2.50

Internal Perception and Bodily Functioning

+Internal Perception and Bodily Functioning

By

Russell E. Mason

INTERNATIONAL UNIVERSITIES PRESS, INC.

NEW YORK

To the many who have encouraged or hesitated
to inhibit independent creative work

Contents

PART I
Conceptual Approaches in the Consideration of Internal and External Awareness

PART II
Various General and Theoretical Approaches Involving Concepts of the Noncognitive Area of Internal Perception

PART III

Physiological Changes Associated with General Noncognitive Internal Perception

PART IV

Physiological Changes Associated with Internal Sensations

PART V

Differentiation of Noncognitive Psychological States by Means of Physiological Reactions and Internal Sensations

Preface

The genesis of this book was in a paper written in 1941 (876) but the review of related literature, as well as the research on internal sensation that is included, was begun in 1948. The earlier paper represented an attempt to synthesize briefly my own knowledge and understanding of human experience whereas the later work that went into this book represents attempts to discover and to synthesize concepts and observations of others that relate to human inner experience and functioning. The knowledge and perspective derived from this study have been most useful in my clinical experience. By the end of 1952, it seemed apparent that the approach to the understanding of human functioning as presented in this study was sufficiently unique in comparison to other current trends in psychologic thinking for its compilation and presentation to be of value. This task has been accomplished along with full-time clinical responsibilities and under relatively unfavorable conditions. Thus, this book doubtless contains many imperfections and lack of elaborations that could be remedied in the future.

In the course of this undertaking, the assistance of so many people has been requested and obtained that complete acknowledgment of my deep appreciation of these favors is not feasible. Particular thanks are given to the many librarians in the United States who have made the reference material available, particularly at the Armed Forces Medical Library, Southern Methodist University, Purdue University, Langley Porter Hospital, the University of California at Berkeley and at Los Angeles, the University of Kansas, and the Veterans Administration Hospital, Brockton, Massachusetts. Readers of the first draft included Dr. Allen K McGrath, Jr., and Dr. Harold Borko, who also gave fruitful suggestions for changes. At an intermediate stage of development, Dr. Donald B. Lindsley and Dr. Robert Hart assisted in looking over the work and discussing it. As the book neared completion, Dr. William A. Hunt read it and offered encouragement, as did also Dr. Richard S. Lazarus, who was able to read part of it. A copy of the final (unedited) draft was read by Dr. Lawrence E. Hinkle, who offered constructive criticism and suggestions, and by Dr. Sidney L. Marvin, who expressed approval of the work.

I am grateful to these people, to my wife, to my editorial mentor, Louise Barker Fred, to the publishers and their readers, and to many others for their encouragement and assistance.

R. E. M.

March, 1958
Brockton, Massachusetts

Introduction

GENERAL CONSIDERATIONS

Concepts and research findings that should be of value to most academic, professional and other persons interested in human personality and psychological functioning from either applied or theoretical standpoints are presented in this book. Human awareness is viewed as being directed in relative degrees toward the individual's external environment, toward his cognitive (ideational) activity, and toward his noncognitive inner experiences. Noncognitive inner experience includes so-called feelings, drive states, internal (organic) sensations, and so forth.

Much has been written in the professional literature concerning overt behavior and symptoms, sensory and perceptual processes relating to external stimulations, and conscious and unconscious ideation and mental mechanisms. Little, however, has been written specifically concerning noncognitive states and processes. This book is primarily devoted to the understanding of these noncognitive states and processes and to the presentation of related physiological findings. Since all human experience, however, is interrelated, and since most theoretical approaches to the understanding of personality have usually made reference to noncognitive inner experience in association with cognitive and behavioral experience, Parts I and II of this book are devoted to explanation and re-evaluation of these various approaches in terms of internal perceptual analysis. Parts III and IV consist of a review of the literature concerning noncognitive internal perception as associated with physiological changes. Parts V and Chapter 22 attempt to synthesize some of these findings and to show their implications.

"Internal perception" refers simply to an individual's awareness of his own internal environment, as contrasted to that of his external environment; this includes awareness that is entirely conscious and specific, or is only vaguely perceived, or is a relatively nonconscious or "unconscious" reaction at some neurophysiological level in response to significant and otherwise meaningful bodily changes. Thus, the range of internal perception concerned in this definition is broad, including, for example, vaguely perceived "feeling states" as well as specifically perceived bladder tension, abdominal cramps, or heart beats. The term "perception" is employed broadly here, since any awareness can become significant only in so far as some relatedness to other functions of the organism exists. Also, by definition, any degree of awareness of such relatedness, whether it is conscious or nonconscious ("unconscious"), may be called cognitive. There exists at this time no good basis for applying a name other than "cognitive" for any given level of neurophysiological functioning, since the nervous system is a continuous and highly interrelated system as shall be described later (see p. 201).

PERSPECTIVE

In the field of medicine, the increased attention to functional disorders has been exceeded only by the growing recognition of psychosomatic relationships and the interdependence and unity of bodily and psychological functioning. In the field of psychology, the recent trend has been away from the former behavioristic denial of the functional value of subjective awareness. Both clinical psychology and psychiatry have underlined the important role played by the individual's relative awareness of his own feelings, emotions, attitudes, and other internal states and processes.

This work is an attempt to collect and meaningfully present most of the pertinent material that has been published in the fields of medicine and psychology and related fields that concerns internal awareness by the individual and that is related to the bodily functioning accompanying or corresponding to such awareness. There is, however, one important exception to the scope of this objective. Material relating predominantly to cognitive, or ideational, processes but not primarily concerned with other types of internal experience, such as feelings, is not included. Thus, those areas of internal perception remaining after the exclusion of strictly cognitive, or ideational, processes may be designated as "noncognitive" areas of internal perception, again using the term "perception" broadly. One area of knowledge is also included here that has been almost completely neglected by psychologists, although it has received some attention in medical research: this concerns the awareness of internal sensations, both of the types stimulated by pathological processes (such as pain) and of the types stimulated by bodily changes accompanying, or corresponding to, different psychological states (such as hunger, fatigue, tightness, and chill sensations).

Psychological and physiological states have been observed to function homeostatically, or "automatically," in many respects. Yet clinical case histories repeatedly demonstrate that with the complex highly evolved cognitive structure of the human being, homeostasis frequently fails, and instead there are seen physical symptoms such as ulcers, hypertension, and diarrhea on one hand, and, on the other hand, symptoms such as acute anxiety, depression, and chronic aggressive reaction. Professional people dealing with these kinds of phenomena have been at a loss to bridge the gap between measurable physiological reactions during changing psychological states and the subjective aspects of these states.

In most research studies concerning such relationships, the physiological changes have been meticulously measured, whereas the psychological states usually have been vaguely, variously, and subjectively described. Thus, the description of psychological states poses essentially a semantic problem, but not one that is easily or arbitrarily solved by the making up of classification systems. Basically, what is needed for the communication of psychological states is a system of differentiated references—of labels—that can consistently describe subjective experiences and can be accepted as describing the same phenomena when applied to different people. Only by this means can those immediate psychological states and experiences that extend beyond cognitive, or ideational, experience be subjected to vigorous scientific scrutiny.

At present, psychologists and psychiatrists rely primarily on clinical impressions and compilations of cases to supply data concerning psychological states, the interrelations of such states, and their dynamics. Even within this vast reservoir of accumulated data and knowledge, the inadequacies of current terminology referring to feelings, emotions, and related psychological states greatly limit communication. Another apparent stumbling block to the understanding of differential psychological states is that of the selective perception, which derives, in turn, from the poorly differentiated psychological states. Especially restricting in this respect is the frequent use of terminology and concepts that unwittingly lump together phenomena, such as the including of different types of feelings with cognitive, or judgmental, phenomena, or even with external perceptions and with strictly behavioral experiences. In this book it is deplored that professional people frequently fail to make certain distinctions between interrelated experiential phenomena and unitary ("homogeneous") experiential phenomena. The attempt here is to re-evaluate the perception of inner experience in such a way that eventually the Gordian knot of semantics concerning feeling experiences and psychological states may be loosened, permitting more precise study of psychological and physiological interrelationships.

CONTENT

The literature was reviewed in the hope of including all major concepts and experimental and clinical findings relevant to the subject matter under consideration. For this purpose, references are cited both to exemplify the concepts and findings noted herein and to provide further reference for given types of theoretical, clinical, and experimental work. Notwithstanding the aim of comprehensiveness in citing past and present studies, an attempt is generally made, when possible, to avoid redundant and multiple references for a given limited subject, and to cite the earliest, the most recent, and the most comprehensive works of given authors and groups, so that the interested reader may easily locate desired detailed references. Therefore, this work is both a textbook for comprehensive references in the areas covered and an attempt to present a concept of psychological functions and of noncognitive internal perception that is somewhat different from traditional concepts. Subheadings are provided primarily as guides or anchorages, to facilitate reading rather than as discrete dividers of content.

Attention must be drawn to the usage of the word "semantics," which in its dictionary definition and in its use by semanticists (536a) most technically refers to the science or study of meanings in communication and of the historical, psychological, anthropological, and other factors in the signification of words and other communication forms. "Semantics" is used here in a colloquial fashion to refer rather abstractly to the content of significant findings and concepts of this "science." For example, on pp. 28 and 29, the elimination of the use of "semantic" would require substitution of a wide variety of terms such as "word usage," "structure," "linguistically," "verbal," "content," "languages," and "verbal concepts."

APPLICABILITY

Recently, professional people in the fields concerned here have not generally thought of psychological functioning in terms of areas of relatively differentiated functions. The focus of study has not been so much on generalizations concerning types of functioning for the individual and for the generalized human organism but rather on (1) holistic concepts concerning personality; (2) classifications of types of personality, or diagnostic constellations, which differentiate groups of people; (3) and studies of dynamic inter-relationships—particularly of cognitive associations and symbolic manifestations—for given individuals and types of individuals seen clinically or psychotherapeutically.

Needless to say, all of these endeavors imply some generalities concerning the human organism, or man, as such. Although there has been an emphasis on *individual* psychological functioning, this has been primarily in terms of differentiating individual differences from group characteristics rather than in delineating areas of functioning within the individual himself. The studies of physiological changes, whether they have been in relation to psychological states or otherwise, have tended toward the usual biological emphasis of delineating the characteristics of the species, and here, too, recognition has also been given to the important phenomena of individual differences as well as to statistically patterned variations.

Parts I and II of this book review different concepts of noncognitive internal perception in an attempt to find what approaches have been employed in the study of, and what agreement may exist for, types of human noncognitive perceptions. For example, it can be seen that concepts of experiences, such as anxiety, anger, and love, are almost universal. In the first section of Part III, it can be seen that many physiological changes in various parts of the body have been associated with psychological states of these types, and in Part IV some internal sensations are seen to have similar associations. When bodily changes associated with such well-known feeling states as joy result in consciously perceived internal sensations, a most simple and clear-cut example of noncognitive internal perceptions, or awareness, is presented. Less easily grasped, but possibly of greater functional significance, is the probable importance of patterns of continually changing neural impulses, which are stimulated by changes in bodily functioning, in association with differentiable psychological states, or types of noncognitive internal experience.

Irrespective of the controversial origins and of the complex neurophysiological relationships involved, the fact remains that the measurement and the perception of such differentiable physiological changes may provide a basis for the establishing of normative classifications for psychological states and reactions. The establishment of definitive classifications for psychological states, which can be subject to measurement and scientific comparisons, has as yet eluded psychological study. For example, a state, or feeling, of anxiety has not been clearly differentiated from other psychological states, such as "fear" or "tension," in so far as individual internal perceptions or total physiological reactions are concerned, nor have reliable criteria been established whereby specific internal perceptions or physiological reactions may be interpreted to indicate the existence of anxiety in an individual as a member of the human species generally (as contrasted to the criteria that may have been established for individuals or for certain types, or diagnostic classifications, of people).

It is the underlying thesis of this book that a good possibility exists for the establishment of specific criteria for psychological states of the human organism and that thereby psychological states and human functioning generally may be subjected to far more precise and accurate scientific study than has heretofore been possible. Also on the basis of such knowledge, it would be possible to screen and to classify personality and diagnostic types by means of physiological measurements and also in combination with introspective reports. It is not purported that all the data necessary to achieve this goal are presented here; however, an approach to the study of human functioning is presented whereby achievement of this would seem to be possible. First, a semantic distinction must be made between terms that have been loosely used to represent presumed psychological states and are derived more or less from traditional or historical habit, as contrasted to *actual* internal perceptive functioning. Because the anatomy of the human organism, like that of other species, has been fairly constant in structure for a very long time, it can be presumed that fairly constant types, or areas, of internal functioning and reactivity exist for the species generally, notwithstanding individual differences.

Thus, on a statistical normative basis alone, it may be possible to differentiate *types* of psychological states for human beings generally. For example, one may postulate an experimental (or clinical) situation, wherein a substantial majority of people can *clearly* classify the situation that arouses the feeling of anger (as *definitely* differentiated from other types of psychological reactions), and one may postulate also that a substantial majority of individuals so studied react with colonic hyperactivity in this situation, whereas when there are *clearly* established depressive reactions, colonic hypomotility occurs. These physiological reactions could be evaluated as one part of a multiple profile consisting of many other physiological reactions in given psychological states. The minority of individuals who have different physiological reactions in the same given situation may be presumed to be experiencing fundamentally different psychological states. Their psychological state might be delineated by some other profile of physiological reactions that could also be established on the basis of normative reactions in other relatively clear-cut psychological situations. This same type of normative classification may be established for the relative perception of internal sensations, which are presumably stimulated by the physiological changes involved in different types of situations.

As will be seen on pp. 298 and 353, the fact that significant differences do exist in the perception of internal sensations for psychologically different types of situations emphasizes the importance of bodily functioning in differentiated internal perceptive experience. These examples, however, somewhat oversimplify the facts, and the conclusions of this work are stated before the details are presented. Nevertheless, comprehension of the ultimate usefulness and applicability of the data and theories that will follow may be necessary in order to maintain interest in material that is frequently complex. At times this material may seemingly be of remote significance to some professional people for whom it is intended since the content is broad and the aim is to coalesce psychological and physiological (including medical) knowledge.

Part I

Conceptual Approaches in the Consideration of Internal and External Awareness

CHAPTER 1

Philosophy and Theory

ORIENTATION

First of all, it is necessary to set forth a clear distinction between "external perception" and "internal perception." Simply, it may be stated that "external perception" refers to the meaningful assimilation of those stimuli that arise from the environment outside the body, and internal perception refers to the meaningful assimilation of those stimuli that arise from the environment within the body. Perception may be considered the initial reaction (or change) of the cognitive processes to sensory impulses. Both philosophical and clinical approaches to the conceptualization and understanding of the significance of this differentiation concerning areas of perception are presented in Part I.

Part II shows how the various theorists and experimenters in psychology, psychiatry, and psychoanalysis have dealt with internal perceptive experience.

The remainder of this book presents factual findings concerning internal perception and bodily functioning that have been gathered from psychological, psychiatric, and general medical literature, including that of so-called psychosomatic medicine. The emphasis throughout is on the delineation of types of psychological states, or areas of internal perception, and on the differential relatedness of physiological changes to such states. In Part I, both the most theoretical point of view and the most immediate practical applications in conceptual approaches to the understanding of noncognitive internal perception are presented as a "philosophical approach" and a "clinical approach," respectively.

A PHILOSOPHICAL APPROACH

CONSENSUAL VALIDATION AND PURPOSEFUL ACTIVITY

A philosophical approach, just as any series of ideas purporting logical connection, is based upon certain assumptions. In the final analysis, however, the conclusions reached must eventually be accepted or rejected on the basis of empirical consensual validation. So it must also be in this consideration of the dimensions of human awareness. Nevertheless, a logical approach may lead interested people to think along lines in which empirical evaluations can be more accurately formed and thereby may allow penetration into areas in which otherwise selective perception or habits of thinking tend to block and preclude new or untried perspectives.

One of the most fundamental characteristics of life is activity. This activity is of a purposeful character, the most fundamental purpose, or function, being ultimately the survival of the organism that otherwise would not be reproduced and continued. Thus in the very simplest forms of life, this purposefulness is easily seen in the directing of movements toward nourishing environments and away from irritants. In man, of course, the ascertaining of the purposefulness of a given behavior is not so simple. Nevertheless, almost any person can recall some kinds of specific situations concerning which he either strove to attain or to avoid, day to day, week by week, or year by year. If a person has a fair imagination, he can with some vividness recall situations in his past experience for the attainment of which he devoted some time, effort, or planning, and then having attained the situation or goal, felt some satisfaction in it. Similarly, one can recall situations in which much dissatisfaction was experienced and that one then strove to avoid.

Such situations can provide for the individual (as well as for the science of psychology) an opportunity to analyze the more immediate factors in the purposefulness, or motivation, of individual behavior, setting aside for the moment consideration of the deeper, relatively nonconscious factors. To actually analyze what the differences are in such types of experiences, one needs to contrast different ones by recalling, as vividly as possible, first one type of experience and then another. It becomes apparent that a person is not striving to attain or avoid given situations simply because of given external stimuli, or environmental objects and people, or simply because of the cognitive content, or ideas, concerning the experience at the time. This becomes apparent because, among other things, a person can recall different situations in which the predominant inner experience was of the same type, but both the external stimulus conditions and the cognitive content of internal perception were different from those in another situation. For example, one may have experienced feelings of happiness in different situations that involved entirely different environmental circumstances, objects, persons, and even different thoughts (such as a family picnic, or job, or scholastic achievement resulting in happiness); the same would apply for anger or other feelings. In order to compare such situations then, one must focus awareness on noncognitive internal perceptual experience.

All terms and names are cognitive in nature, so the mere enumeration of terms for feelings, emotions, and so forth, will not go beyond cognitive experience. Instead, one must simply be immediately aware of his noncognitive internal state. The contrast of these states in different situations may be conceptualized in terms of "feeling," or anything else, but certainly one must take note of a difference in internal sensory experience, as, for example, in the marked sensory difference between tense and relaxed muscles. In this way, one is able to recognize the predominant noncognitive inner experience of some situations as being similar to, or essentially the same as, that of other situations, such as the examples of "happiness" and of "anger" mentioned above.

"ENDS," "AVERSIONS," AND MEANS

The specific *types of inner experience* one strives to attain may be termed "ends," and those one strives to avoid may be termed "aversions." By the comparing of different types of noncognitive experiences, one may be able to recognize internal sensations as being consistently either relatively strong or qualitatively different in given areas of the body for different types of ends or aversions. As will be seen in the next section concerning clinical findings, many people will not be able to analyze and compare their experiences in this manner for various reasons; however, evidence will be presented later (see pp. 298 and 353) to indicate that the vast majority of people are capable of this type of analysis.

The human organism's states of continued activity are most frequently explained or understood, apart from subjective analysis, by postulated concepts of goals or of needs that most frequently are inferred from the direction a given behavior takes. Generally, that thing or situation toward which an individual directs his activity is considered his goal. Motivation is a term that is based on the fact that different people may direct their efforts toward the same objective goal but for different subjective reasons or purposes. Certain motivations, such as hunger, thirst, and sex, are universally recognized, but what other organic processes and functions this generalized term may represent in its various usages are not universally agreed on. Therefore, additional concepts of basic motivational behavior must be considered only in terms of hypotheses or theories. The criterion employed in this "philosophical approach" is that motivations must ultimately have physiological bases, and that motivational symbols lacking specificity in this respect are intermediate to the final goal of ascertaining basic motivations for which differentiable physiological bases can be demonstrated. Understood in this way, the motivation concept is most frequently employed as a negative word, or symbol. It usually symbolizes something that is not identified, or is only partially identified, in terms of specific phenomena from which it is abstracted and into which it can be specifically and immediately analyzed or translated, whenever used in a given connotation. For example, different people may go to a football game apparently for the attainment of noncognitive inner experiences of excitement, or companionship, or expression of pent-up anger, and the like; whereas in more conventional psychological terminology it would be said that they go to satisfy motivations, such as gregarious needs, ego identifications, or aggressive impulses.

Nevertheless, all of these terms represent only vaguely conceptualized references to noncognitive inner experience, and none of these have been clearly and scientifically delineated in terms of relative areas of inner experience, nor are they used consistently by different people in different situations. Especially, the lack of knowledge concerning basic physiological processes, needs, or events to which these "motivational" terms may refer must be emphasized.

It may eventually be possible to avoid in part such ambiguity of reference by the identifying of motivational states in terms of pleasant or unpleasant feeling experiences in combination with perceived patterns of internal sensations corresponding to, or associated with, such experiences. Also, since internal sensations can presumably be shown to have physiological bases, they may provide a clue for, or may directly represent, basic physiological motivational states, or reaction patterns. Such sensory experiences may be considered as corresponding to, or correlating directly with, motivational states because the direction of a given human activity is usually based, either immediately or ultimately, on the experiencing of noncognitive "ends," such as happiness, love, sexual feelings, and so forth. With this conceptual approach it is important to differentiate means from ends. The pros and cons of such an approach, however, need not be considered in this section, as the traditional objections will be somewhat considered in the course of the outlining of the various theoretical and experimental undertakings related to internal perception.

VARIETIES OF ORIENTATIONS

It is apparent from what has already been presented that people do not generally focus awareness directly on the noncognitive area of inner experience, yet it is also apparent that this area of experience is of central importance in the functioning of the individual (167, 168, 759, 835, 907, 908, 909, 1135a). How various personality factors affect the individual's directing of awareness toward the different areas of his experience will be elaborated in the next two chapters. Cultural and historical considerations, however, are probably of even greater importance than individual factors in the understanding of why people are either aware, or not aware, of various aspects of their daily experience.

First, the more primitive cultures that in the past few decades have been so numerously described by anthropologists may be considered (101, 102, 673, 712, 734, 801, 889, 1321). In most of these cultures, the peoples who were studied usually focused awareness on external perceptual things and events to attain a basis for the understanding of important experiences in their lives. Thus, they related, as some persons still relate, their experiences in terms of external sensory changes, natural omens, geographical features, physical maturational changes, age differences, and traditional ways of making and doing things. To the relatively primitive mind such external things take on rather magical significance in their relatedness to inner experiences and to important events in life (1102), all of which are seen in the use of various objects, masks, and movements for primitive "medical" treatment; in "rain dances"; in the "magic" of the planting of crops under various specified, but scientifically unbased, physical conditions; in the attributing of ill-fortune to physical occurrences or omens; and in the simpler, more physical rites and ceremonies that are thought necessary to accompany important events in life, such as the coming of puberty.

Even among the relatively primitive cultures, however, there was, and is, great variation as to how much emphasis (focus) is placed on cognitive experience that may be either more or less mystical (as in the Sioux culture) or "logical" and "rational" in nature (as in the Yurok culture) (339). There is, of course, a line of continuity between such relative emphasis on external perception for purposes of rationalizing or "understanding" experience and the relative emphasis on cognition or ideation, as seen in folklore and primitive religions. Perhaps the best known example of the latter emphasis is Greek folklore, which at one time was accepted by the Greek culture as explaining many experiences. An example of still greater emphasis on cognitive experience that has existed for centuries is seen in Confucianism and Buddhism, in which knowledge of voluminous writings is highly valued. The Hindu culture, on the other hand, places a relatively greater focus of awareness on noncognitive internal perception than do most other cultures, but even here the religious cognitive associations are also greatly emphasized (57, 665, 1124).

Within American subcultures similar variation is seen. For example, groups enthusiastically interested in sports, natural phenomena, horticulture or craftsmanship tend to focus awareness predominantly on events and activities in contrast to groups primarily interested in history, literature, psychological theories, mathematics, and the like, who tend to focus awareness predominantly on cognitive internal perception. Perhaps the only definitive group in Western culture that places relatively great focus of awareness on noncognitive internal perception is comprised of those persons participating, or who have participated in, psychotherapy, but even here cognitive emphasis plays a very important role. Also, any activity that emphasizes physical exertion or (pleasurable) feeling states seemingly includes a partial focus of awareness on noncognitive internal perception.

Of course, in all cultures, as with every individual, there must be some awareness of all areas of experiences, and the variations of emphasis are relative (126). In addition, no culture that is in competition with other cultures can place predominant emphasis on noncognitive internal perception for the simple reason that the focusing on the other areas of experience is necessary to provide the means for survival. At the same time, the results of modern psychotherapy show that great efficiency can frequently be attained by focusing of attention on noncognitive internal perception to an extent greater than that which is commonly undertaken.[1] Thus, the relative emphasis, or focus of awareness, on the different areas of experience depends in part on the culture milieu in which the individual finds himself.

Historically, the contrast in respect to the relative emphasis that is placed on different spheres of experience is even more striking. It will suffice, here, however, simply to note the contrast in emphasis on cognitive ideation in our modern civilization as compared to that of the primitive civilizations that are known to have preceded even the so-called modern and ancient

---

[1] Humanity's need for greater understanding of inner experience for attainment of survival itself is certainly emphasized by the confused states of mind and emotionality that have played important roles in promoting and permitting the costly wars of past and recent times.

civilizations. Relatively greater modern cognitive emphasis is seen in the refinements of literature, theoretical and applied science, mathematics, law, religion, and so forth. Relatively greater modern noncognitive, internal perceptive awareness is seen in the analysis of so-called feelings, emotions, impulses, drives, internal sensations, and the like. It would seem that, for survival at least, primitive man would have had to focus awareness primarily on his environment.

Up to this point only gross differences in relative awareness of different areas of experience have been considered. The main purpose has been to define the directions in which awareness may be focused, to point to their relativity, and to provide a perspective for the understanding of these differences. There remains the matter of relative awareness within each of these areas of experience itself. It has already been noted that when one channels concentration of awareness in one direction or area of experience, there is generally only a relatively vague awareness of the other areas of experience. For example, if one is deep in thought (cognitive awareness) about given problems or plans, he is less likely to notice noises, light changes, and the like in the environment (external perceptual awareness) than if the focus of awareness was reversed. The same principle applies within each of the perceptual areas. Thus, if one is concentrating on visual stimuli, such as a moving picture or a television program, unrelated noises, such as from a passing vehicle, will usually be unnoticed. Similarly, within the area of cognitive experience, if one focuses awareness on one idea (obsessionally), methodology, theory, dogma, past experience, or the like, he is less likely to become aware of other cognitive activity than if he freely associates or considers several alternative possibilities or solutions. Somewhat less clearly recognized or understood is the way that this principle operates in noncognitive internal perceptive experience. Nevertheless, if one is extremely aware of hunger, certainly, other feelings, internal sensations, and the like, are relatively blocked or less intense in one's perception. Similarly, if one is contemplating an experience of love, most frequently he is not aware of ambivalence (or anger) or anxiety when it is associated therewith. A given quantum of the mental characteristic "awareness" appears to exist for a given individual at a given time that limits the number of things to which he may attend, but the relative concentration of awareness on a given thing also limits its scope.

Other factors determining the scope and direction of an individual's awareness are his values (or "ends") and aversions. Selective perception can be exemplified simply by the difference in areas of awareness of a typical couple who are window shopping; the man notices sporting goods, automobile accessories and the like, and the woman notices feminine apparel, housekeeping accessories and the like. The relatedness of such individual values and aversions to cultural values and mores is obvious, and, of course, these are dependent on the historical development of a given culture or civilization. Apart from the individual personality factor, all of the factors in selective perception that have been mentioned have a common denominator—the semantics, or language usage, of the culture in which a given individual finds himself (536a, 646, 720, 721, 762).

SEMANTICS

The semantics of a given culture is an outgrowth, or aspect, of many factors within the culture, such as the language, the economics, the literary and religious traditions, and the like. Although the word usage and ideas embodied in the semantics of a given language tend to focus perceptions selectively, it is still possible for an individual to be immediately aware of areas of experience that are not semantically defined. Nevertheless, even in such a case, the individual is unable without a semantic vehicle to specifically communicate such experiences to others and thereby to direct the attention of others to new areas of experience.

The semantics of languages in use today enables one to differentiate rather definitively various aspects of external sensory experience, such as different colors, shapes, movements, and so forth. Less definitive are the words relating to cognitive experience. This is true for both the defining of the different subdivisions, or aspects, of cognitive experience and for the defining of mutually exclusive concepts. An example of the former is the ambiguity of experience implied by such terms as imagination, fantasy, impulses, and unconscious tendencies or memories, not to mention ego, libido, organizational abilities, and "g" and "s" factors. Examples of the difficulty in the defining of mutually exclusive concepts are seen in the multiple concepts of freedom, democracy, fidelity, psychology, human nature, and religion. Thus, within the framework of Western semantics one is able to focus rather specifically on external sensory experience and to communicate it. The awareness of cognitive experience and content must at this time, of necessity,—due to the limitations of semantics if nothing more, —be rather vague and generalized, and as a consequence the communication of such experience must necessarily be less definitive, more voluminous, more ambiguous and more subject to different interpretations by various persons than that for the external environment and especially so in the area of noncognitive internal perception. Terms such as anxiety, happiness, good feeling, pleasant sensations, tension, and "butterflies" or "sinking in the stomach" are extremely vague, nondefinitive and subject to different interpretations as compared to the sensations of external perception.

It can be surmised from the examples given that real deficiencies in our knowledge and even greater difficulties in consensual validation are limiting factors in the formulating of definitive semantics for the areas of internal perceptive experience, both cognitive and noncognitive. In regard to the semantics for cognitive experience, however, this state of affairs does not now seem to pose as formidable a problem as formerly. The semantics employed are for the most part centuries old, whereas since the turn of the twentieth century almost immeasurable progress has been made in both the understanding of the cognitive area of experience and in the defining of everyday, as well as social and technical, concepts. Also, many refinements have been made in the semantics relating to the cognitive area of experience, and the possibility of redefining and systematizing the semantics of this area of experience for the purpose of more efficient thinking and more definitive awareness exists even now. Such a project, however, would first face the problem of clearly differentiating the cognitive area of experience from those internal perceptions that are noncognitive in nature, and these latter perceptions at this time present the greatest stumbling block to a redefinition of semantics generally and to the possibility of more clearly defined perspectives and communications. With present semantics, all these different areas of experience are almost invariably bound together and confused by most terms relating to feelings, attitudes, drives, motivations, and emotions. Consequently, the social scientist works and thinks with terms that do not necessarily represent functional entities or relationships. This is analogous to the time that the physical scientist worked without knowledge of specific elements or of specific molecular relationships and the alchemist dealt with crude substances.

UNIVERSALITY

It is in reference to noncognitive internal perception that a lack of consensual validation at present limits the possibilities of definitive delineations and, consequently, the possibility of communication and of scientific scrutiny. Once this obstacle is overcome, and some progress in the scientific study and classification of noncognitive perceptual experience is made, the possibility of effective reorganization of semantics generally will exist. The implications of effective semantic reorganization, with resulting effectiveness in communication, are tremendous in terms of the probable world-wide acceptance of those values and ideas that may prove to be more effective and rewarding in everyday living as well as in scientific pursuits and philosophical formulations. Later we will discuss the possibility of the attaining of consensual validation for noncognitive internal perceptual experience in terms of differential reports of internal sensations and also the possibility of the measureing of the physiological changes that are apparently the basis of specific internal sensory experiences.

If, as hypothesized earlier, noncognitive internal perceptual experience constitutes the "ends" of day-to-day motivations and if such experiences can be identified and differentiatedly delineated, it can be surmised that semantics based on such fundamental personality characteristics would have universal implications. Also, the probable effect would be to reduce conflicts in cultural perspectives and to de-emphasize external perceptual experience and "material" values in favor of internal perceptual values or "ends." This last point may not be very clear, but in any case, to clarify understanding of the scope, content, and functioning of internal perceptual experience to any substantial degree would constitute important progress in the science of psychology.

CHAPTER 2

Biological and Historical Perspectives

AWARENESS

Another essentially theoretical or "philosophical" approach to the evaluation of relative external and internal perceptive tendencies is the consideration of biological and historical perspectives. The point of origin of the characteristic of awareness in evolutional development is highly problematical. Certainly, it is considered only a characteristic of animate beings. Since the single-cell organism is reactive and is "purposeful," or selective, in its activity, it is possible to postulate awareness even at this level. The same is true of the single cell that is a part of a complex organism such as the human. However, with a multiple-celled organism, and especially where the rudiments of a nervous system exist, different parts of the organism take on specialized functions, and these activities become co-ordinated so that there appears to be a kind of awareness at a higher level.

For humans, awareness is most frequently thought of in terms of the highest cortical functions, including abstract thinking and symbolical differentiations. Of course, in itself the term "awareness"—the concept—is a symbolic abstraction, and as such it is subject to those mental characteristics at the level of language development. At the same time it is quite evident that most all macroscopical animal organisms, at least, possess the characteristic awareness of the environment although most of these creatures do not even approach the level of symbolic association that is seen in the human. Similarly, awareness at various levels remains with the decorticate animal, and even as successively lower portions of the neuraxis are removed, some kind of awareness, or reactivity, remains virtually until the death of the organism. Thus, awareness, in the most practical and immediate sense of the term, appears to exist at all levels of structure of the organism.

In the more complex organisms, not only does each cell show a reactive type of awareness, but the electrical charge of each cell apparently contributes, by means of the nervous system, to more integrated awareness at evolutionally and functionally higher levels, since there is a greater succession of such levels as the organisms become more complex. The critical question here is whether awareness as commonly applied to the human is comprised of all these levels or whether it is restricted to some of the higher levels. The conventional answer, of course, is to refer to the concept of sensory receptors, but this does not really solve the problem, and it will be noted later that this concept itself has many limitations. Since almost all levels of reactivity exist in the human, from the very simplest to the most complex, it would seem that an awareness of some kind must exist at all levels. Also, since such reactivity, even for relatively localized areas, has a feedback effect on the neural activity of the whole nervous system, it would seem that even the simplest level of awareness becomes integrated, or associated, with the higher levels of awareness in complex ways.

From a subjective point of view, one can become immediately aware of such common sensations as fatigue or tension in remote parts of the body, such as a finger or the calf of the leg, without any apparent immediately integrated or higher-level significance. Nevertheless in the human at least, the potential awareness of a given experience or sensation at a given time is dependent on *all* of the nervous system that is functioning at the time. This would seem to be the case not only because the nervous system is highly integrated and reverberatory in nature, but also because the afferent neural impulses from a given area, as, for example, the lower leg, will most likely undergo modifications of some kinds at different neural levels. An example of this effect on subjective experience is seen after lobotomies have been performed for intractible pain, with the result that the "pain" sensation still is recognized but the patient no longer "suffers" from it (165, 329, 344, 426, 607, 719, 806, 1043).[1]

Thus, human reactivity and awareness exist at different phylogenetic levels of development, and, apparently, at the higher levels of human awareness, modifications are made in the perception of lower-level reactivity.

NONCONSCIOUS FUNCTIONING

Humans are not consciously aware of most of the reactions taking place at lower neurological levels within their own bodies. Co-ordination of most physiological and mechanical changes and reactions that take place in the organism is accomplished by nonconscious integrative activity called homeo-

[1] The possibility, however, remains that the "intractable" aspect of the pain may have been central in the first place.

stasis, which has been given much emphasis in recent decades (113, 193, 291, 426, 893d, 1135a, 1293). The term "awareness" will generally be employed in this book, as most commonly used, to refer to a conscious process that apparently represents a rather high level of neurological development. Nevertheless, it has just been noted that in regard to internal perception, this higher level of awareness is interrelated with, and perhaps dependent on, lower levels of integrative neural activity. These lower levels of neural activity can also be thought of as levels of nonconscious awareness, which are at times subject to conscious awareness.

The fact is that humans can, and frequently do, become consciously aware of both cognitive activity or thoughts, and of noncognitive internal activities, such as feelings, that have usually gone unnoticed. Such *cognitive* awareness is exemplified in psychotherapy by the process of free association revealing previously unrecognized attitudes and motivations, as well as long-"forgotten" experiences, which were, and had been, playing important roles in the individual's functioning. Such *noncognitive* internal perceptions are exemplified by one's occasional awareness of increased respiration or palpitation in stress situations or of "warmth" and orgasmic potential in situations of sexual excitement. Thus, the common dichotomy of voluntary-involuntary reactivity does not adequately demarcate the areas or levels of potential conscious awareness. It may well be that most people have the potentiality for becoming consciously aware of most reactivity within the internal perceptive environment.

It is obvious, however, that if the individual attempted to focus awareness as completely as possible on the myriad reactions taking place within the internal perceptive environment for any given time, he would fail to accomplish anything else. For the organism to function, to provide for its physical needs, to compete and defend itself against other organisms, to co-operate with others, and to procreate and reproduce the species, conscious awareness must be focused on the external environment. The opportunity for the organism to focus awareness on the external environment is provided for by the integration of the internal environment by homeostatic types of reactions, requiring relatively little conscious awareness at a given time. As pointed out, however, as early as 1870 to 1872 by Herbert Spencer (1176), it is with the failure of effective integrative activity in the internal perceptual environment that the process, or faculty, of conscious awareness is usually directed internally. This can be exemplified by pathological pain syndromes; by hunger and fatigue; by the introversive tendencies in consequence of emotional conflicts; by the thought and analysis required upon the failure of a given plan; by newly found difficulties in visual-motor co-ordination, such as the learning of new dance steps or participating in sports; and by one's attempt to re-evaluate his feelings, attitudes, and reactions upon having experienced a stress situation because his aim is to react more effectively to such situations in the future.

In light of the growing recognition that man's internal functioning is far from perfect and that dysfunction of the internal environment, "emotional dysfunction," is the basis of many present-day problems, it may be worth while to direct the collective awareness of psychological investigators to the internal perceptual environment in an effort better to understand its nature and to find means of attaining more effective functioning.

HISTORICAL PERSPECTIVE

Many theorists will question the value of emphasizing the analysis of the individual's internal perceptual environment in order to approach the broader problems of interpersonal and social maladjustments. The same logic that underlies such objections also will be the basis of other opinions that may dispute the theoretical and practical, or therapeutic, value of the individual's analyzing his internal perceptual environment. The first point of view refers to those investigators who in their theoretical approach to human problems stress interpersonal relationships almost to the point of denying the importance of the internal structure and functioning of the individual personality (600, 777, 1219). The second point of view refers to the more extreme Gestaltists who place such great emphasis on the configurational and holistic aspects of perception that the importance of functional units and processes within the internal environment is denied (717, 718, 777, 1308, 1312).

Both of these points of view arose as valid protests against earlier relatively rigid and somewhat limited theories that emphasized analytically isolated associations and mental faculties on the one hand and psychoanalytic psychosexual stages of development and the Kraepelinian clinical nosology on the other hand. Thus, both points of view represent protests to specific limited theories that utilized analysis and classification of functions, yet these protests went beyond the specific theories and attempted to a degree to exclude in general from theoretical usage the analysis of component functional aspects of the individual and the analysis of the individual human as an independent functional unit in society.

The fundamental fallacy of these extreme points of view is that the scientific method itself is comprised of the analysis and classification of phenomena in terms of functional units (715, 727). In denying the functional approach, one is forced into emphasizing "unknown" quantities and into relying on intuitive conclusions in order to explain holistic phenomena. This is exactly what is done in theoretical works encompassing these extreme points of view. However, when scientific investigations are undertaken and when differential theoretical conclusions are drawn, the experimenter and theorist must resort to analysis and classification at some level.

These antianalysis-and-classification points of view fail even when the positive aspect of their theories is carried to its logical conclusion. The positive aspect of these theoretical approaches stresses the interdependence of phenomena and of human development and relationships. However, if interdependence is to be the ultimate criteria of theoretical "goodness" or acceptability, one need not logically stop with interdependence of persons or of perceptual phenomena, since, ultimately, every experience and the existence of every individual group and culture is interdependent with all the universe, its every functioning aspect, its stages of development, and its probable partial disintegration, on this planet at least. Analysis is the very essence of the scientific method, and classification is the handmaid of functional analysis. The individual is subject to analysis both physically and psychologically and perhaps even to the point that the twain shall meet.

By all standards of "common sense," past experience, and future probabilities, the individual can be considered a basic functional unit in the analysis of human phenomena, including interpersonal relationships, and group and cultural dynamics. Even though the health and development of the individual are dependent in great part on the group in which he finds himself, it will not be possible thoroughly to understand any group without first understanding the individual of the group. Similarly, changes cannot usually be effected in group dynamics unless they are effected through individuals.

Thus, the limitation in one's understanding of an individual and of his internal perceptual environment in turn limits the extent that one is able to understand interpersonal relationships and group functioning. Interpersonal relationships and group functioning, along with materialistic construction and destruction, receive most public and professional attention today. To effect commonly desired changes in interpersonal and group relationships, however, it would seem to be necessary to focus more attention on the functioning of the individual, including especially his internal perceptual environment.

Within the history of modern science there has gradually been a shift from more complete focusing on the external environment to an awareness of the internal environment. Man's scientific concern has progressed gradually from the study of things most remote from man himself, namely, astronomy, to the study of things most close to him, namely, his mental and psychological processes. Close study of human anatomy was for centuries prohibited by law and by social pressure. Still later, to subject the "mind," or "soul," to scientific scrutiny was considered irreverent and irreligious. Darwin's evidence that disputed the rational nature of man was first ill-received, and, until relatively recently, Freud's concepts of unconscious processes and of socially taboo impulses were hotly criticized. Also, Fromm has suggested that there are certain psychological factors in the Western culture that make it difficult for individuals to introspect (396). Bakan (59) presented the idea that introspection was psychologically threatening to the psychologists who started to explore his area of experience.

In view of this slow progression of study from that which is outward and apart from man to that which is within man and integral to man's psychological functioning, it would seem only natural that those inner experiences of the individual that can be subjected to scientific inquiry should be relatively late in coming under scrutiny. This area of study appears to be even now in its infancy and the following chapters will attempt to present most of the known important knowledge and theories relating to noncognitive internal perceptual experience.

CHAPTER 3

Clinical Concepts

PERSONALITY AND RELATIVE AWARENESS

In order to evaluate relative internal and external perceptive tendencies in terms of psychological and psychiatric clinical observations and classifications, brief consideration must first be given to related clinical concepts and to factors that underlie the development of the personality tendencies, or types, to be described.

For the greatest quantum of time, people generally direct their attention toward things that are taking place in the environment about them. Whether it be work, play, social activities, or recreation, a person's awareness is most noticeably directed toward external perception. The next most frequent, or most constant, direction toward which the individual focuses his awareness is that of his own cognitive processes. His attention may be completely or just partially devoted to thinking, to planning, to learning, to memories, or to fantasy activity.

The individual's ideational activity, as well as his perception of his external environment, not only includes an awareness of those things on which his attention is most directly or consciously focused, but an additional periphery of awareness that extends even to subliminal perceptions and most closely relates to perceptual "sets" and deep personality factors of which the individual is not usually cognizant. Psychological research and clinical practice give many examples of these relatively nonconscious, or "unconscious," processes that are as much an aspect of everyday normal experience as they are of clinical cases. Simply stated, people generally tend to perceive things that are of meaningful interest and value to them and tend to overlook things that are meaningless or distasteful to them. Thus, in perception, and in the directing or awareness generally, complex factors relating to personality and to the inner state of the individual are operating.

Both clinical experience and psychological measures reveal that there are

37

great individual differences in the quantum of time that different people and different types of people devote to the different directions of awareness. In this respect, people may be differentiated in terms of rather broad personality types, a classification system that is not restricted to pathological clinical cases. The hysterical type of person, for example, represses cognitive associations to his immediate experiences, and he directs his awareness more toward external perception (and actions). The introverted (or "schizophrenic") type of persons shows just the opposite tendencies in his directing of relative awareness. Personality types can therefore be classified in terms of the relative directing of awareness without carrying the stigmata sometimes associated with such clinical terms as "hysteria" and "schizophrenia." The etiological relationships and implications, as well as the functional similarities, between clinical personality classifications and classification of personality in daily, or "normal," contacts should be recognized as they pertain to the relative directing of awareness. In everyday experience one can easily differentiate at the extremes some people who are busily preoccupied with the things that take place in their environment, for example, external perceptions, and others who are seemingly more concerned with things that take place in their own inner experience, for example, internal perceptions.

In the study of cognitive functions and processes, including their relationship to external perception, much greater progress has been made than in the study of other inner experiences. When other areas of inner experience (for instance, "feeling and emotion") have been studied, the orientation has most frequently been toward either their relatedness to cognitive processes or to "objective" physiological measurements, with the consequence that practically no clear delineation of areas of inner experience exists at this time. Nevertheless, it is generally acknowledged that the terms "feeling and emotion" refer to a unique and differentiated area of inner experience, the exact nature of which has not been clearly understood. The nature of such experiences, however, has as yet eluded any psychological study that could clearly differentiate it from other internal perceptions. Of course, many studies emphasize, and all recent studies tend to underline, the integrated nature of total human experience, including inner experience. Nevertheless, it is only by means of analysis and differentiation that precise relationships can be established and thus allow scientific progress.

One type of internal perception that can be clearly differentiated concerns internal sensations, yet relatively few studies that relate these to other types of experience have been made. It is possible to approach the differentiation of types of experiences by the process of elimination. One can consider psychological states in which neither the awareness of external perception nor of cognition is involved. One such commonly experienced state is that of marked fatigue, either physical, "mental," or "nervous." In this state a person most frequently has little interest in environmental happenings and may even close his eyes and minimize his awareness of audition and the like. At the same time, cognitive activity may be at a minimum. Of what, then, is the individual aware at such times? Certainly, he is at least aware of bodily sensations, for instance, internal sensations of fatigue. At such times then, the relative quantum of awareness is directed more toward internal sensations and less toward external sensations and ideational activity. It would seem then, that just before sleep there may be a greater relative awareness of internal sensations, whether of fatigue or of other types of sensations. Also, in studies on starvation, a greater awareness of internal sensations is seen, along with a relative constriction and specificity of external perceptions and of ideation (89, 367, 825, 905, 1079). In situations of bladder and rectal tension or of physical pain, the relative focusing of awareness may be similar.

The problem of deciding whether the sphere of internal perception should be given major classifications other than those of cognition and sensation and the problem of classifying the so-called area of "feeling and emotion" relative to differentiated internal perceptions must await not only further elaboration in the chapters to follow, but also must really rest upon future experimentation. Nevertheless, much more has already been revealed along these lines than is commonly realized.

In summary, a given individual is recognized to possess a limited scope and quantum of awareness at a given time. This awareness is directed in relative degrees toward external sensations and toward internal perceptions, the latter having at least two subdivisions, cognition and internal sensation.

It may be contended, however, that it is possible for a person in an awakened state not to be aware of anything, and of course such a contention may rest on the semantic usage of the term "aware," as well as on the term "awakened." Setting aside the relatively well-known evidence demonstrating that mental activity takes place on a relative continuum of conscious-unconscious levels, it will be shown in Part III how higher levels of neural activity continually react to changes taking place within the internal environment, suggesting a kind of "awareness."

Many psychologists, and particularly Titchener (1249, 1250, 1251), have spent years attempting to define experimentally a third dimension of inner experience in terms of feeling or of emotion that would extend beyond the dimension already termed ideational, or cognitive, and distinct from the dimension of internal sensation. Since, as shall be elaborated on in Part II, these experimenters succeeded finally only in delineating the process of the making of judgments (95), either "aesthetic" or "feeling quality," and since this process falls in the classification of cognitive experience, no third dimension of psychological experience has yet been clearly delineated either functionally or experimentally. More recent psychological studies, although rejecting Titchener's concepts and ignoring his findings, have continued to employ the same assumptions and semantic methodology. Thus, such concepts as "conflict situation" (911), "positive and negative valence" (776, 777, 778), and "ego involvement" (1135) are all frequently used to make reference to experience states other than those of external sensation or cognition.

Frequently, with such terminologies, the concept of motivation is added. Motivation itself, however, has not usually been defined as a discrete dimension of experience. Rather, it has usually been considered either teleologically, as that which the organism seeks out (714, 715), or ideationally, as that ("level") to which the individual aspires (776). At times, the idea is also added that the hypothetical entities of motivation relate to "feeling and emotion" (544, 624, 1135a, 1223, 1382a), or to nonconscious physiological processes that operate homeostatically (195, 372).

Of recent growing popularity is still another concept "the intervening variable" (or "hypothetical constructs") that refers to hypothetical events or processes within the organism that are inferred from the observable behavior or reactions of experimental subjects or from statistical correlations of reported characteristics of individuals. This is again a concept of relationships that are observed in the ideational dimension, but "intervening variables" are most frequently studied as operating on levels not necessarily subject to direct awareness by the individual (112, 158, 218, 378, 608, 1254). It is possible, then, to conceive of a fourth dimension of psychological functioning that refers to factors beyond the *possibility* of any degree of conscious awareness on the part of the individual, and thereore such factors would have to be inferred completely from overt behavior and measurable physical and physiological reactions. As yet such a potential fourth dimension, or dimensions, of psychological functioning has not been clearly differentiated in psychological thinking from the dimensions of experience already hypothesized, nor have the functional interrelationships of these dimensions been fathomed to any considerable extent.

The problem presented by the different conceptual approaches to inner experience and behavioral functioning points to the need of thinking in terms of clearly delineated areas of experience and functioning and in terms of specific relationships between experimentally established and consensually validated classifications. To circumvent this requirement by the making up of new phrases and terminologies without clearly relating the new classifications to the established ones just adds semantic confusion. Similarly, the extent to which any conceivable intervening variable might or might not affect the different types of awareness classified here would need to be established experimentally. A similar view has been expressed by Bergmann, namely, that the "behavior theory must distinguish between its intervening variable emotion, and the response ordinarily called conscious (perceived) emotion" (112, p. 456).

DEVELOPMENT OF AWARENESS TENDENCIES

These concepts provide a basis for briefly considering factors in the development of human personality that influence the relative tendencies of individuals to focus awareness on their internal and external environments, respectively. William James referred to the experience of the newborn infant as a blooming, buzzing confusion, and Hebb (544) has summarized experimental evidence in some detail that has demonstrated the relatively undifferentiating nature of the experience of the newborn human. Psychoanalytic literature has similarly emphasized the lack of differentiations in an infant's perception (353, 385, 386). Certainly, it is clear that infants are not capable of making the subtle distinctions between types of awareness just presented. In the infant's experience it is assumed and inferred that at most there is a very indistinct differentiation between external sensations and internal perceptions, either sensory or cognitive. It might be well, then, to consider briefly how, if at all, these differentiations are achieved by the developing individual.

The central nervous system of the infant receives both external sensory stimuli and internal sensory impulses, arising from homeostatic and other physiological changes. For the young infant these multiple sensory impulses and sensations are apparently not organized meaningfully and his cognitive capacities are very limited. The infant, then, is probably aware of sensory stimulation in the most elementary sense. The term awareness used in this way does not necessarily imply cognitive meaningfulness, but rather it is used in the sense of "immediate awareness" by the experiencing organism.

This precludes the necessity of being differentially aware of the sensations experienced or of identifying them.

A person can be considered to be aware of sensations to the extent that they constitute a focus of experience at a given time. Thus, the infant may be quite aware of warm sunshine or of cold water. Similarly, he may have awareness of urine, feces, milk, or contact with the mother. Of course, the infant learns gradually to differentiate these external experiences and gastro-intestinal functions and eventually learns to identify them and to think and talk about them. This process of differentiation, identification, and labeling, however, applies primarily to external sensory experience and overt behavior, which present a need for and a relative facility in communication to others.

With the probable exception of such elementary states as fatigue and hunger, the infant's differentiation of internal states proceeds more crudely, is later in development, and is subject to more incorrect identification and communication than is the case with external perception. This is also true because these internal states are less subject to consensual validation and, also being variable, are more subject to distortion, neglect or oversight (with constriction), and to blocking or inhibitions (with repression) that may be fostered by parental and other environmental factors. In our culture, emphasis on the awareness, differentiation and communication of internal states is slight compared to emphasis on differentiation of external sensory experiences. Probably, in no culture at this time is any great emphasis placed on the differential analysis of internal sensory experience. Nevertheless, as the child develops, he usually becomes more aware of different psychological states, and he more frequently uses the rather crude and vague terms commonly employed to communicate them, namely, love, anger, fear, happiness, irritation, indifference, and the like.

The pros and cons of the relative emphases on external sensory experience and internal perception, both cognitive and sensory, are matters of both practical and philosophical consideration that need not be weighed here. However, the important fact should be emphasized that in our present culture the child's early learning revolves, first, around external sensory experiences, second, around differential perceptions and relationships of that experience, and third, around further cognitive relationships leading to abstract symbols and ideas. Finally, the child's early learning revolves around the vague identification of internal psychological states in which the identification of internal sensations is de-emphasized, probably because such differential identification has not as yet been proved to him to be of any great practical value except in association with hunger and thirst.

It should be added also that even in the learning of the identification of internal psychological states, they are not usually clearly differentiated from more complex and involved cognitive associations or even from some external sensory associations. For example, when the child thinks of the term love, he will most probably associate this in an undifferentiated manner with the giving and receiving of things and privileges, or with certain specific persons rather than think of love in terms of the inner feeling itself. Such lack of differentiation of inner experience doubtless applies to many adults. Nevertheless, in the actual experiencing of these things, the differential nature of the experiences involved needs to be kept in mind if one is accurately to perceive and evaluate the functioning of a given individual. Thus, the experience of love may well be associated at a given time, or even frequently, with given cognitive and external sensory circumstances, whereas at another time the same psychological state will probably be associated with different perceptual and external sensory circumstances. The psychological state, or feeling, itself is a differential aspect of the individual's experience, and it is conceivable that such psychological states may be subject to more precise and differential description by the individual than has so far been achieved if research is squarely focused on this need.

PERSONALITY CLASSIFICATIONS

The bridge from these conceptual and developmental considerations to psychopathological clinical considerations is an easy one to make (338). Reference has just been made to the narcissistic nature of the small infant. He is egocentrically concerned primarily with his own needs, demands, and body distinctions. To this extent, he is more aware of internal sensory experience than of external sensations, although early in life he seemingly lacks the cognitive ability to make clear-cut distinctions between either his internal or external environment. These preoccupations seemingly gradually lead to meaningful learning in the respect that the infant comes to distinguish his body from his crib, his toes from his feet, and even perhaps his colic from his hunger. Gradually, and to some extent simultaneously, he is able to differentiate his external sensory environment and distinguish between his mother and other adult figures. Thus, in the normal course of development there is a shift from almost complete self-occupation to interest in the external environment and in other people. The individual slowly becomes mature to the extent that he can value, and identify with, other persons, things, and ideals, and to the extent that he can delay his own immediate impulses and demands in order to achieve a final goal that is to the best interest of himself and all concerned.

Some clinical standpoints tend to place more emphasis on the gradual and comprehensive nature of such maturing in the infant's learning and development (396, 398, 438, 439, 598, 600, 789, 890, 891, 1219) whereas others place somewhat more emphasis on certain stages of psychosexual development (oral and anal) (299, 337, 353, 384). In the consideration of psychopathology, however, the final result is about the same irrespective of this difference in relative theoretical emphasis. From all points of view, the individual's relative awareness of himself and of his environment, and the individual's tendencies to focus his awareness in different directions, are recognized to be important factors both in development and in the etiology of psychopathology. Some of the diagnoses that more readily lend themselves to analysis in these respects will be considered in general and simplified terms.

The *schizophrenic* and the *character-disorder* personality types reflect a relative lack of progress in the individuals concerned beyond the infantile, narcissistic stage of development. The common denominator here is their preoccupation with their own needs and impulses and their relative inability to identify, empathize, or value (that is, invest emotional interest in) other people. The focusing of awareness by these two broad diagnostic types, however, is quite different. The schizophrenic focuses his awareness predominantly on his own ideational processes; the early or latent schizophrenic is preoccupied much with fantasy activity, and the more acute schizophrenic is preoccupied with symbolic, confused and relatively arbitrary thought processes. In some types of early schizophrenics, particularly the paranoid, their cognitive orientation appears to be in part an aspect of a constriction, or "cutting off" of awareness of other internal perceptions. Beck describes such internal perceptions as "the complex of organic sensations, with their affective quality, which I have identified as the substance of emotion, and which is represented by 'C' " (or color, on the Rorschach inkblots) (94).

The character-disorder personality types tend to focus awareness more on the external environment in an effort to perceive and manipulate it to their own ends. Neither of these two broad personality types is generally very aware of his feelings, impulses and internal sensations that extend beyond the cognitive dimension of experience. The character-disorder personality types generally "act out" the changes that are taking place in their internal environment without actually focusing much awareness on the origin or nature of these internal changes.

The schizophrenics, in their various stages, are much more complex in this respect. Frequently, these patients bring out rather startling cognitive insights, even at times relating them to ideas concerning feelings and impulses. More frequently, and, certainly, in reference to the acute stages, there is an apparent dissociation between the cognitive processes and other dimensions of inner experience, including "feeling and emotion." Physiologically, there is some evidence (see p. 126) for thinking of this clinical dissociation as reflecting dissociation between cortical activity on the one hand and peripheral sensory impulses (and perhaps also facilitating or redirecting midbrain activity) on the other hand. In this connection, it should also be emphasized that the frequent somatic delusions described by schizophrenics are probably more truly cognitive than sensory.

The *neuroses* are considered to represent predominantly stages somewhat farther along the course of ontogenetic development. Again the multiple combinations and variations of psychopathological diagnostic types shall not be discussed; one must realize, however, that none of these diagnostic classifications are truly mutually exclusive, but rather represent rough classifications of constellations of observed personality characteristics. The neuroses represent stages of development in which the individual has become more aware of his environment, is capable of making emotional investments in it, and is even more aware of cognitive values that signify the assuming of responsibilities toward others (the "superego"). What the neurotic is unable to do, without inducing conflict, is to focus awareness on certain aspects of his internal environment that involve noncognitive internal perceptive experience, or "feelings" and "impulses." Thus, the neurotic is said to be unable to recognize and accept certain feelings or emotions, as well as certain associated cognitive content (impulses, wishes, etc.) that are connected with his conflictual affects and etiologically underlie them.

Instead of focusing awareness on these affects, and associated cognitions, the obsessive (and phobic) neurotic individual focuses awareness predominantly on other ("displaced") cognitions. To the extent that these neurotic persons are also compulsive, the obsessions are acted out by repetitious or meticulous behaviors of various kinds. In some cases this preoccupation with cognition is similar to that of the schizophrenic, and indeed sometimes regression to the schizophrenic levels takes place in an obsessive-neurotic personality, although the mental integration of the obsessive-compulsive neurotic is better than that of the schizophrenic.

The hysterical neurotic, on the other hand, apparently lacks the ability to focus awareness predominantly on ideational or fantasy cognitions as a mechanism of escaping awareness of unacceptable affects and associated cognitions. Therefore, the focus of awareness toward all aspects of internal perception is relatively reduced and is shifted in the direction of the external environment (including even his own body parts). This emphasis on external perception is similar to that seen in the character-disorder personality types to the extent that inner experiences are *accessible* to immediate awareness, i.e., they are "felt" but are not recognized or given attention, and are acted out in part by manipulation of the environment. However, the hysteric is more capable of making true emotional investments in dependency relationships than are the antisocial or asocial types of character disorder. The hysterical neurotic at times makes his extreme demands upon the environment by manifesting so-called conversion syndromes by which he is functionally incapacitated in one way or the other, such as blindness or a paralysis of the leg. Most frequently, the manipulative aspects of such symptoms are considered to be secondary, since the affective conflict of which the hysterical neurotic is unaware (because he has repressed it) is considered to be the primary factor, and therefore the symptom simply seems to provide a place to focus external awareness instead of permitting awareness of the ("threatening") internal environment. The more traditional view is that some sort of "libidinal energy" is channelized into the nonfunctioning body area. There appears to be little physiological basis for such a theory, but neurophysiological functioning reveals that such types of organ "paralysis" might take place at the cortical or thalamic levels within the *projection system* for bodily awareness.

In the neurotic, as in the schizophrenic and the character-disorder personality types, there appears to be a relative lack of awareness of the non-cognitive aspect of internal perception, whether it is constituted by internal sensation, feeling, or anything else. With the possible exception of the severe chronic types, however, the neurotics experience awareness of the noncognitive (the "feeling and emotion") aspect of the internal environment to a greater extent than the psychotics. This awareness, which involves conflictual associations, constantly threatens them and frequently results in overactive responses to stimuli.

A reaction that cannot be so readily classified in terms of relative awareness is the state of *depression*. By this is meant not only clinical depression but any feeling of extreme nonagitated sorrow or sadness. In this clinical state, cognitive activity is greatly reduced, and there is even less relative awareness of the immediate external environment. What, then, is the predominant content of awareness in such depressive states? Two alternatives are presented: either the individual is aware of nothing at all, or he is focusing awareness on the noncognitive area of internal perception that is implied by the concept "feeling of depression"; this last alternative appears the most reasonable. To what extent this may also be true for elated or manic states is difficult to postulate; it is clear, however, that in such states the focus of awareness on external sensation, as well as on ideation, is not fixed or consistent, leaving open the possibility of a relatively great focusing on internal, noncognitive experience. Although in the manic and depressive psychoses, as in all psychoses, there is a certain disorganization of cognitive activity, the relatively favorable initial prognosis in these cases may have some connection with this apparent difference in the focusing of awareness in comparison with the schizophrenic reactions.

The relatively *normal,* or *mentally healthy,* person is seen to be more capable of focusing awareness on the various aspects of his external and internal environment without being overly disturbed by what he perceives. Thus, he is better able to integrate the various aspects of his personality into comfortable and efficient functioning. It is apparent that the ability to focus awareness on the noncognitive internal environment, and to do so without associated cognitive conflicts, is essential to healthy "mental" and "emotional" functioning.

RELATIVE AWARENESS AND PSYCHOLOGICAL INSTRUMENTS

Findings by means of clinical psychological instruments support conclusions that have just been made that indicate the relative direction of awareness by the different psychopathological types. The concepts presented here are greatly simplified and are based on a composite of clinical experience and of general clinical research findings. In early schizophrenia, ambulatory schizophrenia, and the so-called "overideational preschizophrenia" (1019), the Rorschach experience balance is generally introversive, emphasizing the "M" orientation toward cognitive activity (fantasy, obsessive preoccupations, delusions, etc.), and personalized preoccupations are likely to result in a low A% and may even embody unconventional attitudes, lowering the P%. Also these cognitive preoccupations tend to enhance the verbal score on the Wechsler

Intelligence Scale, whereas the patient's withdrawal from environmental interests and activities tends to lower his performance score. This cognitive orientation apparently constitutes a defense against unacceptable noncognitive perceptions, for in the acute schizophrenic state the "M" activity is not so frequently reflected in the Rorschach protocol but instead uncontrolled inner emotionality and impulsivity are reflected in the "C" and "CF" predominance of color responsivity. This, of course, does not negate the possibility of active fantasy or of symbolic cognitive activity. The relative absence of "M" is an aspect of the withdrawal of the schizophrenic, with the result that he can no longer accurately perceive and integrate the external stimulus and can no longer so easily fantasy relationships with other people.

The schizophrenic patient's fluctuating withdrawal from the external perceptual orientation is also reflected in his fluctuating performance on all psychological instruments, and this is usually demonstrated quite well by his response pattern on the Wechsler Intelligence Scale. In this connection, on all such instruments, the schizophrenic produces content that indicates a withdrawal from a consensual validation orientation into his own peculiar cognitive orientation (e.g., bizarreness, clang associations, arbitrary responses, negativistic thinking, and so forth). Similarly, the content of the Rorschach protocol may show dehumanization, morbid deterioration, sex responses, poor anatomy responses, and the like. On such projective instruments as the Thematic Apperception Test and the Sentence Completion Test, the schizophrenic's cognitive orientation is frequently reflected in productions that suggest the presence of remarkable insights or reveal extremely strong aggressive and sexual impulses. The remarkable insights are usually indicative of cognitive "intellectualization," and the aggressive or sexual impulses are indicative of a yielding of the defensive cognitive orientation to unacceptable noncognitive perceptions (e.g., "emotionality" and "impulses"). Productions that are slightly less pathological in this respect are indecisive and markedly fluctuating themes presented with several alternative responses, reflect a weakening of the cognitive defenses.

Paranoid schizophrenia, and other so-called paranoid or paranoiac conditions, differ somewhat from the other schizophrenic types, and this difference permits much more diverse personality constellations and much less uniform psychological productions than are generally produced by schizophrenic types that are not predominantly paranoid in nature. With the paranoid condition, the predominant cognitive orientation is generally limited to a constellation of fantasies, delusions or phobic apprehensions that are somehow relatively isolated from most of the paranoid individual's cognitive activities and abilities. The paranoid individual is usually able to focus awareness on external sensations, even though he may guardedly refuse to communicate his perception of them at times. He will therefore usually be able to show relatively good intellectual functioning on structured materials because these do not usually invade his isolated area of pathological cognitive orientation.

Frequently, the paranoid patient's internal cognitive orientation is not reflected by the Rorschach "M," which represents percepts including human movement, because he is so fearful and hostile about people that he has difficulty in perceiving them, and frequently his percepts are confined to heads or to distorted human figures. Since the paranoid patient's cognitive abilities remain fairly well intact, he frequently realizes that his isolated area of pathological cognitive activity is unacceptable, at least to other people. It is partially for this reason that he is so guarded in his unstructured perceptual productions. This is so much the case that frequently in mild or early condition, the paranoid himself does not seem to be clearly aware of his own underlying (pathological) cognitive activity or tendencies. In such cases, this activity apparently takes place at relatively nonconscious cognitive levels. It is also conceivable that an individual's personality dynamics are such that a pathological paranoid process may be in the making but may not have reached the stage of cognitive (delusional) development. Thus, an orientation toward a paranoid process is more frequently reflected in the associative content of the material produced than in the format of the psychological protocol. Yet, records obtained during the mild or early paranoid process show on the one hand an extremely conventional emphasis, whereas on the other hand there is usually greatly decreased productivity and emotional constriction, and along with this, sex-role confusion is usually seen. In acute or chronically severe cases, a more obvious kind of guardedness or evasiveness is seen, although psychopathological cognitive preoccupations are also suggested by vague perseverative responses (such as "maps" or "heads") along with a frequent inability to give conventional percepts. Some paranoid individuals focus relatively less attention (awareness) on internal cognitive activity, and externalize their rather specific delusions by focusing awareness either on the environment, usually on other people (with "projection") or on somatic delusions (hyochondriacal pains, odors, and so forth). Thus, with the paranoid personality type, awareness is directed in various ways depending on many factors in the given case, and they range from those approximating normal functioning (except for a limited area of pathological process) to those resembling the deteriorated generalized schizophrenic condition. The psychological protocols will vary accordingly.

The predominant orientation of the character-disorder personalities is usually toward the environment and this is shown by a color ("C")-weighted experience balance on the Rorschach protocol. The de-emphasis on cognitive activity usually, but not always, results in a relatively lower verbal score on the Wechsler Intelligence Scale and in a comparative emphasis on visual-motor co-ordination and skill in environmental perception, thus producing a relatively high performance score on these instruments. Because cognitive processes are intact, the intellectual functioning is fairly even, and with bright subjects it is often at a high level throughout all psychological instruments. The structure of the personality is generally reflected in the content of projective productions, as for example on the Thematic Apperception Test, the Make-a-Picture Stories, and the Sentence Completion Test, as well as by the performances already noted.

The productions of the hysterical neurotic resemble those of the character-disorder type in the extrotensive perceptual orientation, as well as in many other respects. There is a major difference, which is that at some level of internal perceptual organization there exist conflicts that result in some degrees of guilt and anxiety. Therefore, although the general orientation of the hysteric is extrotensive, there is some distraction by conflicts in the internal environment, resulting in such things as lowered digit span and arithmetic scores on the Wechsler Intelligence Scale, some difficulty on the tachistoscopic presentation of the Bender—Gestalt drawings at times, and low productivity on unstructured projective instruments. Due to lack of cognitive awareness, the hysteric manifests rather immature content material, stereotyped ideas, vague conventional thinking, and also blasé, optimistic attitudes, which are in accordance with the denial and repression of his own conflicts. These characteristics are reflected by their recognized correlates on the psychological protocols, and they frequently tend to raise the hysteric patient's score on the comprehension subtest of the Wechsler Intelligence Scale, whereas his extrotensive orientation, or lack of cognitive orientation, tends to lower his information and vocabulary scores.

The psychological protocol of the obsessive neurotic will vary with the amount of compulsivity also manifested in his personality, and of course the directing of awareness will vary accordingly. When little compulsivity is present, the characteristics of the obsessive neurotic's record resemble those described for the early or latent schizophrenic except for the fact that the neurotic's cognitive functioning is less disturbed, and indeed his perceptions may be rigidly and defensively accurate. According to the degree that obsessive-neurotic patients have compulsive characteristics, they will show features in their psychological productions of the type described above for the hysterical neurotic. The individuals who have both hysterical and obsessive-compulsive features are appropriately labeled "mixed neurotics."

The individual who really shows more pronounced compulsive symptoms is more frequently described by writers when the diagnosis of obsessive-compulsive neurosis is considered. With this neurosis, there is great fluctuation in the direction of awareness between cognitive obsessions (reflecting "M" on the Rorschach protocol) and the compulsive acting out by overt behavior that directs awareness externally (reflecting "C" on the Rorschach). This directing of awareness externally represents a further displacement and externalization to avoid the conflictual internal perceptual area. The undecided, fluctuating state of mind is frequently reflected throughout all the psychological instruments. As already noted, a marked degree of such fluctuation is very pathological and is indicative of a failure of the displacement mechanism, which leads either to cognitive disorganization and psychosis or to further externalization of a paranoid nature. The cognitive orientation of the compulsive neurotic usually enhances intellectual achievement, which in turn, in the form of intellectualization and pedantic meticulousness, is used as a compulsive defense, further emphasizing cognitive awareness. Therefore the verbal score on the Wechsler Intelligence Scale is likely to be elevated, even though anxiety and inner distractibility may lower the digit-span score and, to a lesser extent, the arithmetic score. At the same time the extrotensive orientation also enables the compulsive-neurotic patient to do well on the performance scale of this instrument, particularly where critical analysis of details is concerned, as in the picture-completion subtest; however, cognitive distractibility and indecisiveness may slow him, thus lowering the scores on some of the other performance items. On the Rorschach protocol, the combination of cognitive and external perceptive orientation usually results in very high productivity despite the compulsive neurotic's indecisiveness, criticalness, excessive elaborations, and frequent emphasizing of small details. Usually, the cognitive emphasis is reflected in the predominance of "FC" Rorschach-protocol responses (or good color usage), but the usage of color is dependent upon the continuum of relative compulsive characteristics of the individual neurotic.

In depressed patients the lack of cognitive and of external sensory orientations, reflected by an absence of "M" and "C" on the Rorschach protocol, has already been noted, and this lack is also reflected in very limited and slow productions on all psychological instruments. In agitated depressions, however, there is generally an obsessive ("M") orientation, but frequently a predominance of a less mature type of cognitive activity is reflected by "FM" responses on the Rorschach protocol. The productions that are forthcoming from the very depressed person usually clearly indicate his depressive feelings and associated ideation. These are reflected in the themes of the Thematic Apperception Test stories, and Sentence Completion Test productions, as well as in inquiries to Sentence Completion and responses to the Cornell Index. This is also reflected by the relatively "pure C" responses that are occasionally given to the Rorschach test as well as by the relatively frequent blackness (C') responses. In manic, or elated, states the relative diversity of awareness is much more complex, and similarly, the psychological productions are complex to analyze.

NOSOLOGY

It should again be emphasized that the diagnostic types described here are not usually seen as mutually exclusive entities in the clinical settings or in everyday experience, but rather a particular personality may combine any number of the characteristics that were presented, as well as other characteristics. The basic personality characteristics that have been noted can be employed in analyzing the psychological productions of any person, and a nosological classification need not necessarily be used.

Actually, a classification of personality with a nosological system based on the relative focus, or "direction," of awareness on the part of individuals and of groups of individuals may be of more functional value, as well as of more practical usefulness, than the conventional diagnostic classification referred to in this section. Thus, reference may be made to *cognitively oriented* individuals of relatively psychotic, neurotic, or normal types, respectively. Similarly, one might refer to *externally oriented* individuals of hysterical, character-disorder, or normal types. Also, individuals with *fluctuating orientation* would include compulsive, mixed-neurotic, schizoid, and perhaps, manic-depressive types. The last, however, as well as anxiety states, depressive states, and possibly other states of clinical significance, which may not as yet have been clearly differentiated, perhaps fall into the *noncognitive-inner-orientation* classification. Such a classification system would avoid the stigma and the erroneous implications of the conventional diagnostic classifications when applied to relatively normal individuals.

In practice, the use of personality classifications for a given person, whether the classification is considered "abnormal" or not, usually hinges on one of two factors. Either a person feels so uncomfortable with his own internal environment that he seeks help in a medical or neuropsychiatric setting, or the person's behavior is so disturbing to other people that he is sent for personality evaluation. This unacceptable behavior, of course, arises out of disturbances in the internal environment.

It is apparent that the emotionally healthy person is relatively more comfortable with his internal environment and has more ready access in awareness to it. The value of focusing awareness on perception of the internal environment has received increasing emphasis in psychotherapeutic techniques in recent years (8, 384, 661, 662, 937, 1014, 1219, 1237). Awareness of the noncognitive area embodying "feeling and emotion" has been found to be particularly important in this respect (125, 321, 366, 808, 1022, 1023, 1050, 1051, 1052, 1053, 1053b, 1119).

Part 11

Various General and
Theoretical Approaches
Involving Concepts of
the Noncognitive Area
of Internal Perception

CHAPTER 4

Orientation

INTERRELATEDNESS AND ANALYSIS

Most psychological references and studies do not evaluate inner experience in terms of having characteristics functionally distinct or separate from ideational experience. Indeed, the usual emphasis is quite the opposite in portraying the integrative nature not only of all inner experience but of all experience, including external sensory and perceptive experience. The point of view presented here does not deny the essential truthfulness and importance of the integrative aspects of all experience. It will simply be emphasized here that analysis is essential to understanding and to scientific investigation. So it is that internal experience needs to be analyzed to the extent that differential aspects can be determined in order really to understand the composite functioning.

Much has been done, and is being done, in this respect with cognition and perception studies, such as those involving learning, problem solving, attitudes, psychometrics, abolition influences, and semantics. Not for many years have experimental psychologists to any great extent attempted to analyze noncognitive aspects of inner experience. As shall be demonstrated, the studies allegedly relating to "feeling and emotion," or "affect," that were done by psychologists in the early decades of this twentieth century, embodied a frame of reference so very different from that of the modern psychologist that their results are of limited meaningfulness today.

Some theorists have proposed that instincts constitute the noncognitive sphere of inner experience, but such classifications were vague, rather arbitrary judgments without semantic substance in terms of consensual validation or experimental references (828, 829, 830, 848).

More recently, considerable literature has been devoted to drives, needs, motivations, and so forth, but studies concerning these constructs have

57

usually been related to cognitive experiments involving learning, problem solving, physiological changes, deprivations, and the like. Nevertheless, all of these concepts are considered in different ways by different people to relate somehow to inner experiences that go beyond the sphere of cognition. The literature and studies that most people are likely to consider foremost in this respect are those concerning "feeling and emotion." Studies and concepts relating to this field will be presented first.

TERMINOLOGY

The preceding section gives some hint of the semantic confusion concerning the noncognitive area of inner experience. Many authors have exemplified the equally great confusion concerning the more generally recognized field of "feeling and emotion." Landis reviewed the usages of the term "feeling" to include: (1) experience less vivid than emotion; (2) vaguely perceived kinesthetic and organic sensations; and (3) a general attitude favoring either positive or negative reactions to possible future stimuli or situations (746). Similarly, Ruckmick (1071) indicated that there have been four meanings attached to the term "feeling": (1) any kind of experiences or awareness; (2) practically identical with tactual sensations, with touch; (3) an impression of bodily welfare as we become aware of it (as "better" or "worse") ; and (4) a cognitive element or choice (as "right" or "wrong"). It should be added that the terms "affection" and "affective experience" have been used in many ways, ranging from specific judgments of "pleasantness" to total emotional experiences.

Many modern psychologists, such as Rapaport (1020) and Hebb (543) used emotional terminology primarily to refer to "violent and unpleasant emotions." In contrast is Lindsley's (795) broad use of the term "emotion, ranging from unanticipated sensory stimulation, as in 'startle,' to ideationally maintained tensions," as in chronic "anxiety states." A more extreme view maintains that emotion is an "inference" or "scientific construct," meaning that the term represents a cognitive abstraction derived from external perceptive experience (158). Masserman (880, 881) presented other variations in the use of the term "emotion."

Perhaps the most common usage of the term is set forth by Papez (968), who differentiates between "emotion" as emotional expression and "emotion" as emotional experience or subjective feeling. The term "feeling" can perhaps most appropriately be employed to designate the internal perceptive act, reserving "emotion" to include, and to refer to, the behavioral expressions that may accompany feelings. The exact nature of the concept "feeling" and the specific physiological changes to which it may refer still remain unclear.

TYPES OF APPROACH

One aspect of the variety of meanings that are associated with the semantics of the noncognitive area of inner experience is the multiplicity of approaches that scientific and clinical people have taken. Before going into details concerning the work done with any one approach, it will be well to note what the various approaches have been. The first approach in experimental psychology was what might be called the stimulus-reaction analysis, which was employed in the general dispute between Titchener and Wundt over feeling dimensions as opposed to affective quality. This approach can be considered as only one type of a broader approach that utilizes the study of immediate awareness of inner experience by human subjects. At the same time a clinical approach, which later became very extensive, started to emerge. During this late nineteenth-century period the "phenomenologists" also studied inner experience. At the turn of the century, the Gestaltists also referred to phenomena that fall in the category of noncognitive internal perception. To some extent psychologists and geneticists with a maturational or developmental emphasis have presented views relating to noncognitive inner experience. Several different approaches that employ the more general technique of making inferential constructs concerning noncognitive inner experience also exist. Other workers interested in this area have made more direct behavior inferences, and still others draw conclusions from what can be called judgmental reactions.

Another approach toward the understanding of inner experience, and more specifically "feeling and emotion," has been the correlations of physiological reactions and changes corresponding to psychological states. This approach, however, is really separate from the study of inner experience per se and will be so presented in Part III. Finally, the approach that deals with study of the sensory aspect of inner experience constitutes a rather specific and relatively well-defined area and therefore it can be presented separately in Part IV.

CHAPTER 5

The Immediate-Awareness Approaches

THE STIMULUS-REACTION ANALYSIS APPROACH

WUNDT'S CONCEPTS

The earliest organized scientific studies attempting to analyze internal non-cognitive experiences were carried out in Wundt's laboratory in Leipzig and, more particularly, in Titchener's laboratory at Cornell. These studies usually employed simple sensory stimuli, such as pieces of colored paper or chemicals with strong odors. When the experimental subject perceived one of these stimuli, he then described his internal state or reaction. Frequently, textbooks refer to this type of approach as the "method of impression"; however, the methodology of these early studies generally was limited to the presentation of stimuli and the recording of the subject's description of his reactions.

Studies employing the methodology followed in the wake of Wundt's three-dimensional theory of feeling that he put forth at the turn of the twentieth century. At first, Wundt subscribed to the view that feeling is merely a quality of sensation, but he later gave it a separate status (591). He also distinguished feeling from ideation, and maintained that feeling is immediate to experience and palpable. E. H. Hollands stated also that Wundt held "pure sensation" to be the original element of the perceptive process. Feeling and sensation were considered to be the subjective and objective aspects respectively of the classification "pure sensation." Wundt's theory of feeling was formulated subjectively. It was thus purely hypothetical and was similar to the views of some of his predecessors. Nevertheless, his theory was the basis for the first experimental work in this field, and it may be considered the forerunner to subsequent theories that relate "feeling and emotion" to internal sensory perceptions. Wundt maintained that feelings vary in quality and intensity and that feelings are experienced in three primary dimensions, each dimension being polar and varying in two extremes. The dimensions included: pleasantness-unpleasantness, arousing (exciting)-sub-

60

duing (depressing), and strain-relaxing (1373). His theory also included the combining of these dimensions into more complex "compounds of feelings."

TITCHENER'S CONCEPTS

Most of the experimental work that was done concerning Wundt's theory came under the influence of Titchener. Titchener employed the stimulus-reaction analysis technique described above, mostly using the method of paired comparisons. His conclusion did not support Wundt's theory; however, Wundt asserted that the technique employed by Titchener would tend to produce a "complex" or a "fusion" of feeling and could not therefore constitute proof or disproof of the existence of the feeling dimensions or "affective qualities" that were postulated (1071). The further theoretical and experimental developments that relate "feeling and emotion" to internal sensory experiences will be outlined in Part IV.

In 1899, Titchener asked a subject to make observations of his actual emotional experiences for the period of a year (95). This subject was able to analyze his experiences in terms of Wundt's dimensions only by the employing of sensory terminology. Titchener and those who supported his view, however, defined feeling as a faculty that excludes the faculty, or experience, of sensation, and therefore they maintained that feeling could not be described. In the final analysis, the only terms that these psychologists would accept for a description of feeling were "pleasantness" and "unpleasantness." Thus, their conclusions were limited by their definition of the term feeling.

Many experiments to investigate "feeling," as defined to exclude sensation, were performed by Titchener and his students at Cornell. As noted above, they usually employed the technique of paired comparisons and presented such simple stimuli as colored paper, geometrical forms, odors, and so forth. The results were almost always the same: the subjects reported various internal sensations, as well as "pleasantness" and "unpleasantness" and other descriptions of their reactions. When it was indicated that the internal sensations were not to be considered, the subjects finally restricted themselves to the acceptable terminology of relative pleasantness. Titchener maintained that since the subjects could report their "feelings" in terms of "pleasantness-unpleasantness" while ignoring the internal sensations, the latter were not basic and necessary to the experiential quality, "feeling." He termed this experience "affective quality," differentiating it as a faculty or dimension of experience, separate from sensation and from cognition.

The basic fallacy in Titchener's logic was that he thought in terms of coequal faculties or dimensions of experience. It was as though dimensions of experience could be "horizontally" classified at the same level. This overlooks the possibility of what might be called "vertical" classification wherein the semantics at various levels of abstraction are based on, and derived from, more concrete experiences at lower levels. Thus, it may be that the term "feeling," as used by Titchener, is derived semantically from more concrete, or less abstract experiences, such as internal sensations.

Titchener believed that feeling differs from sensation in that it cannot be made the object of direct awareness. Feelings, he maintained, lack the quality of "clearness" (1249). Actually, Titchener's view was not very different from that of Wundt. Titchener proposed that "simple feelings" blend with sensation to produce "sense feeling" of six classifications: agreeable and disagreeable, exciting and subduing, and, finally, straining and relaxing. Note the similarity of these polar concepts to those of Wundt. Except for the definition of the term "feeling," Titchener had completely accepted Wundt's theory. He also held the view that organic sensations play a large part in emotion as kinesthetic sensations do in perception (1249).

By 1926 Titchener (1250, p. 226) proposed "that there is an elementary affective process, a feeling-element, which in our minds is coordinate with sensation and distinguishable from it, but which is nevertheless akin to sensation and is derived from the same . . . kind of primitive material: this elementary process is termed affection." Here he appears to be thinking of "feeling" as a higher-order abstraction that is derived from more concrete experiences, including sensation.

ELABORATIONS AND DECLINE OF TITCHENERIAN CONCEPTS

After Harlow and Stagner reviewed the literature in the Titchenerian tradition, they "attempted to show that there are four differentiated feelings: pain-unpleasantness, pleasure-pleasantness, excitation, and depression" (524, 525).

Also in 1932 and also in the Titchenerian tradition, Beebe-Center proposed the use of the term "hedonic tone" (95). He accepted Titchener's affective-quality concept and conceived of the term "feeling" as an abstraction. After a consideration of the multiple uses of affective terminology, Beebe-Center proposed that the multiple implications of the well-known terms could be avoided by using the term "hedonic tone," which should apply strictly to the quality "pleasantness-unpleasantness" as "algebraic variables."

Ruckmick also adhered to the Titchenerian concept of feeling. He drew on more recent organic theories and experimentation to support the view that "affective quality" has an organic basis that is beyond the scope of conscious differentiation. His phylogenetic theory was presented as follows (1071, p. 214):

1. The affective life begins with consciousness itself in the lowest forms of animal life. The simple or elementary feelings, or the affective processes, are to be identified with this early form of experience. In other words, consciousness is nothing more than feeling in the technical sense of the word.

2. As the mental life develops, this elementary phase of consciousness spreads from whole to part in the sense that it becomes attached to, that it permeates through, every succeeding phase of developing conscious processes. On the neural side, therefore, no such receptor or effector mechanism is required, since none was needed in the first place when the animal was nothing more than a single cell. It uses, however, all existing channels for the conveyance of electrochemical energy, especially those structures like the sympathetic and parasympathetic branches of the autonomic system and the plexuses, which most speedily transmit energy from the whole organism to the part.

Ruckmick clearly brought focus on the issue of whether or not "pleasantness" and "unpleasantness" are unconsciously formed judgments beyond the possibility of elementary analysis, or whether they are based on more elementary experiences, such as internal sensations, of which the individual may become aware.

The methodology employed by Titchener and his students resulted in reports of internal sensory experience along with the other subjective terminology. Finally, these sensory experiences were proclaimed by Nafe and others as being important aspects of feeling experience. These developments, however, will be presented in more detail in Part IV.

The stimulus-reaction approach, along with impressionistic and subjective methodologies in general, lost popularity, partially due to the influence of behaviorism, and disappeared from general experimental usage. More emphasis came to be placed on the study of various physiological reactions that ensue from the presentation of stimuli, such as sudden noises and movements, moving pictures, frogs or worms on the hand, and so forth. Such stimuli were usually presumed to produce certain emotions or feelings in the experimental subject. The interest in this type of experimentation was enhanced by the controversies over the theories of men such as James and Lange, who proposed a peripheral physiological and sensory basis of "feeling and emotion," as opposed to the theories of men such as Head and Cannon, who proposed a central-nervous-system physiological basis for "feeling and emotion." These developments will be considered in detail in Part III.

THE HEDONIC THEORY

A "hedonic theory" of motivation, which places primary emphasis on noncognitive inner experiences, has been proposed by P. T. Young (1382a). Primary motivation was considered to lie in the "affective processes" that include awareness of feelings of delight, distress, anger, anxiety, embarrassment, and the like. Such affective processes were thought to have "objective existence," and the human organism was viewed as behaving in a way to maximize positive affective arousal (delight, enjoyment) and to minimize negative arousal (distress). Thus, affective processes arouse, sustain, terminate, and direct patterns of behavior. Acquired motives represent preparatory sets of the organism that are associated with persistent tensions from the proprioceptors and visceral structures. The strength of such tension was thought to be in proportion to hedonic intensity and to the duration and frequency of affective arousal. Young felt that stimulus-response theories are inadequate to explain the psychological factors he set forth.

THE HORMIC THEORY

McDougall's hormic theory conceived of human functioning as being directed by drives, impulses, propensities, or instincts, and affection (or pleasant and unpleasant feelings) was thought to depend on the success of conation (will) (361a, 828, 829, 1370). In this tradition, an introspective study was done by Flugel with nine subjects and produced the following "feeling" classifications: (1) for pleasant states: interest, joy, contentment, pleasant sensations (emphasizing muscular ones), "positive functional feeling," food; and (2) for unpleasant states: unpleasant sensations (emphasizing aches and pains), anxiety and worry, anger (and irritation), fatigue, boredom and depression (361a).

INDIAN CONCEPTS

Mention should also be made of psychology in India, which at this time is in a very early stage of scientific development but promises to be a significant new contribution to the science of psychology because it stems from a tradition quite different from that of Western culture. It has an introspective emphasis and includes many concepts and subtle differentiations regarding noncognitive inner experience.

Scientific scrutiny of noncognitive inner experience as it is conceived by Indian psychologists is difficult for Westerners because the concepts are so closely related to ancient religious beliefs and are supposedly comprehended only by contemplation and "revelation" (57, 57a, 1124). An emphasis on noncognitive inner experience is clearly seen (57, p. 103):

> Thus according to Indian psychology, *samkalpaka* or cognition, including perception and volition, is only a small part of the whole mind. Mind is essentially, and for the larger part, feeling. Feeling is the background and source of all the activities and experiences of the animal. The animal is made up of a scheme of feeling which means self-expansion, consisting in breaking the barrier of the external world and attaching it to the being of the self. With such a meaning of the animal and its mind, an act of perception or volition is much superficial to the whole mind. The whole mind is a process of breaking into feeling by the execution of volition, the external object given by perception.

Bagchi lists thirty-three "passing feelings" of "dullness" arising from chemical changes going on within the body, such as "exhaustion," "self-disparagement," "apprehension," "rapture," "contentment," "gladness," "sorrow," and "eagerness." Eight "permanent feelings" representing the "permanent unconscious wishes of the animal" and constituting the "permanent fundamental motive-forces" underlying all the experiences and activities of man are presented: "*rati*-love; *hāsa*-laughter; *śoka*-grief; *krodha*-anger; *utsāha*-inspiration; *bhaya*-fear; *jugupsa*-disgust; *vismaya*-wonder." Finally, the classification of "mental feelings," consisting of "the feelings of fullness of feeling" and conceived of as spiritual feelings was presented.

THE "CONSCIOUS APPROACH"

I have presented another conceptual approach that utilizes the individual's immediate awareness of his own experience for the study of noncognitive internal perception. This may be called "the conscious approach" because an emphasis is placed on the individual's becoming conscious (or aware) of as many aspects as possible concerning his own functioning personality dynamics and especially becoming aware of his noncognitive internal perceptive experiences, including feelings. One method of accomplishing this awareness has been presented in Chapter 1, and the implications for such study both on the part of the individual and on the part of psychology generally are suggested in the Introduction and in Part I.

CHAPTER 6

Nondefinitive Approaches

GENERAL CONCEPTS

The classification "nondefinitive approaches" refers to those theories that approach the noncognitive area of inner experience in a nonanalytic manner by either avoiding direct reference to it or by implying that it functions in such a way that consciousness (or awareness) of it is of little or no consequence. Close study of any psychological theory, however, will reveal that the noncognitive area of experience has not been completely overlooked, and the nondefinitive types of theories usually make indirect, and seemingly unwitting, references to types of noncognitive inner experiences in their semantic usages. Thus, there is no sharp line of distinction between those theories that consider noncognitive internal perception analytically and those that are relatively nondefinitive about it, but there exists instead a continuum of relative consideration and of nonconsideration of this area of inner experience. At the same time, approaches that are nondefinitive concerning noncognitive inner experience may nevertheless be very analytic concerning the cognitive and external sensory areas of experience.

Aristotle was among the first observers to report that simple feelings of pleasantness and unpleasantness arouse desire and aversion respectively and that these feelings accordingly result in bodily movements. This view also became a part of most of the so-called "hedonistic" doctrines throughout the history of philosophy.

Young, working in the Titchenerian milieu, concluded from his experimentation that a fundamental characteristic of the unpleasant responses was a tendency to withdraw, either reflexly or deliberately, from the stimulus object (1378). He reported pleasant reactions to be "an acceptance of the situation and a passive yielding to it." He gave no support, however, to the concept that pleasant reactions involve movement toward the stimulus.

66

THE JUDGMENTAL THEORY

In light of this background, with the gradual weakening of the Titchenerian tradition and with the increasing behavioristic movement, it is not surprising that in 1925 Carr formalized the concept of pleasantness and unpleasantness as representing directional reaction tendencies. He presented this as the judgmental theory: pleasantness and unpleasantness "are attributes which we ascribe to any stimulating situation in virtue of our normal reaction tendency toward it" (209, p. 290). Pleasantness was considered to be a "positive reaction" and unpleasantness, a "negative reaction."

Although Freyer (403) expressed a similar point of view in 1930, it was Peters who in 1935 really gave body to the judgmental theory (988, 989). Peters added to Carr's exposition and asserted that the meaning of "pleasantness" and "unpleasantness" is as follows (988, p. 357):

The judgmental theory acknowledges that pleasant and unpleasant are first of all words and that they, like all words in the language, have meanings gained through experience. . . . When the process by which these terms gain their meanings is analyzed, the general nature of affection will be exhausted. . . . A majority of human acts can be classed as either approach or withdrawal movements—either activity which continues the experiences or activity which cuts it short.

Peters expressed the belief that pleasantness and unpleasantness are not "ultimate experience," because they come under the broad concept of meanings. In other words, he maintained that they are cognitive, or ideational, in nature. This theory then places emphasis on cognitive experience and, more specifically, on semantics, and it de-emphasizes the importance of the noncognitive aspects of internal perception.

GESTALT CONCEPTS

Two other types of well-known psychological theories, the Gestalt and the phenomenological, are nondefinitive in their approach to the noncognitive area of inner experience. In referring to cognitive and external sensory experience, the Gestalt psychologists are relatively specific in hypothesizing different functions, such as Prägnanz, closure, and so forth. In referring to noncognitive internal experience, however, both the Gestaltists and the phenomenologists use vague subjective terminology that does not have consistent semantic content.

Gestalt psychology arose as a protest against associationism and against the analysis of sensation, images, and feelings. Analysis of these "elements," it was thought, would result in an artificial psychology of compounds, "mosaics," or "bundles." The principle of the Gestalt theory, the law of field properties, states that the whole is more than the sum of its parts (717, 1156). Nevertheless, the Gestalt theory, as all theories, does allow recognition of some analysis, and the irreducible elements of experience are considered to be perceptions, ideas, emotions, and actions. Theoretically, one can discover relations between the elements and study their development, but to analyze them further is to destroy their nature. Yet, Wertheimer's principles are certainly analytic in describing differentiated types, or areas, of perceptual functioning that apply at least to external sensory perception (332, 940, 1267). Several writers (583a, 961, 986) have recognized a limited type of analysis in Gestalt psychology.

Concerning the noncognitive area of inner experience, the Gestaltists most frequently simply refer to "tensions." This reference is exemplified by "the law of maximum work," which states that responses are made that best relieve the organism's tension toward a goal (717). In another context, Krech and Crutchfield make reference to "tension" in their Proposition III: "Instabilities in the psychological field produce 'tension' whose effects on perception, cognition, and action are such as to tend to change the field in the direction of a more stable structure." In elaborating on this, reference was made to "vague feelings of restlessness, dissatisfaction," and so forth, as well as to feelings of desires, wishes, wants, and needs (731). These approaches to internal perception avoid the focusing of awareness on, and the analysis of, noncognitive internal perception; they are thus nondefinitive in this respect.

PHENOMENOLOGICAL AND OTHER CONCEPTS

The early phenomenological psychology, just as the Gestalt, represented a protest against the traditional psychological analysis of the "mind" (140, 561, 1370).

More recently, there has been increasing emphasis on ideational activities and processes, particularly on that referred to as "ego" function (31). Thus, many theorists subscribe to nondefinitive concepts concerning noncognitive inner experience that combine the older phenomenological approach with holistic Gestalt concepts and with Allport's emphasis (30) on "functional autonomy." In these approaches, primary emphasis is placed on cognitive functioning, but at the same time some reference is made to the noncognitive internal perceptive area. This reference is exemplified in the views of

Snygg and Combs that "a very large part of what a person is describing when he speaks of his 'feeling' is made up of his awareness of the bodily conditions he differentiates at that moment out of his field" (1165). Following this statement, the importance of the noncognitive perceptual area is minimized by the assertion that behavior is not motivated by feeling but is a result of the perceptions in the field at the moment. A still more traditional type of phenomenological psychology exists in Europe (185), and vague, relatively nonanalytic references are made to all types of perceptual experience.

Also nondefinitive and very mystical are Sartre's existentialist notions concerning emotions (53a).

CHAPTER 7

Inferential-Construct Approaches

OBSERVATIONS ON BEHAVIOR

Psychologists of various orientations have employed the technique of postulating constructs concerning noncognitive internal experience on the basis of inferences from observed behavior, judgments, or statistical techniques. Brief reference has already been made to the concepts of "intervening variable" and "hypothetical construct" (see p. 40). Such constructs range from those very subjective and arbitrary in nature to those carefully postulated on the basis of statistical analysis of scientifically gathered data. An early example of the former was seen in J. B. Watson's arbitrary classification of an infant's behavior reactions in terms of love, anger, and fear (1281). In developmental studies, such as those of Bridges (149, 150), feelings and emotions of other types also were frequently inferred on the basis of given behavior. In order to study the validity of such judgments, many studies were made concerning the relative agreement of different judges in their inferring of feelings and emotions from given behavior or motor expressions.

In experiments with infants, Watson and associates employed loud noises and loss of support by the infant to produce "fear," restraint of the infant's movements to produce "rage," and tickling, stroking, sucking, and similar somesthetic stimulation to produce what they labeled as a "love" response (128, 1285, 1286). Subsequent investigators failed to find any consistent response patterns on the basis of this stimulation (293, 1004, 1233, 1243). The later experiment seemed to indicate that almost any type of stimulation, if not too extreme, results in random mass movements by the infant without any particular pattern of emotional expression, and that observers can consistently name the emotional reactions of infants only when the stimulus is known (543, 544).

Many different techniques were used to study the judgments of so-called

70

emotional expression. Boring and Titchener made up 360 interchangeable features that could be inserted in a human profile (142). The subjects did not put them together in a consistent way, but rather put them together in every conceivable way to match many common emotional terms that were listed. Similarly, Rudolph made pictures of several emotional poses of the types seen in the early moving pictures (1369). Despite the exclamatory character of the pictures, the subjects were unable to identify them "correctly." Also, Sherman and Merry conducted an experiment on emotional identification by voice inflection without significant results. It should be noted, however, that in most of these experiments the criteria of correctness were arbitrarily established in the first place.

Morgan has pointed out that lower animals certainly possess rather definite modes of emotional responses and that they should not probably be entirely dropped in man (928). Hebb has presented much evidence to the effect that "emotions" can be inferred from behavior patterns to a degree, such as is the case in common everyday social intercourse, including laughter, frowning, and so forth (544). One somatic reaction pattern of the human that is universally recognized as being consistent and therefore presumably basic to the organism is the "startle pattern" (615, 749). It consists of closing of the eyes, head movement, raising and bringing forward of the shoulders, abduction of the upper arms, bending of the elbows, pronation of the lower jaw, clenching of the fists, forward movement of the trunk, contraction of the abdomen, and bending at the knees. The pattern appears at about four months of age and continues into adulthood. A fearlike or startle state is usually inferred from this reaction, which follows at times from sudden strong stimuli.

More recently, many studies, such as that by H.E. Jones (653), have indicated that judges can agree very closely on inferring psychological states from behavior, and particularly from behavior during normal social interaction. It has become widely recognized that classifications of extreme types of any phenomena can easily be made by persons who have some general familiarity with the given phenomenal field, whereas on subtle distinctions between different phenomena it may be difficult to find agreement among those most expert in the given field.

PHYSIOLOGICAL REACTIONS IN GENERAL

Inferences were made on a somewhat different basis in the numerous physiological studies that will be considered in Part III. In a great number of these studies, the "feeling" or "emotion" of the experimental subject was inferred from the nature of the stimulus that evoked the physiological reaction studied. For example, the reaction of "fear" might be inferred from an accelerated heart-beat rate occurring after a sudden loud noise. From electrical skin-conduction changes Schlosberg inferred an emotional "dimension" of a "general level of activation" implicating "a number of physiological processes" and has inferred "dimensions" of "pleasantness-unpleasantness" and of "attention-rejection" from facial studies, thereby postulating "three dimensions of emotion" (1099).

ANIMAL STUDIES

In the area of study involving animal experimentation, changes in internal perceptive states, such as "feeling" or "emotion," have been inferred from changes in the behavior or the physiological reactions of the experimental animal. A good example of this is seen in the inferring of rage, or "sham rage," from the reactions of decorticate animals to certain stimuli (71, 196, 880).

Masserman presented a strong argument for this type of approach (881, p. 47). He rejected the common concept of "emotion" and proposes that behavior be analyzed into other more basic determinants, namely, "(a) the physiologic motivations of behavior, (b) its orientations and symbolisms (milieu interpretations) as derived from the unique capacities and experiences of each individual, (c) the effects of environmental frustrations in deviating behavior into re-exploratory techniques or substitutive goals, (d) the role of insoluble conflicts of motivation in producing various types of maladaptations and aberrations of behavior which we term neurotic or psychotic" (881).

Here Masserman has defined the methodology he employs, as well as that employed by psychologists studying "learning." In most such animal experimentation, the noncognitive internal experiences that are involved include the common strivings for food, water, and sexual objects; however, Masserman postulated much broader types of inner experience, such as aggressivity, hostility, "attachment," "joyfulness," and "affection." The primary purpose of this type of experimentation, however, is not usually to postulate types of noncognitive inner experience, but rather most frequently to derive generalized principles of "motivation" or learning (1194). For example, Masserman includes in his experimental procedure: adaptive learning, "social" interaction, induction of experimental neuroses, and experimental therapy. Nevertheless, inferences involving the noncognitive area of internal perception are made wittingly or unwittingly (881, 882).

Such inferences from animal behavior were felt to be justified because of "the basic uniformity of all organismic behavior." In addition, however, it should be recognized that the semantics of the "affective" terminology employed must derive either from the external sensory experience, the cognitive experience or the noncognitive internal perception of the individual who makes reference to noncognitive inner experience. It would seem probable that the constructs noted do involve noncognitive inner experience, irrespective of the fact that agreements concerning them may have been established experimentally on the basis of "objective" behavior.

STUDIES BY WATSON AND OTHERS

Watson (1283) followed Thorndike's use of animals for psychological study (1242) and adopted Pavlov's concept of conditioned reflex (973). In proposing a behavioristic psychology, he rebelled against faculty psychology, against introspection, and against the making of inferences concerning inner experience. Theoretically, he favored basing all psychological conclusions on objectively observed behavior. Nevertheless, as has already been noted, he at times employed the common "emotional" terminology that appears to have had a basis in noncognitive inner experience. Watson distinguished between instinct and emotions: "An emotion is an hereditary 'pattern-reaction' involving profound changes of the bodily mechanism as a whole, but particularly of the visceral and glandular system" (1281, 1283). This was thought to differ from instinct in having a "chaotic state" for the moment at least. In drawing conclusions primarily based on children's behavior, Watson differentiated the following states: fear, rage, love, jealousy, and shame (1281, 1282). As already noted, the behavioral basis that was postulated for some of these states was not validated by others.

LEARNING PSYCHOLOGY

Watson's early vision of a psychology based on behavior observations has reached fruition, from a theoretical standpoint at least, in current learning psychology (29, 183a, 294, 340a, 458, 509, 510, 511, 561, 608, 800, 826, 913, 914, 1174, 1174a, 1175). Nevertheless, each worker in this field makes reference to the noncognitive area of inner experience, and the postulated characteristics are usually inferred from the observation of experimental behavior.

In speaking of anticipatory responses, or readiness reactions, Guthrie stated that these consist of tension in the muscles (509, 510, 511, 561). Hull's postulated innate "primary drives," such as pain, thirst, hunger, and sex, as well as such "secondary" or acquired drives as anxiety, fear, and so forth (561, 608) seem to relate directly to noncognitive internal perception. In addition, Hull spoke of such characteristics as drive strength, drive reductions, and inhibitions.

B. F. Skinner proposed constructs that broke with the traditions of stimulus response psychology (561, 1155). In addition to elicited responses ("respondents"), he postulated emitted responses or "operants." The operant is a construct based on spontaneous behaviors that are presumably, at least at times, related to noncognitive changes occurring within the organism. Operant responses are emitted independently of any initial stimulus but can become associated with given stimuli and then are reinforced by the (rewarding) stimuli. Conditioning of operants involves approximately the same factors as Thorndike's law of effect and Hull's principle of reinforcement. Most human behavior was thought to be of an operant type. Also involving the noncognitive area of inner experience was Skinner's concept of "drive" which was hypothesized as a state to account for the variability of the "reflex strength," or effort, of the responding organism, and this "drive" is not thought to be equated to the stimulus. He distinguished the separate effects of "drive," "conditioning," and "emotion," and considered emotion also to be a state rather than a response.

These learning theories are primarily concerned with what has been identified as cognitive experience; however, the terminology and concepts presented frequently are not distinctive of any particular area of experience, as for example those concepts apparently derived from physiological or neurological laws, such as Skinner's law of refractory phase. At the same time, the current trend is definitely away from Watson's rejection of any constructs concerning inner experience and is in the direction of dealing with the area of noncognitive internal perception as such.

Mowrer's work clearly demonstrates this (936). He postulated that many conditioned responses represent solutions to secondary-drive problems, acquired by way of the "law of effect." Yet the law of effect cannot, he believed, account for the origin of the so-called secondary drives (such as fear) themselves, and he took a position similar to that of Skinner in reserving the term "conditioning" for the process of secondary drives deriving from primary drives (which appear to be of a noncognitive internal perceptual nature). After the differentiating of voluntary from involuntary, or homeostatic, responses, Mowrer stated, "when visceral and vascular responses occur on the latter basis, as *anticipatory states,* they produce, rather than eliminate, physical disequilibrium and are consciously experienced as emotion." This noncognitive internal experience was thought to play a "motivation role." Mowrer believed that all emotions, including fear, anger, and "the appetites," are basically painful in the respect that they have a drive quality. Thus in postulating a dual nature of learning, Mowrer expanded "effect learning" (or "solution learning") to include those situations in which the motive or problem is learned drive, and "conditioned learning" (or "sign learning") was restricted to responses involving visceral and vascular tissues—responses that are experienced subjectively as emotion. "Solution learning" was believed to involve the central nervous system and the voluntary skeletal musculature, whereas "sign learning" was restricted to the involuntary autonomic nervous system and visceral-vascular tissues (936a, 936b). Mowrer's theory and the James—Lange theory (see Chapter 10) were interpreted as compatible (936a), and Mowrer applied his theory to the empirical data and inferences of clinical psychology and psychiatry (936a, 936b).

Similarly, Dollard and Miller have applied the "four fundamentals of learning," namely, drive, response, cue, and reinforcement, to clinical concepts (304a). Noncognitive inner experience is implied in reference to "primary drives" that include, for example, pain, thirst, hunger, fatigue, cold, and sex. Also, fear, anger, nausea (associated with disgust), and the "appetites," as well as sex, are considered innate, but they are "learnable" in that the content with which they become associated takes the characteristics of secondary (learned) drives. Innate drives vary with the physiological state of the organism, whereas learned drives vary with the principles and conditions of learning. Thus, learned drives should be weakened by non-reinforcement, but innate drives should not. Fear was thought to be a component of many socially learned drives such as guilt, surprise, pride, and so forth.

In addition there have been many learning experiments employing animals, as well as experiments of related types, that have made reference to experiences of "fear" (544, 786, 787, 912). The recent trend in "learning" and inferential construct theory has placed emphasis on physiological, and particularly on neurophysiological, constructs (254, 434, 727, 728, 729, 730, 731, 1005).

INSTINCTS AND DRIVES

There are a number of theoretical viewpoints that, although postulating constructs of noncognitive inner experience primarily on the basis of experimental observation and reviews of "objective" studies, nevertheless remain more theoretical than specifically experimental in setting forth their constructs. A functional (or "dynamic") type of psychological theory was presented by Woodworth in 1918 wherein "drive" was substituted for, and supplemented with, the older term "instinct" (1367). He used Sherrington's (1141) distinction between "preparatory" and "consummatory" reactions, considering the latter to be those that satisfy basic drives or needs. Basic drives relate to noncognitive inner experience. Noncognitive inner experiences were assumed to exist also by the traditional functional psychologists (47, 48, 210, 626, 1370).

Similarly, virtually all theories concerning personality functioning have presented concepts involving noncognitive internal experience, such as seen, for example, in McDougall's extensive list of "instincts" (828, 830). Most frequently, of course, no clear distinction is made by these theorists between cognitive and noncognitive inner experience. For example, Allport's "functional autonomy" (30, 31) which involves the continuing of striving toward goals after the original "drive" has ceased, more probably has a greater basis in cognitive goals, or levels of aspiration, than in immediate noncognitive needs or drives.

TOLMAN

One point of view combining behavioristic and Gestalt theory systems is that of Tolman. However, Tolman rejected introspective methodology, proposing that "intervening variables" relating to the inner functioning of the organism be inferred from observations of behavior that originates from given stimulus conditions (1254). Drives were conceived to produce tensions that result in the demand for goal objects and activate the cognitive structure. Tolman set forth many "laws" or principles, most of which are cognitive in reference and were inferred primarily from animal experimentation. In addition, however, he referred to "feeling," including "pleasantness and unpleasantness," and to "emotion," such as fear, as being essentially alike, both resulting from stimuli that release relatively generalized "sign-gestalt expectations." These were thought to produce incipient visceral and skeletal movements going off appropriately to the "sign-gestalt expectations" (e.g., expectation of goal achievement) that result in auxiliary sets to organic and kinesthetic sensations, functioning as "discriminanda-expectations."

LEWIN

Lewin's psychology is often considered to be a further development of Gestalt psychology, yet his concepts concerning personality are so much broader and his constructs concerning noncognitive inner experience are so much more specific that a separate classification of his psychology is in order (776, 777). He designated as the most important problem in psychology the differentiation of "specific psychical units, personality spheres and behavior wholes," which include human activities, emotions, and aspirations as these are reflected in real-life experiences. His personality constructs included: needs and quasi-needs, tension systems, perception (cognitive structure), valences, boundaries, and a complexly structured ego system. Lewin's most fundamental inner-experience construct was that of a "needs-tension" system that is related to specific goals in terms of varying strength of "valence." In his system, emphasis shifts to the noncognitive area of inner experience since both the activation of cognitive activities and changes in them are believed to depend on aroused needs or "tensions."

Harms has presented a view proposing a differentiation of various categories of psychical processes or functions (526). Only limited progress has been made, however, in experimentally differentiating "specific psychical units" as regards the noncognitive area of experience.

STATISTICAL STUDIES

Quite a different technique from any discussed so far is the use of statistical analysis to infer constructs concerning inner experience, although here again the constructs are not usually specifically designed to refer to noncognitive inner experience as such. Statistical techniques began to assume an important role around the turn of the twentieth century in the inferring of constructs concerning the cognitive area of experience (and particularly concerning intelligence).

In England, Burt's factor-analysis studies led him to emphasize a hierarchal structure of the "mind" and central nervous system that differentiated between cognitive and noncognitive experience, the latter combining the traditional affective and conative classifications that he found "so closely related that they virtually form a single aspect" (182, p. 18). This noncognitive area of experience was designated as the "orectic sphere," and a statistical assessment of "emotional traits" by Burt appeared to demonstrate three kinds of factors: general, specific (group or bipolar), and unique factors (179, 180, 181). At that time and subsequently, Burt's studies have systematically assessed the following traits: joy, sorrow, sex, fear, anger, curiosity, disgust, sociability, tenderness or affection, self-assertiveness, and self-submission. More recently, these studies have also applied factor analysis to what are considered to be acquired emotional characteristics, as, for example, interests, preferences, and psychoneurotic tendencies. Several types of physiological measurements, psychological instruments (or "tests"), questionnaires, and ratings were employed for the raw data of statistical measurement and analysis.

The more recent studies suggest that 40 to 50 per cent of the total variance seen represents the factor of "general emotionality." Burt believed that this may be the same as McDougall's construct, "a common fund of emotional energy," and as Jung's concept of libido. About 13 per cent of the total variance appeared to represent a *"sthenic,* or demonstrative, type of personality at one end of a polar continuum and an *"asthenic,"* or inhibitive type at the other end of the polar dimension. Finally, about 6 per cent of the total variance appeared to represent a *euphoric-dysphoric* dimension, or emotional continuum, which was thought of in terms of a pleasurable-unpleasurable feeling-tone continuum. Burt stated that a number of similar investigations subsequently confirmed the more important aspects of these conclusions and that the majority also confirmed the general factor of emotionality. Also, another factor dimension, the "algedonic" or "euphoric-versus-dysphoric" factor was suggested to some degree, and this is exemplified by the difference between optimism-pessimism, sanguine-melancholy, and so forth. The attempt of this group to classify temperamental types by means of statistical factors is also relevant to the noncognitive area of internal functioning. The usual complexity and predominant overlapping of types was found. In the factor analysis of correlations about 15 to 25 per cent of the total variance was found to represent a "general factor of neuroticism." On subsequent investigation, however, this factor appeared to be the same as the factor of general emotionality, or temperamental instability.

Studies with psychoneurotic patients indicated two other factors. One of these, an extrovert-introvert factor dimension, was found also among "normal persons," though it accounted for a far greater proportion of the common factor variance in the psychoneurotic studies. The other factor found in the psychoneurotic studies subdivided both the extroverts and introverts into two subclasses. The extroverts were divided into those characterized (1) "by strong sexual propensities, relatively joyful moods, and conspicuously social or gregarious behavior," or (2) "by aggressive, assertive, and inquisitive tendencies, and a relatively morose and unsociable disposition." Most of the hysterical cases were of the former type, and most of the obsessional and compulsive cases fell in the latter classification. The introverts were divided into those characterized (1) "by fear or anxiety, together with a marked degree of affection and desire for affection," or (2) "by disgust, fatigability, submissiveness, a strong desire for comfort, and a marked lack of persistence." Almost all of the "anxiety states" were in the former subclassification, and most of the "neurasthenic" types were in the latter subclassification.

These results were based on a relatively small number of cases and therefore are considered tentative. Yet, Burt feels that his classifications are similar in nature to Cattell's factors, which indicate some twelve "primary source traits," including cognitive traits and conative traits, as well as affective traits. Burt identifies his factor of "general emotionality" with Cattell's "factor III or C," namely, "demoralized general emotionality *versus* emotionally stable or mature." The introvert-extrovert factor dimension is identified with Cattell's "factor I or A," "cyclothymia *versus* schizothymia," and it is also thought that Cattell's factors "IV or E" and "IX or H" could be included in the introvert-extrovert dimension. The melancholic-pessimistic, or sanguine-optimistic, factor dimension is thought to be virtually the same as Cattell's "factor V or F," "melancholic desurgency versus surgency."

In the United States, Cattell has made many studies attempting to infer personality characteristics and "traits" from objective behavior ratings, self-inventory ratings, and objective-test measurements (62, 216, 217, 218, 219, 219a, 834, 1239). Personality measures of a cross-sectional type that correlated into clusters are called "surface traits." Cattell maintained, however, that statistical factors are more appropriate for the measuring of personality traits than are correlation clusters because: (1) correlations are often highly intercorrelated, (2) they are concerned with only a few trait elements, and (3) they are simply statements of literal going-togetherness. Factors, on the other hand, are analytical of covariance, and Cattell believed therefore that they reflect more basic "source traits." In order to translate factors into traits, Cattell employed Thurstone's principle of simple structure that assumes that the most likely solution is that which gives the most parsimonious explanation with regard to a simple matrix of correlation. In addition to this, Cattell set forth his own "principle of proportional profiles" (or "simultaneous simple structure"), which encompassed parsimony relative to the plurality of matrices of separate studies considered together. This reduces source traits to the fewest dissimilar factor loadings for all the matrices considered together. In addition to choosing factors by making statistical rotations to agree with factors found in earlier factor-analysis studies and by attempting to put the statistical axes through the center of correlation clusters, Cattell also attempted rotations to agree with clinical and general psychological findings. When traits are so chosen, they are considered to be "mental structures," i.e., relatively fixed characteristics, which are inferred from observed behavioral functioning. The efficacy of such a given functional unity is conceived of as varying in degree at various levels, and it would be considered greatest when the traits indicated covary in each and every situation.

Cattell sets the task of psychology to seek the most widely useful, *influential* functional unities as they are based on their recurrence with different researches in accordance with the above-mentioned "principle of proportional profiles." When he found clusters from different researches showing a 50 per cent or greater overlap of variables, they were listed as probable single clusters and called conglomerate nuclear clusters. He stated that any device directed to measure personality along given dimensions has to be subjected to dual validation: (a) correlation as a true psychological functional entity (called "internal or essential validation") and (b) correlation and standardization as a prediction of performance in real-life situations (called "peripheral or external validation"). "Functional unity" was defined as referring to both the functional behavior as a unity, comparing person-to-person variation, and to the growth (longitudinal or maturational) within one person.

On the basis of "common sense," Cattell postulated constitutional and environmental mold traits. He maintained that if source traits found by factoring are pure, independent influences "as present evidence suggests," a source trait could not be due both to heredity and environment but springs from one or the other. Also based on "common sense" were his subdivisions of constitutional and environmental mold traits into: (1) dynamic modality,

(2) temperament modality, and (3) ability modality. These modalities were defined by "field characteristics": (1) with dynamic traits, variables change most in response to change of incentives in the situation, (2) with ability traits, variables change most in response to the complexity of path to goal, and (3) with temperament traits, variables change least in response to any changes in the field.

Three levels were postulated at which dynamic traits are manifest, the first two of which are not overtly observable: (1) ergs (dispositions), (2) sentiments, and (3) attitudes. Ergs were thought of as "innate" drives or needs, and basic "learned," or acquired, reactions are called metanergs. Ergs were further defined as innate psychophysical dispositions that permit one to acquire reactivity (to attend) to certain classes of objects more readily than others, to experience a specific emotion therefrom, and to enter into activity that ceases more completely at the attainment of one specific goal than at another goal. Ergs were subdivided into appetitive needs (viscerogenic needs) and nonappetitive needs (drives). A "sentiment structure," which involves more than one emotion or drive, is "deep" and widely ramifying. An "attitude" is more transient and emotionally more superficial, and it arises from the impact of "sentiments" on a particular situation. Thus, it is Cattell's postulated "ergs" that appear to be most closely related to the noncognitive area of inner experience, and his other constructs include combinations and associations of "ergs"; most of these constructs would seemingly involve cognitive experience in varying degrees.

Cattell listed the personality traits found through various studies with alphabetical labels in descending order of relative magnitude of variance for "a typical adult population." The "purely descriptive or historical labels" were listed with each "for those who prefer verbal forms, and therefore must be accepted as contingent or temporary." The source-trait titles, as well as their constituent elements, were listed in bipolar fashion. It was added that the order of listing should not be accepted too rigidly since in different samples, ages, and social groups, it will vary somewhat. Approximately fourteen source traits were consistently found in various researches. The six indicated by italics in the following list were "repeatedly configured," and Cattell believed that they are unmistakable. The source traits listed below were factored from surface traits reflected in "twenty topologically and psychologically distinct" regions, called "personality spheres," which were derived from fifty nuclear clusters of different research studies. The titles aim at maximal literal descriptiveness:

A. *Cyclothymia vs. Schizothymia*
B. *Intelligence, General Mental Capacity vs. Mental Defect*
C. Emotional Mature Stable Character vs. Demoralizing General Emotionality
D. Hypersensitive, Infantile Sthenic Emotionality vs. Phlegmatic Frustration Tolerance
E. Dominance-Ascendance (Noneuphoric) vs. Submissiveness
F. *Surgency vs. Agitated Melancholic Desurgency*
G. Positive Character Integration vs. Immature Dependent Character
H. *Charitable, Adventurous Cyclothymia vs. Obstructive, Withdrawn Schizothymia*
I. Sensitive, Anxious Emotionality vs. Rigid Tough Poise
J. Neurasthenic vs. Vigorous "Obsessional Determined" Character
K. *Trained, Socialized, Cultured Mind vs. Boorishness*
L. Surgent Cyclothymia vs. Paranoia
M. *Bohemian Unconcernedness vs. Conventional Practicality*
N. Sophistication vs. Practicality

Factor analysis of self-ratings produced twelve sufficiently confirmed factors, two of which have no clear counterpart in behavior ratings, and therefore were thought to be much "larger," if not more defined, in the introspective realm than in overt behavior. These were "free anxiety" and "general neurotic maladjustment" (or depressive tendency, or emotionality and self-deprecation). Analysis of self-ratings produced at least four other factors that had no well-defined equivalent in behavior ratings, namely, radicalism, adventurous self-sufficiency, will control, and tenseness-and-restlessness. It is to be noted that these statistical procedures do not in themselves differentiate the basic "ergs" of Cattell's theoretical system, but rather these source traits would appear to involve various areas and levels of inner experience. Further elaboration therefore will be required in order to clarify the role of "ergs" in Cattell's theoretical and statistical approach.

Cattell maintained that people acquire interests in intrinsically uninteresting activities as a last resort when the direct path to the satisfaction of innate drives is blocked, which he called "long-circuited" or "metanergic" behavior. During such activity there is an increase in cognitive content, and concrete cues become symbolic. There are attenuation and combinations of primary emotions in secondary-derived emotions. He stated further that a habit acquired for one reason often happens later to satisfy some other motive, and therefore functional autonomy does not exist (without satisfaction of some drive). Cattell discussed the modification of drive as it affects stimulus perception (cues), the intensity and complexity of emotions, and the complications of behavior by long circuiting. Also in rare instances, the goal itself is replaced by a substitution, and the aim at such times is the inhibition of a drive. If the new goal is socially valuable, this substitution is called sublimation; if it is socially disapproved, it is called perversion. By the various processes of the modifying of drives, the unitary character of the sentiments is likely to appear in a common variation of those attitudes that "subsidate" to the purpose of maintaining the object of affective existence. It was thus postulated that attitudes would be proportional in strength to the love of an object (goal) and that hatred (fear and anger as used by McDougall) would be proportionally directed toward that which threatened to destroy the object valued.

Such a vectoral, ergic theory of attitude measurement, Cattell stated, permits any attitude to be analyzed by the usual factorial specification equation, in which factors are ergs. For example, in an experiment measuring strength of attitudes by objective criteria (PGR, etc.), the motivation behind a sports interest (attending football games) was found to have the following order of loadings: first, gregarious satisfaction, secondly, assertive erg, and thirdly, sexual interest. By this method of detecting ergic structures among general dynamics observed in the dynamic lattice, one is said not to arrive at innate patterns of ergs, but instead the patterns of investment of the ergs in behavior acquired within a given culture are obtained. Cattell cited many of the well-known studies in psychological literature as throwing some light on the inherited, the innate, and the maturational aspects of drives, or ergic patterns. He stated that the main problems that still call for more exact formulation and solutions in the realm of dynamic-trait action are: (1) analysis of the action of innate drives (ergs), (2) formulations of principles governing "learning" or modifications of single drives, and (3) formulation of principles governing the general interaction of dynamic traits with one another and with traits of other modalities.

The study of personality and behavioral functioning by means of statistical techniques such as those employed by Cattell is coming into rather widespread application (181, 219, 936b, 1196). It should always be kept in mind, however, that the original correlations from which factors are derived are based on ratings and judgments in response to specific categories of classification which, from their inception, are limited by the semantics employed in constructing them. Cattell himself called attention to the limitations of the self-rating measures available, especially in regard to attitudes, and he noted that the items reflecting social and intellectual pros and cons that have been collected are superficial and oblique from the standpoint of personality structure. In part because of the limitations of the raw data on which these studies were based (508), there is necessarily a great hiatus between Cattell's precisely outlined methodology for the discovering and interrelating of facts about personality and his rather eclectic concepts concerning the nature of personality that are based on "common sense," "clinical experience," and general psychological knowledge.

Perhaps the most fundamental weaknesses of building a system on the basis of statistical factors are the limitations of the measures used and the necessity of rectilinear relationships for (significant) correlation coefficients. Any measure that may be taken is limited by the small aspect of individual personality that a given instrument can comprehend. All of the psychological instruments are thought to be very limited in respect to precise quantitative measurements of personality. When rating sheets are used, the measurements and the factors are limited by the meanings of the words employed; thus it is not possible really to add much beyond the inherent meanings of the terms employed. Finally, any measures that are limited to rectilinear relationships are most certain, on the basis of frequent findings in psychological measurements, to overlook vast areas of personality function. In addition, there are many other statistical requirements that circumscribe the applicability of factor analysis. Notwithstanding the fact that many of the considerations raised here limit most psychological studies, it can hardly be presumed that one method so circumscribed as factor analysis, or even the technique, can be adequate as an exclusive measure for the study of something so relatively uncircumscribed as personality. At the same time the application of such techniques may be helpful in the delineating of areas of function concerning noncognitive internal perception, for they have already contributed much where cognitive functions are predominantly involved.

CHAPTER 8

Maturational and Developmental Approaches

GENERAL CONCEPTS

This approach to the evaluation of noncognitive inner perception is a relatively specific subtype of the "inferential-construct-approach" classification. However, in maturational (or developmental) studies, specific constructs concerning noncognitive inner experience frequently are not systematically postulated. More often the development of certain behaviors is described, and common affective terminology, implying types of noncognitive internal experience, is employed. Thus, noncognitive internal perception is not ignored, nor are systemic constructs usually postulated, but rather behaviors apparently reflecting experiences of this type are described. There exists, nevertheless, a theoretical aspect to the maturational approach even though in general a hiatus exists between the theoretical concepts and the actual developmental observations made concerning noncognitive inner experience.

A current theoretical emphasis on inherent maturational development had its more recent origin in biological and physiological experimentation that began around the turn of the twentieth century (116, 240, 241, 313, 332, 421, 466, 1173, 1301). Later, these findings were incorporated into the Gestalt theory in the manner already noted, and maturational aspects of human development were especially emphasized by Wheeler (1311, 1312, 1313). As has already been indicated, the principles derived were applied more to cognitive experience than to noncognitive internal perception. Many developmental studies referring to noncognitive inner experiences, such as those of Bridges (149, 150), followed in the wake of the behavioristic tradition rather than as an aspect of the development of the maturational theory. Gesell's extensive work in genetics and child development represents a culmination of both traditions as well as a fulfillment of practical medical and clinical needs (436, 437, 438, 439, 441, 442, 443, 444, 445).

It is generally acknowledged that inner experiences correspond with some aspects of physiological make-up, and that one's constitutional make-up is dependent to a great extent upon inherited gene characteristics. The fundamental concept of the maturational approach was presented by Gesell, maintaining that maturation is the net sum of gene effects operating in a self-limited time cycle (440). These effects were postulated to be manifested in a lawful manner so that the emotional characteristics of the infant, child, and adult are subject to the laws and principles of a developmental morphology.

He believed that the genesis of emotion is seen in the fetal period. As early as twenty weeks after conception, the fetus shows a tonic-neck-reflex pattern that is fundamental to subsequent postural and prehensory behavior, and Gesell found many evidences of affect associated with this growing "motor" behavior. He delineated no general emotions of fear, anger, or joy, but rather conceived of all "emotions" as being formed and formative phenomena that are primarily the outgrowth of maturity and of a "growing action system." This was exemplified by a "self-contained" attitude in a sixteen-week-old infant, by a tendency to disequilibrium in a twenty-week-old infant, by a more affectionate, smiling response in a twenty-eight-week-old infant, and by overexcitability in a thirty-two-week-old one.

Such descriptions leave little doubt that changes take place in the noncognitive internal perceptual environment of the infant and child. Similarly, the maturational point of view does not maintain that such changes are entirely dependent upon constitutional factors, even though the basic patterns of development are thought to be delimited by inherited characteristics.

REFLEXES, RESPONSES, AND EXPRESSIONS

The early work of Watson (1281, 1284, 1286) and the subsequent studies of Bridges and others (149, 150, 492, 802) concerning the "emotional" expressions of infants involve a fundamental problem in the understanding of internal perceptual experience. Many differentiated psychological states have been postulated for the adult human, and by contrast the infant's perceptive experience would seem to be much less complex. What, then, is the ontogeny of the differential aspects of noncognitive inner experience? Complicating the study of such development is the inability of the infant to communicate directly and the consequent necessity of relying on inferences based on observations of the infant's behaviors and reactions. Most studies in regard to this question were made in terms of "feeling and emotion," and there is the consequent difficulty in conceiving and in labeling the inner experiences of infants and children since the adult must think and communicate in "adult" terms. It may be presumed, however, that the infant's internal environment is in many respects like that of the adult and for this reason, since reactions and communications of experiences can be observed as they progress gradually from stage to stage throughout the life span, it would seem that the expert and experienced observer should be able to, and in fact can, make substantially valid inferences concerning the inner experiences of the infant.

It is first of all assumed that all changes in muscle tonus and physiological functioning constitute, at least in part, the inner experience and psychological state of the infant. That is to say, the infant organism is in some ways immediately aware of the changes taking place within it. Further understanding requires that two lines of development be studied. One line of development involves (1) the discovery of early differentiated patterns of responding, (2) the delineation of subsequently developing differentiated patterns of response, and (3) the consideration as to whether these patterns are innate in maturational development or whether they are culturally learned modes of response. The other line of development to be studied involves the consideration as to which responses and processes in noncognitive inner experience are essentially of reflex types and which of these are relatively more organized and differentially selective in terms of perceptual inner reactivity.

One must not draw too sharp a line between reflexes and other reactions. Goodenough has noted that with any stimulus of moderate intensity, the response is most pronounced, and appears most consistently, in the part of the body stimulated, and also that with any response there is a tendency of spread into adjacent areas (470). It should be added that the results of modern researches in physiology emphasize the extensive, diffuse, and reverberating nature of neural stimulation. Morgan sums up the significance of human reflexes in stating that the assumption that reflexes are dominant in the behavior of human beings as these appear in lower animals is unwarranted (930, p. 43).

In order to study infant behavior, one must nevertheless determine what reflexes exist. Notwithstanding the definition of a reflex as being automatic and at times unconscious, the possibility that more extensive inner experiences may be involved with the reflex must be considered. One may react to a situation, reflexly or otherwise, and only afterward become aware of the situation or of his internal state. A concept of the manifestation of reflexes in the young infant can be formed from some of Sherman's findings (1138).

Blanton's observations of newborn infants included (127): sneezing before the first cry; hiccoughing, the earliest at six hours and commonly after feeding; yawning, two times within three minutes after birth; crying, essentially as an accompaniment to the taking of air into the lungs and rarely spontaneous; tearing, by one subject at birth and by most at two weeks; and smiling, rarely spontaneous and the earliest at four days. The newborn infant's reaction to dropping was a marked movement of arms and a brief holding of the breath; the reaction to a touch on the cheek and chin was to move the mouth in the direction of the touch as early as five hours after birth. Sucking when a nipple was placed in the mouth was exhibited by most infants within half an hour after birth.

Thus are exemplified some of the early findings concerning relatively reflex behaviors and reactions of the infant. Such behaviors grade gradually into those that seemingly play a broader and more extensive role in the perceptual inner experiencing of the infant. Goodenough set forth a distinction between wakefulness and sleeping of the infant when she described the latter as a recuperative mechanism that occurs whenever the combined effects of the internal and external stimuli become too weak to arouse fully co-ordinated activity (470). Wakefulness was described as "generalized activity." Bridges observed that the hungry child before feeding would often show restless activity, squirming, mouthing and crying (150). When the nipple was placed in his mouth, the infant would breathe quickly, cry a little, wave his free arm, and kick in excited agitation. After lying in one position a long time and before going to sleep, the infant would show "emotional agitation" by a "cu-cu-cu-ah" cry, by throwing the arms out, and by irregular movement of the legs. She noted further that the baby two to three months old may be seen to suck his thumb or finger in times of stress and that gradual subsiding of emotion followed. It may be presumed that at such times the infant is learning to eliminate uncomfortable states and to substitute a more satisfactory inner state. Bridges also reported that a hungry, annoyed, excited, or restless infant might rock rhythmically and give forth rhythmic vocalizations for minutes on end. The "rhythmical" movements appeared not only as apparent outlets for emotional excitement, but also they were seen to have a soothing and pacifying effect.

A more controlled experimental approach is exemplified in a study by Bayley (85). During a series of examinations, psychologists and medical examiners noted the crying of infants, from three days to one year of age, in terms of the cause, the duration, and the intensity of crying. The classification of stimulus situations was pragmatically determined and included: specific test situation; continued handling; fatigue at the end of the test; internal conditions, such as colic, sleepiness, and hunger; strangeness of place and purpose; being put down; interference with play activities; postural discomfort; "spoiled" behavior, e.g., crying to gain ends; adverse conditioning, i.e., response on first sight. The specific test situations were the most frequent causes of crying at all ages, as judged by the cessation of crying when the stimulation ceased. Such crying was produced by restriction of the infant's movements, by handling, and by changing its position. In the early months, fatigue was a main cause of crying, but this rapidly disappeared with age. The infant's "spoiled behavior" was judged to increase about the middle of the first year. Interference with the examinations by the infants and adverse conditioning to the different examinations appeared only in the last two and three months of the year, respectively. These observers noted relatively little change in the affective disposition of the individual infant from month to month; some were almost always calm, "good," and others "high-strung" and difficult to handle. Bayley stated that it was characteristic of most infants that they should cry some but could easily be comforted. There was some consistency in the causes that elicited crying in any given child. In this study the infant's reactions were differentiated on the basis of internal and external stimulus conditions. The observers who made separate ratings were in close agreement.

Other types of factors that affect the psychological state of the infant were reported by Gesell (439). The full-term, forty-week neonate suffers a more difficult, or traumatic, birth than the premature infant, and approximately four weeks are required for the functioning of the organism to again become stable and uniform. He stated that the amount of initial activity depends upon the amount of anesthesia and sedation used during labor and delivery, that most infants are "knocked out" and somnambulant from twenty-four to forty-eight hours after birth, and that irritability and restlessness are found at the other extreme. During the first four days of postnatal life 6 to 9 per cent of the infant's weight is lost, and it is not until seven to ten days later that this loss is recovered. Gesell stated that during the period of postnatal transition, food hunger and "sleep hunger" seem to compete so that full satisfaction of neither is obtained. By the fourth week, the infant has assumed what is known as the "t-n-r," i.e., the tonic-neck-reflex attitude: he lies on his back with his head averted to the preferred side and with the arm of that side (which is usually the right side) extended and the opposite arm flexed. Gesell has also observed that the infant emerges less decisively out of sleep than in falling to sleep, and that, during wakeful interludes, there are lengthy moments of visual and auditory awareness, as well as heedfulness of his own state of being on the part of the infant. Gesell stated that the infant's face assumes passing shades of expression that suggest "inner springs of reactivity," and the infant seemed to attend pleasurably to internal organic states after feeding.

Goodenough noted that sometimes change in the infant's activity takes the form of sudden and temporary *inhibition of bodily movement* in response to a change in the quality of a stimulus, and a tenseness, similar to "set" or "attention," seemed to be represented (470, p. 190). Such responses are occasionally seen in newborn infants, and with age they increase rapidly in frequency.

Another apparent manifestation of change in noncognitive inner experience is the Moro response, which is considered to be a universal reaction. With certain sudden stimulation, the young infant first extends his body full length, arms over head and head in mid-line; he then relaxes and the arms tend to bend toward the head. Carmichael compared this reaction with that of fear or "startle" in the adult (207). Although young infants may show both types of reaction, at about four months of age the Moro response gives way to the startle reaction, which remains throughout adult life. The startle reaction, which was first described by Landis and Hunt (749), is a sudden movement toward a "crouched" position, the body bending slightly forward, knees flexed, arms held to the side and elbows bent, fists clenched and palms up. Several stimuli have been found to produce these reactions in infants: loud sounds, sudden movements, cold, water, and so forth.

NONCOGNITIVE INTERNAL PERCEPTION

In addition to the relatively generalized observations of the types just described, others have attempted more specifically to differentiate psychological states in the scope of infant's experiences on the basis of behavior observations and interactions. Stratton, at the Wittenberg Symposium in 1928, laid the foundation for the widely prevalent concept that the original "emotional" experience of the infant is one of "undifferentiated excitement" (1211). He believed that this original emotional experience subsequently became differentiated into experiences of "depression" and of "elation," the former forming the basis for "unpleasant emotions," and the latter forming the basis for "pleasant" ones. The acceptance of these concepts was enhanced at that time by the refutation of Watson's limited classification of the emotions of infants into love, fear, and anger by Sherman (1136, 1139) and others (938a).

A few years later Bridges crystallized the concept of "undifferentiated excitement" by a very thorough analysis of infant behavior, noting the indications and the sequences of various "emotions" that she believed evolved from the "original undifferentiated excitement" (149, 150). Bridges's earliest observations were of week-old infants, and at that age she found that the infants already manifested two "emotions," namely excitement and distress. She stated that (150, p. 327):

> It may be that it [distress] is a part of the general emotional response of excitement which copes more satisfactorily with obnoxious stimuli. Tense muscles resist or remove pressure; activity warms a chilled body and reduces tension; and cries, at first reflex due to the rush of air in and out of the lungs, bring comfort and aid. The responses become differentiated from excitement, associated together and conditioned to the disagreeable stimuli as a result of experience. If such differentiation actually takes place, it must begin immediately after birth. For the two emotions of excitement and distress are always distinguishable in a three-week-old infant.

It would seem that in alluding to an earlier state of undifferentiated excitement, Bridges was stating a theoretical position rather than reflecting her own observations. Behavior that reflected distress included: muscle tension, difficulty in movement and breathing, closing of eyes and loud, rather high-pitched crying. Also, in the month-old infant the cry of distress was said to be recognized by short intakes of breath and long cries on expiration, with the eyes "screwed up tight" and the face flushed, the fist often clenched, arms and legs still or kicking sporadically, mouth open and corners usually down, and the crying high pitched. Concerning the young infant, she observed that (150, p. 238):

> The crying of the infant *under a month* or even six weeks often seems to be part of the general activity of excitement. Breath comes more or less regularly, the cry emerging on both intake and expiration of air. There are no tears and the skin is not flush. Movement is free though rather jerky and the mouth is held open in an elliptic, round or square shape.

When the infant is three months of age, Bridges believed that (150, p. 329):

> The slight change in vowel sound of the cry, the long holding of breath

combined with more than usually vigorous leg thrusts and arm movements, seemed to suggest the emotion of anger is beginning to evolve
from general distress at about this age.

At five months of age the infant was noted to be concerned with small
objects and with food tastes. Since the infant rejects these things at times,
Bridges suggested that this might be the beginning of the "emotion form
of disgust," even though the more complete revulsion at nauseating sights
and smells is not seen until two years of age or more. Fear was differentiated
at about six months of age when, after the attentive watching of a stranger
for a few moments, the infant either begins to cry slowly or bursts into
tears suddenly and then his whole body becomes rigid and inactive. Usually,
the eyes close tightly, and the head bends, and if touched, the infant turns
and draws away.

Bridges asserted that delight is much later in being differentiated from
general excitement than distress. At less than a month of age, gentle stroking, swaying and patting of the infant soothes him and makes him sleepy.
When seemingly satisfied, the infant often appears to be just emotionally
content and either tranquil or busy, mouthing and staring at distant objects.
At two months the infant gives fleeting smiles upon being nursed, patted,
wrapped warmly, spoken to, or rocked. Perhaps, Bridges stated, this is the
beginning of the emotion of delight. At three months of age the emotion
of delight is more clearly differentiated from agitated excitement and from
nonemotional quiescence. Delight is indicated by crooning sounds and smiles
that appear in response to persons, feeding, and moving objects, and the
infants' eyes are wide and the mouth round and open. Also at times the
infant breathes fast, or inspires deeply, and utters murmuring of "uh-uh-uh,"
while the arms wave up and down and the legs kick alternately. The seven-
month-old infant was observed to be interested in small objects, and his
success in the attainment of these was shown by smiling, the taking of deep
breaths, and the expression of satisfaction in a sort of grunt. Bridges believed
that this is probably the beginning of the emotion of elation. It is to be
noted that in elation, Bridges began more definitely to include the stimulus
in addition to the response in the criteria in the delineating of types of
emotional responses; this was seen even more clearly when, in the eighth
month, the infant, when watching and exploring the person who was nursing
him and when patted gently and smiling, was thought to demonstrate the
beginning of the emotion of affection. Similarly, affection for other children
apparently follows in about two or three months. Also between fifteen and
twenty-one months, the infant knocks on objects in play, collects things, and

finds pleasure in throwing and scattering things about, which are, Bridges stated, the precursors to the emotion of joy. Between fifteen and eighteen months of age the infant showed distress when attention was paid to other children, and this was considered as the beginning of jealousy. These latter differentiations made by Bridges appear to be based more on differentiations in external circumstances and cognitive relationships than on noncognitive inner experiences. For example, there is little to suggest that the non-cognitive inner experience in elation or affection differs greatly from that of delight. Needless to say, all of such differentiations require more experi-mental or clinical verification before being accepted even tentatively as valid.

Bridges elaborated on the development of other emotions. Hope was distinguished as the anticipating of pleasure or of the imaginative release from disagreeable circumstances. Shame and disappointment were postu-lated to derive from distress in the observing of distress combined with sub-mission and with responses to check assertion and display. Anxiety was thought to evolve from distress in a problematic or uncertain situation causing conflict of impulses or anticipatory doubt. The possibility of another emotion was suggested, namely, "pain," which differs from distress, since response to painful stimuli was described as having its own distinguishing characteristic. Depression also was postulated as deriving from distress in the thwarting of self-assertiveness combined with a sense of insecurity. Envy and revenge were seen as deriving from anger.

In the first place it must be noted that Bridges has assumed that excite-ment is more basic than distress, for in her earliest observations she found both present. Toward the end of her expositions, Bridges seemed to be find-ing explanations for conventional terms of "emotion" rather than empiri-cally differentiating the infant's reactivity. Nevertheless, Bridges's study was the first relatively thorough attack on the important task of differentiating the development of inner experience and associated reactivity, and this is a task that remains uncompleted (43, 1035). Subsequently, Blatz and Milli-champ reported eighteen specific emotional reactions, involving "negative" responses, after the observing of five infants, starting at the age of one month, for the next two years (129a, 938a).

Carmichael cited several more recent investigators who, in connection with infant behavior, favored the use of the term "emotion" to refer to purely descriptive accounts of the "organismic involvement" rather than using it to include the external circumstances at the time of reaction (207). That is, "emotion" should be descriptive of the individual's response and not of the stimulus conditions. Descriptions of such responses, however, would not be meaningful in themselves except in so far as they could be identified with differentiated psychological states or functions within the individual.

The psychoanalytic developmental studies have placed little emphasis on differentiating the development of noncognitive inner experiences or the expression of them, but rather the focus has been upon the ways such experiences are controlled (by "ego" and "superego" development) and upon the direction (or "cathexis") of the affect (or "libidinal" energies) (153a, 379, 379a, 624b, 624c, 893c, 893d, 1060).

Nevertheless, from observations of 239 infants, aged ten days to one year, and of forty-five babies delivered without anesthetics, Spitz classified the reactions of the newborn into "unpleasure" and "quiescence" (1060, 1180, 1181, 1182, 1182a). A "narcissistic stage" was postulated within the first three months of life when the internal needs of the infant appear to dominate his behavior completely. The first "pleasurable responses" were seen in association with the presence of the mother during the second and third months; and "anxiety," as such, seemed to appear after the sixth month in association with the approach of a stranger. About this time, the development of a rudimentary organized, structured, conscious, "central steering organization, the ego," was postulated, and the need for a substitute ego of an adult, the mother figure, was emphasized (1182a, p. 255). The term "somato-psyche" was employed for the infant, the psychic system not yet being differentiated from the somatic; and the wrong kind of mother-child relationships results in the "psychotoxic diseases of infancy" classified tentatively to include the following symptoms and etiological factors: (1) coma in the newborn (1034a) with overt primal rejection; (2) three-month colic with primary anxious overpermissiveness; (3) infantile neurodermatitis with hostility in the garb of anxiety; (4) hypermotility (rocking) with oscillation between pampering and hostility; (5) fecal play with cyclical mood swings; and (6) aggressive hyperthymia with hostility consciously compensated. The "emotional deficiency" from restriction of mother-child relationships was seen to result in marasmus with complete functional deprivation and in anaclitic depression with partial emotional deprivation. Anaclitic depression occurred within four to six weeks in infants when they were separated from the mother figure at the ages of six to eight months for periods of from three to five months. Severe mental and physical symptoms were reported for this condition. A study by Fischer (359a) supported this concept, though there has been some debate concerning the generality of the anaclitic-depression studies (153a, 996a, 996b, 1182b).

In the elaborating of psychoanalytic concepts of infant development, Schur emphasized the genetic, biological, and maturational aspects (1110b). The "emotional" reactions of the infant were conceived of as occurring mainly in response to homeostatic disturbances, and the responses in turn may create more profound disturbances, in this equilibrium. Normal development "tends toward maximal use of integrated automatization of muscle action towards replacement of action by thought and reduction of vegetative discharge phenomena" (1110b, p. 123).

Other clinically based psychoanalytic formulations that relate to development are presented in the next chapter and in the appropriate chapters of Parts III and IV.

CHAPTER 9

Clinical Approaches

GENERAL CONSIDERATIONS

The clinical approach is the most eclectic in conceptualizing inner experience. Growing out of the practical need for care and treatment of mental and emotional conditions, the clinical concepts are frequently limited and lacking in completeness from a theoretical standpoint. At the same time, however, the clinician has at his disposal a Gestalt of deep contact with human experiences and behavior, as well as of long-term, longitudinal contact. This provides first-hand information and perspectives that can never be duplicated by textbook study or experimental procedures. Of course, it is the partial lack of duplicability of clinical data that makes them difficult to fit to experimental procedures and that at times permits considerable personal bias in the formulation of theoretical positions. Nevertheless, concepts of noncognitive inner experience that have been formulated out of clinical practice are worthy of detailed consideration. The extensive wealth of such material, however, will be only briefly outlined here.

Clinical concepts most frequently apply to whole behaviors or to constellations of symptomatologies, and therefore they are not always clearly differential regarding the various areas, or spheres, of experiences that are being distinguished here. Even so, it is usually possible to discern reference to noncognitive experiences in clinical classifications.

In 1899 Kraepelin decribed the manic-depressive psychosis, which includes the two states implied by the name and which was differentiated from dementia praecox (schizophrenia) (722). Also by this time, Janet had observed the importance of emotional factors in hysteria (629, 630, 631), and Breuer and Freud assigned "the first rank to the affective processes" in this condition (148, 381).

96

APPROACH OF FREUD

Freud's therapy first emphasized the release of pent-up emotion. He conceptualized the construct "libido" as a reservoir of emotional energy within the individual, having all the attributes of quantity and being capable of change like "fluid electric current." This was distinguished from the cognitive entity of "ego" and most of Freud's mental mechanisms of psychic defense were strictly of ego origin. Originally, Freud conceptualized libido primarily as "sexual energy," embodying the instinct, or drive, for procreation. Another instinct recognized was that of self-preservation, which was conceived of primarily as an ego function. Fear, guilt and the like, however, were viewed as aids in causing the individual to avoid dangerous situations. Later, the superego was also conceived of as serving this function.

Terms such as "love," "hostile feeling," and "distress," were employed, but these were not at first included in Freud's theoretical framework. Later, his concept of sexual energy became less specific in the sense of erotic, genital sexuality, and came to be considered as any pleasurable body sensation. This concept also embraced emotions not identified with any particular part of the body, such as "tenderness," "affection," and "satisfaction." Later, also, a specific erotic component generated by the various organs of the body themselves was postulated, and this was thought especially to include the mouth, the anus, and the genitals, with each receiving successive emphasis in the development of the child. The quantity of libidinal energy within the individual was conceived of as representing "self-love"; and, as the libidinal energy becomes attached to other persons or things, a person possesses a lesser quantity of libido and suffers feelings of unworthiness (383, 937, 1237). Then with rebuff by the love object, the person may withdraw the libido and return to a relative narcissistic, self-love state.

Early in his development of theory, Freud had thought of aggression as an aspect of constitutional development that stemmed from the libido. Clinical experiences of World War I and the consideration of masochistic tendencies resulted in a re-evaluation of the nature of aggression, and Freud began to question the theory that the dominating human drive was to obtain pleasure, or "sexual" satisfaction (353, 380). He postulated a "death instinct," which embraced both aggression and the tendency to repeat certain behavior. The primary drive of life was seen to be that of relieving tension, which extends beyond sexual tension to the general tension of living. A second basic instinct then was conceived of to include the libido and part of the self-preservation (ego) drive, and this was called the "life instinct," or

Eros. The outward expression of aggression was thought to be a defense against masochistic self-destruction.

Another change in Freud's theory about this time involved his concept of anxiety to which he had previously given little consideration, thinking of it primarily as a physiological reaction to sexual frustration. He had noted that anxiety and fear seemed to be related emotions, but was unable to place their common factor. Fear was seen as a reaction to danger, being part of the instinct of self-preservation, and, in 1926, anxiety was conceived of as a signal of danger from within (382). He at first speculated that anxiety represents a transformation of libido; subsequently, however, his writings referring to the nature of anxiety became less clear. Anxiety became central to Freud's concept of neurosis, since neurotic symptoms were viewed as attempts to cope with anxiety, which stems from conflicts of the instincts.

Rapaport has traced the complex and overlapping development of Freudian psychoanalytic concepts of "affect," which refer to the noncognitive area of experience (1022). He summarized three stages of such theorizing (1022, p. 187):

> In the first theory, affects were equated with drive-cathexes; in the second theory, they appeared as drive-representations, serving as safety-valves for drive-cathexes the discharge of which was prevented; in the third theory they appear as ego-functions, and as such are no longer safety-valves but are used as signals by the ego.

Some idea of the complexity of these concepts can be seen in the following excerpt (1022, p. 186):

> This conception of the guilt affect was further extended, in regard to both its origin in conflict and its multiple layering, by Jones in his "Fear, Guilt and Hate" [649], which already makes use of Freud's major contribution to the third phase of affect-theory, i.e. *The Problem of Anxiety* [382]. It is to my knowledge the first study of affects in the literature to make use of this advance in affect-theory. Jones shows that fear, hate, and guilt are multiple-layered, in that any one of them may appear not only under the basic dynamic conditions which usually give rise to it, but also as an outcome of defense against any of the others. This conception implies, besides the conflict origin of these "secondary affects" and their hierarchic layering, the concept of defense against affects.

Thus, it is apparent that in clinical elaborations, descriptions, and theorizing, the concepts involving noncognitive inner experience are frequently combined with various concepts of complex cognitive structures (including "ego" and "superego" functions), as well as with references to etiological and ontological development, so that a clear-cut analysis of the content and reference areas of such concepts is frequently difficult to achieve. In comprehending this practice, the practical use of these concepts for the understanding and treating of still more complex individual personalities must be appreciated. Nevertheless, from a theoretical standpoint, the frequent lack of clarity or consistency in the use of clinical concepts defeats the attempts to employ them for comprehensive personality theory.

APPROACHES OF ADLER, JUNG, AND RANK

Early in psychoanalytic development, Adler disagreed with Freud's concept of libido, and he postulated "inferiority feelings" to explain his clinical observations (6, 7). With this, he de-emphasized the role of sexual feelings, or drive. He also postulated a "herd instinct" (8).

Jung, too, disagreed with Freud's sexual emphasis, and at an early date he recognized the importance of the child's affective state in his relationships with the parents (659). Although Jung placed much emphasis on cognitive symbolic activity, he also conceived of "primal" libido as being "undifferentiated energy," of which sexual libido is only one manifestation (661). Jung differentiated pleasure from sexual satisfaction. Also, he brought out the distinction between introvert and extrovert character types, subdividing each of these types into thinking, feeling, intuition, and sensation types (660). Since such characteristics were found to some degree in every individual, the typological classifications were distinguished by the relative emphasis of a given characteristic in the personality of the individual (663). In addition, relative characteristics of masculinity and femininity, which presumably embody noncognitive features, were postulated.

Rank believed that a "primal anxiety" stemmed from the trauma of birth and considered this the basis of all neurosis (1012). He conceived of this as a reservoir of anxiety that becomes gradually reduced in anxiety-producing situations. The trauma supposedly derives from the physiological and psychological aspects of being separated from the mother, and there is postulated a strong craving within the individual for reunion with the mother, which acts as a motivating force in respect to symbolic representations of the mother. Rank also placed much emphasis on "will," but it was conceptualized as a cognitive, guiding, integrating characteristic (1014).

Personality was conceived of as being constituted in terms of impulse, emotion, and will (937, 1013, 1014, 1015). The "impulse" was believed to be of a primitive, innate nature that is expressed in motor discharge, with a feeling of gratification following discharge. This impulse excitation was said to have two phases of tension and discharge, these being experienced as pain and pleasure respectively. The postulated essence of emotion is the prolonging of the tension in order to continue the pleasure up to the point that the tension becomes unbearable and must be discharged. Thus, emotion was thought to arise out of the blocking of impulses by the ego, which is in accordance with the will. Two kinds of "emotional formation" were conceived of, one being the "uniting emotions" such as love, gratitude, and tenderness, and the other being the "separating reactions," such as stubbornness, rage, fear, and hate. Emotional life was said to be the strongest inner force, being more powerful than the sexual instinct.

APPROACHES OF HORNEY, FROMM, AND SULLIVAN

By the 1930s anthropological studies had come to exert a strong influence on psychological thinking. Relativity was seen in human values, customs, interpersonal relationships, and behavior, but little that was new was added concerning the noncognitive area of inner experience except within the perspective that certain psychological (or affective) states are given greater emphasis or prevalence in some societies than in others (673, 1321). Some of the psychoanalysts themselves moved from Europe to America, accentuating their cultural perspective (937).

By this means, Karen Horney broke with conventional psychoanalytic theory, and she postulated that anxiety, being synonymous with fear as an emotional reaction to danger, constitutes the original basis of neurosis (598, 599). More recently, she has set forth a detailed theory of neurosis that contains many concepts relating to the noncognitive area of experience (600). The most basic characteristic of personality was conceived to be an inherent constructive force that drives the individual to realize his given potentialities. Given the chance, the individual supposedly will develop his peculiar potentialities, his "real self," which includes feelings, thoughts, wishes, interests, abilities, and so forth. For such development there was seen to be required an "atmosphere of warmth," specifically the good will and help of others, which permits a "feeling of inner security" and inner freedom. Without this, the infant does not develop a "feeling of belonging," but instead experiences profound insecurity and vague apprehension, which is called "basic anxiety." The child who suffers from a lack of love and understanding tends to develop a "reaction of hatred" toward people, which increases his insecurity in his relationship with the parents.

Horney discussed hostility in terms of conflictual hostile impulses producing anxiety (598) and in terms of "self-hate," which stems from conflicts involving tendencies that conflict with the "real self" and that result in feeling "guilty, inferior, cramped, tormented." This concept was believed to account better for the phenomena that Freud related to the "death instinct."

Horney discussed the various roles that love, sexuality, and the like may play in the personality; concerning "morbid dependency," she conceived of a need for love being fed by a "longing" for surrender and for security. It is not clear whether the "longing" is conceptualized as a cognitive or non-cognitive experience. Sexuality was believed to involve a natural function of satisfaction, intimate human contact, and feelings of self-confidence if the sex relation is satisfactory; however, it can also be used as a vehicle for releasing nonsexual psychic tension of various types.

Erich Fromm, especially, drew information from related fields, including anthropology and social psychology (396, 397, 400, 937). His concepts and personality classifications, even to a greater extent than those of Horney, were based on the relationship of the individual to the other persons in his environment and society. Fromm's holistic emphasis was somewhat similar to that of the Gestaltists. Nevertheless, liberal reference is made to what would seem to imply noncognitive inner experiences.

Fromm rcognized two types of needs, one type being relatively inflexible (hunger, thirst, and so forth) and including the most primary need of self-preservation, and the other type being flexible (love, destructiveness, sadism, and so forth) and being culturally determined (396). Also he spoke of "temperament," including endowment and all constitutionally inherited psychic qualities and referring to the individual's mode of reaction to experience (398). In this connection, Fromm adopted Hippocrates's classifications of choleric, sanguine, phlegmatic, and melancholic. He placed greater emphasis on character types, however, and these involve the relatedness of the individual to other people and to the world. Because of this latter emphasis, it is not always clear whether his concepts refer to noncognitive inner experience or to cognitive (and therefore behavioral) relationships or both.

Fromm viewed sex as one of the imperative needs, and the essence of pleasure, including sexual pleasure, was thought to be relief from painful tension. Concerning this, a distinction was made between physiological needs and irrational psychic tensions. Pleasure was also conceived of as deriving from the use of surplus energy along with, or after, the satisfaction of bodily needs, and the pleasure in the "abundance" of energy beyond that required to relieve tension needs of hunger, sex, and so forth was called "joy" (396, 398, 399). He thought of love as a very specific feeling, yet believed genuine love to be rooted in productiveness and in the characteristics basic to productivity. Pleasure he considered not the aim in life but an inevitable accompaniment of productive activity. In Fromm's words, "Happiness is the criterion of excellence in the art of living, of virtue in the meaning it has in humanistic ethics," and the opposite of this is depression (398, p. 189). It is clear that he considered happiness more than a state of mind, as he stated that "happiness and unhappiness are expressions of the state of the entire organism, of the total personality" (398, p. 181).

Masochism and sadism, which were associated with hostile feelings, were considered to be attempts to escape from "unbearable feeling" of "aloneness" and "powerlessness" (396).

The basis of neurosis was conceived of as a "struggle" for freedom (a "struggle" that one may presume to be accompanied by an appropriate feeling of some sort). Discussing the emotionally constricting factors in Western culture, Fromm stated, "It is not only hostility that is directly suppressed and friendliness that is killed by superimposing its counterfeit. A wide range of spontaneous emotions are suppressed and replaced by pseudo feelings" (396, p. 244). He postulated a "humanistic conscience" (presumably cognitive in nature), which is the reaction of the individual's total personality to its proper function or dysfunction. With dysfunction, including the constriction of spontaneous emotional functioning and the like, "guilt" ensues, producing feelings of anxiety.

In Sullivan's theory of personality, which similarly emphasized interpersonal relationships, the concepts were also frequently ambiguous in respect to distinction between cognitive and noncognitive inner experience (937, 938, 1217, 1218, 1219). His "three modes of experience," namely, prototaxic, parataxic, and syntaxic, seemingly refer to degrees of cognitive organization. The first represents undifferentiated infantile perception, the second represents internal (or self) and external differentiation, and the last represents abstract thought processes.

All experience was thought to involve two types of pursuits, or end states. One pursuit is for "satisfactions," such as sleep, food, and sexual fulfillment, which are connected with the bodily organization of man. Included in these was a state of "loneliness" as a "middling example." The other pursuit was conceived of as being one for "security," which relates to the individual's culture and to his socialization and involves the individual's "state of well-being," "good feeling," and "euphoria" (1217). Inversely related to the state of "euphoria" is the state of "tension" (1218, 1219).

The experience of "tension" was said to constitute one of the two most basic characteristics of personality, the other being the experience of "energy transformation." These were conceptualized as physical and physiological, and "tension" is the potentiality for action, the transformation of energy, and it may or may not have a "felt" (representational, cognitive) component. Sullivan stated that the infant's tensions arising in association with "his relationship to the physiochemical environment tend to be relatively localized and marked with the prototype of what later we call emotional experience" (1219, p. 42).

In the infant's realm of experience was postulated a "fear-like" state, which may be precipitated by a violent disturbance involving contact with the physical environment or by certain types of emotional disturbance within the mother figure. The latter type of experience is made possible by the (cognitive?) characteristic of "empathy," which can only be "felt" (presumably meaning perceived) in parataxic experience (937, p. 529). Any threatened precipitation of this primitive infantile "fear-like" state arouses "uncanny emotion," which refers to "an indeterminately large group of feelings," the most common being "awe" and also including "dread" with "horror" and "loathing" (1219).

It is to be noted that all these concepts do not refer just to the infant's experience but rather refer to infantile experiences of which all persons are capable. Anxiety opposes and interferes with the tension of needs and with the actions appropriate to their satisfaction, even to the extent of "opposition to the tension of tenderness in the mothering one." Prolonged severe anxiety produces a state of "somnolent detachment," and this is distinguished from the state of "apathy" resulting from long-unfulfilled needs. It would seem that these states refer to noncognitive functions. In discussing "anger," "resentment," and the like, Sullivan seems to refer primarily to behavior and to cognitive "felt" perceptions rather than to noncognitive experiences.

LATER PSYCHOANALYTIC DEVELOPMENTS

Elaborations and variations of the psychoanalytic theories that have just been presented have been numerous. Some more general ones relating to noncognitive processes will be considered here; references to others are made in appropriate chapters of Parts III and IV.

Specific concepts by Spitz and Schur have already been presented (pp. 94, 95). Psychoanalytic developmental theory has placed primary emphasis on stages of erotic fixation and on differentiations involving ego and id processes. Anna Freud emphasized the overlapping of developmental stages, noting a particularly wide overlap between the oral and anal stages (379, 379b). From twelve to eighteen months, behavior was seen to alternate between the "primary processes" with the pleasure principle and the "secondary processes" with the beginning of the reality principle; subsequently, the latter comes to predominate, normally.

Glover identified instincts in Freudian terms as "sources," acting as "quantities of continuous psychic stimulation (excitation) to be distinguished" from the more intermittent sensory stimulation (experiences) (460b, p. 33). Active instincts were thought to be manifested through affective experience, mental images and ideations, and verbal and actual behavior. Two kinds of affect are induced by instinctual excitation and its accompanying processes of tension and discharge, one being mostly but not exclusively painful and the other being mostly but not exclusively pleasurable in proportion to the quantity of discharge. Simple affects were conceived of as a specific emotional response to any given vicissitude of a particular instinct, and these tend to merge and form compound or fused affects. Primary and secondary affects were postulated according to the sequence of arousal from given instincts. Anxiety was seen as one of the commonest components or accompaniments of various affects, its nature and origin being obscure but generally being a reaction to danger and having a close connection with the experience of birth. Guilt was considered a highly specialized form of anxiety. Primitive instincts, all in existence at birth, were seen to obtain maximum expression at different times as described in Freudian theory. Behavioristic evidence suggested "that the most important zonal sources of instinctual excitation are cutaneous, respiratory, oral, gastro-intestinal, urinary, anal, muscular and genital" (460b, p. 97). Variations in the distribution of libido or of aggressive charges throughout the different body organs or zones were considered responsible for characteristic affective experiences, and a possible association of this sympathetic stimulation was suggested (460c). Glover emphasized the need of clinical research to isolate and identify "specific tension affects."

Hartmann, Kris, and Loewenstein (533a-f, 733a-c, 808) developed Anna Freud's (379) focus on "ego psychology." The id was conceived of as centering around basic needs, rooted in instinctual drives and their vicissitudes, and striving for gratification with mobility of cathexes of the instinctual tendencies and with their mental representations (e.g., primary processes)

(533e). Differentiation and integration in early development were seen to be partly regulated by maturational sequence, but even where these are influenced by environmental conditions, a principle regulating the interaction was assumed to exist. Taking issue with Freud's early concept of "gradual differentiation of the ego from the id," they postulated an "undifferentiated phase" of development during which both the id and the ego are gradually formed. Setting aside the problem of whether or not instinctual drives tending toward destructive aims are part of the original equipment of man, they observed that in the infant's earliest phases, any transition from indulgence to deprivation tends to elicit aggressive responses that were equated with ambivalence. Energy ascribed to sexual impulses was designated libido in Freudian terms, but no similar term was adopted for the energy of aggressive impulses (533f). The energy of this drive was simply called "aggression." Also, factors contributing to survival were considered as the functions of the ego rather than a separate instinct. Neutralized energy, which Freud identified as sublimated or desexualized libido, was "assumed to provide the cathexis of the ego and partly of the superego" and to account "for a large number of psychic activities both in the individual's relation to his environment and within the ego and superego" (533f, p. 15), (the latter being called "intersystemic" conflicts) (533b). Neutral energy vested in ego and superego was thought to stem from and to be retransformed into either libido or aggression. Freud's four characteristics of drive, namely, impetus, source, aim, and object, were accepted. The question of specific aims of the aggressive drive could not, however, yet be answered even though degrees of discharge of aggressive tension could be distinguished. Aggression was closely associated with the apparatus of the ego, specifically with the muscular apparatus. It seemed that aggressive energy not discharged in fighting might be internalized and used as cathexis of the superego, becoming the source of guilt feelings. To the degree that "ego strength" exists, neutralization of this aggressive energy may take place, and in lieu of this, internalized aggression tends toward self-destruction. Discharge of aggressive tension was thought to be pleasurable (but sadistic impulses were differentiated by the presence of libidinal elements). Although libidinal gratification was conceived of as being partly zone specific, and aggressive gratifications as not being zone specific, it was thought "that in the same way as libidinal cathexis follows in many instances the pathways established by physiological processes, so aggressive cathexis follows the pathways of certain phases of physiological maturation and also of the stages of libidinal development" (533f, p. 33). Hartmann postulated that the ego's countercathexis against drives (including aggressive ones) (533b) was likely to be fed by some shade of neutralized aggression, still retaining some characteristics of the original drive (fight) (533c). Conversely, occasional regression in the service of the ego can be tolerated by the adult ego, provided its functions are unimpaired. It was left undecided whether all of the energy at the disposal of the ego originates in the instinctual drives (533b).

Jacobson (624c) described the gradual development of "specific affect qualities and more sustained emotional states" from the early prevailing pleasure principle and primary process (624c). At the climax of infantile sexuality was postulated the fusion and neutralization of sexual and aggressive drives and the merging of single affects into compound fusions along with the establishment of emotional control and increased tension tolerance and with an increasing awareness of the qualities of emotional experience.

Brenner believed that anxiety, as such, is not present in early infancy, and that the infant experiences only the "emotions" of pleasure or unpleasure (147b). Anxiety develops with increased ego functioning so that an ability to predict or anticipate a state of unpleasure exists.

Paralleling the three phases of libidinal development, namely, orality, anality, and genitality, Margolin postulated the psychosomatic developmental processes of (1) the initial involuntary, (2) the combined involuntary-voluntary, and (3) the voluntary, which were conceived as being always present, interacting, and interdependent but with the dominant properties of each being identifiable (870a). Initially, the involuntary functional and narcissistic phase predominates, but the ego develops progressively as a "patchwork" of ego boundaries between the structural and the topological aspects of the personality, and its relative maximum is achieved during the voluntary psychophysiological phase. The basis for this occurs with psychic differentiations in the first three years during the libidinal stages of orality and anality. These events were thought to be analogous to the field theories of embryology, which maintain that in relatively undifferentiated states of development certain tissues exert a predominant "organizing" influence that results in heterogeneous differentiations. Such "organizers" can exert their influence only at an optimal stage of development if conditions are favorable. Margolin viewed the instincts as having a similar organizing influence in the psychic sphere that serves "to mobilize constitutional and biological and environmental factors into a variety of differentiates of function, behavior and psychic representation" (870a, p. 20). Although it was believed that the variety of involuntary processes themselves have no primary psychic representation, the manifestations of such functions can reach consciousness by means of the subjective sensations that they arouse (as by means of respiratory reactions, muscle tone, shivering, heart rate, and vascular tone). Innumerable psychic components were thought to fuse with relatively few somatic effectors to produce limited numbers of psychophysiological states (moods and affects) such as anger, laughing, weeping, depression, elation, and anxiety.

Colby has presented a relatively systematic, rather comprehensive theory emphasizing hypothetico-reductive constructs and postulating the two general drive categories of maintenance and reproduction (244a). Maintenance drives include breathing, sleeping, ingesting, and excreting, whereas the reproductive drives are more complex, variable, and plastic, and include a mating drive and a drive to "rear." Conscious pleasure experiences accompany drive fulfillment.

Blau hypothesized that emotion derives from two sorts of autonomic visceral responses that are represented psychologically as pleasure and displeasure; he differentiated affects, as inner kinetic reaction, from emotional expression, an outward manifestation (129b). Enteroceptive, proprioceptive, and visceral components of affect were postulated. Anxiety was thought to be the primary, innate emotion of displeasure that acquires a signaling function that calls forth more directed and highly organized secondary and tertiary emotions, namely, fear, rage, and depression for the former, and guilt, shame, and disgust for the latter.

CLINICAL PSYCHOLOGY

Most clinicians of various disciplines and points of view working in the field of personality and mental health have made liberal use of the psychoanalytic concepts presented above and have also added numerous variations in concepts concerning the noncognitive area of experience. Some concepts of different types have derived from the interpretation of psychological instruments for personality evaluation (42, 93, 96, 711, 1019, 1090). These concepts include standard noncognitive clinical terms, such as free-floating anxiety, depressive feelings, dysphoric moods, affectivity, emotional lability, and affect needs (or "craving" or "hunger"); however, the more unique concepts, such as "emotional constriction" and the various "fantasy" operations, primarily involve cognitive functions.

Clinical concepts were involved in some of the psychological theories presented in Chapter 7. Most current psychological texts and personality theories draw eclectically from experimental, developmental, and clinical data (304a, 686a, 936a, 940a). The constructs of noncognitive inner experience for such formulations can be exemplified by Sherif's list of biogenic motives: hunger, thirst, activity-sleep (rest) cycle, breathing, sex, temperature regulation, suckling of young, evacuation, and "avoidance of organic injury(?)" (1135a). Other noncognitive perceptions, such as anxiety and elation, are usually presented in accordance with the developmental or clinical data just reviewed, and varying degrees of distinction between cognitive and noncognitive functions are reflected. Rogers postulated that the "core of personality" is positive, meaning basically socialized, forward moving, rational, and realistic; and, therapeutically, his client-centered group places primary emphasis on the therapeutic subject's awareness and acceptance of himself and on his "getting back to basic sensory and visceral experience" (1053a, 1053b).

Part III

Physiological Changes Associated with General Noncognitive Internal Perception

CHAPTER 10

Concepts Concerning Developments in
Medicine, Physiology, and Psychology

ORIENTATION

In Parts I and II various theories and studies that have approached, or handled, the understanding of internal perception in different ways have been reviewed. In Parts III and IV the literature concerning the relationships between bodily functioning and noncognitive internal perceptive states that have been inferred by many different techniques but mostly by means of clinical studies will be reviewed. The findings from these studies promise to reveal the physiological bases, or corresponding physiological reactions, of many noncognitive psychological states, some of which are elaborated in Part V. As has been noted in the Introduction and in Part I, and as will be discussed in Chapter 22, such knowledge should eventually lead to better means of classifying, comparing, and screening of individual internal perceptive characteristics and personality features by the use of physiological measurements and, possibly, by combining these with reports of internal sensory experiences. In Parts III and IV also will be provided reviews and references for the understanding of psychological factors in the functioning of the various body areas and processes, as well as for the occurrence of sensations in various body parts.

CLINICAL CONSIDERATIONS

PSYCHOPHYSIOLOGICAL "IDENTITY" OR INTERRELATEDNESS

Today, most people who are interested in mental health and personality are quite familiar with the fact that close relationships exist between psychological states and physiological functioning. Early theorists thought in terms of "emotions," or psychological states, causing physiological changes or vice versa. Later, the basic physical nature of the human organism suggested a

111

correspondence, or *identity,* between all psychological states and physiological functioning.

More recently, the complex interrelationships between psychological states and physiological functions have been somewhat clarified in the conceiving of internal perception as being dependent upon various phylogenetic levels of neurological functioning that are related to somatic and visceral functioning in various degrees of complexity. Also in this connection, the distinction already noted between cognitive and noncognitive, or more *immediate,* awareness should be kept in mind.

PSYCHOSOMATIC EXTENSIVENESS

The clinical importance of the interrelationships between psychological and physiological functioning has been brought to the fore in terms of manifest symptoms, disabling conditions, and medical costs of considerable significance involving so-called "psychosomatic" conditions (21, 239, 297a, 318, 319, 321, 352a, 376, 453, 1038, 1083, 1131, 1144, 1256, 1300, 1319).

Weiss and English (1300, p. 4) classified three areas of psychosomatic medicine; the first includes patients who have no definite bodily disease and who constitute about a third of the patients who consult physicians. Another classification also comprises about a third of the patient consultations, and these patients' symptoms are "in part dependent upon emotional factors, even though organic findings are present." It was believed that the psychological factor with the latter type of patients is capable of doing even greater damage than is the case with the patients of the first classification. The last grouping concerns conditions such as migraine, asthma, and essential hypertension, which, the authors stated, are generally considered to be "physical diseases," but, as shall be demonstrated, their relatedness to psychological factors is suspected and is being explored.

Emphasizing the importance of psychological factors in clinical practice and prefacing his own extensive survey of medical literature in this connection, Altschule stated (38, p. 3):

Practicing internists, and also discerning surgeons, are plagued by the fact that daily they see evidence of the influence of emotion on visceral function in healthy and in sick persons but have at hand no extensive body of physiologic data that might illuminate their clinical observations . . . It may be taken for granted that the course of any illness can be influenced by emotional factors; accordingly, the physician must seek evidence of their presence in every case. The lack of adequate data for systematizing information about patients' reactions to emotional factors makes it essential for physicians to understand in general what these factors might be and to learn as much as possible about the life and personality of each patient in particular.

PROBLEMS AND APPROACHES

Today the importance of psychological factors in physiological functioning and in clinical symptomatology is beyond question. Two major unsolved questions are presented, however; one is the understanding of the specific interrelationships involved in physiological and psychological functioning. Since these relationships pertain directly to noncognitive internal perception, they are the primary subject matter of this section. These relationships are also closely associated with the other question presented, namely, why psychological factors in a given individual present a given type of symptomatology rather than another type? The answer to the first question can be approached by studies of immediate (cross-sectional or horizontal) functioning. The second question involves not only possible constitutional factors but also dynamic (ontogenetic or longitudinal) factors that, by the requirement of memory and associative relationships, place somewhat greater emphasis on cognitive functioning.

HISTORICAL PERSPECTIVE

Since the time of Hippocrates, speculations attempting to relate psychological states and personality types to various physiological functions and constitutional body types have been made (780, 1083, 1384). Following the great progress in evolutionary theory and in the biological sciences of the nineteenth century, Adolph Meyer formulated and taught a "psychobiological" approach for psychiatry that has had marked influence upon the study of physiological-psychological (and social) relationships in the United States during this century (789). Meyer simply emphasized the interrelatedness of such functioning and brought awareness of this to clinical practice so that the total life history and personality patterns of the given patient would be studied to bring increased understanding and better treatment of his symptoms. At the same time in Europe, Kraepelin (722) and Bleuler (132, 133) called attention to physiological and constitutional factors in personality.

The physiological manifestations of anxiety states and the numerous cases of "neurocirculatory asthenia" of World War I also helped focus attention on psychophysiological relationships. It was the relationship of "psyche to soma" that early attracted Freud's attention; and it has been within the psychoanalytic tradition that much of the theorizing about "psychosomatic medicine" and "organic neurosis" has been formulated, most of which originated in the 1930s. Just preceding this period, Abraham postulated character types centered around fixation on the body areas involved in the Freudian psychosexual stages of development, namely, oral, anal, and so forth, and physiological, as well as behavioral, symptoms were thought to stem from such fixation (2).

Grinker (499) credited Alkan (27) for the first clear outlining of how organic pathology may stem from psychogenic disturbances. At the same time, Alexander's psychoanalytic experience led to his believing first that gastrointestinal disorders, and then, later, that respiratory and vasomotor symptoms frequently have etiology in psychological conflicts (22). A major step in the demonstrating of the extent of psychophysiological relationships and their clinical significance was then made by Dunbar, who, in 1935, reviewed the "psychosomatic" literature, citing particularly German literature and including many hypnosis studies. Dunbar herself studied hospital cases of different diagnostic types in terms of personality differences and of functional etiological factors relating to the particular illnesses (321). This work has been called "the beginning of a formalized approach to comprehensive medicine" (500, p. 19).

Since the 1930s, a steadily increasing abundance of clinical studies along these lines has been produced, and many theoretical formulations placing different weights on symbolic, constitutional, neurological, and direct physiological expression of "emotion" (or "affect equivalents") have come forth (23, 131, 173, 297, 353, 1083, 1131). Those findings that most directly relate physiological functioning to immediate psychological states, or conditions, will be outlined here. Relatively little concerning the etiological, symbolic, or cognitive factors will be included.

Most all modern theorists recognize the existence of various functional and homeostatic aspects of the different symptom complexes, even if these are considered to be only symbolic in nature. Also, more recent views have placed emphasis on multiple etiological factors in psychosomatic conditions (1204).

METHODOLOGY

Since the first early vague reference to the existence of some relationship between psychological and physiological functioning, clinical studies have employed to an increasing degree more precise experimental methods in the studying of these relationships, even to the inclusion of factor-analysis techniques (1002). Nevertheless, it shall be readily apparent from the studies to be cited that much remains to be done in the way of the refining of experimental controls for these studies. One of the greatest defects of most of these studies has been the failure to include control subjects, or conditions, along with the experimental subjects or variables, when the need for such controls has been repeatedly recognized (471) as a requirement for the accurate evaluation of experimental and clinical findings. A much more difficult problem, inherent in these studies, is the need of evaluating the individual's psychological state with respect to the fact that the "feeling or emotion" at the time of study may be different from that which is consciously reported or which is surmised by the experimental or clinical observer (871, 998a). Hamilton has reviewed the psychosomatic literature from the standpoint of the placing of primary emphasis on statistical validation (517a), and others have leveled severe criticism at psychosomatic theory (893b).

LEVELS OF PSYCHOSOMATIC RELATIONSHIPS

There has been much confusion and controversy in the literature over the concept of "psychosomatic." Some have maintained that this term implies a dualism of "mind" and "body," although it is almost universally agreed that all psychological functioning has some physiological correlate. This confusion disappears when one considers the interrelationships of various levels of neurophysiological and somatic functioning. For example, a psychological *state* of anxiety may conceivably have an etiological origin in some pattern of neural organization within the cortex or other brain structure of the individual, but this must be differentiated from the immediate occurrence of changes in heart beat, blood pressure, gastric secretion, perspiration, and so forth. Similarly, still another distinction must be drawn between these characteristics and the behavior manifested by the individual, which again presumably has a basis in his existing neural brain patterns. Patterns of these types, however, would seem to be primarily cognitive. The distinction between cognitive and noncognitive inner experience should be kept in mind. It is this very practical distinction that provides a theoretical basis for psychosomatic studies in which a differentiation is made between psychic (or cognitive) "functional" etiology and inadequate physiological functioning of nonpathological origin at more elementary phylogenetic levels.

The interrelationships between the higher neurophysiological levels, which apparently embody the basis of cognitive functioning, and the phylogenetically lower neurophysiological levels, which may be limited in function to manifesting more direct and immediate physiological changes, are of course extremely complex, as shall be shown in subsequent sections. The determination of the levels, along the neurophysiological continuum of the human organism, at which noncognitive inner experience and "psychosomatic" symptoms (representing direct "emotional expression") can be differentiated from the cognitive (neural-ontogenetic or "symbolic") etiology of symptoms, respectively, is one of the most fundamental problems presented in this work.

It has been with the psychoanalytic theories and studies that the greatest emphasis has been put on the relating of somatic symptoms to symbolic, or cognitive, factors (298). One of the most striking examples of this thinking is demonstrated in the concept of somatic displacement, in which the symbolic significance of a part of the body to a given individual results in its unconscious "selection" as a site for the expression of emotional conflicts; such bodily locations are reported to change at times with the changing conditions and circumstances of the individual (694).

In his *Interpretation of Dreams* (384), Freud developed the concept of affects as "motor and secretory (discharge) processes that are controlled from the unconscious" (1022, p. 180), and more recently there has been a plea for greater emphasis on physiological studies in psychoanalysis (166).

In the last chapter, psychoanalytic formulations that involved developmental stages and relative voluntary-involuntary reactivity were presented. Most psychoanalytic concepts of psychosomatic conditions, or organ neuroses, involve the idea that the patient has regressed to a degree to earlier developmental stages or fixations (299, 299a). In regression and disease, Meerloo conceived of a "rudimentary alarm system" that becomes activated, and that is a form of "archaic communication" and a rudimentary remnant of animal signals that manifests such signs as fear melanosis, fainting, goose flesh, and several types of dermatoses (893a). In regard to bodily feelings, Szasz defined three sorts of relationship of the ego to the body: (1) a silent feeling of well-being, (2) feelings associated with increased interest in the body, including an "almost limitless diversity of affects" such as pain, itching, paresthesias, anesthesias, and feelings of bodily estrangement, and (3) feelings associated with decreased interest in the body, such as a stoical attitude of "feeling no pain," or as a "hysterical anesthesia" (1227a).

In Chapter 8 was noted Schur's concept of infantile somatization with disturbance of homeostasis. The desomatization of responses was related to the ego's faculty of using secondary processes and of neutralizing energy; conversely, resomatization was linked with a prevalence of primary-process thinking and of the use of deneutralized energy (1110b). On the assumption that neutralization follows the model of homeostatic regulators, it was proposed, consistent with clinical reports, that in children with innate or early acquired abnormalities of homeostatic mechanisms, inhibited development of the ego function of neutralization occurs. Such failures, however, do not always result in physiological regression since innate and emotional factors seem to have a role in predispositions as well as in choice of organ.

DEVELOPMENTS IN GENERAL PSYCHOLOGY AND PHYSIOLOGY

HISTORICAL PERSPECTIVE

The experimental approach to psychophysiological relationships is rooted in events that also took place about the turn of the twentieth century, even though considerable "psychophysical" experimentation in evaluating external sensory perception had already taken place (140, 349, 350, 623, 1290, 1291, 1292). Several relatively independent activities in addition to those already noted focused increased attention on psychophysiological relationships. Of these, perhaps the greatest influence on psychophysiological experimentation in the United States stemmed from the "controversy" concerning the theories of William James, the psychologist and philosopher (625, 626, 627), and W. B. Cannon, the physiologist (190, 191, 195), concerning peripheral versus central physiological factors in emotional experience and expression. The neurologist, H. Head, also played an important role (538, 539, 540, 541). About the same time a physiologist, I. Pavlov, developed conditioned-reflex experimentation that exerted a considerable influence on subsequent theoretical and experimental work (973, 974, 975, 1235). Also, relatively simple studies of physiological relationships to psychological states were beginning (49, 352, 1134). Much of the early experimentation involving psychophysiological functioning took place in the 1920s and, more especially, the 1930s, and it was augmented by the general protest against introspective psychology and by the general behavioristic trend already described.

The negative protest against introspective psychology, combined with the positive difficulty in evaluating subjective reports of experimental subjects, resulted in the virtual omission of experimental study of psychological states while attention was focused almost exclusively on the stimulus conditions and on the physiologic and behavioral reactions of experimental subjects. Nevertheless, it was most frequently the relationships of "emotion" to physiological functioning that were described in psychophysiological experimentation, and it was necessary to infer or postulate given types of emotional, or psychological, states. With the animal experimentation, of course, there was no other alternative anyway. It remained for the clinicians to explore more scientifically the psychological states of subjects in connection with psychological reactions and changes by both evaluating the judgments of subjects and by accepting, and even comparing, the judgments of experienced clinical observers in "life-situation and emotion" studies.

One underlying aspiration of the psychophysiological experimenters was to discover physiological changes that would be better indices of psychological states than are the variable subjective reports of subjects, and would thereby make way for a more highly developed scientific approach to psychophysiological relationships (1197, p. 48). Because they attempt to avoid judgments of psychological states, rather than scientifically including them as a basis for evaluating their physiological findings, these experimenters failed to achieve this ambition. The early experimenters were also greatly limited by the lack of instruments that would precisely measure the many, varied, and complex physiological changes that occur simultaneously in the organism. Even now experimentation is limited in this respect.

Nevertheless, the findings and views of such experimenters so greatly influenced psychological thinking that they are incorporated to some extent in practically every current psychological theory, and include even those with primary social and interpersonal emphasis (656, 707, 777, 1165, 1312). Especially important in this respect was Cannon's concept of homeostatic functioning, in which he proposed that fluctuating physiological changes are supposed to vary and to interreact in the direction of maintaining a constant physiological state within the organism and to protect the organism from foreign intrusion (193). Foreshadowing this concept was Claude Bernard's "general law of constancy of the internal environment" (113, 114), Herbert Spencer's theorizing on the physiological nature of emotion in the middle of the nineteenth century (1176), Charles Darwin's views on the functional nature of emotional behavior a few years later (277), and a general functional emphasis in psychology, biology, and neurophysiology early in the twentieth century (46, 48, 240, 300, 301, 539, 626, 1141).

The concept of homeostasis has been extended by some writers to include all human behavior (271, 373, 998), and other theorists have combined the homeostatic concepts with concepts embodying universal regulating forces or principles (333, 1024). Some have placed much emphasis on the adrenal cortex as a homeostatic regulator (1120, 1121, 1122, 1123); more recently, however, it has been viewed as functioning integrally with other organs and processes (334, 365). A similar emphasis and subsequent de-emphasis occurred earlier in regard to the thalamus, which was at one time considered by many theorists to be the "center," or key organ, for "feeling and emotion."

JAMES AND CANNON

Much misunderstanding has centered about the theories of James and of Cannon because of failure to distinguish that James's theory primarily concerned "emotional experience," feelings, or noncognitive inner experience, whereas that of Cannon primarily concerned emotional behavior. James maintained that the individual reacts physiologically and behaviorally directly in response to the stimulus and that the conscious, or feeling, aspect of this experience *is* the awareness of the physiological changes taking place (627, 628). At first James believed such experiences to be localized in visceral and muscular tissues, but later he modified his theory to include pleasant and unpleasant affective sensory experiences due to "nerve currents" (1071).

Lange (751) of Denmark and Sergi (1071) of Italy independently set forth similar theories about a year after James. Lange believed that emotional experiences were localized in the vasomotor areas, and Sergi localized them in the cardiovascular and respiratory systems. These concepts have been called "peripheral theories of emotion." James also distinguished emotions from instincts, believing that these shade imperceptibly into each other and that every object that excites an instinct, excites an emotion as well.

Cannon was the first to maintain that the thalamic region is the center of emotional experience (195). Such viewpoints have been termed as "central theories of emotion." It was from Head (539) that Cannon got a clue as to the importance of the thalamic region. Late in the nineteenth century, Head made observations concerning changes in sensation, perception, and expression of "emotions" in patients with thalamic lesions. Cannon confirmed and elaborated Head's findings by experimenting on animals, principally on cats and dogs. Head observed that the destruction of the cortex alone does not disturb the threshold for the painful or uncomfortable aspects of sensation, and that thalamic lesions cause an excessive response to affective stimuli. A person with a thalamic lesion might laugh or cry in situations that would stimulate only mild feelings in others. Head concluded that the lesion enhances hedonic tone by impeding the inhibitory effects of the cerebral cortex on thalamic activity and that the thalamus is the seat of the neurological process involving hedonic consciousness.

Cannon and his co-workers skirted the conscious aspect of the problem and accepted the bodily changes, which could be studied, as reflecting "emotion" when preceded by certain familiar stimuli. Cannon employed two methods primarily: one was the puncturing of brain tissue, particularly the thalamus; and the second was the removal of brain tissue, preceding from the more highly developed cerebral cortex to the thalamus and then to the brain-stem tissues of lower phylogenetic development. Under these various conditions, he observed the reactions of cats and dogs to such common stimuli as food, pinching, and being confronted with cats or dogs. He was principally concerned with the visceral manifestations of emotional reactions, although he recognized that emotional expression involved both the visceral and skeletal-muscle anatomy.

CONCEPTS OF AUTONOMIC FUNCTIONING

Cannon emphasized the role of the sympathetic nervous system on visceral reactions in emotional responses—reactions that had earlier received the attention of Sherrington (467, 796, 1141).

Parenthetically, it should be noted here that although the nervous system is one continuous structure, for purposes of analysis it is divided into three parts: the central nervous system, which includes the brain and spinal cord; the autonomic nervous system, which includes the nerves leading to organs and glands; and the peripheral nervous system, which includes the remaining sensory and motor nerves. The autonomic nervous system is subdivided into the sympathetic division and the parasympathetic division, the latter being made up of sacral and cranial subdivisions. Both the sympathetic and the parasympathetic systems are apparently connected to all of the internal glands and organs, and they are in many ways antagonistic, or opposite, in function, maintaining a relative balance in the innervation of a given organ. A persistent tendency in the past to overgeneralize from experimental data has led many theorists, including Cannon, to assert or assume that these systems are absolutely differentiated and antagonistic. As shall be demonstrated, more recent research indicates that these systems are interrelated in a much more complex manner.

Cannon found many physiological reactions upon presentation of the stimuli that he used, and he generalized that the sympathetic nervous system is *characterized* by diffuse conduction. Thus, he concluded that in "major emotions" there are not specific visceral changes corresponding to specific patterns, but rather that there is a simple pattern of changes for all emotions that results from sympathetic innervation, namely: an acceleration of the heart, constriction of visceral blood vessels, dilatation of the pupils, inhibition of stomach contraction and of intestinal and gastric activity, secretion of adrenaline in the blood and release of increased blood sugar, and the raising of the hair in animals. It should be kept in mind, however, that the "major emotions" that he observed were in the nature of fear and rage. By 1926, it was already apparent to some observers that these workers were oversimplifying their concept of "emotional upset" and of physiological reactivity (745).

Concerning "fear," Kling has taken issue with Cannon in noting that the sympathetic-innervation syndrome accounts for hardly more than half of the total visceral changes that occur (710). The other changes stem from parasympathetic innervation, and Kling proposed that these parasympathetic changes characterize the bodily expression of fear and that the parasympathetic innervation is dominant over the sympathetic and it is this relative predominance that differentiates "fear" reactions from "rage" reactions as well as from other emotions. Also, findings of increased hydrochloric acid secretion in the stomach during sustained experimental stress conditions were presumed to be a result of parasympathetic stimulation and were interpreted by Mahl as proof against any extension of Cannon's theory to include "chronic" emotions (856).

Bender (98) and Gellhorn (426, 429, 430) have demonstrated by experiments on animals and humans that both sympathetic and parasympathetic innervation are involved in response to emotional stimuli, and the complex nature of this innervation, as well as of the associated hormone reactions, has been increasingly emphasized (478). Clinical examples of parasympathetic participation in such reactions are seen in blushing, lacrimation, fainting, vomiting, and involuntary urination and defecation (710, 1144).

In contrast to Kling's view, Morgan once hypothesized that parasympathetic activity is the basis of "pleasantness," making the following observations: warmth stimulation, when not painful, stimulates this system and produces a pleasant feeling; functions connected with eating are parasympathetically governed, as are generative and evacuative functions; in sexual behavior, the vasodilatation and certain muscular responses leading up to orgasm are of parasympathetic origin (928). Morgan cautioned some hesitancy, however, in expecting a simple correlation between relative pleasantness and the two autonomic subdivisions.

More recently Arnold has associated "fear" with preponderant sympathetic activity and "anger" with preponderant parasympathetic excitation, and has proposed "that the most favorable conditions for activity are found in a moderate stimulation of the cholinergic (parasympathetic) mechanism resulting in facilitation of action by 'excitement' without untoward secondary adrenalin effects (at least for the duration of the activity)" (52, 53, 54). An experiment by Ax has been interpreted as opposing Arnold's theory (55). Also, there have been several other attempts to classify types of personality or types of emotion on the basis of differential autonomic reactivity (409, 411, 1215). Subsequent elaborations on physiological functioning during various psychological states will perhaps clarify somewhat these differences in theory.

CONCEPTS DEVELOPED FROM ABLATION STUDIES

Cannon and his co-workers found by the removal of parts of the brain that no definite co-ordinated response, such as is implied in emotional behavior, was found in the central nervous system below the medulla. When the medulla was left intact, reactions were easily elicited by the stimuli employed, and although these reactions were rather extensive, they were not considered to be sufficiently co-ordinated to be called "emotions." With the metencephalon, including the pons and cerebellum, still intact there was increased co-ordination in the nature of "emotion," but the reactions were still not sufficiently co-ordinated for the making of generalized and intensive responses. Also, at this phylogenetic, neurophysiological level were found some centers of facial expressions, together with modified vocal utterances. Leaving intact the next brain-stem section between the cerebellum and the thalamus, namely the mesencephalon, certain so-called pseudo-affective reflexes occurred in the cat and dog, such as mewing, clawing, snapping of the jaws, barking, and growling. But it was with the inact functioning of the diencephalon, including the thalamus and hypothalamus, that "infuriated rage responses" and the majority of the so-called physiological signs of emotional behavior occurred. Bard localized this critical area principally in the hypothalamus, and he distinguished the animal's responses from true rage by terming them "sham rage" (68, 71, 72).

Cannon interpreted his findings as a refutation of the James-Lange theory and as proof that the sympathetic nervous system gives expression to the emotions, and believed that these emotions originate in, and are co-ordinated by, the thalamus. Such reactions to stimuli are first made in the thalamus, according to Cannon, and from there the reactive impulse is sent over the sympathetic nervous system to produce the observed emotional behavior. Cannon believed that the center for emotions was the thalamus, although he credited the cerebral cortex with the inhibiting of emotions in certain ways. He also postulated that the stimuli might at times pass directly through the thalamus to the cerebral cortex where conditioned responses would in turn excite the thalamus, producing emotional reaction patterns. Cannon maintained that from the reaction in the thalamus, an epiphenomenal impulse was transmitted to the cerebral cortex and from this a person experiences awareness of the emotional reaction (191, 192).

Lindsley has summarized the points that Cannon believed negated the James-Lange theory as follows (796, p. 501):

(1) Total separation of the viscera from the central nervous system does not alter emotional behavior. (2) The same visceral changes occur in very different emotional states and in nonemotional states. (3) The viscera are relatively insensitive structures. (4) Visceral changes are too slow to be a source of emotional feeling. (5) Artificial induction of the visceral changes typical of strong emotions does not produce them.

RECONSIDERATIONS OF JAMES'S AND CANNON'S THEORIES

Wenger has also summarized Cannon's major criticism of James's theory along with the evidence for the rebuttal that has gradually accumulated to negate Cannon's argument (1304). Concerning Cannon's point that emotional behavior is not altered by separation of the viscera from the central nervous system, Wenger stated that, notwithstanding this, conditioned cortical responses could still exist and could even involve fibers arising in the thalamus and medulla, as well as involve instinctive somatic reflexes that Wenger believed constitute the basis of the so-called "emotional behavior" of the ablated animals. He also noted Cannon's own inconsistency in stating that the same visceral changes occur in very different emotional states when he also added that there are "minor variations." It shall be seen in this text that the variations are considerable. Issue was taken by Wenger with Cannon's belief that viscera are relatively insensitive structures and that visceral changes are too slow to constitute emotion. Concerning Cannon's last criticism, which refers primarily to the attempted stimulation of "emotional" reactivity by injection of adrenaline into human subjects, Wenger noted that many complex factors are involved in such attempts to induce "emotion," which he distinguished from true emotional reactivity.

Hebb has pointed out the fact that whether emotional responses are organized and patterned by the thalamus, as Cannon had hypothesized, or by the hypothalamus, is irrelevant to James's view that afferent excitation produces feeling, or "emotional" awareness (542, 543, 544). It is important, however, to decide whether such feeling, or awareness, is to be considered merely epiphenomenal and insignificant or is to be considered of significance to the individual. Yet, Cannon's theory can also encompass significant aspects of such awareness by reference to the postulated conditioned reflexes, which, being associated with afferent stimulation through the thalamus (and hypothalamus), send impulses back into it, setting off further emotional reactions or behaviors.

Lindsley (796) has noted that the details of neuroanatomy and neurophysiology were largely unknown at the time of James's theorizing (626), and he questioned the relevancy of Cannon's experimentation (191) to this theory. Lindsley asserted that James's theory is by its very nature an untestable hypothesis since it is virtually impossible to eliminate all visceral afferent impulses in experimentation. He added that the emotional expressions observed by Sherrington (1140) and Cannon (197) in animals were nevertheless diminished only in those areas where autonomic and somatic efferents had been eliminated.

Golightly's analysis of the James-Cannon controversy pointed to four interrelated problems: (1) James's attempt to consolidate and simplify the conceptual approaches of nineteenth-century introspective psychology; (2) the problem of what causes emotions; (3) the problem of a criterion for what emotion is; and (4) the problem of the relationships between mind and body (467, p. 287).

The theories of James and Cannon are not fundamentally incompatible, and each was aimed primarily at explaining different phenomena, with one pertaining primarily to feeling and the other to "emotional" reactions, or expressions. Thus, the protest against James's theory by proponents of the thalamic theory has usually been directed against "a straw man." This is even more the case with the numerous treatises concerning postulated "organizing," or disruptive, aspects of "emotion" (314, 315, 316, 544, 763, 796, 1288, 1381, 1382). These arguments have been predicated on the assumption that "emotion" is a *thing,* a psychic entity. It has become increasingly clear, as shall be demonstrated in this book, that no such entity exists; feelings refer to one type of inner experience, and emotional expressions and behaviors refer to the final efferent manifestations of complex interrelated functions that include various phylogenetic levels of relative involuntary-voluntary neural reactivity and integration, different learned associations and cultural reaction patterns, and various reverberating neural circuits and neural-impulse firing patterns that are not yet completely understood.

MORE RECENT CONCEPTS

A somewhat different approach to the conceptualizing of organismic reactivity was presented in a generalized concept of a general adaptation syndrome (GAS) by Selye (1120, 1122a). This theoretical construct encompasses a reactivity to so-called "stress," whether physical or otherwise. The concept of "stress" is also very general and may be defined "as the state which manifests itself by the G.A.S." (1122a, p. 47). Three stages of the GAS were postulated: (1) the alarm reaction (AR), (2) the stage of resistance (SR), and (3) the stage of exhaustion (SE). Tissues that were more directly affected by a given stress were conceived of as developing a local adaptation syndrome (LAS), which is closely co-ordinated with the GAS and produces "alarm signals" by nervous-system stimulation and results in the secretion of "adaptive hormones," including especially pituitary and adrenal secretions. Two groups of "adaptive hormones" were distinguished: "the *anti-inflammatory hormones* (ACTH, cortisone, COL), which inhibit excessive defensive reactions, and the *proinflammatory hormones* (STH, aldosterone, DOC), which stimulate them" (1122a, p. 47). The effects of such substances are modified by other physiological conditions and past experience. Organismic resistance and adaptation were thought to depend on the proper balance of these factors, and imbalance was conceived to be the basis of "diseases of adaptation," a term that substitutes for the more common term "psychosomatic diseases." The term "stress" has been used by Lazarus to represent a psychological *state*, involving cognitive and noncognitive reactivity, whereas the term "stressors" was used for stimuli producing "stress" reactions (758a, 758b).

The most promising method for ferreting out and differentiating physiological functions, neural and somatic, at the various complex levels from peripheral to central, appears to be that of electrical measurements of changes in organs, structures, and neural pathways, including even the measurement of electromagnetic and electrostatic fields (121, 686). Such measures constitute a bridge between the as yet incompletely understood electrochemical changes from which they arise and the as yet inconclusively classified behavior, or organismic reactions, with which they may correlate. Concerning the coalescence of these two variables, G. H. Bishop stated as follows (122, p. 161):

Two developments are necessary, however, before the electro-physiologist can function successfully as the middleman. Both involve giving specific meaning to what is still largely a nonspecific electrical potential. On the one hand we must have the chemical information in terms of observable neural functions. It is not enough to know, for instance, that certain enzymes accomplish substrate oxidation in nerve; we must know how these chemical reactions result in electrochemical excitability and response. On the other hand we should have mental behavior broken down into components capable of corresponding to practicably recordable patterns of neural behavior. That such a breakdown should be possible follows from the premise that mental behavior is a function of nervous tissue. It is difficult to conceive of a neural pattern corresponding to anxiety, or to a dissociation from reality; if there is one, it must be too hopelessly complex to be recorded by any current apparatus. There must be simpler mental components conceivable, as there will certainly be more complex electrical recordings possible, in terms of which the neurophysiologist and the psychologist can find a common ground; but this common ground must be approached from both directions.

Similarly, there have been other recent advocates of the studying of differential physiological changes for different psychological states (500) and for the employment of simultaneous multiple physiological measures to accomplish this (55), and to this purpose the balance of Part III is devoted.

The relationship of noncognitive inner experiences to the various levels of neurophysiological organization will be considered secondly, and following that the physiological changes that take place in different body areas and parts with different psychological states will be presented. Finally, following Part IV, which concerns internal sensations, an attempt will be made to synthesize the findings that have been presented for the purpose of understanding what simultaneous physiological changes take place *throughout* the body with the different psychological states, including the major types of "feelings." It would seem that studies of such simultaneous physiological changes (which may correspond to experimentally established differential psychological states) may reveal "simpler mental components," or feeling components, such as just quoted from Bishop. Studies of this type would seem to be required for more refined electrophysiological formulations, as well as for neurophysiological and psychological theories concerning human functioning.

CHAPTER 11

Neurophysiological Developments

THALAMIC ("HYPOTHALAMIC") THEORY AND VARIATIONS

The Cannon-Bard thalamic theory focused attention on the critical neurophysiological aspects of inner experience, and subsequent studies and theories concerning the noncognitive area of inner experience have placed major emphasis on neurophysiological relationships. Masserman's extensive experimentation led him to oppose the thalamic theory, and he integrated the evidences of physiological reactions in emotional states into the psychoanalytic theory (881). It was observed that the quasi-aggressive behavior previously described with hypothalamic stimulation was neither object oriented nor goal directed, and similarly "sham fear" was diffuse and apparently undirected. Except for mechanical interference, normal behavior patterns were hardly modified, so that "a cat would continue to lap milk, clean its fur, or even purr in response to petting while at the same time reacting to direct hypothalamic stimulation with horripilation, widened pupils, arched back, unsheathed claws, snarling, and other peripheral manifestations ordinarily indicative of rage, or fear"; furthermore, the reactions ceased abruptly when the stimulation was discontinued (881, p. 45). Nevertheless, these reactions were thought to be consistent with the concept of emotion proposed by some psychoanalysts, which contrasts the rational behavior of "ego" with the "diffusely impulsive and intrusive 'emotional' eruptions of the 'id.' " Masserman asserted orthodox Freudian theory to assume more meaningfully that, once experienced, an emotion becomes associated with various sensory configurations constituting a "complex" and modifying all subsequent relevant behavior. He interpreted the failure of a conditioned reflex to be formed between visual stimulation and the physiological reactions produced by direct stimulation of the hypothalamus in cats as negating the James and Lange theories. Although he did not conceive of the diencephalon as a site of emotional "drive" or expression, either by itself or as part of the

127

"thalamic-frontal-paleocortical-diencephalic" tracts proposed by Papez (968), the experiments indicated that it is an important integrative ganglion on the peripheral arc of the neural mechanisms governing emotional expressions (881).

Papez (968) had made the distinction between using the term "emotion" to imply a way of acting or to imply a way of feeling. He accepted Bard's evidence that emotional expression depends on the action of the hypothalamus rather than on that of the dorsal thalamus or cerebral cortex; however, he added that for subjective emotional experience, or "feeling," the participation of the cortex is essential. After describing the afferent routes leading to the mammillary body and the hypothalamus, he summarized as follows (968, p. 729):

> It is thus evident that the afferent pathways from the receptor organs split at the thalamic level into three routes, each conducting a stream of impulses of special importance. One route conducts impulses through the dorsal thalamus and the internal capsule to the corpus striatum. This route represents "the stream of movement." The second conducts impulses from the thalamus through the internal capsule to the lateral cerebral cortex. This route represents "the stream of thought." The third conducts a set of concomitant impulses through the ventral thalamus to the hypothalamus and by way of the mammillary body and the anterior thalamic nuclei to the gyrus cinguli, in the medial wall of the cerebral hemisphere. This route represents "the stream of feeeling." In this way, the sensory excitations which reach the lateral cortex through the internal capsule receive their emotional coloring from the concurrent processes of hypothalamic origin which irradiate them from the gyrus cinguli. . .
>
> It is proposed that the hypothalamus, the anterior thalamic nuclei, the gyrus cinguli, the hippocampus and their interconnections constitute a harmonious mechanism which may elaborate the functions of central emotion, as well as participate in emotional expression.

This theory has subsequently been extended in a proposal that a phylogenetically old brain structure, the rhinencephalon (called the "visceral brain") may be largely concerned with emotional and psychosomatic manifestations (840, 852) (see p. 137).

The thalamic theory underwent a series of criticisms and rebuttals (68, 69, 192). In 1938, Lashley (756) raised serious questions concerning some of the thalamocortical mechanisms postulated in support of the thalamic theory and concerning the ability of the thalamus to control patterns of emotional expression or to produce the wide range of affective states observed in human personality (796). Lashley interpreted evidence cited from cases with clinical brain lesions as opposing not only the James-Lange theory, as Cannon believed, but also the thalamic theory. Although thalamic lesions may result in marked and unusual emotional expressions, Lashley pointed out the inconsistency in believing that the thalamus, as one example, would discharge one pattern to the musculature in producing laughter, while simultaneously discharging an entirely different pattern to the cortex, so that the patient felt sad and depressed in referring to his very difficult home situation. As a better explanation for such symptoms, Lashley proposed that a correct cortical evaluation and feeling initiated the appropriate corti-cothalamic impulse, but the brain lesion forced the impulse into an abnormal pathway in the thalamic relay station.

Morgan emphasized the strategic location of the thalamus, as a main way station for all afferent pathways to the cerebral cortex, and he believed that the thalamus is no more important in emotional experience than its function as a relay station would suggest (928). He considered it important that somesthetic impulses constitute a battery of excitement continuously impinging upon the central nervous system, forming a sensory background for other sensory effects. With this, the effects of specific stimuli fit into, and are determined in part by, the pre-existing and ever-present somesthetic stimulation. Thus the thalamus, along with the hypothalamus, may be considered as a critical relay station interacting with both efferent and afferent neural impulses, and, with this, adding its own appropriate effects in terms of its level of phylogenetic organization. Nevertheless, differences in opinion concerning the roles of the hypothalamus and of the diencephalon in emotional experience still exist, and therefore it may be worth while to consider some of these developments in more detail.

DECORTICATION AND THALAMIC FUNCTIONING

Although Goltz observed the effects of stimulation on a decorticate animal as early as 1884, it was not until the 1920s that experimentation involving decortication and thalamic stimulation was undertaken extensively (67, 73, 196, 325, 577, 675, 676, 677, 881, 898, 1016, 1046, 1062, 1178). Spiegel, Miller, and Oppenheimer commented on various findings in ablation experiments in regard to the involvement of different brain parts in the reactions of abnormal emotional hyperexcitability that resulted from slight and innocuous stimuli as follows (1178, p. 538):

Whereas Goltz [468] observed it after ablation of the frontal lobes and anterior sigmoid gyri, a number of observers (Barris [80]; Magoun and Ranson [851]) did not obtain these reactions even after extensive lesions of the frontal lobes. The experiments of Cannon and Britton [196], Bard [67], and Bard and Rioch [73] indicated that these fits of rage are due to the release of subcortical ganglia from cortical inhibition, particularly a release of the posterior hypothalamus as far as the vegetative component of these reactions is concerned, the somatic component probably having its center in the mesencephalic tegmentum and its continuations into the hypothalamus (Hinsey, Ranson and McNattin [578]).

In order to ascertain which part of the forebrain is critical in the precipitation of "rage" reactions, Spiegel, Miller, and Oppenheimer, working with 66 cats and 12 dogs, systematically explored by ablations and lesions the various parts of the forebrain that are involved in the sending of efferent impulses to the hypothalamus and to the midbrain tegmentum, respectively. Their ablations and lesions involved the frontal lobe, parietal lobe, temporal lobe, occipital lobe, gyrus cinguli, olfactory tubercle, the hippocampus-fornix system, the striatum-pallidum system, and the amygdaloid nuclei. They found that (1178, p. 546):

> Lesions restricted to neocortical areas failed to produce rage reactions. Following lesions of the frontal poles hypermotility could be observed but no convincing outbursts of rage. Definite manifestations of rage appeared if the lesions (*e.g.*, extirpation of the frontal lobes) encroached upon the olfactory tubercles or followed isolated lesions of the tubercles, whereas destruction of the olfactory bulbs or section of their stalks, had no or only slight effects. After acute lesions of the hippocampus-fornix system rudimentary, or in some animals marked, rage reactions appeared, particularly in cases in which the lesion of the fornices encroached upon the septum pellucidum. Definite outbursts of rage were observed after bilateral lesions of the amygdaloid nuclei. Lesions of the pyriform lobes, as long as they remained superficial, evoked only slight and transitory symptoms of rage.

No additional stimuli were employed to precipitate the behavior of these animals, and it was felt that the rage reactions relate to phylogenetically old forebrain parts involving the central olfactory system (namely, the olfactory tubercles, the amygdaloid nuclei, and, to some extent, the hippocampus-fornix system). After the considering of both the excitatory and the depressant aspects of the cortical impulses, as well as the complex innervations and functions of subcortical areas, Spiegel, Miller, and Oppenheimer favored the traditional view that: (1) the subcortical "rage" reaction is generally inhibited by the cortex; and (2) that ablation of the forebrain, or the presence of intervening lesions, results in release of this inhibition, permitting the free expression of "rage" patterns and the like. Subsequent studies related such defensive reactions, showing integration of somato-motor and autonomic mechanisms, to the perifornical area of the hypothalamus, the preoptic and ventral septal region, and the central (periaqueductal) gray matter of the midbrain, whereas electrical stimulation of the following areas failed to produce these reactions: dorsal thalamus, striatum, cornu ammonis (hippocampus) and mammillary bodies, and the anterior and orbitofrontal cortex (559b).

These experiments serve to illustrate the relativity, the overlapping, and the complexity of neurophysiological interactions. A stimulus at one point, whether it is direct as with needle electrodes, or indirect as with the scarring that results from lesions, is likely to result in neural impulses that affect other brain parts, making it difficult to distinguish which part is actually producing the observed physiological or behavioral changes. Similarly, a lesion at one point might interrupt reverberating neural circuits that involve brain parts well removed from the area of the lesion. Also in this type of experimentation, it is usually only possible to determine the actual location of lesions and the extent of tissue damage by autopsy, which makes uniform experimentation with different subjects difficult. Finally, with studies using experimental animals, caution should be taken not to necessarily relate the findings for a given brain part with the same functions in human subjects, since with each step in phylogenetic evolution, given brain parts take on slightly different functions. The degree of caution or of generalization actually expressed in the drawing of conclusions from experiments of these types also depends, of course, somewhat on the personality (and physiological knowledge) of the theorist. Notwithstanding these limitations, much valuable knowledge has been derived in recent years from experiments involving direct and indirect stimulation of brain parts.

Specific circuits of interaction between the thalamus and the cortex have been demonstrated, though independent electrical activity within each of these brain sections is also seen (291, 426, 1179). Jasper postulated "a separate regulating system in the thalamus which may time and control the resting rhythms of the cortex analogous to the alpha rhythm in man" (633, p. 236). He also noted "that the neural mechanism underlying the regulation of alpha rhythm is susceptible to conditioning and that practically all varieties of Pavlovian conditioned reflexes" have been demonstrated (497, 638, 1125, 1126).

HYPOTHALAMIC FINDINGS

In regard to hypothalamus, Bard has reported that "rage reactions" could be evoked in cats when only the posterior hypothalamus was destroyed (70). Obrador found that lesions in the hypothalamus (and also in the thalamus and in thalamocortical pathways) abolished electrical activity in the cortex of cats (958). Employing electroencephalographic measurements, Murphy and Gellhorn demonstrated that strychninized impulses in the hypothalamus result in neural firing in various parts of the cortex, and here again the dorsomedial nucleus and the ventrolateral nucleus of the thalamus played predominant roles as intermediate relay stations (941). Thus, not only have efferent functions of the hypothalamus been demonstrated, but "upward discharges" into the cortex are seen to produce quantitative changes in cortical functioning. The experimenters added, however, "It will be difficult, if not impossible, to show by physiological experimentation that thalamic discharges may lead to *qualitative* sensory changes," even though these were considered probable.

Relevant to this consideration was White's experiment, reported two years earlier, wherein he stimulated the hypothalamus electrically while human patients were conscious under local anesthesia (1316). These patients apparently experienced no emotional changes, sensations, or variations in consciousness. No changes in alertness were seen, in contrast with animal experimentation where alertness and excitement were seen on electrical stimulation. Manipulation near the anterior hypothalamus did produce drowsiness that merged at times into unconsciousness, and this was interpreted as stemming from a depressing, or inhibiting, effect on the "waking center" in the posterior hypothalamus. Manipulation of the hypothalamus during surgical operations has been reported to produce "maniacal excitement" (306, 413).

Clinically, lesions in the hypothalamus have been related to a wide range of personality changes and symptom manifestations (37, 693, 707, 1316), many of which are similar to symptoms produced by damage in other brain areas (796). These symptoms include such things as restlessness, lack of social inhibition, mood swings between depression and excitement, emotional lability with a low threshold for uncontrolled laughter and at times apathy.

Gellhorn believed his experimentation demonstrated not only that cortical activity inhibits "downward discharge" from the hypothalamus, but that it also holds in abeyance the "upward discharge" to the cortex (424, 425, 426,

427, 428) and "facilitates" cortical functioning (426, 942). The functioning of the hypothalamus has also been found to be important in connection with certain types of convulsive seizures (448), with the regulation of afferent impulses that affect seizures (426), with states of sleep and wakefulness (426, 621, 709, 949, 1017), with food intake (288), and with temperature changes (426, 481, 1018).

Arnold has formulated the implications of some of these findings in supporting an excitatory theory of emotion (53). The expression of rage or the explosive reaction to sound in decorticated animals was thought to result from a "short circuit" or direct connection between two thalamic relay stations, one being sensory and one being autonomic-motor; whereas ordinarily a longer circuit including the cortex would be involved. It seemed unlikely that this longer circuit switches from excitation to disinhibition at some point, so instead the hypothesis was presented that emotional expression is the result of *excitation* of autonomic effector patterns, either directly or indirectly via corticothalamic pathways.

Thus, the thalamus and especially the hypothalamus are seen to function normally in connection with the cortex, as well as with all other neural structures, adding degrees of integration that are appropriate with their level of phylogenetic development. The fact that the electrical activity of the hypothalamus is in turn influenced by afferent nerve impulses has also been demonstrated (427).

THE HYPOTHALAMUS AND THE PITUITARY GLAND

The hypothalamus is in an especially critical position also because of its close proximity and interconnections with the pituitary gland, or hypophysis. As has been described, the hypothalamus receives afferent impulses from all somatic and visceral modalities as well as efferent impulses from the thalamus and the cortex, and its efferent fibers affect the entire autonomic nervous system and extend into the hypophysis (968). The anterior hypophysis (pituitary) releases ACTH (which stimulates the adrenal-cortex gland), by way of hypothalamic stimulation (287, 334, 478, 609, 1123) as well as by other mechanisms. There are also indications that the hypothalamus to some extent influences the secretion of gonadotropic, thyrotropic, and pancreatic hormones (426). A differential hypothalamic effect on epinephrine and norepinephrine secretion with separate representation in the hypothalamus has been suggested (346a, 410a, 559b).

The proximity of the hypothalamus to the hypophysis makes it difficult to establish the exact source of particular syndromes that stem from lesions in this area since the pituitary gland, in addition to its other important functions, is the master regulator of the various endocrine glands. The endocrine glands release hormones into the blood stream that affect a great number of bodily functions and tend to maintain internal stability in a homeostatic manner. Grinker postulated a close functional relationship between these two brain parts as follows (499, p. 23):

> According to modern endocrinologists, the endocrines fulfill a three-fold function of communication, correlation and catalysis which contribute to the mechanisms concerned in the preservation of an adequate internal milieu of the body, but are relatively slow acting and chronic in effect. Hypothalamic structures through their neural connections with the autonomic nervous system, innervating all smooth muscles and glands, regulate and integrate the internal milieu with greater speed and less lasting but more violent effect. It has been found that denervation of most endocrine glands, which also means removal of central influences from the hypothalamus, produces no profound insufficiency. This signifies that although the rapid, often emergency effect of their activities is lost, their constant activities are preserved as long as the pituitary is intact. Parasympathetic posterior lobe and probably adrenal cortex functions are, however, dependent on an intact nerve supply.

It should also be noted that neural conduction is affected directly by certain hormones and other secretions, as will be discussed in later sections. On the other hand, ACTH (adrenocorticotropic hormone) has been shown to have an effect on electrical brain activity (311, 335, 585), which can be reversed with the administration of ACE (adrenal-cortex extract), suggesting a complex interrelationship between such hormones and neural activity rather than any simple regulatory mechanism.

HYPOTHALAMIC SUBCENTERS

Grinker (499) described the hypothalamus as balancing the innervation of the sympathetic and parasympathetic nervous systems, the former having an anabolic effect and the latter having catabolic effect in the stimulating of vegetative functions and the depressing of energy expenditures. These functions are frequently considered to be antagonistic (as was discussed briefly in the preceding section), but their relationship is actually much more complex than this and can better be thought of as reciprocal in function: to maintain a stable internal milieu and to react to perceived threats to the organism. Opposite effects in innervation of these two systems have been specifically shown only in regard to bladder, gastrointestinal, arteriolar and vasomotor functioning.

Two general autonomic centers within the hypothalamus have been postulated as having reciprocal functions, with each having its own afferent and efferent connections. Thus, the posterior hypothalamus is thought to contain a symypathetic center and the anterior hypothalamus is thought to contain a parasympathetic center (330, 426), though some functional overlapping is reported (237a). The finding of independent electrical rhythms in these subsections is also suggestive of differential functions (491).

Evidence has been submitted for an anterior sleep center and a posterior waking center of the hypothalamus (426); however, the arousal system ("ergotropic system") has been found also to involve the periventricular gray matter of the mesencephalon, and the anterior extension of the system could not be perfectly elucidated (559a). Hess believed the "sleep mechanism" ("trophotropic center") to function antagonistically to the arousal system, and he localized it (in the cat) lateral to the massa intermedia and limited caudally by the habenulointerpeduncular tract and rostrally by the mammillothalamic bundle (although stimulation of the anterior thalamic nuclei also had a depressive effect) (559a). This stimulation contrasted with that of the "dynamogenic field" of the posterior and mesial part of the hypothalamus, extending to the central gray matter of the mesencephalon and anterior rhombencephalon, which produced the dramatic "fear and fury" excitability of defensive and aggressive types of reactions.

Electrical stimulation in the low mid-line axis of the hypothalamus (of monkeys) produced gastroduodenal lesions, whereas such stimulation outside the central hypothalamic region failed to produce these results (376d). Three mechanisms of hypothalamic functioning have been found to affect gastrointestinal functioning: (1) stimulation of the anterior pituitary body to release ACTH, inducing secretion of adrenocortical hormone (ACH), which causes a delayed hydrochloric acid secretion and possibly impairs the healing process in the gut wall; (2) stimulation of the vagus nerve, resulting in a rapid increase in hydrochloric acid production and changes in gut motility; and (3) stimulation of reticulospinal pathways of the splanchnic nerves, resulting in modification of gastric motility and vasomotor activity (376b, 376c, 805a).

As an aspect of the findings just presented, the thalamus (742) and hypothalamus (1194) have been theoretically considered to be crucial centers in motivation (1194). Stellar postulated different centers in the hypothalamus for different kinds of basic motivation (1194). Also, for each kind of motivation, there was proposed to exist in the hypothalamus one main excitatory center and one inhibitory center, which functions by depressing the activity of the excitatory center. The amount of motivation present at a given time was thought to depend on the level of excitability of the hypothalamus, which was believed to be determined by the sum total of afferent impulses arriving there. Finally, different parts of the cortex and thalamus were believed to operate selectively in the control of motivation via excitation and inhibiting influences on the hypothalamus.

BROADER THEORIES

Penfield has proposed that the highest level of neural integration lies within the diencephalon (982, 983). A somewhat broader variation of the "thalamic theory" has been presented by Gellhorn, who postulated that the basic physiological patterns of the emotional process are represented in the autonomic-endocrine and the somatic "downward discharge," and in the hypothalamic-cortical "upward discharge," the former providing bodily expressions of emotions and the latter accounting for "feeling tones" and for the mental changes that accompany emotions.

On the other hand, some opinions have already been presented to the effect that the role of the hypothalamus and thalamus in human functioning has frequently been overrated, and the evidence of efferent neural pathways and autonomic effects of the cortex that bypass the thalamus and hypothalamus (744) has frequently been overlooked or de-emphasized. Also, impulses from the reticular activating system of the brain stem may reach the cortex by way of the subthalamus and hypothalamus through the internal capsule, thereby bypassing the thalamus (426, 1191).

More recently, much attention has been given to the brain-stem reticular formation (BSRF) (287b, 331a, 331b, 376a, 969a, 1100a, 1191, 1191a). This interest began with the observation that direct electrical stimulation of the reticular formation induced changes in the EEG seemingly identical with those produced by waking from sleep, or alerting to attention, which have been referred to as "activation," "desynchronization," "EEG arousal," or "the blocking reaction" (850a, 934). Brain-stem parts producing such EEG arousal include the reticular formation, the tegmentum of the lower brain stem, and, in the diencephalon, the subthalamus together with the dorsal hypothalamus and ventromedial thalamus (850a). Magoun stated that influences leading to desynchronization are transmitted to the cortex by way of an extrathalamic route from the subthalamus to the internal capsule and by way of the nonspecific thalamic nuclei, and possibly others, which, however, generally lie dorsal and lateral to the most excitable zone (850a, 1191, 1191a). The reticular influence is tonic in nature, with wakefulness depending on an uninterrupted stream of ascending impulses and with postural tonus depending on a balanced distribution of tonic discharges descending through facilitating and inhibiting reticulospinal pathways (933a). Some evidence has been presented, however, that behavioral wakefulness can accompany reduction of activity in the BSRF (1100a). Bremer emphasized that arousal excitations reach the BSRF through both direct sensory channels and cortical neuronal networks, and he, as others, believed that "full consciousness requires an incessant cross-fire of intracortical and intercortical as well as cortico-thalamic facilitating interactions" (147a, p. 151). Conversely, the physiological process of falling asleep was explained "without necessary recourse to the hypothesis of a hypnogenic center, by the cumulative de-activation (de-facilitation) of the encephalic neuronal networks resulting from synaptic fatigue and favored by a reduction in the exteroceptive and proprioceptive sensory afflux," with emphasis on the fact that the BSRF's central location plays an essential role (147a, p. 158).

From experiments with 200 rabbits, Gangloff and Monnier presented evidence that "arousal" involves at least three mechanisms: (1) a reticulocortical desynchronizing mechanism; (2) a thalamocortical synchronizing mechanism; and (3) a rhinencephalic mechanism showing high-voltage fast activity and synchronized with the thalamic rhythm (413a). These widespread electrographic changes suggested that the arousal system may be activated by sensory afferents and also by higher, corticodiencephalic and rhinencephalic systems associated with the control of attention and emotional behavior.

THE LIMBIC SYSTEM ("VISCERAL BRAIN")

More recently, emphasis has also been placed on the limbic system, which has been referred to earlier in association with the rhinencephalon, also called the "visceral brain" (41a, 460a, 771a, 805a, 841a, 841b, 962a, 1091a). The limbic lobe and its subcortical cell stations have been found to constitute a functionally integrated system (841a). This system is composed of the limbic lobe of Broca and the following subcortical cell stations: the amygdala, the septal nuclei, the hypothalamus, the anterior thalamic nuclei, parts of the basal ganglia, and perhaps also the epithalamus (841b). Fifteen years of experimentation led MacLean to the conclusion that this system is anatomically a common denominator in all animal brains and is physiologically a common denominator of a variety of viscerosomatic and emotional reactions (841b). Electrical stimulation by multilead electrodes implanted in different parts of the limbic system of 25 cats and 13 monkeys showed that stimulation in frontal-lobe structures generally resulted in a rise in blood pressure, and in temporal-lobe structures resulted in a fall in blood pressure, but temporal polar stimulation produced a rise in blood pressure in cats and a fall in monkeys(41a). Both increases and decreases in heart rate without regard to blood-pressure changes were elicited in all regions, and respiration was inhibited for the majority of temporal-lobe stimulations and accelerated for the majority of frontal-lobe stimulations with opposite effects also occurring.

In 1953 it was discovered that electrical stimulation of parts of the limbic system, especially the septal area, could constitute "reward" and result in reinforcement behavior with experimental animals (962a). The amygdaloid complex and ventromedial nucleus of the hypothalamus also showed "high reward" value. Septal stimulation with 23 (human) patients resulted in: (1) their becoming less tense and fearful or angry and frightened; (2) often a "pleasurable" reaction to stimulation; (3) their becoming at times more alert and recognizing more things; (4) increases in motor activity and speech; (5) sensation descriptions such as "warmth, faintness, a glowing feeling, anxiety and a queer feeling" (541a, 962a). Distinct, reproducible changes in electrical recordings, localized in the amygdaloid and rostral hippocampal regions, that correlated with both spontaneous and elicited thought activity during directed interviews have been reported, and it was suggested that this activity is related to emotionally significant memories (771a). Four patients participated in this study, and changes in the EEG pattern consisted of distinct bursts of 14-17/sec. waves from the rostral hippocampus and 20-30/sec. waves from the amygdala along with increases in amplitude, which suggest more synchronous activity. The duration was from several seconds to twenty minutes, and this change did not spread to other subcortical areas studied nor include the cerebral cortex.

Not only have different subcortical areas (in the rat) been found to be differentially sensitive to different chemical or electrical stimulation, but specific types of implanted stimulation, including hormones, were seen to produce maternal behavior with medial preoptic placement and sexual behavior with lateral preoptic placement (360a).

ELECTRICAL POTENTIALS AND RHYTHMS

In 1933, Bartley and Bishop reported that cortical rhythms are partially controlled by subcortical pacemakers through neural circuits between the thalamus and cortex (81). Subsequent studies supported this concept, indicating that the principal pacemaker for neural impulse rhythms is in the thalamus, with secondary ones in the hypothalamus (327, 635, 931).

In 1938, Hoagland et al., with human subjects, took simultaneous EEGs from the occipital area over the cortex and from the nasopharyngeal area near the hypothalamus, and they found similar, although slightly different, activity in the two areas (582). Subsequent studies suggested, however, that nasopharyngeal tracings represent the activity of the mesial inferior temporal cortex more than that of the brain stem (331a). Delta waves were seen in both areas, with a slight time precedence in the "hypothalamic" region, and it was thought that the waves probably originated there, going then to the cortex and being associated with emotional reactivity, as was reported in the study by Hoagland noted earlier (581). A relationship between the cortex and subcortex was also seen in the destruction of subcortical tissue to the point of eliminating the "hypothalamic-lead" waves, which had a frequency of 4 to 5 per second and were 75 per cent the amplitude of cortical waves; this destruction resulted in cortical alpha rhythm of clear, frequent types and of unusual amplitude *"in the hypothalamic lead"* (499). It was concluded that "cortical rhythm thus enters into the normal resting hypothalamus but dominates it only when the hypothalamus is injured." It was also noted that the resting human "hypothalamic pattern" varies more with the individual than do cortical patterns, suggesting a clue to individual differences. Electrical stimulation through the "hypothalamic lead" resulted in general autonomic visceral changes and in various emotional reactions, all involving a quality of fear and none involving emotional expressions of anger. With this stimulation, fast waves were reflected from the "hypothalamic lead" along with the disappearance of its usual "cortical" alpha rhythm; marked cortical response to the "hypothalamic-lead" stimulation was seen with the variability of rhythms in both areas, suggesting an interacting effect. Similarly, various drugs were seen to affect the electrical potentials of the "hypothalamic lead" and of the cortex, having in some instances differential effects. The inducing of anxiety in a patient resulted in similar effects in the "hypothalamic lead" and in cortical excitation as did the electrical stimulation described above.

Gellhorn's early demonstration of "upward discharge" from the hypothalamus to the cortex has already been noted, and he concluded that cortical activity normally inhibits such discharge as well as the "downward discharge" from the hypothalamus (424).

Lindsley et al. experimented on cats with the successive removal of brainstem sections from lower to higher levels, which resulted in corresponding reduction of afferent sensory impulses (797). This revealed a gradual shift from the "activation" pattern (e.g., the relatively flat EEG record with almost no alpha rhythm that was seen with "emotional excitement" or "anxiety") to a pattern of increased synchronization, representing the "spontaneous rhythms" of the thalamus and cortex, respectively. A complex interrelationship was suggested as follows (796, p. 500):

> With regard to emotion it appears that the sensory influx via the reticular formation in the intact organism may initiate antonomic reflex effects in the hypothalamus—for example, the galvanic skin response to sound stimulation, or the startle response and other visceral changes—but at the same time the cortical activation effect may induce cortical inhibition (or facilitation) of hypothalamic mechanisms.

Darrow has emphasized the over-all relationships of the EEG to other physiological functions and has suggested that the EEG reflects "facilitative and homeostatic regulatory processes which contribute to, but which are not essential to, integrative cerebral function" (271). After referring to the well-recognized homeostatic "feedback" mechanisms of various physiological processes, Darrow emphasized the coincidental effect of these upon the central nervous system, and he listed five modes of such reflexive regulation associated with emotional reactions: neural, hydrostatic, chemical, autonomic, and humoral (273). Darrow presented evidence showing that these mechanisms all affect central activity and the EEG. An example of such effects was seen in the reduction in amplitude with bursts of slow activity of the electrocortical potentials for patients taking ACTH or cortisone (311, 365, 496, 585, 1241, 1258, 1366). After elaborating the physiological conditions that modify alpha activity toward either extreme, Darrow observed that "normal alpha rhythm thus apparently requires that there be neither great excess nor great deficiency in conditions favoring cortical activity" (271, p. 162).

Not only do the various bodily functions (including the many changes associated with psychological states and emotional reactions) influence brain functioning directly with afferent impulses through the reticular formation into the hypothalamus, thalamus and cerebral cortex, as shown by the work of Lindsley just cited, but they also exert such influences indirectly by means of changes in blood chemistry and content and by changes in the blood vessels supplying the brain. In addition, it should be considered that by means of the sensory projection system in the brain, differential physiological changes may be meaningful to the individual and may result in psychological states (as well as in changes of activation of neural circuits), by means of cognitive associations at different relative levels of consciousness-unconsciousness.

From the facts presented and the conclusions drawn, it would appear that the functioning of the cortex in these respects is of at least equal, if not greater, importance than the subcortex and, in the changes considered, the entire nervous system is involved, along with the functioning of each body organ and process. The fact that the various physiological changes may have complex effects on brain functioning, and thereby may involve noncognitive internal perception, should be recalled as the various physiological processes and body areas are considered in the sections to follow.

The functioning of the cerebral cortex itself will be considered briefly at the beginning of the next chapter, since there is a growing supply of electroencephalographic data involving direct measurements related to localized functions.

FUNCTIONAL INTEGRATION

It should be kept in mind that at each level of the nervous system, regulation and integration of autonomic activity exists, the complexity being generally proportionate to the phylogenetic level. Also, at each level the autonomic system is intricately interrelated with the somatic (peripheral) nervous system (405, 423, 815). Thus, "it is generally impossible to evoke a somatic reflex that does not have an autonomic concomitant of central origin," and this "makes for unification of reaction in the organism as a whole" (405). Even the separation of motor and sensory processes has been considered "to be more a necessity of analytic research and didactic simplification than an adequate description of the immediately given data of the physiology and pathology of movements" (426, p. 70).

The traditional view is that higher, or evolutionarily more recent, levels of encephalization act to inhibit the lower, simpler, quicker reflex functions by long-circuiting of the neural impulses to higher central-nervous-system levels.

Grinker presented the following theoretical implication of this (499, p. 42) :

> Psychoanalytic theory of symptom-formation implies that the repressed or
> undischarged energy must escape elsewhere than through the motor
> activity of the ego—that it returns modified as a symptom. The same
> phenomenon has been described by Pavlov, for when reflexes are inhibited
> from one skin area, they are increased elsewhere. In neurological terms,
> Jackson stated that diminished action in one part of the nervous system
> results in exalted action in another part, but this so-called new action
> takes place on a lower level. Neurologically, release of lower levels results
> in greater preponderance of visceral participation in reflex activity and,
> psychologically, alloplastic reactions are replaced by autoplastic innerva-
> tions. Innervations engage organs whose functions represent the level of
> psychological activity to which the psychic life has regressed, thus produc-
> ing sucking, biting, soiling and retaining psychologically, as Alexander has
> shown in his vector analysis. Thus, functional innervations of various ap-
> propriate organs, released from inhibition, set into effect the first link in
> the causal chain of events that end in visceral disease. Regression in the
> psychoneuroses and organ neuroses probably does not extend lower than
> the hypothalamus. Evidence of preservation of its integrating function
> in the visceral systems and personality indicates its intactness.

An alternative type of concept should be considered, however, in the
evaluating of the relatedness of the psychological states and physiological
functions described in the sections to follow. This is simply the concept that
certain, as yet undetermined, differential physiological changes may *correspond to* given types of feelings or of other psychological awareness of
functional significance. This concept is consistent with Meduna's theory of
psychosomatic disorders, which envisioned continuous, conflict-stimulated
reverberations of neural impulses among the cortex, hypothalamus, and
thalamus acting to block physiological homeostasis (893).

Even though Grinker considered the "drives" of the hypothalamus to be
"synonymous with id demands or necessities of the instincts," his formulation
is not incompatible with the concepts proposed in the preceding paragraph
(499). The main difference between his view and the concept of correspondence between certain feelings and physiological changes is that the latter
view does not necessarily imply a defense, an escape, or a regression from
psychic conflicts when pathological stages are reached, but rather the physiological function is considered to be chronic because of its relationship to a
sustained conflict and associated feeling state.

Arnold integrates the functioning of the entire nervous system in her
excitatory theory of emotion (53). She postulated the formation of an

"emotional attitude" (e.g., anger, fear, or disgust) that follows selective perception and evaluation and that initiates nerve impulses from the cortex to centers in the thalamus-hypothalamus, touching off the appropriate patterns of emotional expression and peripheral physiological changes (e.g., in muscle tone, blood pressure, and heart rate). Such changes are reported back to the cortex via afferent pathways with resulting perception and re-evaluation (e.g., "how it affects me"). It might be well to make a distinction between Arnold's "emotional attitude," which is a cognitive function, and the term "feeling," which perhaps may better represent the "perception of organic changes." Whether one may consider such a usage justified may depend on his evaluation of the clinical and experimental material that will follow in this and the next chapters.

CHAPTER 12

Clinical and Physiological Studies in Terms of Extensive Bodily Processes

GENERAL ORIENTATION

Studies that relate physiological changes to noncognitive inner experiences will be analyzed where possible in terms of body location, which are classified in Figure 1. This is a departure from the references to physiological functioning usually encountered in most of the literature. One reason for this type of analysis is to enable the comparison of the physiological studies presented in this and the next chapter with the studies involving the perception of internal sensations to be presented in Part IV. An analysis of physiological reactions by specific body areas, including those organs and processes within each given area, makes it possible to consider how these changes may be perceived by the individual, as well as how they may be measured by the experimenter. Also, such an analysis may make more meaningful the specific symptoms that are reported by different individuals in given areas of the body.

The particular areas of Fig. 1 were selected on the basis of differentiating the various body organs and processes, and notwithstanding the overlapping inclusiveness of the areas, a given organ or physiological function will usually be classified within the area where it is primarily located.

First, however, consideration will be given to those generalized physiological processes that cannot readily be classified by body area. Summaries of the findings presented will not be made for each body process or area considered, but an attempt is made in Part V to integrate the physiological changes found to occur in different types of psychological states.

This manner of presentation departs from the assimilation of material exclusively in terms of the conventional medical classifications of "organ systems," but at the same time cross-references are made to functionally related data, organs, and systems. Also, some of the material is duplicated under different headings so as to show functional interrelationships. The body-area classifications employed herein are research oriented and were designed to facilitate differential awareness and measurement of physiological changes and associated sensory experiences. Even though, on the one

FIGURE 1

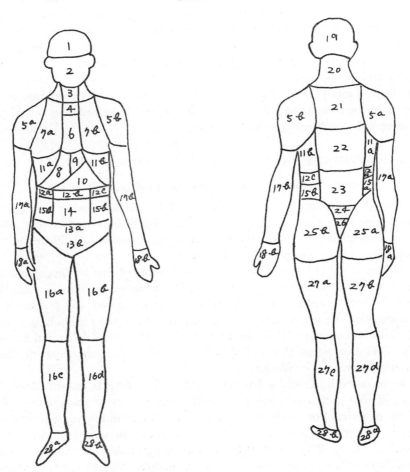

hand, a given body-area classification may involve several organs and systems and, on the other hand, a given physiological change may result in sensations in several areas of classification, the data presented generally tend to indicate that the given body area employed for the presenting of data relating to a given organ best differentiates that organ from other organs in terms of measurements or of awareness. Thus, the focus of this work is not so much on the didactic functional interrelatedness of systems as on the differential (sub)functioning of specific organs and "subsystems."

The body is an integrated whole, and many organ systems are readily evident and functionally meaningful; however, it will become apparent that much of the research presented here is contaminated by overgeneralization to and from organ systems, which thereby ignores the possibilities of further differentiations and differential functioning. Examples of this are seen in inferences of generalized autonomic (sympathetic or parasympathetic) reactivity and of colonic reactivity from measurements of one portion of the anatomy. Finally, it should be noted that the terminology employed is designed to be descriptive for a wide audience and therefore does not always correspond to conventional medical usage.

THE CEPHALIC AREA (AREAS NOS. 1 AND 19)

UTILIZATION OF THE ELECTROENCEPHALOGRAPH (EEG)

Though much data concerning neurophysiological functioning have already been presented, there remain to be considered several studies that relate brain functioning to noncognitive perception. Especially significant in this respect are electroencephalographic studies.

Electrical potentials from the brain were recorded first by Berger in 1924 in the form of "waves" on a kymograph. He published the data in 1929 that related these potentials to neuronal tissue and showed the potentials to change with the age of the subject, with external sensory stimuli, and with physiological changes (105). In 1931, Adrian (13) and Adrian and Buytendijk (14) discovered that isolated ganglia and brain parts show rhythmic electrical-potential oscillations.

More recently, Lindsley has stated "that very little is known about the basis of the electroencephalogram, both with respect to the precise origin of the electrical potentials (for example, whether from axons, dendrites, cell bodies, or synaptic junctions) and to the function subserved or signaled by them" (795, p. 238). It is believed that autonomous electrical potentials arise from cell bodies and that synchronous activity of many cells summate to reflect the recorded rhythms.

On the electroencephalogram the most prominent "normal" wave rhythm for the human in the resting state is 10 per second, called *alpha,* but it may range from 8 to 13 waves per second. The waves of about 18 to 30 per second, called *beta* rhythm, are prominent only in the anterior-head region.

The *delta* rhythm ranges from 2 to 3 per second or less and is associated with normal sleep or with pathological conditions. An intermediate rhythm of 4 through 7 per second has been designated as the *theta band* (667, 1112, 1278), and the unusual frequencies of over 30 per second are designated as the *very fast band,* and the band of 14 through 17 per second has remained unnamed (1112).

EEG REACTIONS

It was early recognized that the perception by subjects of external stimuli, such as light, abolishes the normal alpha rhythm, and in 1933 Berger reported that fright, stemming from a firecracker explosion, also had this effect, and the rhythm then increased to almost double the frequency (108). Others have reported a similar disappearance or reduction of the alpha rhythm during startle (634), during embarrassment and apprehension (794, 810, 1327) and with "stimulating" word association (784, 952) and other "tests" (389a). Conditioning of such effects has been reported (271, 690, 1264).

The alpha rhythm was also stopped by a subject who imagined himself in a terrifying situation, but there was only a momentary effect during the third trial, when he found the fearful "phantasy difficult to repeat" (1327). The same experimenters found that attention to the point of getting "rattled" stopped the alpha waves, but this was not the case with ordinary attention to listening, reading, reciting, adding, and so forth. Even in regard to external perception, it has been shown that it is the attention—the heightened level of consciousness—that suppresses the alpha rhythm rather than the stimuli themselves (146, p. 190). For example, concentrated efforts to see under pitch-dark conditions abolish the alpha rhythm, whereas the wearing of frosted glasses, which blur the vision, permits the alpha rhythm to persist even in bright light. Williams believed that the combination of stimulation and attention are necessary to abolish alpha rhythm, and also described a psychological facilitation effect (1327).

Beta waves were said by some experimenters to be little influenced by sensory stimulation in any case, but it is, however, common knowledge with every electroencephalographer that the initial anxiety, or apprehension of subjects who are having EEG recordings abolishes the alpha rhythm until such time as the subject feels at ease (795). Much evidence of this type leads to the conclusions that beta potentials displace the waking alpha activity during increased "tension" or excitation (271).

Thus, it is apparent that internal perception of some type affects the EEG rhythms, and evidence suggests that this perception is of a noncognitive type. Studies concerning this have been generally of two types, one involving subjects in different psychological, or "emotional," states and the other involving subjects of different degrees of emotional or mental health. These additional studies will be described separately and in approximate chronological order for each type.

Using heart rate and EEG measurements during personal questioning with normal and psychotic subjects, Hoagland et al. showed an increase in heart rate and in delta index after strong emotional stimulation (581). Lindsley has raised some question that this delta increase might have been an artifact of skin potential, but noted that the finding of these experimenters of greater delta changes over the motor regions of the brain than over the occipital area favors cortical origin rather than skin origin of the delta change (794). The following year, five experienced judges were able to detect lying, presumably associated with artificial "guilt," by observing alterations in alpha rhythm during key word associations (956). Jurgens found the most marked inhibition of alpha rhythm from stimuli that had the greatest effect on the vegetative functions (as indicated by several autonomic measures), implying emotionally toned "psychic meaning" (664). In this connection, a "U"-curve relationship between alpha rhythm and palmar conduction has been found with four conditions producing a variety of arousal states (1195a). Darrow et al. reported that beta waves increased and alpha waves decreased in response to emotional stimulation (276).

In a careful study of 10 normal subjects, Thiesen failed to confirm Hoagland's finding that there was increased delta index in emotional excitement (581, 582), and he suggested that it may have been an artifact of scalp potential, or the use of psychotic subjects, or the heart rate, which Thiesen found to be reflected in waves on the EEG (1236). Although he interpreted the EEGs during sustained emotional excitement to be within normal limits despite "flat" records of reduced rhythmic and serial components extending at times to the greater part of the cortex, he commonly observed a specific and localized effect involving depression of fast activity or beta rhythm from the frontomotor region primarily, which was observed at times in the absence of depression of the occipital alpha rhythm.

In general, the reduction or abolition of synchronized, alpha rhythms and the induction of low-amplitude fast activity is called an "activation pattern" (796).

Before we evaluate these findings, the studies involving different personality and diagnostic characteristics will be considered in approximately chronological order.

In 1936, abnormal findings were reported with psychotic patients (689). In the following year, EEGs taken in connection with psychoanalytic treatment by Saul revealed differentiated EEG records associated with two opposing personality trends, namely, low alpha index in active, independent, aggressive individuals and high alpha index in passive, dependent, receptive individuals (1086). The "alpha index" refers to the percentage of time, or amount of time, that alpha rhythms are present over a substantial period of the record, and its reduction in this study may be interpreted as being associated with activity and excitement (795). Follow-up recordings were made on the 66 psychoanalytic-patient subjects of this study; along with this, other patients also undergoing psychoanalysis (totaling 136 adult subjects) were studied for possible EEG and personality correlations over a five-year period (1087). The EEG patterns for every individual remained basically the same throughout the study, but different major personality characteristics were correlated with three types of EEG patterns: (1) a very high alpha index with very "passive" individuals, including traits of dependency, submissiveness, and escape-from-stress; (2) low alpha index with women having strong masculine trends, including traits of independence, dominance, activity, and leadership; and (3) a mixed type of EEG with women having traits of frustration, demanding impatience, aggressiveness, and hostility. Concerning the last type (3), very prominent fast-frequency waves with very little alpha were seen in the women who had the most pronounced traits. Similarly, Berger related the "better," more pronounced, alpha rhythm of the feebleminded to their passivity in comparing their records to those of more active intelligent persons (110).

Jasper et al. (639) reported 71 per cent of abnormal EEGs in a group of children with behavior disorders, and Kennard and Willner (689, 692) found 68 per cent of abnormal EEGs for 202 children having behavior disorders, with the schizophrenic subjects showing 80 per cent abnormality (775).

Jost submitted an experimental group of 18 schizophrenic, neurotic, and behavior-problem children and a control group of 20 relatively well-adjusted children to frustration tests involving learning, and he found that the alpha rhythm was significantly dominant for 85 per cent of the total time in the control groups as contrasted with 62.1 per cent in the experimental group (655). Findings from several simultaneous physiological measures, presumably indicating changes that also send neural impulses to the central nervous system, suggested to Jost that "since stimulation of the exteroceptors will suppress these (alpha) waves it is probable that stimulation from the interoceptors (and of the autonomic nervous system) may also have the same effect," and the effect will be greatest with those who are more continually emotionally disturbed. Sherman and Jost confirmed these results a year later using three frustration tests and employing 10 adults and 48 children (1137).

Many studies report degrees of abnormal electroencephalographic activity with the diagnosis of psychopathic personality and behavior disorder. A consistent, though only casually emphasized, finding with these and other studies was reported to be increased cortical reactivity and lowered thresholds of reactivity for psychopathological conditions of all types (689, 692). Gastaut (419) has generalized the desynchronized "activation pattern" as common to individuals who experience intense and lasting anxiety-provoking sensations, including particularly anxiety states and usually also psychosomatic affections, such as asthma (967a) and arteritis (229a). Theoretically, and on the basis of a probable optimal speed of neural transmission and "coding," Gastaut postulated three electroencephalographic syndromes: (1) hyperexcitability, showing rapid, feeble background rhythms (alpha 11 to 13 cycles/sec. in the posterior regions and beta 15 to 20 cycles/sec. in the middle regions) coming in short bursts with intervals of complete desynchronization, and corresponding to exaggerated perceptive functioning; (2) hypoexcitability, showing rather continuously distributed slow strong background rhythms (alpha 8 to 9 cycles/sec. without beta), and corresponding to calmer and slower perceptive functioning; and (3) instability (lability or versatility), a less well-defined syndrome, showing both low frequencies (especially theta) and high frequencies (especially beta) with a background of alpha rhythm 9 to 11 cycles/sec. and with the whole varying in amplitude from moment to moment, and corresponding to psychomotor versatility and paroxysmal liveliness of reactions (419a).

Psychological measurements and EEGs were given by Kennard and Levy to 27 "normal" control subjects and 70 clinic patients; 47 of the latter had the EEGs redone in a month and some had 3 to 5 EEGs over a period of 2 to 4 months (691a). "Anxiety, lability, and aggressivity" were all related to "poor EEGs." Also, significant correlations between the EEG and psychological findings differentiated between acutely disturbed individuals and those with chronic less violent disturbances. A similar study by Rabinovitch,

Kennard, and Fister in which 64 consecutive psychiatric admissions, 33 prison inmates, and 50 "normal" subjects were included revealed that the psychiatric patients' EEGs, as compared to those of "normal" subjects were less well organized, had more electrical activity in all frequencies except the 16 to 20 range, had more multi-peaks in the alpha range, and had more left-right dyssynchrony (1007a). Compared to the prisoners, the psychiatric patients' EEGs showed less organization, fewer high alpha pictures, more activity in all frequencies except the 16 to 20 range, and more left-right dyssynchrony, and the prisoners differed from the normal subjects in showing more high alpha pictures and more theta activity.

Concerning the Rorschach-protocol findings, the "no-M" subjects showed more activity in the 16 to 20 range than did the subjects with three or more "M," and the "no-S" subjects had less well-organized graph profiles than did those with two or more "S" responses; however, it was thought that these statistically significant findings could have occurred by chance. Global Rorschach indicators of maladjustment and of anxiety correlated with EEG findings of the general types previously described for such conditions, and "introversive experience balances" (e.g., much more "M" than "C" response) corresponded with more harmonizing activity from various cortical areas, more high alpha, and less activity in the 16 to 20, 5 to 7, and 22 to 30 frequency ranges.

Ulett et al., rating 191 flying personnel on an 8-point scale for anxiety proneness by means of interview and psychological measurements, found significant correlations between anxiety-proneness ratings and: (1) amount of subjective dysphoria during photic stimulation; (2) amount of harmonic EEG response in the 20 to 30 range to flicker frequencies one half and one quarter that rate; (3) displacement of the centroid of driving from the normal range; and (4) percentage of abnormal and low alpha records (1269b). A check list of EEG anxiety indicators showed a .48 correlation with the criterion ratings, and the threat of electric shock resulted in "power reduction" in both occipital driving response and alpha rhythm. Subsequently, scales based on EEG records, EEG response to photic stimulation, and subjective sensations induced by the photic flicker, identified 59.4 per cent of anxiety-prone normal subjects and 65.5 per cent of anxious patients, with an occurrence of only 11 per cent "false positives" (331a, 1269a)

A relatively high percentage of alpha activity, measured in the occipital area, has been found for peptic-ulcer patients, and Rubin and Bowman related this to the passive, dependent, nonaggressive personalities of these types of patients (935, 1065). Kirschbaum and Stehle noted the reports of the Gibbses (448, 451) that 14-per-second and 6-per-second positive spikes originate in the thalamus and hypothalamus and are distorted from the normal pattern (as seen in animals), and in a study of 50 patients with peptic ulcer and 10 with functional gastric disorder, Kirschbaum and Stehle found an 8 per cent occurrence of such waves, which they interpreted as reflection of a disturbance of the autonomic nervous system (706).

Rubin and Moses reported a "definite relationship" between bronchial asthma and dominant alpha record, with about three times as many dominant alpha records being found in the asthmatic group as in the normal group, and the association of alpha records with passive, receptive types of individuals was noted (1066). Holmgren and Kraepelien found "pathological EEG of different degrees and types" in 36 of 100 cases of children, aged 2 to 15 years, with bronchial asthma after careful scrutiny to eliminate any subjects with a family history of convulsive manifestations; the EEG abnormalities were comprised partly of a slow dysrhythmia (with two thirds being mainly occipital), partly of focal spikes or sharp waves (3 cases), and partly of general wave and spike episodes (3 cases) (596).

EEG FINDINGS IN NEUROTICS, CHARACTER DISORDERS, AND OTHERS

Cohn studied the EEGs from a group of patients with diagnoses of anxiety states and determined two types of EEG records (244). One type was relatively normal, but the other was characterized by diminished alpha activity and the presence of low-amplitude, high-frequency (beta) waves that were associated with somatically tense individuals; the tenseness presumably produces internal sensory impulses that depress alpha activity. Brazier, Finesinger, and Cobb compared the EEG records of 100 neurotic subjects with those of 500 normal adults (147). Although they reported that the neurotics' EEGs were generally normal, the incidence of fast activity was significantly greater in the neurotics' records than in those of normal subjects, which was also noted by Finley (357). Varying percentages of abnormal EEG records with neurotic subjects have been reported by others (702, 1214), and obsessive-compulsive neurosis has been associated with a very high percentage of abnormal EEG records that included, among other things, paroxysmal cerebral dysrhythmia (964, 1049). In reviewing the literature on the relating of EEG findings to personality characteristics, Kennard observed that the variety of reports dealing with abnormal EEG patterns with neurosis is probably no greater than the variety of clinical, diagnostic criteria in use (689).

Hill found that psychopathic soldiers showed abnormal EEG records in

32 per cent of the total measures and in 65 per cent of the measures of subjects having more serious disorders with hostile, aggressive features (563, 565). This finding was supported by Levy and Kennard, who studied over 1000 EEG records with different types of neuropsychiatric patients, between the ages of five and fifty-five years, from four different institutions (775). They found a significant relationship between abnormal fast frontal activity among the schizophrenics and high alpha index and theta activity among the "so-called psychopaths," with the high incidence of abnormal theta activity being seen only among criminals confined in the penitentiary. For children and adolescents, the incidence of abnormal EEGs was over 50 per cent in both schizophrenics and the behavior disorders, whereas between the early twenties and mid-fifties, the incidence of EEG abnormality fell between 20 and 30 per cent, then rose for higher ages. These findings were noted to be consistent with Denis Hill's concept that a "delayed maturation" (563) was responsible for disorders of behavior among adolescents, delinquents and psychopaths, and with a previous study that suggested the possibility of a progressive deteriorating organic disease process among schizophrenics (691).

EEG FINDINGS WITH PSYCHOSES

In the comparing of EEG records of 500 schizophrenic patients with those of 215 control subjects, Finley and Campbell found the former to show a greater incidence of abnormality of a nonspecific type (359). In another study, Finley concluded from a large number of EEG records that high-voltage activity of 15 to 40 per second, mainly over the anterior half of the scalp, is characteristic of psychotic patients, especially with manic-depressive, involutional, and paretic psychoses (357). The pattern occurred to some extent with catatonic excitement, and it was also seen to some extent in all psychoneurotic disorders. This feature disappeared between some of the manic-depressive episodes. Under the influence of drugs, rapid activity occurred with excitement or depression, whereas slow waves occurred with confusional or comatose states.

Davis found that the EEG records of schizophrenic patients showed fewer records with slow alpha activity and twice the number of fast alpha rates in comparison to those of manic-depressive patients (284); however, Lemere reported a relatively low state of cortical activity with schizophrenic patients (767), and Kennard found paroxysmal, abnormal patterns (689).

Although Davis observed that manic-depressive-depressed psychotic patients tend to show frequencies of alpha rhythm of 10 per second or slower, whereas manic-depressive-manic patients tend to show alpha frequencies of 10 per second or faster, there were no indications of shifts in alpha frequency corresponding to psychotic phase changes (283). These findings were confirmed by Hurst et al. in a study of 117 manic-depressive and involutional-melancholic patients (with a mean age of fifty-five years) and 160 normal control subjects (with a mean age of twenty-two years) (617). Among the psychotic patients significantly more low-voltage, fast irregular EEG patterns, which did not appear to be related to age, were found than among the normal subjects.

In 1944, Greenblatt, Healey, and Jones reported abnormal EEG findings in 20 to 54 per cent of the records of 1593 adult neuropsychiatric patients, of whom there were 23 per cent with schizophrenia, 31 per cent with depressed manic-depression, 42 per cent with manic manic-depression, 51 per cent with involutional psychoses, and 34 per cent with psychoneurosis (493).

In connection with these findings, it should be noted that several organic abnormalities have been reported in the study of the brains of patients with psychotic disorders (82, 903); however, many complex factors enter into such studies, making it difficult to draw inferences concerning causal relationships. Thus, for example, in the words of Wolf and Cowen, "in the great majority of subjects in whom the diagnosis of dementia praecox is made, no obvious morphological changes in the brain have been encountered," and the changes that have been "described are of a more subtle and debatable nature" (1340, p. 469). Lindsley (794) has summarized several rather contradictory EEG studies involving complex personality and diagnostic features (109, 280, 359, 473, 554, 636, 765, 766, 767, 793, 846, 1277, 1375).

EEG FINDINGS WITH EPILEPSY

It is with epileptic conditions that abnormal EEG patterns are most commonly associated, and in this connection the EEG finds its greatest employment. Petit-mal epilepsy is characterized by high-voltage alternate waves and spikes occurring at the rate of approximately 3 per second; grand-mal epilepsy is characterized by increases in the frequencies (from 15 to 25 per second) and increases in the voltage of waves that fuse into 3 to 6 per second, high-voltage waves; the psychomotor seizures are generally characterized by abnormally large-voltage, slow waves of from 3 to 8 per second (769, 794).

Epilepsy is most often considered to be primarily constitutional and, to some extent, hereditary, and the abnormal EEG is usually presumed to reflect an organic basis (768). In contrast to this are the facts that about 20 nonepileptic persons show cortical dysrhythmia in comparison to each person with epilepsy and that about 15 per cent of patients with epileptic seizures have normal EEGs (as taken from the scalp) (768). Also, according to various estimates, 5 to 15 per cent of the normal population with no known focal organic central-nervous-system pathology or overt psychopathology show abnormal EEG records; similarly, the EEG records of children are more variable and less stable than those of adults, but generally show predictable EEG changes with growth until a stable pattern is reached about the end of adolescence (689). Other studies also indicate a complex relationship between electroencephalographic activity and epilepsy.

Psychoanalytically oriented writers have frequently proposed the existence of a basic psychological disorder underlying epileptic symptoms while at the same time acknowledging that, as with any disorder, some organic predisposition may exist (233, 353, 641, 921). The psychological factors proposed are repressed hostility, extreme narcissism, and the regressive nature of the epileptic seizure (201). More recent evidence, stemming from photic experimentation, suggested that many, if not all, personality types possess thresholds for convulsive seizures, and therefore the precipitation of epileptic attacks is probably relative to both the individual's threshold and to given types of psychological stress (419).

Other psychogenic factors in epileptic or epilepticlike seizures have also been suggested (63, 201). Gibbs, Gibbs, and Fustrer reported that approximately 42 per cent of patients with psychomotor epilepsy have personality disturbances of various types (447). A past history of irritability and of childhood behavior problems was frequent, as well as adult features of passive aggression, dependency, poor interpersonal relations, and hypochondriacal complaints (416).

Here the traditional classifications of epileptic-seizure discharges into grand-mal, petit-mal, and psychomotor types should be recalled (449). In psychomotor epilepsy, temporal-lobe abnormal paroxysmal activity on the EEG has been related to the aggression of such patients, and theta activity at the rate of 5 to 6 waves per second was reported to be directly associated with this diagnostic type (562, 689, 1001, 1031, 1184).

In 1951, in 6 per cent of patients with epileptiform disorders and in 2 per cent of normal subjects, Gibbs and Gibbs discerned a type of spike discharge during sleep studies that consisted of (1) 14-per-second positive spikes with an unusual "flat-topped" episode and (2) a component of 4-to-6-per-second positive spikes (448). These spike discharges were thought to originate in the thalamus and hypothalamus. Although there was no history of convulsions in 35 per cent of the 100 patients showing the 14-per-second positive spikes, 87 per cent had symptoms such as fainting attacks, crying spells, and rage attacks, and 7 per cent reported attacks of severe pains in the arms, legs, or trunk that are otherwise rare in epilepsy. It was thought that this finding may relate in some way to the close association of convulsive electrical activity and seizures to afferent neural impulses noted by Gellhorn (426).

In 1945, Kupper reported a case of classic grand-mal epilepsy with abnormal EEG findings, the condition having been precipitated six years earlier by an emotional upset (741). When the patient was under hypnosis, the EEG readings would become normal when it was suggested that the patient regress to an age before the time of the precipitating conflict, which related to anger and guilt involving his father, and a convulsive seizure could be produced only by association with this conflict.

In 1949 Barker and Barker made EEG recordings of convulsive patients at daily and weekly intervals, noting at the same time, by means of interview, significant life events that would increase or decrease the patient's sense of security and well-being; they found bursts of abnormal waves to accompany disruption of integrative mental activity, as for example, "sudden, conflicting and intensely distressing thoughts and feelings" (77). Also, abnormal waves were produced "by subjecting the patient to stimulus-events designed to startle, disturb, irritate, and annoy," such as sudden noises, temperature change, and pinpricks. Abnormal waves were preceded by bursts of muscle potential and fast frequency waves and by a "sudden decrease of wave amplitude suggesting a sudden arousal of attention and alertness and sudden intensification of integrative effort," and, apparently, the momentary disruptions allowed the discharge of tension, reducing stress and making possible the resumption of activity (77, p. 110). On the basis of several similar studies (74, 75, 76, 78, 79), the following conclusions were drawn (77, p. 91):

> The wave abnormalities were more closely related to specific subjective and objective events than to the larger pattern of life situation. Thus, paroxysms of abnormal waves were observed as (1) disruptions of the elaboration into awareness of thoughts and feelings painfully unacceptable to the patient; (2) response to environmental stimulus-events when the patient, for one reason or another, could organize no other reaction; (3) at moments of phase-change in relatively brief or enduring activities; and (4) in periods of inactivity such that "spontaneous" eruption of some intrinsic pathological neuronal activity seemed the only reasonable explanation.

The finding that with the aura of psychomotor epilepsy occurs an alternation of opposite "feeling" states such as warmth-cold, fear-anger, and familiarity-unfamiliarity (1196a) suggested to MacLean that a neuroanatomical substratum for the reciprocal innervation of "feeling" states (similar to muscular innervation) exists and that the limbic cortex is implicated in epileptic-seizure discharges with the spread of discharge corresponding here to the "march" of the many "feelings" (841a).

SUMMARY OF EEG FINDINGS

In summary, there is general agreement that alpha waves are abolished or decreased by emotional excitement. Because a decrease or abolition of alpha rhythm can be caused by attention to external stimuli, several experimenters, by analogy, have concluded from carefully documented experiments that the decrease of alpha rhythm during emotional excitement is caused by internal sensory impulses. Thiesen has emphasized that this decrease in alpha rhythm is occipital (1236). These findings are consistent with studies involving personality types in which low alpha rhythm was associated with active, aggressive individuals (Saul, 1086, 1087), with anxiety (Cohn, 244), and with emotionally unstable patients (Jost, 656; Sherman and Jost, 1137), in comparison to more pronounced alpha rhythm in normal controls (Jost, 655, 656), passive individuals (Berger, 110; Rubin and Bowman, 1065; Saul, 1087), in less tense patients (Cohn, 244), and in asthmatic patients (Rubin and Moses, 1066) who were thought to be passive. Although Hoagland (581) thought that delta rhythm increased with emotional excitement, this has been questioned by Thiesen (1236) and Lindsley (794). Darrow (276) reported an increase in beta waves with emotional excitement; but Thiesen (1236) found a decrease in the frontomotor region, Jasper and Andrews (634) found beta waves to disappear with "startle," and Cohn (244) associated these beta waves with somatically tense, anxious individuals. Finley (357) observed high-voltage activity of 15 to 40 per second in anterior-head regions in psychoneurotic disorders and, especially, in psychoses, and other fast (147) and abnormal (702, 964, 1049, 1214) rhythms were reported in psychoneuroses. High alpha index and theta activity have been found with psychopathic, aggressive tendencies (563, 565, 775). Several abnormal EEG findings were reported in psychotic conditions, including slower alpha rhythms in depressed patients than in manic patients (283, 617). Different epileptic types were recognized to have characteristic EEG records that especially involve high-voltage activity. In epilepsy, a relationship of EEG changes to emotional changes was seen, and the possibility of a precipitating

emotional "trigger mechanism" was suggested (741). Temporal-lobe abnormal paroxysmal activity and theta waves were thought to be characteristic of psychomotor epilepsy and to be related to the aggression of these
patients. Some trends in the relating of electropotential activity, as measured
from the scalp, are therefore evident even though differential findings for
different head regions are not as yet entirely clear.

DIFFERENTIAL CORTICAL FUNCTIONING IN GENERAL

The history of attempts to localize behavior and emotional functions in
relation to different brain areas extends back at least to the eighteenth century (640), and in fact valid localization of sensorimotor areas has been
established for many years. Only recently, however, has some progress been
made in the localizing of more complex personality functions, and most
studies of these types have employed EEG measures that reflect cortical
activity.

Studies of the cortex have usually employed the conventional brain-lobe
classifications of frontal, parietal, occipital, and temporal (172). Around
1951 or 1952 with the work of Kaada (666), Dell (290), and a group led
by MacLean, Pribram, and Wall (289, 840, 841, 842, 843), functional
interrelationships between the autonomic nervous system and the cortex
were assigned to the older limbic system (see p. 137) that was made up
of medial and orbital structures. The older limbic system was functionally
differentiated, in Fulton's words, from the neocortex as "comprising centers
of the lateral surface and contiguous gray matter within its sulci-centers
which function through projections to and from the lateral nuclei of the
thalamus and also through connections with other parts of the cerebral
hemispheres" (407, p. 305). Strychnine neuronography of the limbic and
extralimbic cortex, involving the medial and basal aspect of the cerebral
hemispheres, indicated six regional systems: (1) frontotemporal, (2) medial
occipitotemporal, (3) medial parieto-occipital, (4) medial frontoparietal,
(5) medial frontal, and (6) hippocampus (682a, 1046a). Bilateral synchrony of the cortical EEG reflects and exemplifies subcortical influences, and
this is also seen in the fact that "flat," "desynchronized" EEG activity can be
resynchronized in the occipitoparietotemporal regions by visual flicker stimulation ("photic driving") (419a). Similarly, alpha rhythm is notable for its
bilateral synchrony, and beta rhythm is notable for its lack of bilateral
synchronization, indicating that cerebral electrogenesis depends on both
specific and nonspecific projection systems (419a). Jasper's elaborations are
informative in respect to these findings (633, p. 236):

It seems, therefore, that the diffuse thalamocortical projection system may exert a regulatory action, either by enhancing or depressing the elaboration of nerve impulses after they reach their primary projection in the cortex, even though it cannot apparently exert any effect upon the arrival of such volleys to the cortex. The elaboration of cortical response to incoming afferent signals is, therefore, modified by the regulating influence of this separate central integrating system. The thalamic portion of this system may exert its effect only on a small restricted area of the cortex, while the more caudal portions of this system in the brain stem have a more diffuse and undifferentiated action on the cortex as a whole.

Conversely, specific neocortex regions, which are capable of influencing brain-stem reticular formation, have been delineated (in the monkey) as the frontal oculomotor area, the sensorimotor cortex, the paraoccipital region, the superior temporal gyrus, the cingulate cortex, and the posterior orbital surface of the frontal lobe (376a, 805a).

As has already been noted, the EEG wave potentials themselves can be differentiated for different head areas. Berger first concluded that only one type of brain bioelectric activity exists because he obtained both alpha and beta rhythms from various head areas (105, 106, 107, 108, 634).

Subsequently, many technical and mechanical advances have been made in the analyzing of EEG-wave characteristics. Jasper nevertheless has supported Berger's view and noted the difficulty in localizing the origin of potentials that may be detected for a given area, and therefore disputed the claims of several experimenters (15, 16, 1257) that the alpha rhythm appears to originate in the occipital region (634). He found the occipital and precentral regions each to have different characteristic activity, each having alpha potentials of different, distinctive cortical origin, and with the precentral region showing a greater proportion of beta potential at an average frequency of about 25 per second.

Many studies show that alpha waves tend to be strongest in occipital regions and that beta waves are more prominent in frontal regions (271). Darrow has presented some evidence suggesting that sensory stimulation of emotionally unstable individuals tends to increase slow alphalike or theta activity in precentral portions of the brain, which possibly indicates an increased anterior dominance (271). This supported the theory that in the more stable nervous system, "activation" and postcentral alpha "facilitation" prevail, which possibly indicates some postcentral alpha dominance to be a defense against repeated and expected disturbing conditions.

FRONTAL LOBE FUNCTIONING

In regard to the frontal lobes, much data have been obtained from lobotomy and lobectomy studies, wherein some frontal-lobe tissue or tracts are surgically severed or removed. Lobotomies are performed usually to obtain either therapeutic personality changes in neuropsychiatric patients or to obtain relief from intractable pain (514, 1275, 1356). Many general personality changes following operations of this type have been described (4, 28, 374, 517, 522, 523, 747, 863, 897, 971, 990). The psychological and physiological complications involved, however, have made it difficult to draw definite conclusions concerning localization of function; moreover, most effects appear to be mediated primarily through changes in cognitive functions. One of these affects is usually considered to be a decrease in "anxiety"—at least the individual usually appears to be less upset by those things that had previously disturbed or obsessed him. Also, there is reported a decrease of enthusiasm and zeal (747), and the common factor involved here would seem to be a "lessening of inner tension" (28) or "sustained tension" relating to motivation (4, 215). Similar changes have been described for 8 patients following bilateral ablations in the anterior cingulate gyrus; these patients were reported not to show the "frontal lobe deficit," which is expected with lobotomy operations (1260). Perhaps these findings may have some relationship to the report of a high percentage of fast electroencephalographic activity in the frontal area of schizophrenic patients (691).

Surface and depth exploration of the frontal lobes in 9 conscious subjects, including 5 psychotics and 4 nonpsychotics, with multilead needle electrodes showed no correlation between electrical activity and either (1) the depth of the frontal lobes or (2) motor movements, sensory stimulation, or "changes in the mood of the patients" (289b).

TEMPORAL LOBE FUNCTIONING

In regard to the temporal lobes, abnormal focal electroencephalographic findings are seen in about half of all epileptic seizures that have cortical foci (637, 667) and have been associated with psychomotor seizures (412, 446, 447, 450, 563, 564). Focal theta activity in this area has been related by Hill to aggressive, paroxysmal rage patterns or to a low frustration level (563, 564, 775). Patients showing "impulsive-compulsive" behavior were reported to have a high incidence of 6-per-second and 14-per-second positive spikes in the temporal and occipital region (1114).

After the use of direct electrical stimulation of the cerebral cortex of patients who were only under local anesthesia and who were subject to psychomotor epilepsy, Penfield reported in 1938 as follows (982, p. 421):

> Response is obtained from the human cortex most easily from the vicinity of the central fissure of Rolando, that is, from areas 4 and 6 of Brodmann anteriorly and areas 1, 2 and 3 posteriorly. These responses are not obtained from exactly fixed areas, like the keys of a piano, but vary considerably from one patient to another. During a specific operation the sites of elicitation remain constant, but the responses can be influenced by facilitation and inhibition. Outside the motor cortex, the same area in different brains may show marked differences in response, depending apparently on the frequency of some previous experience, such as the aura of an epileptic seizure. These unusual responses may well be explained by the process which Pavlov termed "conditioning."

In a later report summarizing the results of stimulation of the temporal lobe of patients subject to temporal-lobe epilepsy, Penfield noted that recollections of past experiences, as well as similar psychical experiences, could be obtained only from stimulation of the temporal cortex (983). Some of these recollections had been forgotten by the patients, and some seemed to be associated with their seizures. Similarly, many changes involving apparent "emotional" behavior were observed after the bilateral removal of the temporal lobes in monkeys, but such symptoms did not appear with unilateral removal (713).

Kubie cited Penfield's work, as well as electroencephalographic studies of MacLean (840), that concerned the basilar areas of the brain and the structures deep within the temporal region, and he emphasized "the fact that the temporal lobe complex constitutes the mechanism for integrating the past and the present, the phylogenetically and ontogenetically old and new, and at the same time the external and internal environments of the central nervous system" (736, p. 31). Integration at this locus was particularly emphasized because it appeared that here the "gut component of memory enters into our psychological processes and the symbol acquires its dual poles of reference." Earlier, Alford had reported that it seemed to be left capsular injuries that were associated with definite and permanent confusion of consciousness (26).

In view of the importance of gastrointestinal functioning in noncognitive internal perception, it should be mentioned that a localized area in the frontal-lobe cortex has been determined in animal experimentation that results in gastric secretion upon stimulation (278).

Finally, in regard to physiological changes concerning the upper-head region, mention should be made of the common observation that relatively great sweating of the forehead frequently occurs with emotional reactions (341, 838) and is seen particularly in clinical anxiety reactions.

CIRCULATORY SYSTEM

GENERAL CONSIDERATIONS

One of the most critical of the bodily processes is the circulatory system, which transmits, via the blood, nutritional and hormonal substances as well as the blood cells themselves that have metabolic and protective functions. Relationships between circulatory functioning and "emotional" factors have long been recognized (38, 321, 770, 771, 1289). This section, however, will be concerned only with the more diffuse aspects of the circulatory system, leaving consideration of the heart itself to that section that deals with the central-chest area.

It should be remembered that parts of the circulatory system are involved in every body area that will be considered in this discussion. Thus, the circulatory system may or may not play a particularly important role in the differential perception of physiological changes in a given body area, even though no studies may have been available for presentation to show the specific role of circulatory processes in that area. For example, adequate circulation for the brain, which is essential for its functioning, depends primarily on blood pressure; consequently, with reduced blood pressure at the carotid sinus (in the carotid artery), the brain (and heart) are relatively favored in a general reflex increase in systemic blood pressure, and thereby the homeostatic functioning of the central nervous system is enhanced (426).

Two primary mechanisms are involved in circulatory regulation: one is the heart beat; the other is vasomotor innervation, which regulates the size of the blood vessels. Vasomotor innervation is autonomic and maintains a certain tonus of the smooth muscles that regulate the size of the vessels; increased sympathetic stimulation results in vasoconstriction whereas relatively increased parasympathetic stimulation causes vasodilatation. Circulatory functioning is complex and is still not completely understood, as can be seen in the following studies that involve several circulatory variables.

MULTIPLE VARIABLES

An animal study with measures of pulse rate and amplitude demonstrated that the removal of any one of parasympathetic, sympathetic, or adrenal factors did not markedly reduce the effects of emotional stimulation; however, the removal of any two of these factors affected the reactions about 50 per cent, and the removal of all three resulted in a negligible response to the stimulation (821).

In a study of 23 healthy medical students who experienced "anxiety" before taking an oral examination, there was an increase of 10 per cent in mean arterial pressure, of 27 per cent in heart rate, of 16 per cent in stroke volume, and of 48 per cent in cardiac index, and a fall of 23 per cent in peripheral resistance (560). The fall in peripheral resistance was generally proportional to the increase in cardiac index (which is a measure of the volume per minute of cardiac output per square meter of body-surface area, normally averaging 2.2 liters). The extremes of the reactive types were shown by, on the one hand, 4 subjects who reacted with a slight to moderate increase in peripheral resistance and no increase or a slight fall in cardiac index, and, on the other hand, 3 subjects who reacted with cardiac indexes between 35 and 56 per cent.

Another study intercorrelated the following measures taken from children before and after a psychological examination: pulse rate, systolic blood pressure, diastolic blood pressure, pulse pressure, blood-pressure changes, and several galvanic-skin-reaction indexes (267). Systolic, diastolic, and pulse pressure were found to correlate with each other and to form a grouping differentiated from the intercorrelations of galvanic reactivity and conductance level even though all of these types of reactions involve vasomotor innervation.

Measures were taken on 62 student nurses during preadmission examinations and on 17 student pilots before flight tests (experiences that seemed to involve some stress) (933). The following results were reported: little change in diastolic pressure; an increase of 10 to 30 per cent in systolic pressure; a variable pulse rate from 20 per cent deceleration to 40 per cent or more accelerations; and no correlation between variables and subsequent adjustment at work.

Brown and van Gelder cited the results of many studies of this type (156). General agreement with these studies was seen in the following conclusions that were drawn from their own carefully planned and statistically analyzed study, employing multiple physiological measures and involving 78 students and 4 different examinations of different degrees of difficulty designed to provide an index of stress (156, p. 8):

From the above findings it is evident that some students are emotionally aroused before examinations with increased systolic blood pressure, increased pulse and respiratory rates, increased blood sugar, and that some students show glycosuria before examinations. The degree of the above changes is dependent on the difficulty and length of the examination and on the individual. If the student is taking an examination that covers two days, he tends to be excited before the examination on the first day, and much less excited before the examination on the second day. There is no change in blood pressure, pulse, and respiratory rates after the examination as compared to normal. There is no change in erythrocyte or leucocyte counts or diastolic blood pressure before or after an examination as compared to normal readings.

Other authors have also emphasized individual cardiovascular patterns of stress reactivity (742a).

CARDIAC OUTPUT AND PULSE RATE

In an early study, 3 normal males showed an increase in cardiac output with apprehension of fainting (1188). Altschule (38) referred to several studies showing rises in cardiac output with emotion (65, 90, 465, 847). An experiment by Skaggs involving "startle" and a "state of expectancy" of an electric shock showed the greatest increase in pulse rate during "excited expectancy" and a smaller increase during "mental work" as compared to a relaxed condition (1153).

Kinsey et al. summarized six studies involving pulse measures during sexual arousal, showing an increase during "erotic arousal," especially to the point of orgasm, of as much as 150 per minute or more from norms of 70 to 80 (705). These findings are indicative of increased heart work under these various conditions.

VASOMOTOR FUNCTIONING

Numerous studies relating to vasomotor circulatory functions have been made. Vasoconstriction was seen with startle and with anticipation in very early studies (38, 118). Peripheral vasoconstriction-dilatation has been inferred from measures of skin temperature even though blood and body temperature are dependent upon many factors. Conflict and emotional stress usually result in vasoconstriction and a fall in skin temperature (but this effect can be eliminated by blocking of sympathetic innervation), and the opposite effect is seen with absence of conflict and emotional security (796, 920, 922). Blood volume and distribution are affected by pain, tension, excitement, and cold stimuli, which all tend to decrease the blood supply to the skin surface, the extremities, and the visceral region, and tend to increase the supply to the head, brain, lungs, and large skeletal muscles (821).

Cutaneous vasoconstriction, and consequent cooling, in the hands and feet with emotional excitement are commonly seen (38, 601, 1025). Such changes are said to be the result of both arteriolar and venular constriction in the hands (38) and primarily of venular constriction in the forearm (3, 203) with only one of four arteries being involved (558). The vasoconstriction effect of anxiety in normal persons was seen to be limited to the skin, whereas the blood flow in the forearm was seen to be increased (494). Ulcerative-colitis patients, however, have shown finger dilatation with "anxiety and fear" that lead to no effective action or relief (678a).

Differential vasomotor innervation for different body areas results in shifts of blood volume and flow; with constant body temperature, colonic and cutaneous blood flow are seen to vary inversely (486). Emotional changes and, specifically, resentment were seen to correlate with increased blood flow in the wall of the vagina of a patient with pelvic congestion (324, 1360). On the other hand, a decrease in renal blood flow, stemming from renal vasoconstriction, has been found during emotional stress (38, 130, 489, 602, 603). Carotid-artery dilatation occurs with stress and occurs also as a precursor of migraine attacks, suggesting a causal relationship involving blood flow (38). Forearm-skin studies and experimentally induced emotional disturbances in 19 patients, predominantly of psychosomatic types, showed "an attitude of hostility" and also "an attitude of anxiety" to be associated with constirction of arterioles and increased tone of minute vessels, whereas states of "depression" were associated with constriction of arterioles and decreased tone of minute vessels (479a). It was suggested that Raynaud's disease, involving constriction of both arterioles and minute vessels, may involve the skin generally, and hostility was found to be an "invariable accompaniment" of major disease attacks.

BLOOD PRESSURE

Increased blood pressure has long been associated with emotional stress (including the stresses of deception and of so-called "mental work"), and these findings usually revealed a rise in systolic pressure but little or no change in diastolic pressure.

The fact that more pleasant psychological states of excitement also involve increased blood pressure was exemplified by the summary of Kinsey et al. of twelve studies concerning sexual arousal in which it was noted that diastolic blood pressure, normally as low as 65, may be raised from 120 to 250 or more during orgasm (705, p. 599). Also, blood shift to the peripheral vessels was noted in orgasm, increasing surface temperature and leading "to tumescence of all distensible parts of the body" (705, p. 602).

Using diastolic and pulse-pressure measures, among others, Brower found differential circulatory and respiratory reactions, in which the predominant circulatory reactions apparently reflected an "emotive" type of psychological change as contrasted to an "orientive" type with predominant respiratory reactions (155).

Stress arising from the endurance of painful stimuli, namely, headscrews and radiant heat on the forehead from a "Wolf-Hardy" apparatus, resulted in increased blood pressure but no significant pulse changes (36). Increased blood pressure in response to the cold-pressor test has been found significantly greater following the discussion of stressful topics than during control periods (257). A fall of hepatic blood flow during fainting has been reported (90).

Clinical assessment of 69 students in terms of the "direction" of their anger under the stress of mathematical problems accompanied by derogatory remarks indicated that "anger out" was manifested by moderate increase in blood pressure, more marked increases in diastolic blood pressure, mild pulse increases, and decreases in cardiac activity, whereas "anger in" corresponded with mild to moderate increases in diastolic pressure, moderate to marked increases in pulse rate, and moderate to marked increases in cardiac activity (411a). Systolic blood pressure has been found to be lower in 190 females showing overt anxiety than for 120 nonanxious ones (1072a).

NEUROTIC AND HYPERTENSIVE PATIENTS

Many relevant circulatory studies involving various diagnostic groups have been made. Comparing a mixed neuropsychiatric group of children with normal children during a frustration-learning experiment, Jost found that with sensory stimulation (type unstated), the diagnostic or "emotionally unstable" group had significantly higher blood pressure (655). A study of 2000 neurotic patients in a military hospital revealed higher blood pressure than normal (837), and other studies of emotional reactions of neurotic patients showed that excessive acral vasoconstriction occurs and that vasoconstriction sometimes produces fever (38).

Essential hypertension, which has been associated with over 25 per cent of deaths in persons past the age of fifty, is a condition of chronic high blood pressure that some authorities believe to be related to organic changes in the kidneys. The importance of emotional factors in this condition, however, is generally recognized (321, 346, 668a, 668b, 1349, 1357), even though the physiological complexity of circulatory functioning gives rise to much difference of opinion as to the degree and the mechanism of involvement of psychological states (38). Smith stated that the etiology of essential hypertension is unknown and that increased diastolic blood pressure is its *sine qua non* (1159).

Wolff also noted the undetermined state of the pathogenesis of essential hypertension and pointed to theories relating hypertension to two mechanisms, namely, "neurogenic" and "humoral" (or endocrine) (1358). He believed that these mechanisms act together to constitute a characteristic biological pattern of defense for threats to security in individuals having the following, empirically determined, personality characteristics: tense, poised and "calm"; constant alertness and readiness to spring into offense; and, frequently, signs of excessive skeletal-muscle tension. Thus, physiologically and psychologically, hypertensives are mobilized for combat and poised to strike but withhold with a guilty fear of the consequences. When instead of reacting with mobilization, these patients reacted with a feeling of defeat or of being overwhelmed, a depressor reaction occurred, lowering the blood pressure (560, 1342).

Characteristically for hypertensive patients, however, and notwithstanding increased cardiac output and blood pressure, blood is shunted from the kidney by renal vasoconstriction, involving both afferent and efferent arterioles (1358). Only the latter effect is relieved by lumbodorsal sympathectomy, and the former effect is presumed to be the result of endocrine secretions (991, 1358). In establishing these findings, Pfeiffer and Wolff studied renal blood flow and filtration rates for 35 subjects with and without arterial hypertension during the discussion of personally threatening topics, and 6 hypertensive subjects were studied before and after lumbodorsal sympathectomy and splanchnicectomy (991). Also, less blood flow through skeletal muscles has been found in hypertensive patients than in nonhypertensive subjects (1349).

Stevenson et al. found mean blood pressure slightly elevated and peripheral resistance slightly lowered in a group of 20 hypertensive patients and in one of 28 normotensive individuals following exercise in a relaxed atmosphere, with no significant difference between the groups (1201). During emotion-provoking discussions of stressful life situations, the hypertensive patients showed a greater rise in blood pressure in proportion to the increase shown by the normotensive subjects, although under these conditions both groups showed an increase in cardiac output, a rise in blood pressure and a fall in peripheral resistance. When the subject's reaction to conflictual stress was one of restraint, with little overt expression of anxiety, the tendency toward vasoconstriction with increased peripheral resistance was even greater. On the other hand, when the hypertensive subject felt "utterly defeated or overwhelmed," he responded hypodynamically with decreased blood pressure, cardiac output, or both.

Wolff showed that hypertensives, in relation to normotensives, reacted with greater intensity and duration, with stroke-volume increase, a slight initial peripheral vosadilatation followed by a general vasoconstriction, and a decrease in effective renal blood flow due to vasoconstriction (1357) ; the decrease in effective renal blood flow is not a primary factor since after sympathectomy the reaction to discussion of traumatic material is a pressor response despite an actual increase in renal blood flow.

The importance of emotional factors, and particularly of unexpressed hostility, in essential hypertension has been emphasized in many other studies (22, 888, 1082, 1108). Smith noted a hypertensive reaction with the occurrence of "fright" in a nonhypertensive subject, the reaction being reversed with relaxation (1159).

Harris et al., in a carefully planned study, compared 40 undergraduate college women, who showed elevated blood pressure upon their initial physical examination, with a group of 40 matched women, who showed normal blood pressure (530). The former, so-called prehypertensives, were differentiated by their characteristic response to a psychiatric interview and to interpersonal situations involving stress by behaving less effectively as judged by observers and by their own self-appraisals, and their response was similar to clinical-hypertension patients.

After a ten-year psychoanalytic study of 8 patients, who had a minimum of 6 experimental sessions, and 2 long-term experimental patients, Moses, Daniels, and Nickerson formulated the following psychodynamic-hemodynamic correlations for essential hypertension, in which there was amelioration with treatment: (1) rage and resentment predominated with blood pressure elevations of 160-211/100-130 mm.Hg that were related to increased peripheral resistance (with normal stroke volume and heart rate) ;

(2) anxiety with minimal overt expression predominated with minor blood-pressure elevation of 140-160/90-100, and was related again to increased peripheral resistance; and (3) anxiety more overtly expressed was associated with minor blood-pressure elevation with increased stroke volume and heart rate (and with normal peripheral resistance) (935a).

Weiss and English have noted the importance of cultural factors relative to hypertension as follows (1300, p. 304) :

> Hypertension is a disorder largely confined to occidental civilization. There is a good deal of evidence to support this. Thus studies of African natives, the Chinese, Buddhist priests in Ceylon, and Egyptians of the laboring classes all indicate that hypertension is very rare among those peoples. In this connection it also seems important that the blood pressure of foreigners living in China and in the tropics is lower than when they are living in a temperate zone.
>
> Related to these questions come the important observations of Schulze and Schwab [1110], who found the incidence of hypertension in the American southern Negro two and a half times greater than that of the southern white. They and their associates also showed that the tendency to hypertension, as determined by the Hines and Brown ice-water test, exists to a greater degree in the American southern Negro. This bears on the question of heredity because it is acknowledged that the ancestors of these Negroes could not have had hypertension since the Negroes in Africa do not have it now. Thus it would seem that the American southern Negro in his contact with our civilization over a period of 200 years must have acquired hypertension to an even greater degree than the white American. Kesilman found hypertension three times as common in Negro males in a survey conducted in a northern prison (699). It is also interesting to know that hypertension runs a more severe course in the Negro (Metropolitan Life Insurance statistics).

The possible relatedness of these cultural considerations to the factor of repressed or suppressed hostility, anger or aggressive drive as described above is obvious. Fishberg also noted the same findings, but he favored an emphasis on a hereditary factor (360).

In a rather extensive study involving both hypertensive patients and control subjects, Jost et al. found with healthy controls an increase in blood pressure during sensory stimulation, questioning, and periods of successful test performance, and a marked drop in blood pressure at failure (657). During periods of control and periods of sensory stimulation, the control group showed practically no blood-pressure change, whereas the hypertensive group showed much more labile changes. The hypertensive group displayed a marked drop in blood pressure during the initial control period, and they showed the same trends, but with much greater degrees of change, during the other periods in comparison to the control subjects.

Duncan, Stevenson, and Wolff studied 35 subjects, including 11 with symptoms (usually called neurocirculatory asthenia) of dyspnea, dizziness, and effort intolerance, but without evidence of heart disease, and 16 subjects with hypertension or evidence of various degrees of structural heart diseases, and 8 healthy young hospital workers without complications or complaints (323). They found in every subject that significant changes in exercise tolerance were related to changes in emotional state, and they concluded that investigation of both structural factors and life stress in patients with symptoms of cardiac insufficiency is essential for correct prognosis and treatment.

NEUROCIRCULATORY ASTHENIA AND "FUNCTIONAL CARDIOVASCULAR DISEASE"

Altschule has noted that neurocirculatory asthenia is related to neurosis "not only by the nature of its symptoms but also by the fact that the physiologic changes induced by exercise in patients with various types of neurosis are similar to those considered characteristic of neurocirculatory asthenia" (38, p. 35). In summarizing the literature on neurocirculatiory asthenia, however, Cohen and White stated that a relationship of this disorder to life situations and emotion-provoking situations has been neither proved nor disproved (243).

Many studies cited by these authors as well as other findings (56a, 123, 234, 392, 393, 1215) favor an emphasis on the psychogenic aspects of neurocirculatory asthenia. Friedman equated this diagnosis with several others including "irritable heart," "disorder action of the heart," "soldier's heart," "the effort syndrome," and "autonomic imbalance," and he proposed for this syndrome the diagnostic term "functional cardiovascular disease" ("FCVD") (393). Although his review of the literature will be considered in more detail under the section on the central chest, dealing with the heart, it should be noted here that patients having this condition are said to "invariably have psychiatric defects—some disorder of the highest level of the central nervous system" (393, p. 109).

Stevenson and Duncan found that 70 patients with a variety of different cardiovascular complaints usually reacted to life stresses involving anxiety and resentment with "cardiovascular mobilization" including increased blood pressure; in some instances, however, where reactions of dejection and despair were involved, a "hypodynamic response" and a consistent lowering of blood pressure were seen (1200, 1201). In regard to neurosis in general, measurement of 2000 such patients in a military hospital revealed higher blood pressure than normal (837).

PSYCHOSES

Arterial pressure has been described as being variable in functional psychoses, though elevation was found occasionally with manic patients and often with depressed patients, and normal or lowered pressure was found most frequently with schizophrenics (38, 356, 861). A lower cold-pressor response with schizophrenic and manic patients than with normal subjects has been reported, and neurotic patients were reported to show an intermediate response level (619). Variable findings concerning circulation time in schizophrenic patients were also reported (356).

Meadow et al. found a statistically significant positive correlation between abstraction capacity on proverb responses by 20 schizophrenic patients and three related aspects of systolic-blood-pressure reaction to Mecholyl, which were the maximum fall, the area (on the graph) under resting blood-pressure levels, and the time for recovery (892). From these results, two polar types of schizophrenia were suggested, in which poor abstraction, disorganization of personality, and slight response to Mecholyl were at one extreme and the opposite characteristics were at the other extreme.

Catatonic schizophrenic patients were found by Gjessing to show increased blood pressure and pulse rate in the states of stupor and of excitement (459). Altschule cited several studies showing diminished acral blood flow in schizophrenia and cited some findings of this type for manic-depressive psychosis; with such conditions, little response to mental stimuli or concentration was noted although vasoconstrictive reactions were at times marked (38). In contrast to this, he cited studies in which neurotic patients frequently showed excessive acral vasoconstriction in reactions involving varying degrees of emotional tone.

HEMATOLOGIC STUDIES

In studies on hematology, a rise in leucocyte count has most frequently been associated with emotional stress as well as with other strong effects (321, 1334), although this is not invariably so (38, 1335). In a period following emotional stress both lymphocyte and eosinophile counts have been found to be low (38). Eosinophile counts have been found to be low with stress (1313a), before stressful examinations, and prior to operative procedures, and this condition persisted in some cases following the examination (312). Wolff has found increased eosinophiles in nasal secretions along with feelings of resentment, frustration, guilt, and humiliation in a patient with rhinitis (1358).

Emotional stress has been reported to increase the red-cell count, neutrophile cells and the clotting time (38). Marked reductions in clotting time and viscosity were reported by Schneider in patients with painful experiences, vigorous effort, alarm or anxiety, and repressed hostility (1104), and implications of this finding for the occurrence of thrombosis during life stress have been noted (1357). Also, feelings of depression and long clotting times were seen to occur together (1103, 1360).

In a study of 6 unselected patients with recurrent thrombophlebitis, which involves the slowing of blood flow and changes in the chemical properties of the blood, Schneider found that attacks were often correlated with sustained periods of emotional stress, characterized by fear, anxiety, and anger, and that the patients chronically reacted commonly with a decrease in clotting time of the blood; these reactions were also seen in stressful interview sessions whereas they were absent in nonstressful interview sessions (1104). Also studied were 4 healthy volunteer subjects and 23 patients suffering from bronchial asthma, migraine headache, peptic ulcer, or hypertension. Under conditions described above, these patients failed to react with a shortening of clotting time, except that the patients with early labile essential hypertension (as contrasted to the chronic, fixed type) reacted with resentment and hostility and with shortened clotting time and elevated blood viscosity, as well as with hypertensive blood-pressure levels.

Cannon early considered the acceleration of blood-clotting time as an adaptive response to danger (198, 1360). Some changes in blood glucose levels with different psychological states are described in the next section, along with other changes in blood content related to endocrine-gland secretions. Altschule thought that most such changes are associated with secretion of epinephrine by the adrenal gland.

ENDOCRINE GLAND FUNCTIONS

GENERAL CONSIDERATIONS

The endocrine glands regulate metabolism, help maintain a stable internal environment, and govern many specific physiological functions by means of hormone secretions into the blood stream. The pituitary (or hypophysis) is located centrally at the base of the brain and is the master endocrine gland.

In addition to other functions, its secretions affect growth and in part regulate the functioning of the other endocrine glands. The thyroid gland, situated in the neck along with the parathyroid glands, affects directly the use of oxygen by the cells of the body, thereby regulating the energy normally produced, and it also secretes a growth hormone. The parathyroid gland controls blood calcium and phosphorus. Located below these in the upper chest is the thymus gland about which little is known, although some believe its secretions counteract sex-gland secretions and delay physical maturity since atrophy is seen with sexual maturity. The sex glands, or gonads, are comprised of the two ovaries in the female, located in the lower abdomen, and the pair of testes, in the male, in the scrotum; and, they are involved in sexual and physical maturation and functioning. The pancreas gland, located at the posterior wall of the abdomen at the level of the epigastrium, secretes digestive fluids into the duodenum and also has the vital function of secreting insulin, which is produced by he islets of Langerhans and which acts to metabolate sugar (glycogen). The adrenal (suprarenal) glands, situated on top of the kidneys, consist of the adrenal medulla, which elaborates epinephrine (adrenaline), and the adrenal cortex, which secretes numerous steroid hormones having multiple and diverse functions.

PITUITARY GLAND

The pituitary, the master gland, has three major subdivisions: the posterior lobe, affecting blood pressure, contractibility of smooth muscles, and renal functioning (via a specific antidiuretic hormone); the intermediate lobe, elaborating a hormone of unknown function; and the anterior lobe, regulating the growth of bodily tissues, controlling the development and functioning of the thyroid, the adrenal cortex, the gonads, and probably the parathyroid glands, and also regulating lactation. The close relationship of the pituitary gland with the hypothalamus has been noted earlier, and some authorities believe that any stress results in stimulation of the pituitary gland (235, 424, 1144). Certain emotional excitations, particularly "stress," anxious anticipation, and fainting, result in the release of the specific antidiuretic hormone (221, 1075, 1234, 1271). One report of pituitary insufficiency in regard to ACTH (adrenocorticotropic hormone) secretion in chronic alcoholism was made on the basis of an eosinophile-count criterion (1163).

ADRENAL MEDULLA

The adrenal glands have received more attention than the other endocrine glands, but still it will be obvious that knowledge concerning their functioning during various noncognitive psychological states remains only fragmentary. Cannon early emphasized the importance of epinephrine (adrenaline) secreted by the adrenal medulla during emotional stress (195). Its physiological effects were seen to be cardiac acceleration, release of glycogen (sugar) from the liver, increased tonus in striped muscles, and constriction of certain blood vessels and arterioles, which results in redistribution of the blood supply, as has already been noted (89, 195). With epinephrine secretion, either vasodilatation or vasoconstriction of the kidneys may result under different conditions (1159). More recently, it has been reported that the infusion of epinephrine results in transient vasodilatation of muscular vessels, but the sustained vasodilator effect upon intravenous infusion of epinephrine is thought to be due to metabolites set free by epinephrine action (341). Injection of adrenaline usually resulted in no introspective emotion or in "cold" emotion that has "no object or reason," although some subjects felt "true" emotion and all experienced physical symptoms of various kinds (201a). Other widespread reactions to epinephrine include decrease in peripheral resistance, relaxation of the bronchioles, decrease in the clotting time of the blood, and change in glucose metabolism (410a). Also, adrenaline excites the hypothalamic electrical potentials and the accompanying cortical response (499) and, on the electrocardiograph, it has been seen to lower T waves (534) and at times to produce extrasystoles (979), which are signs sometimes associated with emotional reactions (1202).

Norepinephrine (a more recent discovery), on the other hand, does not have such widespread effects, and acts primarily to increase peripheral resistance throughout the body (410a) and produce adrenergic nerve stimulation (341). In summarizing ten years of study of norepinephrine and epinephrine, Funkenstein noted von Euler's theory that these are secreted by different types of cells in the adrenal medulla and reported confirmation of earlier findings suggesting norepinephrine to be the resting secretion of the adrenal medulla and epinephrine to be its secretion in "emergency reactions" (410a). Also, innervation of these secretions by different sympathetic nerves has been indicated (426). The metabolic relation of noradrenaline (norepinephrine) to adrenaline (epinephrine) remains obscure, however, and the possibility that noradrenaline may be a precursor to adrenaline has been suggested (128, 426). In an experiment by Funkenstein et al. with 69 students (see p. 166), differential physiological reactions suggested that the directing of "anger out" might be associated with noradrenaline secretion and the directing of "anger in" with adrenaline secretion (410a, 411a).

The amount of adrenaline found in the adrenal medulla and in other sympathetically innervated structures is influenced by the hypophyseal-adrenocortical system, which is activated by sympatheticoadrenal discharges (342, 343, 426). Thus, in animals subjected to emotional excitement, the increased secretion of the adrenal-cortex hormones (stimulated via the hypophysis) was thought to result from epinephrine secretion (424).

It is well established that in the anesthetic state, marked increases in adrenaline secretion occur, primarily as a result of sympathetic excitation (1159). Gellhorn presented more recent evidence that adrenaline secretion may diminish the excitability of central autonomic and somatic structures (426). Earlier, Cannon had maintained that adrenaline put the organism on an emergency footing, but Arnold cited evidence that adrenaline reduces energy output and believed that it is the cortical hormone, cortin, that is instrumental in maintaining muscular strength (52). She associated adrenaline secretion with fear reactions, during which general activity is decreased. It appears that the physiological stress reactions attributed by Cannon to the release of epinephrine also occur in the absence of the adrenal medulla, which supported the view of Selye that the adrenal cortex is of primary importance in stress reactions (1120, 1121).

THE ADRENAL CORTEX IN GENERAL

The adrenal-cortex secretion is regulated primarily by tropic hormones released from the anterior pituitary; however, as just noted, the adrenaline secretion of the adrenal medulla may also indirectly bring about secretion of adrenocortical hormones (426). Differing from the adrenal medulla, the adrenal cortex secretes numerous steroid hormones, some of which are believed to be associated with reactions to stress. Some of these steroids are chemically related to the sex hormones. Also, adrenal dysfunction in females sometimes results in virilism by the stimulating of an oversecretion of androgen (89).

Scant data are available concerning excretion of adrenocortical hormones and their breakdown products during different psychological states, though small increases in 17-ketosteroid output in the urine have been reported in stress (995). It is this by-product that is frequently taken as an index of adrenal-cortex activity, since 70 to 90 per cent of it is of adrenal-cortex origin in men (with the balance coming from the testes) and probably all of it is of adrenal-cortex origin in women (995). Another indicator of adrenocortical activity is the level of 17-hydroxycorticosteroids in the peripheral blood and in the urine. Bliss et al., in a wide variety of studies, have found the levels to increase moderately but consistently with emotional upset, which also suggested that persistent elevations of the blood steroids might occur with prolonged emotional upset (133a). Another group compared these measures with discomfort-involvement ratings based on interviews and psychological measurements of patients prior to thoracic or cardiac surgery (1005a). Significantly elevated steroid levels were found the day before surgery, and lower steroid values were associated with mild to moderate depression. High steroid values correlated with the following Rorschach-protocol indicators: a low percentage of neutral associations, a high percentage of unpleasant content, low form accuracy, and introversive tendencies ("M" greater than "C"). "Degree of emotional involvement," associated positively with these steroid values, was thought to be a more valuable operational concept than "anxiety." Urinary formaldehydrogenic steroid (FS) levels are also taken as indicators of adrenocortical functioning, and this was found to correlate positively with "emotional tension" in a series of studies (1114a).

It has been reported that prolonged adrenal-cortex stimulation produces hypersecretion and hyperacidity of the gastrointestinal tract (38, 521), and, over extended periods, produces alterations in electrolyte and carbohydrate metabolism resulting in alterations in the structure of blood vessels and other organs and in organic pathology (1144).

Selye called such alterations "diseases of adaptation" since he designated adrenocortical reactivity "the general adaptation syndrome" (GAS) (see p. 125) (1120, 1122a, 1123).

Concerning the frequent finding of increased urinary output with emotional stress, such stress has been seen to result in changes in glomerular filtration, in filtration fraction, and in renal blood flow, as will be discussed in more detail later in the section dealing with the kidneys (570, 1160, 1162, 1341, 1349). Related to this are findings that cortisone (an adrenal-cortex hormone) and ACTH (the equivalent of the pituitary adrenotropic hormone) produce increased renal blood flow (620) and progressive increases in glomerular filtration rate and filtration fraction (777); ACTH has also been found to reduce the tubular reabsorptive capacity for glucose (248). Nevertheless, it has been said that changes in water secretion cannot be attributed to changes in glomerular filtration (1161) and that the increased diuresis with stress can be explained by secretion of the antidiuretic hormone of the posterior pituitary gland (570, 1271).

Of the blood-cell changes attributed to adrenal action, an immediate rise in leucocyte count and an accelerated clotting time have been associated with epinephrine action, and delayed decreases in lymphocyte and eosinophile counts were also associated with adrenocortical action, these changes and similar findings having been related to emotional stress (38, 478, 867, 1127). In people in whom chronic emotional variations are known to prevail, the urinary excretion of 17-ketosteroids (an index of adrenal-cortex activity) was seen to be normal or slightly increased for neurotic patients in most studies, and with this, the hematologic changes of the types just noted suggested to Altschule the possibility of some degree of adrenocortical hyperactivity (38).

Using several indices, including blood counts and urinary acid excretion, on 22 patients hospitalized because of anxiety, Cleghorn reported a "striking positive relationship" between the degree of clinical anxiety and the amounts of adrenocortical discharge; the secretion with mild anxiety states resembled that of normal controls, that with moderate anxiety showed a medium degree of responses, and that with extreme apprehension showed marked adrenocortical discharges (236, 478).

ACTH STUDIES

Following the extensive employment of ACTH in medical therapy, there has been considerable variation in reports of the relative psychological effects produced. These effects have been compared to those of Cushing's disease, involving adrenal hyperactivity, and of Addison's disease, involving adrenal hypoactivity (478). Several studies have found no changes, or negligible personality changes, in patients receiving ACTH (184). Other experimenters have described a variety of changes including in some cases "euphorogenic" and "depressogenic" effects (237, 295, 365, 388, 460, 471, 553, 1027, 1057, 1183).

In a study of 80 general medical patients, Goolker and Schein found 54 per cent free of psychological reactions, and only 15 per cent showed distinct aberrant reactions (471). Similarly, Rees observed no change in 52 per cent of 40 mixed psychiatric and general medical patients studied (1027). With the other patients, many different types of reactions were observed, and the primary mental change was described as a state of "cerebral excitability," called "the ready state" (471). This usually began during the first 4 to 6 hours of treatment, and the central clinical manifestation was considered to be affect perturbation with marked lability. Fox and Gifford, in a study of

98 medical patients, supported this primary finding, hypothesizing that the metabolic changes that occur with the administration of ACTH and cortisone "constitute physiological sources of instinctual tension and result in an increased drive to discharge energy or an increased need to obtain instinctual satisfaction" (365, p. 626).

Rome and Braceland have classified the reactions of patients undergoing this therapy into four categories, the first two involving primarily mood and affect changes and the second two, which also included affect changes, involving more comprehensive changes in ideation and behavior in patients who maintained more or less marginal adjustments prior to treatment (1057). On the other hand, Clark et al., in studying 10 patients, found nothing in their premorbid personality structure that would help predict a patient's reactions to these drugs (232). This impression was supported by the study of Goolker and Schein who described the reaction to the drugs as unpredictable (471).

Rome and Braceland emphasized the dependence of personality organization and integration upon the internal environment of the organism and noted that at no phase of growth and development is the organism subject to such a sudden and great hormonic change as it is incidental to ACTH treatment. Widespread metabolic-physiological changes result from ACTH administration (996), and at least 15 adrenocortical hormones are released in response to this administration (597), having far-reaching effects that even include changes in brain physiology (305) and in EEG patterns (311, 585). The personality changes that do occur in a minority of cases upon administration of ACTH or, more particularly, of adrenal corticoids, are generally thought to result from a weakening of defenses that allows an exacerbation of latent tendencies (311).

Despite the great amount of work done in connection with adrenocortical functioning, Engel stated that "we still have little or no real understanding of the precise mechanisms by which the anterior pituitary and adrenal cortex participate in the response to a stressful stimulus" (334, p. 565). He criticized two primary indicators employed to reflect pituitary-adrenal secretion, maintaining that eosinopenia has now been found a "totally inadequate index" and that the levels of adrenal steroids in blood and urine "cannot yet be interpreted unequivocally in terms of secretory rate as long as we know so little about the metabolic fate of adrenal steroids under normal and abnormal circumstances," especially since there is still disagreement concerning the validity of the various methods of analysis.

Cannon early observed glycosuria with fear or rage reactions of experimental animals (195, 199, 568). He and Fiske also reported this condition for several football players and for one spectator following an exciting game (195). The assumed primary mechanism in such glycosuria is the release of glycogen (sugar) from the liver by the action of epinephrine secreted from the adrenal medulla. Glycosuria in normal subjects prior to stressful examinations or following them has been a frequent finding (144, 156, 171, 304, 321, 363, 1247), although there are some negative findings (528). The degree of such changes, among others, was reported to be dependent on the difficulty and the length of the examination as well as on the individual (156).

Glycosuria also has been related to melancholia, and it was presumed to result from contained aggressive impulses (812, p. 311). Both neurotic and normal soldiers showed glycosuria for two to three days after being under fire (321, 902). On the other hand, Marañón reported hyperglycemia (excess sugar in the blood) in aviators to be in proportion to the extent of their fear (870).

A similar mechanism of adrenal secretion has been suggested in studies of diabetes mellitus, a condition of chronic glycosuria, hyperglycemia and, in advanced stages, ketosis (acidosis or excess blood ketone bodies) (247, 257, 346a, 568, 571, 572, 573, 574, 575, 576, 601a, 899, 916). Hinkle and Wolf made extensive observations first on 64 diabetic subjects and later on 80 other subjects and correlated their data with life situations and emotional, or feeling, reactions (576). In nondiabetic subjects the glucose concentration fell with both hunger and stressful situations that involved anger or anxiety without hunger. Diabetic persons reacted similarly to stress but often to a much greater degree. The fasting diabetic subjects usually reacted to conflict situations initially with a transient fall in blood glucose level and a rise in ketonemia, but with continued stress, the blood glucose ceased to fall and at times even rose. In contrast, fasting persons "suddenly made very fearful or angry" showed a rapid rise in blood sugar, apparently as a result of epinephrine secretion. Concerning the ingestion of carbohydrate foods, it was found that "situations associated with loneliness, sadness, and resentment were sometimes associated with a longer and higher ('more diabetic') glucose tolerance curve; whereas situations associated with less stress or with anxiety were associated with a flatter and less elevated curve" (576, p. 517). Major fluctuations in diabetic symptoms and insulin requirements frequently were found to coincide with situations of life stress. Hinkle and Wolf found that diabetes mellitus was related to the following personality factors (576, p. 518):

> A large proportion of the patients had one parent (usually the parent of the same sex) whom they felt to be dominating and restrictive. Toward this parent they exhibited an unusual degree of both dependence and resentment. Periodic outbursts of anger and rebellion directed at this parent had been a feature of their behavior long before their diabetes developed. After the disease began these acute conflicts were accentuated, and were usually accompanied by exacerbations of the illness, including ketosis and coma . . . In diabetics of all ages the onset of the symptoms of the disease usually took place in a setting of stress . . . and it was accompanied by feelings of anxiety, dejection and deprivation. Such feelings often became chronic, and were associated with a feeling of inability to cope with the problems of life.

Although a causal relationship was not assumed, emotional factors were considered to be an integral part of the total process of diabetes mellitus.

In a similar extensive study of diabetic patients and normal controls, Hinkle et al. found a rise in ketones for all persons subjected to stressful situations and a return to a lower ketone level when the stress was subsequently withdrawn (568, 573). Such ketones, when excessive, constitute acidosis, which can result in coma and even death. A complexity of physiological factors may operate to different degrees in different cases. In the study of Hinkle et al. most cases involved an element of anger or hostile-aggressive feeling during stress, and it was noted that in most cases the blood glucose fell as the ketone level rose in unfed individuals under stress. Also in this study, no normal subjects developed significant hyperglycemia, but two developed moderate hypoglycemia, apparently due to the suppressing of fear, a finding similar to that of another study involving suppression (24).

A hypoglycemic condition with certain psychological states has also been reported by others (567). One study of 7 patients indicated that hypoglycemia was associated secondarily with so-called "tension depression," consisting of motor tensions and states of depression, wherein "flat glucose tolerance curves" occurred in symptomatic periods but normal curves were later seen for those patients who resolved their difficulties (24, 1030). Alexander and Portis studied 9 such cases in considerable detail and noted that each one showed the asthenic syndrome in either a chronic form of prolonged exhaustion and apathy or in acute attacks of weakness with tremulousness, sweating, and often anxiety, and the diagnosis was hypoglycemic fatigue (24). Psychodynamically, these patients all showed a striking lack of "zest and interest" in any activity in which they were engaged, which resembled depression in some respects. In most cases, the condition had "developed after a gratifying occupation or a cherished goal or hope had to be abandoned on account of compelling circumstances, and the patient was forced to engage in distasteful routine activity, against which he revolted intensely" (24, p. 194).

OTHER VARIATIONS WITH PERSONALITY TYPES

In asthma and in arthritis some evidence of adrenocortical hypofunctioning has been reported (605), and, in tuberculosis, 17-ketosteroid excretion has also been shown to reflect emotional problems (593a). Pincus and Hoagland (580, 580a, 995) reviewed numerous studies of their own and others that show adrenal-cortex reactions to stress with normal subjects and a lack of adrenal reactivity on the part of schizophrenic subjects. Pincus and Hoagland attributed this unresponsiveness of the adrenal gland to the absence of ACTH.

Altschule, on the other hand, cited many studies as evidence for adrenal hyperactivity in manic-depressive, involutional, and schizophrenic psychoses of recent onset, but he, too, noted that these findings disappear with chronicity in most cases (38). Fry commented on the many conflicting results from studies concerning relative adrenal-cortex secretion in schizophrenic patients (402). He presented evidence to show that in such studies a number of nonspecific stress factors influenced the level of pituitary-adrenal-cortex activity; he also pointed out a tendency for false-negative responses that should be considered in the evaluation of this reactivity.

THYROID GLAND

The relation of thyroid-gland functioning to psychological states, or "emotion," is controversial. Psychic trauma has been related to the onset of hyperthyroid conditions by some observers (247, 320, 919). Graham stated that it has been known for a long time clinically that increased secretion of the thyrotropic hormone from the anterior pituitary gland occurs in response to psychological stress, and with the consequent release of thyroxine from the thyroid gland, there is modification of all cellular metabolism (478). Thyroxine also significantly modifies the physiological responses normally produced by the adrenal steroids (566). This is seen in an antagonism between the effects of the thyroid growth hormone and the increased activity of the adrenal cortex; this antagonism may be implicated in the effects of emotional disturbance in modifying the growth of children (389, 478, 1122,

1323). The fact that the removal of the thyroid gland markedly reduces conditioned reflexes would also seem to be significant in regard to its possible role in human reactivity (426).

In studies of blood iodine content to indicate thyroid activity, Wittkower reported that with emotion, iodine values as abnormal as those in Graves's disease (involving thyroid hyperactivity) were found, and these values returned to normal with the passing of the emotional reaction (1335). In another study no correlation was found with degree of anxiety, but a relationship between the hormone decay and psychodynamics was found (304b). Beach has noted that, in addition to the well-known extremes of thyroid hyperfunctioning and hypofunctioning that result in the abnormal conditions of myxedema and cretinism, respectively, "abnormally high concentrations of thyroid hormone in human beings are associated with hypermetabolism, restlessness, hyperactivity, and often with emotional instability" (89, p. 74).

Altschule, on the other hand, attempted to refute this rather common association (1300) by differentiating the hyperthyroid condition from anxiety neurosis (38).

Lidz and Whitehorn, in a study of patients manifesting hyperthyroidism, concluded that personality factors and constitutional factors are both etiologically important (788). They found continuous stress in interpersonal relationships, including ambivalence toward the mother figure, to be characteristic of such patients. For some women, emotional changes and conflicts associated with pregnancy correspond with the occurrence and reoccurence of hyperthyroidism (787a). Wolff cited an unpublished study of Hetzel and Hinkle in which hourly measures of plasma protein-bound iodine (PBI) were taken for periods of three to seven hours as indicators of thyroid hormone levels in the blood of euthyroid (normal) and hyperthyroid patients (1360). The amount was found to be constant under neutral conditions, but with the stress of discussing distressing personal topics, marked fluctuations in the PBI level occurred and increases of as much as 100 per cent were seen in some subjects. A brief report of Hemphill and Reiss indicated a high incidence of thyroid hypofunctioning with anxiety in male psychiatric patients as contrasted to negative findings for female psychiatric patients (552).

Since the thyroid gland is generally considered to be of primary importance in the regulating of body metabolism, the rather mysterious phenomenon of fevers of unknown origin (FUO) will be considered here in so far as psychological states are implicated. Such findings have been associated with "neurogenic instability" (518). Friedman reported studies of the functional cardiovascular syndrome, including neurocirculatory asthenia, wherein 30 per cent of patients with this condition showed episodic, low-grade fever, rarely exceeding 100° F., which was of functional rather than infectious origin and appeared to result from centrally induced changes in the sympathetic nervous system (393). Similarly, periodic episodes of fever have been noted by Wolff to occur in some persons during sustained stress (1360). Also Goodell, Graham, and Wolff found that a given amount of work resulted in a rise of body temperature that was sustained longer during periods of emotional tension and conflict than during periods of tranquility (469).

SEX GLANDS

The sex glands have rather widespread functions, and it is at times difficult to distinguish their functions from those of other glands, particularly those of the anterior pituitary gland. The anterior pituitary gland releases a gonadotropic hormone, and such secretion can be stimulated by sexual excitement (426). As the sex glands are concerned with physical and sexual maturation, their functioning affects many personality traits. For example, if castration takes place before adolescence, the so-called secondary sexual traits, such as pubic hair and breast development, fail to appear, and castration after adolescence causes the involution of the remaining sex organs of reproduction and a number of other symptoms resembling menopause.

The fact that the characteristics associated with sex differences are less dependent upon the existence of the gonads at higher phylogenetic levels is illustrated by the dramatic changes that take place with castration of lower animals, such as chickens or rats, in comparison to the more moderate changes in humans, where in many cases castration does not necessarily interfere seriously with normal sexual activity (except, of course, reproduction) (97). Nevertheless, castration of the adult male usually results in some diminution of sexual urge, as well as frequent symptoms of "hot flashes," asthenia, and muscular weakness, all of which reportedly respond favorably to treatment with testosterone implants (124, 545, 1003). In addition, Bishop reported that the effect of gonadectomy on females is far less marked than in males, especially in regard to changes in sexual feelings; however, one third of 300 hysterectomy patients that were studied complained of some loss in sexual drive within a short time, which suggested that estrogen secretion is a factor therein. Yet for the evaluation of such studies, consideration must be given to other psychological factors that are frequently involved in hysterectomy patients. Bishop also noted that after the menopause many women show no diminution in sexual receptivity, but for those women who do show diminished receptivity following menopause, the administration of estrogen fails to increase sexual drive. On the other hand, the administration of androgen ("the male hormone") has been found clinically to increase sexual desire in normal females as well as in males (124).

The gonads, however, cannot be considered the primary factor in sexual arousal of adult humans; like many other factors, the gonadal hormones are considered to be one of many additive factors leading to the desire for copulation (424, 544, 1310).

The reverse relationship in which certain stimuli result in glandular secretions has also been demonstrated, as exemplified by an experiment of Clark and Treichler in which the viewing of "pornographic" movies was seen to result in increased acid phosphatase (AP) (indicating prostate-gland secretion) in all males except for one who was "quite embarrassed, almost repulsed," by the movies (231).

In lower animals, secretion of the female ovarian hormone, estrogen, governs the release of reproductive cells as well as the receptivity of the animal to sexual approach by the male—both events occurring about the same time. Human females, however, do not feel their strongest sexual drive at the time of ovulation, which occurs near the mid-point between menstrual periods, but rather just before or after menstruation (89, 282, 302, 1210). Of course, it is possible that this reflects a cultural variable. The relative influence of organic versus personality factors in regard to sexual matters is debatable.

Daniels presented evidence that changes in emotional tone and mood often correspond to specific phases of the menstrual cycles (265). A "regression" with menstruation was reported for patients in psychoanalysis (1146). Stone and Barker have emphasized the shift in interests occurring with the initial onset of menstruation independently of the age factor (1208).

Premenstrual tension has been estimated to occur for at least 40 per cent of all women at one time or another (735a, 743), and is frequently accompanied by headaches, tenderness of the breasts, abdominal swelling, and irritability, which have been attributed to the effect of circulation of a presumed menstrual toxin (124) or of other organic changes (1026). Concerning the phenomena of premenstrual depression, as well as involutional and post-partum depression, it has been suggested that endocrine factors may be involved; however, dynamic personality factors must be considered in the evaluating of these conditions (1093). Lamb et al. observed that premenstrual-tension therapy based on theories of pathologic endocrinologic imbalance, involving particularly estrogen-progesterone levels, has been "singularly unrewarding" in terms of predictable results in large numbers of patients (743).

From a questionnaire survey of 127 student nurses, Lamb et al. carefully selected 5 with symptoms of premenstrual tension and 5 control subjects; these subjects were submitted to extensive psychiatric, EEG, and endocrinologic investigation (743). Endocrine activity (including gonadotropic, pituitary, and thyroid hormones) and also ovarian functions were found to be within normal limits for all subjects as were EEG measures; however, psychiatrically, the subjects with premenstrual tension showed more emotional lability throughout their menstrual cycles as well as in the premenstrual periods, and they were in general less assertive individuals.

Other workers have related the hormonal changes during the menstrual cycle to emotional changes in various ways; an increase in pituitary gonadotropin at menopause is considered by some people to be the basis of emotional instability at such times. The anterior-pituitary hormone, prolactin, is associated with maternal reactions of lower animals (89).

Benedek and Rubenstein have estimated estrogen production in "minimally neurotic women" by the study of vaginal smears and basal body temperatures, and they have found increased estrogen production to correspond to increases in heterosexual tension (33, 100). Ovulation was followed by a release of tension and a feeling of contentment and well-being that may last for several days. Benedek and Rubinstein reported that this change may be accompanied by erotic genital sensations. With the production of progesterone, a tension reappears that is more narcissistic and less heterosexually directed than previously. Conflicts and neurotic symptoms were seen to become accentuated at the height of both the estrogen and progesterone levels. Benedek also related low estrogen and progesterone levels to characteristics such as hostility, infantile demanding dependency, and depressive tendencies (99). Wright raised some questions about the methodologies employed in the studies of Benedek and Rubenstein (1372).

The physiological cycle of menstruation was described by Daniels as follows (265, p. 232):

To sketch the physiology briefly: toward the end of the menstrual period a follicle of one of the ovaries, under the stimulation of the follicular stimulating hormone of the anterior pituitary, begins to mature. As it matures it produces estrogen. The estrogen reaches its first peak at, or about the time of ovulation. A sharp pain called the *Mittelschmerz,* accompanying rupture of the mature follicle at ovulation, has been described. About the time of ovulation the follicle, under the influence of the anterior pituitary, forms a corpus luteum which secretes progesterone. The production of estrogen continues. The progesterone climbs to a plateau on the second or third day of ovulation, falling off two to five days before menstruation.

Werner has also observed that although the normal woman continually excretes estrogen, androgen, and follicular-stimulating hormone in the urine, the peaks in both estrogen and gonadotropin generally coincide at the midpoint of the menstrual cycle, and therefore appear to be related to ovulation (1307). A cyclic secretion of follicle-stimulating hormone for noninvoluted females has been suggested, and in one case the aggravation of the patient's neuropsychiatric condition occurred at times of increased secretion (529, 1000).

These latter studies have emphasized hormonal factors as causing psychological changes, though the reverse emphasis is common in psychological and psychiatric literature. For example, it has been noted by obstetricians (as well as dairymen) that lactation can be suppressed by emotion (38). This function is also affected by a pituitary hormone. Similarly, it is well known that fear and other emotional states frequently disturb menstruation (114a, 426, 683a, 735a, 985a).

Altschule entered the controversy over the physiological versus psychological causation in such changes and, after noting that various gonadal functions may be severely deranged with emotional disorders and after citing mixed physiological findings in regard to pseudocyesis, favored an endocrine origin (38). Kroger and Freed, however, cited pseudocyesis as an illustration of how psychological factors may precipitate endocrine changes (735a). As far as the noncognitive inner experience of the individual is concerned, there need be no conflict between "psychological" and "physiological" factors because at some level correspondence of these factors in human functioning is assumed to exist. Controversy concerning causality relates primarily to etiology, and there can be little doubt that in general both cognitive or "emotional" conflicts can affect sex-hormone functioning and marked alteration of sex-hormone functioning affects the personality.

A similar interrelationship is seen in the study of sex-hormone alterations in males. Reactions to castration after puberty vary from no reduction in sex drive or capacity to different degrees of reduced interest in sexual matters and impotence, and, conversely, the effects of testis hormone may augment aggressive tendencies in both humans and animals (89, 246). In castration of the prepubescent male, traits develop that are neither masculine nor feminine; he is a "neutral" type. His sex organs cease to grow; his voice and appearance do not change; and he lacks the vigor and aggressiveness of the normal male and is phlegmatic.

Daniels and Tauber have emphasized the need of careful preoperative and postoperative personality studies in castration cases, noting that psychotherapy alone may enhance sexual expression (266). After a review of the literature concerning male castration effects, Tauber noted the occurrence of varying degrees of castration, depending on whether all or part of either the testis or penis or both were removed, and concluded that both biological and psychological factors seem to play a definite role in sexual adequacy (1232). Nevertheless, sexual potentialities and experiences were seen in cases including all types of castration, and Tauber believed that most investigations "have neglected to penetrate the individual and social implications of castration."

Precocious male puberty, including precocious sexual advances, has been reported with excess secretion of adrenal androgens as indicated by 17-ketosteroid output (124).

Altschule cited generally normal sex-hormone findings in the following conditions: neurosis; impotence and masturbation problems; homosexuality; and functional psychoses (except for the finding in chronic schizophrenia of atrophy of the Leydig cells that are thought to be the source of the male sex hormone) (38). It should be added, also, that psychoses have often been precipitated by pregnancy (900).

BODY CHEMISTRY AND METABOLISM

GENERAL CONSIDERATIONS

Body chemistry is determined by all bodily functions, ranging from absorption of nutrients and elimination of waste products in the gastrointestinal tract and lungs to the use of energy in the muscle and other tissues, as well as by glandular, neural, and blood products. In so far as psychological states relate to any of these factors, body chemistry will be affected; however, the interrelation of all these functions by means of body chemistry is so complex that it is only incompletely understood at this time. As can be seen in the studies already cited, chemical changes are most frequently analyzed for the purpose of estimating the functioning of some given gland or organ. Similarly, attempts have been made to estimate relative sympathetic or parasympathetic innervation by the measuring of changes following the injection of epinephrine, acetylcholine, pilocarpine or of atropine; however, such methodology has been criticized on the basis that physiological factors other than the particular organ of reference are paramount in the changes that occur, such as enzyme activity, the reactivity of certain end organs, and of neural ganglia (38, 1076, 1167). The chemical findings to be described here are rather heterogeneous. Differential acetylcholinelike and epinephrinelike reactions in the blood have been suggested for different "emotional" states (303).

CARBON DIOXIDE, PH, AND OXYGEN

Hyperventilation, a symptom frequently associated with emotional excitement and with neurotic conditions, lowers arterial blood carbon dioxide tensions and thereby results in decreased cerebral blood flow that may precipitate complaints ranging from fatigue and lightheadedness to fainting and seizures (38). Hyperventilation also has a secondary effect of increasing the fixed acids, primarily lactate. Acid, of course, reduces the blood pH (the reciprocal of hydrogen ion concentration), and pH measures of salivary secretions have frequently been related to changing psychological states (417, 790, 1185, 1330).

Starr found a correlation between salivary pH and the carbon dioxide content of the alveolar air (1185). With emotional stress involving reactions of anger and excitement, Starr found that the salivary pH increased for normal subjects and then returned to normal as they became calm. He also reported abnormally high hydrogen ion concentration of mixed saliva, due to the presence of carbon dioxide, in subbreathers and fatigued individuals whereas these values were abnormally low in "chronically excited psychopaths."

Barcroft differentiated a state, similar to that of drunkenness, with an acute lack of oxygen and a state of fatigue with a chronic lack of oxygen (66). Using an oximetric index of arterial oxygen saturation in a series of 14 observations on 3 female neurotic patients under hypnotic and posthypnotic suggestion, Lovett Doust found this measure to provide an accurate index to the depth of hypnosis, or to the "relative plane of unawareness"

(817, 818). The suggestion of unpleasant emotion was accompanied by relative anoxemia whereas that of pleasant emotion tended to be associated with increased oxygen saturation. A similar reaction to the stress of psychological "tests" was found for 48 control subjects and 98 patients (with the exception of psychotic patients) (818a). The extensive studies of McFarland have demonstrated that the nervous system is very sensitive to oxygen want, the sensitivity varying greatly with the conditions involved (832). The processes affected by lack of oxygen appeared to relate primarily to fatigue and to cognitive changes that result from physiological effects on the central nervous system, especially on the brain; however, the physiological reactions observed have broader implications, as stated by McFarland (832, p. 155):

> Psychoneurotics with objective symptoms of exhaustion and sympatho-adrenal disturbances were observed by McFarland and Barach [833] to be particularly sensitive to oxygen deprivation compared with normal subjects, over 68 per cent of the patients collapsing after 20 minutes in 10 per cent oxygen compared with 14 per cent of the control subjects. The implication that emotional stress may impair one's adaptation to high altitude is strengthened by the observation of Hess [559] who believes the oxygen exchange between the alveolar air and arterial blood is inhibited by vagus action and by Kroetz [735] who reported that the arterial oxygen saturation of neurotic patients showing vasomotor instability might suddenly fall from the normal level of 95 per cent or over to 88 per cent as a result of emotional stress.

OTHER REACTIONS

Along with diuresis and a fall in the specific gravity of urine during stress that involved anxiety and apprehension, Hinkle, Edwards, and Wolf found a fall in chloride concentration (569). With this, the rate of chloride excretion varied; in some cases it rose. Other writers have reported increased urinary excretion of chloride and of potassium during emotional reactions (38). Wittkower reported that emotion caused changes in calcium, potassium and chloride levels of the blood as well as in the hematocrit (1335). As already noted, stress results at times in diuresis, which, with the rapid loss of water, glucose, and chlorides, may be an important factor in the development of diabetic acidosis and coma for diabetic patients (570).

There is general agreement that emotional reactions elevate the metabolic rate, although some cases fail to show this (38). From the reverse perspective, starvation results in a greatly reduced basal metabolism and also in increased lactic and pyruvic acid blood levels and decreased blood sugar level (89, 367). Psychological changes in starvation experiments are marked and include increased irritability and preoccupation with hunger and food-associated interests at the expense of normal sexual activity and of other pleasurable psychological states (367). Similarly, women living on a reduced intake of B vitamins for over a month tended to become more irritable and to complain of fears and depressive feelings that were eliminated when thiamine was added to the diet (1143). Comparable psychological changes were seen in men who were on diets reduced in thiamine, riboflavin, and niacin, but there was a return to normal when thiamine was added to the diet (162).

ALCOHOL AND DRUGS

The effects of the taking of drugs or alcohol vary with individuals, and with most the effect of the drug on psychological states and emotional expression is thought to be indirect from the release of the inhibiting effects of the higher central nervous system. Different drugs, of course, do have a selective action on different parts of the nervous system, and a variety of characteristic cognitive changes have been reported (89, 642). Also, human morphine addicts are seen to show depressed sexual functioning under addiction and show hypersexuality on withdrawal, which is not the case in chimpanzees (89). Mild euphoria is frequently seen clinically with slight alcohol intoxication, and this may be related, among other things, to the reduced supply of oxygen to the brain (831, 832). Slight intoxication may also stem from rarified air, and it results in euphoria at high-altitude conditions. Taking into account the lack of psychological studies concerning alcohol intoxication, Jellinek and McFarland concluded that the evidence at hand indicates a general depressing effect of alcohol on all psychological functions measured so far, but simple psychological functions are less affected than are complex ones in so far as sensory and cognitive factors are concerned (642). There is little direct evidence concerning such changes in noncognitive inner experience.

Masserman has presented strong evidence, using experimental animals, that alcohol may have the effect of relieving neurotic anxiety (880, 881). At the other extreme, it is the release of "normal" anxiety and ego control that is generally believed to be responsible for outbursts of rage or depressive acts frequently seen in clinical alcoholism.

Grinker has described the complex and differential effects of chemical changes on hypothalamic and cortical functioning (499). In the 1950s, the so-called tranquilizing drugs began to play a major role in the treatment of mental and emotional conditions. The tranquilizers are frequently supplemented by other drugs for increased effectiveness (as with niacin) or for counterbalancing effects, as with ritalin to counteract drowsiness. New forms of these drugs are being produced in seemingly endless varieties (363b). Fields's book describes some brain mechanisms involved with these and other drugs (353a).

NEURAL SECRETIONS

Certain chemical substances are liberated by the nerves themselves, and these appear to play very important roles in all neural activity and reactivity. Sympathin is liberated primarily by sympathetic-nerve fibers and only secondarily by other means (426). Fibers secreting sympathin are termed adrenergic. The effect of sympathin is similar to that of the adrenal-medulla hormone, adrenaline. Acetylcholine is secreted primarily by the parasympathetic nerves, but it is also released by some sympathetic nerves (426). All these nerves are called cholinergic. Although Gellhorn believed that acetylcholine played an important role in cellular metabolism, he asserted that it did not, as frequently claimed (260, 939), play a central role in nerve conduction (426). Subsequently, Marrazzi asserted that excitatory effects of cholinergic stimulation and inhibitory effects of adrenergic stimulation reciprocally regulate neural synpatic transmission of impulses and account for a great number of chemical and drug actions (871a).

FINDINGS IN NEUROSES AND PSYCHOSES

Altschule has cited studies on body chemistry in neurotic and psychotic emotional maladjustments (38). Twenty-two references were given for normal metabolic-rate findings in neurosis, six references for high values, and ten references for low ones. Stressful thoughts were noted to have a marked effect in increasing the metabolic rate of neurotics. Variable findings concerning metabolic rate were reported by Altschule for the functioning psychoses; however, findings within the normal range were usual. Many chemical variables in psychoses have been studied (89). For example, a high blood cholesterol level found by Stenberg (1195) and increased phospholipid level found by Randall and Cohen (1009) have been associated with the agitated states of schizophrenia in comparison to the findings in calm states. Similarly, mental disturbances in one type of schizophrenia have been related to changes in nitrogen metabolism (459, 520).

MUSCLE, BONE, AND SKIN

MUSCLE IN GENERAL

Numerous studies have been cited by Berrien relating emotional experiences to disturbances in voluntary musculature (115). Some of these findings will be presented in this discussion primarily under the classification of body-area involved. Muscular reactions, like reactions of other organs and systems, are seen by H. G. Wolff to constitute patterns of personality defense, with sustained contraction of muscles becoming "a source of pain and paresthesia in tense, dissatisfied, resentful, apprehensive, anxious people" (1358, p. 316). Wenger reported a relatively high correlation of traits of "sensitiveness" and "restlessness" with muscle tension and a negative correlation between "emotional control" and muscle tension (1303).

Muscle changes can be measured very specifically by needle electrodes, somewhat less specifically by surface electrodes such as those of the EEG, and more generally by mechanical tension recorders. Travis and Lindsley (792, 1265) and also Malmo et al. (866) have demonstrated that these measures are indicative of muscle tension. In averaging the simultaneous electrical measurements of five muscle groups with 15 normal subjects, the muscle tension was seen to rise steadily with the subjects' activity and to fall more after the completion of the simple drawing tasks than after interruptions. The subjects who showed the greatest tension during the drawing tended most to maintain their tension when interrupted (1158).

Tremors and electromyographic activity have been related to frights and to other emotional stresses, and, similarly, motor inco-ordination is frequently seen during stress (38, 253). Most such studies are based on the measure of skeletal muscles, particularly those of the finger and arms. Tremor should be differentiated from muscle tension since relative degrees of central disorganization may be involved with the former. In the reactions of the circulatory system and of the visceral organs, smooth muscles are involved, and reference has been made, and will be made, to these body areas separately.

Ax carefully studied fear and anger states in 43 healthy subjects using multiple physiological measurement that included muscle potentials taken from the frontal head muscles, and he reported greater muscle-potential increases in anger but more numerous ones in fear (55). Newman found electrical muscle spikes from the temporal head muscles with the presentation of some emotionally loaded words but none with relaxation or with "neutral" words (952). Similarly, Lundervold reported action potentials from limb and trunk muscles with emotional excitement but not with relaxation (822).

MUSCLE CHANGE AND PERSONALITY TYPES

Many muscle studies compare different diagnostic types. Malmo and Shagass attempted to determine the relationship between the severity of anxiety and disturbances in the following functions, which involve various muscles by inferring greater anxiety in anxiety patients than in normal controls: finger movement, head movement, muscle potentials of the neck, and respiration (860, 862, 863, 866). Comparing these and other patient groups, under the stress of a thermal forehead stimulator, they found less control of head movement with anxiety subjects with a concomitant increase in neck-muscle potentials and found tension and increased potentials of neck muscles without head movement, especially for patients with chronic complaints of headache, head tightness, and other tensional symptoms referred to the head (860). In another study Malmo and Shagass and Davis observed that electromyograms taken from several body areas simultaneously showed "subclinical" muscle disturbances in body areas that were at other times the sites of symptoms (865). Such muscle disturbances were seen, independently of complaints, when the patients were discussing distressing life situations; thus there appeared to be a specific lowered threshold for disturbance in bodily areas associated with the symptoms of a given patient. Significant differences in motor activity between psychoneurotics and schizophrenics, as compared to normal controls, were also found with the Rapid Discrimination Tests (864).

Similarly, Holmes and Wolff found increased motor and electrical skeletal-muscle activity in the back to be associated with stressful life situations for patients with backache complaints as compared to patients without such symptoms (595). On the other hand, Wishner compared 11 psychoneurotic patients, having anxiety as their chief complaint, with 10 "normal" subjects, and he found the latter to have significantly higher muscle action potentials in the frontal muscles above the eyebrow but found no significant differences in the masseter muscle, measured on the right side of the jaw (1332).

Functional muscle contractions of the diaphragm have been seen to produce breathing difficulties and other symptoms (1326, 1345, 1365). Pertinent to this was Skagg's observation, in his classic electrical-shock experiment of 1930, that violent contraction of the diaphragm, along with sudden contractions of chest muscles, occur during the state of "startledness" (1153).

Altschule cited several types of deviant muscular activity reported in neurotic patients, including muscular weakness, variability of contractions, depressed flicker-fusion frequency in anxiety states, increased arm-muscle activity with occasional spasms or tremors in association with increased emotional stress, relatively more action potentials during exercise, and greater motor inco-ordination (38). Rheumatoid-arthritis patients showed changes indicating spasm with emotional upset; however, the myograms after hysterical contractures were reported to be normal except that they may have less powerful and less sustained action currents.

During frustration experiments, mixed diagnostic groups of children were compared with normal children (656) and with normal adults and children (1137). The diagnostic groups were found to show greater hand-tremor movements, even though gross movements did not differ significantly; however, schizophrenic children more nearly resembled the normal in these movements than the other patients.

In the measuring of flexor-muscle potentials for the forearm and neck of normal controls, psychotic patients, and various types of psychoneurotic patients under three stress conditions with the Hardy-Wolff thermal stimulator (861), with rapid visual discrimination, and with mirror drawing, Malmo et al. found the tension of chronic schizophrenic patients to be higher than that of control subjects and as high as that of the psychoneurotic subjects (866). With mirror drawing, in several cases, marked alternation in muscle activity of the arm and the neck was indicated. The usual finding of increased muscle tension in psychiatric patients compared to normal controls was reported. However, in preparing for this experiment, both the patient and control groups showed a rise in blood pressure and heart rate, whereas only the patient group manifested marked muscular tension. This was interpreted as indicating autonomic preparatory response in both groups, but greater somatic (skeletal muscle) preparatory response in the patient group. Another finding indicated no significant relationship between the degree of muscular tension in the forearm flexors and the degree of irregularity of finger movements, but considerable individual consistency in muscular tension for different stress situations was seen.

A case of torticollis, in which hostile competitiveness was seen as an important factor, was relieved with psychotherapy (1084).

After thoroughly reviewing the many studies related to muscle tension, Plutchik concluded that (998, p. 58):

Patterns of movement, posture, and facial expression are consistent aspects of personality and have been found in many instances to be more revealing indices of change in personality, than verbal reports.

Chronic tensions arise because adequate motor responses to conditions of conflict or frustration are impeded or blocked. Tensions reflect a continuous state of readiness of which an individual may often be unaware.

Rheumatic disorders, including rheumatoid arthritis, have been related to emotional stress by many investigators (532a). From a series of studies cited, Halliday concluded that emotional inhibition was the common personality pattern with rheumatoid arthritis. Short, Abrahams, and Sartwell associated this disease with a wide variety of stresses of which usually two or more were of long duration, and infection, operation or injury often immediately preceded the onset of the rheumatoid arthritis.

SKIN IN GENERAL

Most studies that relate psychological states to changes in the skin have employed measures of electrical galvanic skin resistance (GSR); however, many other skin changes have also been reported in this respect. Primarily, these other findings have come from clinical observations, though Pattie cited case reports of blisters being produced by hypnotic suggestion in 11 subjects, including 3 normals, 2 "normals" except for hysterical aphasia and neurotic skin gangrene respectively, and 6 hysterical patients (972). He "suspended judgment" on these reports primarily because he could not conceive of a physiological process that "could produce localized and circumscribed erythemas or blisters." Nevertheless, many others have accepted this phenomenon as valid in clinical reports (321). As will be described subsequently, the occurrence of urticaria, as well as other skin symptoms, has frequently been associated with changing psychological states.

ELECTRICAL AND GLANDULAR CHANGES IN THE SKIN

Much space in the literature has been devoted to measurements of electrical changes in the skin under different conditions. There are two primary methods of measuring galvanic skin resistance (GSR): the Féré method, which utilizes an external source of electrical current; and the Tarchanoff method, which measures electrical potentials in the skin.

The various ways that given GSR data may be handled (498, 512) must be considered in the evaluating of the results reported, as exemplified by the findings of Haggard and Jones that revealed significant differences between the following techniques and measures: resistance and conductance changes, log. of the conductance change, change in log. resistance, latent time, responding time, recovery after 5″, and recovery quotients (512). GSR changes appear to be based on sweat-gland activity due to the fact that moisture directly increases electrical conductivity (796). Electrical potentials may also be affected by the contraction of the smooth muscles of the sweat glands since the characteristics of form and time of their wave potentials are similar to those of other smooth-muscle potentials.

Because the sweat glands are like blood vessels and arterioles in being dilated and constricted by smooth muscles, the GSR is frequently taken as an indicator of generalized vasomotor functioning; however, the possibility that differential functioning may apply to given body systems and areas should always be considered. Concerning differential sweating, Shelley et al. wrote as follows (1133, p. 196):

Women normally sweat less than men and may be relatively insensitive to drug stimulation in this regard [489]. Area differences are marked [1166, 1296], sweating on the legs being usually less than elsewhere. Little or no sweating occurs on the tip of the nose, elbow, patella, or dorsal surface of the metacarpal joints [803].

Stimulation of sweating on the palms or soles may be achieved either by inducing pain or emotional changes, or by cholinergic drugs. Such techniques do not permit sustained high sweating rates such as are seen clinically.

Other methods in addition to the GSR for the determining of the secretion of sweat include direct visualization of droplets (free or under oil) and various colorimetric procedures (dibromfluorescein paper; iodine starch paper; starch iodine; cobaltous chloride; and Quinizarline) (824, 1061, 1133). Wenger and Gilchrist (1305) have found that the GSR is more reliable in the case of palmar sweating than the colorimetric method of Silverman and Powell (1147).

Lindsley cited several studies of sweat-gland physiology that indicate that sympathetic nerves supply the sweat glands, but the neurohumoral agent at the effector (as at almost all synaptic neurone junctions) is acetylcholine, which is usually secreted by parasympathetic innervation (796). It should be recalled, however, that some sympathetic fibers are of a cholinergic type, and cholinergic nerves appear to act by liberating acetylcholine from their endings (426). In addition, a localized sweat-gland reflex occurs in the terminal rami of the postganglionic sympathetic fibers and it is entirely divorced from the action of the central nervous system (251, 1133).

It is well known that changing psychological states are reflected by the GSR. GSR changes were seen in emotionally provocative situations with studies of 8 infants and of 61 children (650, 651, 652, 653). The GSR reactions were observed to occur when the child failed to react overtly to the stimuli, and the changes tended to return to normal when overt emotion was expressed, as, for example, in crying or agitation. The most effective stimuli were those producing startle or frustration reactions, which were thought to be associated with fear and anger. There have been numerous GSR studies on adult subjects, which Jones compared with the reactions of infants and found, among other things, that the initial resistance is lower in infants but that the general reactivity to emotionally toned stimuli is similar (650).

Darrow reported increased palmar secretion resulting from a variety of stimuli such as pinprick, loud noises, and a slap on the cheek (268). Darrow and Freeman observed that anticipation, apprehension, and ideation caused increased sweat secretion mainly on the palmar surface whereas muscular activity caused an increase mainly in the nonpalmar areas (275). Lund, in citing Katz's (679) experimental finding of increased tactual discrimination when the hands are moist, inferred a phylogenetic advantage with the palmar sweating that frequently results from emotional stimulation (821), a point also made by Darrow (270). Sweating palms have been reported to occur with "mental strain" (821) and "mental work" (422), and Ruckmick noted a correlation of the GSR with introspective accounts of "common emotions" (1070). To determine relative sweat secretion, McCleary used bags of hygroscopic crystals that were held in the palms by large groups of subjects during military maneuvers; he found greater sweat secretion by the group that was thought to be more anxious (824).

Bayley reported the differentiation of two types of fear, namely, startle and apprehension, by GSR measures (84); however, Hunt found no correlations for fear, grief, anger, and suffering with the magnitude or duration of galvanic deflections (612). On the other hand, Woohsler and Jones, in inferring fear and anger from GSR reactions to 40 stimuli by 35 subjects, obtained a .76 self-correlation of stimulus, .50 intercorrelation of similar stimuli, and a .22 correlation of dissimilar stimuli (1294). In a well-devised experiment including skin-conductance measures from the volar surface of two fingers on the hands of 43 subjects, Ax found a greater number of rises in skin conductance with fear reactions but a greater increase in skin conductance with the anger reactions (55).

Dysinger and Ruckmick measured the GSR while showing a motion picture to subjects of different ages, and noted that individuals differ widely in the extent of their reactions to the same stimuli (328). Conflict and tragedy were most effective in producing reactions in subjects sixteen years of age, as were also love and sex; the latter, however, were least effective in producing a response in subjects below twelve years of age. Male response to danger was greater than that of females, but amorous and aggressive pictures produced the same responses in both sexes. They noted that an "adult discount" for the nonreality of the pictures was indicated.

The common clinical observation of sweating over the face and hands at times of fear and apprehension was observed in a transient reaction of a patient undergoing renal studies (1159). Freeman took measures of palmar-skin resistance and of electromyographic activity in the abdominal and perineal muscles, using 20 male subjects for three sessions each after the ingestion of 1000 cc. of water (369). Measurements were taken during a control period, before and after micturition, and during a delay when micturition seemed imminent, at which time the subjects were given eye-hand co-ordination tests and were subjected to experimental interruptions. A general increment in autonomic-postural activity was seen as a result of the inhibiting of micturition, and the localized muscular measures tended to reflect the inhibition of micturition and its discharge. Interruptions of the tasks also generally resulted in increments in palmar resistance and in muscle action potentials. The level of task performance was adversely affected when reactivity was very great, and the subjects were seen to be nervous and distractible with the inhibition of micturition. Also, if the task was interrupted during this inhibition, there was less likelihood of spontaneous resumption than during other conditions.

A subsequent study with 23 subjects, including 10 of the former group, suggested that the speed of a subject's return to base-line PGR levels upon release from such stress may be an index of his emotional stability (370). In this study, tension was induced by inhibition of micturition while performing co-ordination tests, by attempting difficult visual discriminations with electric shock upon error, or by tests of endurance of electric shock. Concerning the relationship of GSR measurements to inner emotional lability, Poser's observations that such "reduced antonomic activity" frequently accompanied color-form (CF) and pure color (C) responses to the Rorschach test may be significant (1102).

Wolff et al. reported that sebum over the face increased with anger and fell with remorse (1363), and a similar relationship was seen in a subsequent study (833); however, since the sebum-spreading effect was equally great or small on a number of days without apparent deviation in mood, caution in interpreting these findings was advised. Nevertheless, facial-sebum studies on 30 patients with acne vulgaris, who were compared with 10 non-acne control subjects, especially in regard to reactions to stressful life situations, showed a characteristic emotional pattern that consisted of episodes of "anger" followed by periods of "remorse" (guilt and depression) (811). These episodes usually involved conflicts with an authority figure. The control level and marked twenty-four-hour fluctuations in facial-sebum output were the same for both groups, but acne patients uniquely showed lability in the prompt fluctuation of increased and decreased rate at times of emotional stress. Similarly, Lewis stated that clinically localized hyperhidrosis (or excessive sweating) had frequently been found to be psychosomatic (779). Under the stresses of painful cooling of the right hand and arm and of tightening of screws around and over the head, 5 of 7 healthy subjects showed marked sweating, predominantly about the head, hands and legs (36). One subject also exhibited an increased oiliness of the forehead, and three subjects showed pallor of the face, but there was no flushing or increase in skin temperature in any.

A tendency for increased sweating during stress, as reflected by lowered GSR findings, was seen with hypertension patients (657). In a group of predominantly neurotic children, the initial skin resistance was seen to be greater than for the normal group (656, 1137). With psychotic patients, the skin resistance has been reported to be normal or high (38). One study has proposed that the electrical-potential difference between the head region and extremity areas may serve as an index to changes in psychological states as well as to reflect a universal cyclic phenomenon (1024).

SKIN TEMPERATURE

Only limited studies of skin temperature with different psychological states have been made. Although skin temperatures, along with blood and general body temperatures, are regulated by many factors the main factor in skin-temperature variability is local vasoconstriction (798). These vasomotor studies have already been presented under the section on circulatory system. Mittlemann and Wolff made 203 observations on 19 males and 28 females and found a drop in the skin temperature of the fingers to occur with emotional stress in all but three instances involving two subjects, with the greatest drop being 3° C. below the environmental temperature (922). There was great individual variability, though the reactions of a given individual were quite consistent on repetition. Subjects experiencing sustained emotional stress showed a low finger temperature both outside and within the control periods, and the fall was greater during sustained periods of apprehension than during sustained periods of contentment.

With stress, skin-temperature reactions of patients with Raynaud's syndrome were the same as those of other subjects, but major falls in finger temperature were accompanied by pain, cyanosis, and pallor in the patients. Low environmental temperature in itself did not produce these symptoms (when the patients were adequately clad) unless there was emotional stress. Interruption of the sympathetic-nerve supply eliminated the symptoms.

A drop in finger temperature with stress was also seen in patients with gastritis, duodenitis, and peptic ulcer (923). Another group of investigators studied the finger temperature in 38 experiments with 27 "well-adjusted healthy" subjects during control periods and during discussions of emotionally charged material that produced "moderate emotional tension in most subjects" (220). Significant temperature changes were observed to occur during the interviews. These findings, however, did not correlate with other measures of renal plasma flow that were taken (220). Baker and Taylor also noted skin-temperature changes to accompany the presentation of emotionally loaded words (61). In Ax's study of multiple types of changes for 43 healthy subjects with fear and anger reactions, face and finger skin temperature were not found to be clearly differentiating (55).

SKIN CHANGES AND PERSONALITY TYPES IN GENERAL

Saul cited many reports linking clinical skin conditions with psychological changes (1083), and the importance of psychological states in the production or aggravation of certain skin conditions has been widely recognized (321, 356, 434a, 681, 694, 906a, 957a, 1006, 1170, 1182a, 1207, 1209, 1221, 1222, 1300). Skin lesions have also at times been reported to appear as the result of masochistic self-marring.

Lewis noted the following clinical skin conditions to involve psychogenic factors: trauma from a "nervous habit," such as biting or scratching that may lead to infections; feigned eruptions, or self-produced lesions; delusional parasitosis involving complaints of crawling sensation; atopic eczema (neurodermatitis); alopecia areata (the sudden development of bald areas); and local pruritus (itch), usually closely allied to atopic eczema (779). Obermayer also included dyshidrosis, rosacea, and lichen planus, and classified many other conditions according to psychogenic factors (957a). In some of these conditions, particularly atopic eczema, which occurs most frequently in women and especially about the time of menopause and frequently flares up or exacerbates with "emotional stress and strain," Lewis suggested a possible endocrine factor. He observed that any skin condition involves an incidental emotional impact, with the patient's relationships with other people possibly being affected.

In the studying of atopic dermatitis, Greenhill and Finesinger reported the finding of neurotic tendencies in which hostility, a sense of inadequacy, and depressive features were prominent (495, 1222).

Dunbar cited evidence that related atopic eczema to repressed hostility and related pruritus vulvae and pruritus ani to emotional etiology and sexual wishes (321). In connection with emotional factors she also mentioned psoriasis, lichen planus, dyshidrosis (pompholyx), exudative discoid and lichenoid dermatitis, and verrucae (warts); warts responded to treatment with suggestion by Vollmer (1273) and others. In pruritis ani, personality factors, particularly involving some symbolic significance of this condition, appeared to Macalpine to be etiologically important (850).

Schur described cases of dermatosis that reflected somatic discharge phenomena associated with ego regression; itching was related at various times to the expression of aggression, sexual impulses, a masturbatory function, and masochism, and a stratification of different meanings was a usual finding (1110b). Libidinous affect-equivalent was noted particularly in dermatoses such as Sulzberger-Garbe's syndrome, neurodermatitis, pruritus vulvae and ani, and atopic eczema. No specificity of personality, of conflict, or of defense against one phase of sexuality or aggression was found, but certain common characteristics of these patients were observed: (1) a great variety of neurotic symptoms and character traits; (2) a prevalence of narcissistic and pregenital elements, with intensive conflicts around exhibitionism; (3) widespread impairment of ego functions; (4) tenuous object relationships characterized by extreme ambivalence; and (5) early traumatization. Etiologically, both innate and early environmental factors were significant, but in total alopecia and in chronic, exudative discoid and lichenoid dermatitis, genetic factors were not discernible.

Rosenthal, in reviewing many studies, emphasized the probable functional etiology of most infantile eczema, and presented evidence that nervous reactivity, by way of retrograde neural impulses over pain fibers, can cause destruction to adjacent epidermal cells, initiating vesicle formation, and thereby possibly aggravating or producing eczema (1059). He suggested further that the epidermal necrosis within the area of distribution of a given irritating nerve fiber may excite other nerve fibers overlapping into that area, thereby spreading the pathological condition to successive adjacent areas.

URTICARIA

Functional factors in urticaria have been particularly emphasized. Allergens have been reported to be the causative agents in only 10 per cent of chronic urticarias (1220). Wittkower's clinical study of 35 urticaria patients revealed an underlying excessive need for affection from which two types of personality patterns stemmed. One type showed "an ingratiating pleading, or an overaccommodating, pleasing attitude toward their environment" with fearful reactions to criticism or disapproval (1339). The other type showed a demanding attitude with embittered and vindictive reactions to their frequent disappointments. Events entailing anticipated or actual withdrawal of love frequently preceded the onset or relapse of urticaria. These attacks appeared to manifest repressed aggressiveness, masochism, repressed exhibitionism, and infantile skin erotism. Other experimenters have associated urticaria, on the one hand, "with masochism, prolonged unsatisfied sexual excitement, and rejection of responsibility and effort" and, on the other hand, with repressed frustrated sexual desires combined with longings for love and dependency (1083). In one case of the latter type, urticaria was seen to be an alternative to weeping; the urticaria disappeared with the onset of weeping (1220).

Grant, Pearson, and Comeau related urticaria attacks to emotional factors and found these attacks also to occur when acetylcholine was released in the skin by stimulation of cholinergic nerve fibers and when Mecholyl was administered (483). In confirming these findings, Hopkins, Kesten, and Hazel proposed the name "cholinergic urticaria" for this type of reaction (597). Similarly, in contrast to a series of asthma cases tested, Funkenstein found urticaria to be precipitated in one patient by Mecholyl but only during states of schizophrenic psychosis (409); it was thought that this reaction might possibly be an aspect of the frequent finding of relatively greater parasympathetic innervation with this psychosis.

Lewis compared 30 patients with chronic urticaria with control subjects.

He used life-history material, symptom-inducing interviews, and chemical vasodilating agents, which all demonstrated that the symptoms were associated with conflictual states and that cutaneous vascular changes were a factor in the symptom (781). Similarly, Graham studied 30 unselected cases of chronic urticaria and found the attacks to correlate highly with states of resentment in which the patient felt unjustly treated and lacking in recourse (479, 480). Cutaneous-vessel studies indicated that the urticaria symptom involved extreme dilatation of both arterioles and minute vessels in the skin, and the skin showed changes the same as those induced by actual skin trauma. One of the measures used in this study involved skin-temperature reactivity during changing psychological states.

A study by Saltzman also related the onset of urticaria to emotional life situations, but evaluation by psychological instruments revealed little of significance concerning these patients (1078). On the other hand, Moldawsky reported that 112 adults with various types of dermatitis, particularly those with atopic eczema and psoriasis, showed a "greater-than-average degree of psychological disturbance" on the Minnesota Multiphasic Personality Inventory (925).

CHAPTER 13

Clinical and Physiological Studies in

Terms of Bodily Location

THE FACIAL AREA (Area No. 2)

Reference has just been made to this area, among others, in regard to psychological states that involve sweating and other vasomotor and muscle changes, and it seems apparent that no simple formulation of the factors involved in such changes can be made at this time. Changing psychological states have also been related to physiological changes in the eyes, nose, and mouth areas. Studies attempting to relate facial expression to various psychological states have as yet made only limited contributions (1369, 1099).

Lindsley has pointed out that little is known concerning the significance of eye movements; however, recorded data suggest that their movement is related to excitement, embarrassment, and other emotional reactions (798, 799). Godtfredsen has cited some evidence of psychogenic effects on eye functioning (462). Similarly, in connection with Schoenberg's report that emotional disturbances maintain and increase ocular hypertension and act to pecipitate glaucoma, Dunbar noted that central innervation probably affects the level of intraocular pressure (321, 1106, 1107).

Holmes, Treuting, and Wolff reviewed many studies that relate psychological states to patterns of nasal functioning that involve hyperemia, hypersecretion, swelling, and obstruction to breathing (593, 594). Primarily, these changes in nasal functioning were observed to be related to "conflict" and "anxiety" (592, 593), but in the cases cited it is apparent that anger played an important role in the onset of the "hay-fever" symptoms that were investigated (594). From an extensive study of 20 subjects with histories of seasonal "hay fever" and of positive skin or eye tests for ragweed sensitivity and of 11 subjects with no history of hay fever and with negative skin or eye tests to ragweed extract, these experimenters drew the following conclusions: (1) the onset and intensity of hay-fever symptoms and of mucous-membrane reactions relate directly to the magnitude of nasal hyperfunctioning on exposure to pollen; (2) life situations engendering conflict and anxiety result in nasal hyperfunction and exacerbation of symptoms and sensitivity; (3) parasympathetic neural impulses appear to be responsible for nasal hyperfunction of this type (594). Altschule also mentioned that many clinicians have observed emotion to affect nasal functioning (38).

Emotional reactions have long been associated with changes in the moisture of the mouth and throat, and early experiments by Pavlov demonstrated the relationship of salivary-gland secretion to psychological states (974). Lindsley noted the "general observation that emotional excitement, anticipation, fear, and anger often seem to produce a dryness of the mouth," and explained this on the basis that sympathetic stimulation of the salivary glands produces a thick mucouslike secretion, as contrasted with a thin, watery secretion produced by parasympathetic stimulation (796). Clinically, hypersalivation has been associated with personality characteristics involving various oral needs, desires, or fantasies (1226). As has been mentioned, (p. 188) Starr reported that with emotional excitement, saliva normally increases in alkalinity, and he related this to several factors (1185). It has been reported that the teeth may be adversely affected by the chemical changes in salivary secretion, as well as by the mechanical action of jaw movements, which are associated with emotional states (321).

Psychosomatic and neurotic factors in dental conditions and other oral symptoms are gradually being delineated (868a, 868b, 935b).

UPPER-CENTRAL CHEST AREA (Area No. 4) AND THROAT AREA (Area No. 3)

Concerning the throat area (Area No. 3), most of the relevant data available are related to either the thyroid glands, the mouth, or the throat. The data relating to neck muscles and bone structure, however, will be presented separately later in the section on Area No. 20. A case of transient sore throat, diagnosed as "allergic" swelling but associated with conflictual anger in regard to the patient's psychoanalyst, has been reported (694).

Two major structures underlie Area No. 4, namely, the trachea and the esophagus, and although the esophagus extends far beyond this area, most of the material concerning it will be presented here or in Part IV that deals with internal sensations. Material relating to the trachea involves also the bronchi and lungs and therefore will be presented in connection with them under the section on the upper-lateral chest area (Area No. 7).

From observations of the esophagus in various clinical life situations of four persons, Faulkner, Rodenbaugh, and O'Neill drew the conclusion that esophageal spasm and dysfunction can be produced by emotions and that the causal relationship can be observed directly by means of esophagoscopic and roentgenologic examination (348). Several workers have observed the occurrence of esophageal spasm, particularly toward the lower part (or the cardiac end), in association with emotional reactions and with life conflicts (1345). Faulkner reported one case of spasm of the entire length of the esophagus occurring subsequent to the patient's being taken off the pension roll (347). When the patient was asked how he would feel if he were on the pension roll again, the spasm disappeared and the lumen opened, and a similar functional relationship was observed in the bronchus. In this connection, Wolff reported that the mucous membranes in diverse parts of the body showed striking resemblances in function even though at the same time the reactions differ in each area (1358).

Kling has reported a spastic esophagus, which was called "a lump in the throat," in fear states (710). Similarly, Wolf and Almy have made extensive studies of esophageal spasm occurring with stress (1347), but such findings by these and other experimenters will be considered in more detail under Part IV that deals with internal sensations. Altschule (38) cited studies describing cessation of esophageal motility with emotion (1150). He cited the finding of normal esophageal functioning with relaxed neurotic subjects (723, 724), in contrast to the finding of spasm by Faulkner, which was described above.

CENTRAL CHEST AREA

GENERAL CARDIAC MEASUREMENTS

An important role has been ascribed to psychological states in the functioning of the heart since antiquity. In modern times, many measures have been employed to study such relationships, including heart beat, pulse rate, cardiac output, heart size, and electrocardiograph (EKG) patterns, as well as the more general circulatory measures that have been presented in Chapter 12.

Many early studies reported increased cardiac output and other cardiac changes during startle, tension, apprehension, and other emotional conditions (235, 245, 323, 503, 560, 791, 1187, 1193, 1309, 1320, 1342). An early classic experiment by Blatz revealed pulse rate to rise suddenly with startle reactions, then to fall quickly below normal and again accelerate, and a similar, less marked reaction was seen with the anticipation of startle

(129). Also, at times in attempts at deception, cardiac irregularities and inhibitions have been observed (9, 743, 755). Changes in the heart size, involving both enlargement and diminution of the heart shadow, have been reported with emotional reactions (256, 1335). Stead et al., on the other hand, found normal cardiac-output values with right-artery catheterization during presumed anxiety and during tilting (1193).

In 1930, Starr and Collins studied the effects of several variables on the cardiac output of 10 normal males (1188), estimating cadiac output from the ethyl iodide content of mixed venous blood following inhalation of ethyl iodide (1189, 1190). They reported that the results with this method were in agreement with those of other methods, showing cardiac output to increase with food and excitement, to decrease with warmth following chill, and to change in both directions with cold (1188). The "excitement" in this study concerned apprehension over vein punctures, which had produced fainting with some subjects; during "excitement" a markedly increased pulse rate was also noted.

Hickam, Corgill, and Golden recorded cardiac output on the Nickerson ballistocardiograph and took the pulse rate of 23 unselected healthy medical students, 20 to 25 years of age, who expressed varying degrees of anxiety over impending oral examinations (560). These investigations also recorded the cardiac output of hospital and clinic patients by cardiac catheterization with direct brachial-artery intracardiac and pulmonary-artery pressure measurements, in which the patients were made somewhat anxious. Under pre-examination conditions, as compared to postexamination states of relief and satisfaction, the medical students showed an elevation of 10 per cent in mean arterial pressure, of 27 per cent in heart rate, of 16 per cent in stroke volume, and of 18 per cent in cardiac index, and showed a fall of 23 per cent in peripheral resistance, with great variations in the amount of change for different individuals, particularly in regard to the cardiac index. Though complex variables entered into the studies involving the patients, the following conclusions were drawn (560, p. 297):

> In the majority of persons, anxiety has an effect on circulation similar to that produced by small doses of epinephrine. The cardiac output, heart rate, and oxygen consumption are increased. There is a moderate elevation of blood pressure, but the peripheral resistance is decreased. The cardiac output is abnormally high in proportion to the rate of oxygen consumption.

A study by Jost, et al., involving 47 medical students, nurses, and technicians from twenty-one to thirty-five years of age, employed the Keeler polygraph and made several simultaneous physiological measurements under the following conditions: control period; auditory followed by visual stimulation; questions with and without emotional significance; success in the repeating of series of digits; failure in this task; and a final control period (657). No significant changes in heart rate were seen during the control period or during sensory stimulation, but during the questioning, success, and failure periods, the increase in heart rate was significant at the .01 statistical level. The heart rate during success and failure periods was significantly higher than during the questioning period.

When 43 healthy subjects, studied by Ax, reacted with anger toward an obnoxious experimenter, there were found significantly greater "heart-rate falls" than when the subjects were apprehensive (fearful) of incurring physical harm from a supposedly faulty electrical connection (55). No significant differences were found in the heart rate, although it was observed to be faster with fear, and also a nonsignificant rise in stroke-volume index with the apprehensive reaction was seen. A study of 69 students (see p. 166) showed decreased cardiac activity with the directing of "anger out" in contrast to moderate to marked increases with the directing of "anger in" (411a). Hypertension patients have evidenced increased stroke volume and heart rate in overt anxiety in contrast to normal values in "rage and resentment" and in "minimal overt anxiety" (935a).

A subject who experienced strong anger with "no hope for the resolution of his dilemma" was reported by Wolf and Wolff to have a slight pressor response with a fall in pulse rate and a fall in stroke volume (1342). (This study will be presented in Chapter IV, dealing with internal sensations.) Dunbar noted Schultz's report (1109) that "well-trained" individuals were able voluntarily to induce far-reaching changes in the heart rate, and von Wyss (1374) reported that thinking about sad situations slowed the heart rate (321). Also cited were Grollman's studies showing increased cardiac output with "psychic stimulation" (504, 505).

A study of 12 psychotherapeutic sessions employing Bales's interaction analysis associated higher "tension" scores with higher heart rate and associated "tension-release" scores with lower heart rate; the patient appeared to express "tension" more through heart rate than through skin temperature whereas "antagonism" scores showed the reverse (303a). With "tension," the therapist's reactions tended to parallel those of the patient, but opposite tendencies were observed with "antagonism."

Although most studies have involved unpleasant reactions, cardiac acceleration during pleasurable states has also been demonstrated. Boas and Goldschmidt recorded sharp peaks of 143 to 146 heart beats per minute during sexual orgasm, and, similarly, an increase of pulse rate from 64 to 121 beats per minute resulted from listening to a song with pleasurable associations (134). Gladness was reported by Kling to arouse faster and stronger heart beats, presumably reflecting sympathetic predominance, as contrasted to weaker and interrupted heart beats, with an irregular pulse during fright, presumably reflecting vagotonia (710).

GENERAL ELECTROCARDIOGRAPHIC STUDIES

Several studies show electrocardiographic (EKG) changes with different psychological states. Increased bioelectrical output of the heart of healthy subjects has been reported with "mental work," involving the solution of arithmetical problems (364), which is similar to the finding of increased heart rate with the mental work of color naming (422). Mainzer and Krause took EKG tracings from patients, presumed to be fearful because they were on the operating table, immediately before administration of general anesthesia, and they obtained abnormal findings in approximately two fifths of 53 cases, as compared to the EKG tracings taken on the day before (858). Similar EKG changes occurred frequently in other patients with initially normal cardiograms, and the changes that were observed in persons who had cardiac disorders were an accentuation of the pathological character of the cardiogram already existing. Although in a number of patients the abnormal changes disappeared under anesthesia or during the following day, in some cases the changes still persisted twenty-four hours after the operation. These experimenters described three types of EKG patterns for which the following explanations were postulated (858, p. 230):

> In view of the analogies existing between "fear-electrocardiograms" and other types of tracings, it is assumed that the curves of type (a) are brought about by a reduced coronary flow, mainly to be attributed to vagal stimulation; that sympathetic stimulation is responsible for the development of the curves of type (b) ; and that type (c) [a combination of "a" and "b"] is the result of the interaction of both factors. . . . Thus myocardial damage could be induced by the vasomotor fear-reaction, as apparent in cases of type (a), and could be attributed to coronary constriction of vagal origin.

In employing the EKG to study constitutional characteristics of different patient groups, Draper, Bruenn, and Dupertuis described several EKG characteristics and variables, and reported a high degree of constancy in individual electrocardiographic patterns for both unchanging pathological states (331) and the normal heart (307). Significant differences between the EKG curve patterns for ulcer and gall-bladder patients appeared to exist within certain age groups, and both of these patterns differed from the EKG patterns of individuals from a general hospital population who showed normal records (307). These abnormal EKG findings were not considered to be secondary to the symptoms studied, and they included steeper, more abrupt curves from the ulcer patients in contrast to smoother and more rolling curves in the gall-bladder patients, which was emphasized by the descending limb of the T waves.

HYPERDYNAMIC AND HYPODYNAMIC SYNDROMES

Wolf reported that some people show "hyperdynamic reactions to stress" that are evidenced by increased blood pressure and stroke volume and decreased ventilatory efficiency during frustration, tension, and anger as well as during domestic difficulties (1342, 1357, 1359). Both hyperdynamic and hypodynamic cardiac reactions were seen in a study by Stevenson, Duncan, and Wolff that compared the reactions during exercise of 10 patients who had structural heart disease to three groups of subjects that included 18 relaxed subjects, 11 tense subjects, and 13 subjects under psychiatric treatment for anxiety and associated palpitation, dyspnea, and exercise intolerance who all did not have structural heart disease (1203). The slightly emotionally disturbed patients showed greater cardiac output than did the relaxed subjects, primarily due to increased stroke volume, both before and after exercise, and the subjects with overt anxiety showed even greater cardiac output throughout, primarily due to greater heart rate. Changes in emotional state were accompanied by corresponding changes in exercise tolerance, and a close correlation between impaired exercise tolerance and such symptoms as dyspnea, palpitation, and weakness on exertion were seen. These relationships were also seen in the patients with structural heart disease, such symptoms being similar to cardiac failure. These findings were supported in a six-month-to-two-year study of 70 patients having cardiovascular complaints such as palpitation, dyspnea, and weakness (1200). Stevenson and Duncan reported that life stresses, evoking anxiety and resentment, were usually met by cardiovascular mobilization, which included increases in heart rate, blood pressure, and cardiac output, and again, in the few instances that involved dejection and despair, a hypodynamic response with decreases in heart rate, cardiac output, and, usually also, blood pressure was seen (1200). Again there was impaired exercise tolerance during periods of anxiety and resentment, along with an exaggerated cardiovascular response. Disturbances in cardiac rhythm, including extrasystoles, paroxysmal tachycardia, and paroxysmal auricular fibrillation, occurred with stress-invoked anxiety, resentment, and depression. Also, rapid alterations in the electrocardiogram, with changes in the amplitude and direction of the T waves, were observed for these states.

In the comparison of 20 hypertensive patients with 20 normal subjects, a relatively hyperdynamic response of a slightly different type, involving more marked vasoconstriction, has already been described for the hypertensive patients, as has a hypodynamic response in the depressive circumstances (1201).

Another study by Duncan, Stevenson, and Wolff that employed mixed types of subjects and included groups of 16 with hypertension or degrees of structural heart disease, 11 with cardiac complaints but without heart disease, and 8 healthy hospital workers, and used measures of blood pressure, heart rate, and cardiac output, revealed only a small degree of variation in cardiac index and exercise tolerance during comparable emotional states (323). It was observed that with every subject significant changes in the exercise tolerance were related to changes in the subject's emotional state. Duncan, Stevenson, and Wolff reported that attitudes or preparedness and feelings of anxiety or resentment were associated with cardiac hyperactivity; in contrast, attitudes of despair and discouragement were associated with cardiac hypoactivity, with the heart rate and cardiac index then being below the usual values. Similarly, at times of anxiety and resentment, exercise resulted in greater and more prolonged increases in heart rate and cardiac index than normally; this exercise intolerance was also frequently manifested by common cardiac complaints. In the reviewing of a series of these studies by the Cornell University group, Wolff emphasized the homeostatic, adaptive, and protective aspects of such cardiac functioning (1359).

OTHER ABNORMAL HEART SYMPTOMS

Many other relevant findings are presented in studies that concern abnormal heart symptoms and functioning. Master and Eichert noted earlier reviews (885, 887) concerning functional paroxysmal auricular fibrillation and described 5 cases that appeared to have a "psychogenic or nervous" basis and were considered to be generally disabling for military service (886).

Patients with cardiac complaints have been conveniently classified by Burchell into four large overlapping groups in which: (1) all organ systems are functionally disturbed, the cardiac being a small part of more extensive derangement; (2) the circulatory system is chiefly disturbed with numerous manifestations; (3) an isolated symptom is related to the heart, such as heart consciousness; and (4) no cardiac symptoms are present but a phobic fearfulness of them exists (173). He cited two researches in addition to his own wherein follow-up studies were made on patients receiving different treatments for functional heart complaints. It was assumed that the 601 soldiers concerned were usually told simply that they had no heart disease; a five-year follow-up revealed that 15 per cent had recovered, 18 per cent had improved, 56 per cent were unchanged, and 3 per cent were worse (482). With psychoanalytic treatment averaging sixty hours and a follow-up of one year, in a group of 7, 6 patients were reported recovered and 1 unchanged (143). Burchell's series (which was incidental to another study) included 50 cases treated with reassurance or "environment attention," and follow-up periods ranged from three to six years; 24 per cent recovered, 30 per cent improved, 34 per cent were unchanged, and 12 per cent were classified "worse." He thought that it was gratifying to see that simple clinical methods relieved large numbers of patients, and he noted that some of the patients had participated during the entire war on active fronts without incapacity.

Schneck cited many studies of functional extrasystoles, some of which could be induced or treated hypnotically. In the hypnoanalysis of a patient, he found functional extrasystoles to relate to "feelings of tension" (1101).

After noting several other studies relating paroxysmal cardiac arrhythmias to emotional disturbances, Duncan, Stevenson, and Ripley reported a detailed study of 26 unselected cases that included paroxysmal auricular tachycardia, auriculoventricular nodal tachycardia, or auricular fibrillation; some patients had arrhythmias at different times and 50 per cent evidenced structural heart disease (322). Cardiac symptoms and findings were correlated with events in the life situations of the patients and with their attitude, general behavior, and emotional responses. These patients were generally described as "serious, worrisome, conscientious people who were preoccupied with their responsibilities." Covert hostility with superficially pleasant and agreeable attitudes was considered an outstanding feature in two thirds of the cases. Long-standing and pronounced anxiety in 11 cases, along with frequent characteristic somatic manifestations in many cases, was described, and "frequently the patient's anxiety had become focused on his heart with a deep conviction of serious heart disease." The following circumstances were seen to be important in the precipitating of arrhythmias: (1) for 10 patients, settings involving fear, anxiety, or apprehension; (2) for 11 patients, settings involving hostility and resentment that were usually incompletely expressed; and (3) for the majority of arrhythmias, settings involving sustained and mounting tension, although occasionally the arrhythmias occurred during a "let-down" period that followed.

Subsequently, Duncan, Stevenson, and Ripley made an electrocardiographic study of 35 clinic patients, of whom 18 were men and 17 were women and of whom half were over forty-five years of age; in 13 patients only a ballistocardiograph was employed for the measurement of heart rates (1202). The patients included 10 with arteriosclerotic heart disease, 10 with neurocirculatory asthenia, and 6 with bronchial asthma and with no cardiovascular complaints or disease; the rest of the patients had complaints referable to the cardiovascular system. Primarily, heart measures were taken during interviews in which the physician at times directed the topics into areas that were known to be emotionally significant to the patient. The principal state produced by this procedure was thought to be anxiety, but resentment was common and also depressive feelings were apparently involved on occasions. The mean heart rate of patients with arteriosclerotic heart disease was significantly lower at the .05 per cent level of probability than that of patients with neurocirculatory asthenia during both relaxation and anxiety; however, the neurocirculatory-asthenia group did not differ significantly from the noncardiac asthma group in this respect. The fact that the heart changes were related primarily to emotional stress rather than to heart disease was exemplified by the observation that 5 of 6 noncardiac asthma patients showed marked electrocardiographic changes whereas the sixth showed little emotional change during the interview; in the 18 patients whose tracings showed the most pronounced changes, 8 had no evidence of structural heart disease. Although the mechanisms of the observed EKG changes could not be stated with certainty, some changes in the amplitude of T waves and in the ST segments were thought to be related to increases in heart rate. There were indications, however, that the diversity of changes was not due solely to such increases, because, for example, it was noted that epinephrine will lower T waves (534) and may produce extrasystoles (979), and it was suggested that sympathetic stimulation was responsible for the T-wave changes observed during emotional disturbances. The tracings taken during anxiety or resentment were of a type commonly attributed to coronary insufficiency when observed following exercise. It appeared to these investigators that during the discussion of stressful topics, the patients reacted with a symbolic, exaggerated, and disproportionate mobilization of their circulation. The pathological implication of such a reaction was suggested by a finding of significant correlation between tachycardia and subsequent development of structural heart disease (774).

Jelliffe noted that several stimuli may precipitate cardiac arrhythmic attacks, and he expressed the belief that unconscious hostility is the most important factor involved (91, p. 311). He postulated a possible adrenal mechanism for this, stating that the neural stimulation might come from different levels. Arrhythmias, with increased heart rate and shortened P-R interval, have been seen to arise from stimulation of the sympathetic pathways to the heart or from reflex stimulation of sensory nerves; whereas section of the sympathetic pathways to the heart abolishes extrasystolic arrhythmias that arise from chloroform anesthesia, and reduces heart rate and lengthen the P-R interval (91, p. 294).

Nevertheless, both sympathetic and parasympathetic innervation appeared to Katz et al. to be involved in cardiac irregularities (680). After citing several studies, as well as noting the constant medullary regulation of cardiac activity and the evidence of differential effects of anterior and posterior hypothalamic stimulation on the heart, they summarized as follows (680, p. 268):

> Psychic impulses may, by upsetting the tonic balance in the cardioregulatory centers, cause: (1) depression or stimulation of the primary pacemaker of the heart, producing sinus tachycardia, sinus bradycardia, and sinus standstill; (2) increased irritability of subsidiary pacemakers, giving rise to paroxysmal tachycardia of supraventricular or ventricular origin or to paroxysmal auricular fibrillation and flutter, and even possibly to ventricular fibrillation with sudden death; and (3) heart block, i.e., S-A or A-V block, and more rarely, intraventricular block.

An experimentally induced functional-tachycardia conditioned reflex has been produced in dogs, and it was accompanied by many other symptoms of increased autonomic activity such as those seen in humans (414).

OTHER FINDINGS RELATING TO PERSONALITY TYPES

In the consideration of neurocirculatory asthenia, reference has already been made (under the section concerning general cardiovascular functioning, p. 170) to its vague functional nature and to Friedman's classification of functional cardiovascular disease (FCVD), which includes this diagnosis, as well as the earlier ones of "irritable heart," "disordered action of the heart," "soldier's heart," "the effort syndrome," and "autonomic imbalance."

In a study of 50 patients diagnosed as neurocirculatory asthenia, the hearts were found to be normal in size, in structure, and in function both at rest and during effort *when* the patients were free of emotional disturbance (392). Friedman noted, however, that earlier studies had reported heart abnormalities in some patients who had neurocirculatory asthenia and also that the negative electrocardiographic findings of his own study conflict with the reports of Master (884) and Merritt (895) of QRS-complex or T-wave abnormalities. He added, however, that 11 (22 per cent) of the patients exhibited some form of transient arrhythmia during their stay at the hospital.

Subsequently, in his classic review concerning this syndrome, Friedman disclosed that over 75 per cent of these patients were subject to episodic neurogenic cardiac discharges, which were related to the symptom of giddiness that had been mentioned by 91 per cent of an experimental FCVD group (393). Also, 14 per cent of this group experienced severe attacks. The giddiness symptom apparently resulted from cerebral anemia due to the retardation of forward blood flow following "a profound and generalized autonomic discharge effecting arterial and arteriolar constriction" (393, p. 56).

Friedman credited Wood (1365) with first clearly delineating the emotional basis of this syndrome, although a series of reports suggests that this began during the latter part of the nineteenth century (264, 482, 654, 844, 1168, 1338). It has already been noted that over 30 per cent of FCVD patients manifest low-grade fever episodically, which Friedman associated with changes in sympathetic innervation that can be induced centrally (393). He was able experimentally to provoke this symptom in a majority of the patients suffering from it, and therefore considered it to be a "neurogenic manifestation" of the FCVD syndrome itself. In addition to the characteristic symptoms of mental and physical fatigue, Friedman listed as the primary cardiovascular symptoms of this condition: precordial pain, palpitation, tachycardia, and vasomotor changes in the face and extremities; however, dyspnea and tachypnea also occur. Some of these symptoms are produced or aggravated by the tendency of these patients to employ minimally their diaphragmatic muscles in breathing, resulting in fatigue of the intercostal and accessory muscles. Several other frequent symptoms were listed, but, as has just been mentioned, the primary difficulty appeared to stem from emotional and personality features that included: a tendency to mental and physical immobility; a diminution in emotional range; difficulty in concentration and perseverance; disinterestedness and unawareness in certain environmental conditions; partial loss in memory function; and "strange reluctance to consider themselves as psychiatric casualties" (393, p. 112).

Altschule stated that QRS and T waves are usually normal with neuro-circulatory asthenia, as with neuroses, although some authors have described inversion of the T wave in Lead 2 or in other leads (38). Concerning studies with neurotic subjects he added (38, p. 20):

> Arrhythmias are more common among neurotic patients than in normal persons [392, 394, 519, 1318]. The arrhythmias include auricular or ventricular premature beats, shifting pacemaker, sinus arrhythmia, and prolonged P-R interval; auricular fibrillation may occur [1318]. For the most part the abnormal rhythms are those considered to be owing to over-activity of the vagus nerve. Short P-R intervals may occur [820].

The arrhythmias associated with emotion were noted to be usually produced by hyperactivity of the vagus nerve and to involve the S-A node, the auricles, and the A-V node.

A comparison between 11 neurotic patients who manifested anxiety and 10 healthy subjects under a variety of stimulus conditions revealed a higher heart rate for the former (1332).

A study by Sherman and Jost of normal children and a mixed group of emotionally disturbed children found that the heart-rate changes were not uniformly different in the two groups, although there was generally a greater rise for the emotionally disturbed group in the seven situations employed, including the situation of frustration (1137). Similarly, Malmo et al., in comparing 75 mixed psychiatric patients and 21 normal controls, found for both groups marked rises in blood pressure and heart rate during preparation for stress and test procedures, though the rises were approximately equal in the two groups (866).

Word association and interview techniques were employed during two hundred and eighty hours of recorded heart beats by Whitehorn, Kaufman, and Thomas in 48 subjects, 29 of whom were psychotic (1320). Brief cardiac accelerations were seen to occur at moments of fleeting emotion. Profound emotional disturbances were reported to produce marked cardiac acceleration, "which may persist, may be slowed gradually or may be terminated by abrupt, excessive decelerations, depending on the subjects' mode of action" (1320, p. 731). These changes were attributed to changing vagus innervation. Altschule has summarized the cardiac studies for functional psychoses with findings of variability for given patients and with the findings of usual pulse-rate increases for lying but not for hallucinations (38).

UPPER-LATERAL CHEST AREAS *(Areas No. 7a and 7b)*

RESPIRATORY REACTIONS IN GENERAL

Many authors have referred to the complexity of voluntary and involuntary physiological factors involved in respiration measurements (796, 953), but notwithstanding this complexity, significant respiration changes with changing psychological states have long been reported. As early as 1906, Shepard reviewed findings that related feelings to respiratory and other physiological changes in connection with his own experimental data of this type (1134). A few years later, Feleky attempted experimentally to differentiate various "emotional" reactions by measurements of inspiration-expiration ratios (352).

Blatz, during his classic "falling-chair" experiment, recorded a gasp (an "inspiratory stimulus") and a momentary check of breathing with the unexpected tilting (129). Respiratory changes observed by Skaggs in a "startle" experiment involving electric shocks were first a sharp inspiratory movement, stemming from sudden contraction of the diaphragmatic and chest muscles, and then increased rate and amplitude of breathing and sharp, irregular breathing (1153). "Excited expectancy" of the electric shocks also produced similar but less marked changes of these latter types (1154).

From another early experiment employing three subjects, Landis reported the following respiratory changes from "pronounced emotional upset" subsequent to a forty-six-hour fast and thirty-six hours without sleep and with strong electrical stimulation: an augmented respiratory rate, deep gasping, and thoracic respiration followed by an increasing tendency toward rapid, shallow breathing (745). Caster found an increased amplitude of breathing proportional to the intensity of the stimulus when he employed a pinprick, electric shock, and a pistol shot (214). Cason and Cason measured the amplitude of breathing and the gross bodily movements of subjects while showing them a set of emotionally toned pictures (213). The subjects selected the emotion that they felt from a list and rated it according to intensity. The amount of gross bodily movement and the respiration amplitude correlated positively; the strength of the feelings that were rated correlated with the duration of movement and breathing, which lasted longer with unpleasant feelings than with pleasant ones.

By the measuring of circulatory and respiratory changes during guilt feelings and deception, Larson obtained a high percentage in the predicting of deception when a decrease in the ratio of inspiration over expiration (I/E) following the subjects' responses was taken as an indicator (754, 755). These findings were similar to those of Benussi (104) and Burtt (183). Larson added, however, that although the presence of bodily changes under these conditions indicates some emotional excitement, they tell nothing of the cause.

These older studies and others were summarized briefly by Altschule as follows: (1) startle usually causes a cessation of respiration followed by an increased rate above normal with frequent irregularity in rhythm and depth; (2) stress gives rise unpredictably to either increases or decreases in respiratory rate, has variable effects on tidal air volume, and frequently results in more shallow breathing; and (3) lies will cause increased respiratory rate in normal persons (38).

Ax's multiple study of 43 healthy subjects showed a significantly greater increase in respiration rate during a state of fear than during states of anger, in measures that were taken over seven-minute periods (55). In regard to respiration, Burrow reported decreased frequency, increased amplitude of movements, and, with certain subjects, a decreased inspiration-expiration ratio in a relative tension-free state, which he called "cotension" (177). Browner's respiration measures on 18 male subjects during mirror-tracing "conflicts" revealed deviations from basal respiratory measures under "conflict"; however, basal circulatory and respiratory scores were not found to be related (155). Circulatory indices were thought to be more "emotive" and respiratory indices more "orientive" in significance. Concerning respiration, the amplitude and the I-fraction seemed to imply different characteristics, the latter appearing to be an indicator of "frustrationality and emotionality." During painful stress, subjects were observed by Almy and Tulin to breathe more slowly and more deeply, and their respirations developed the quality of sighing (36). Jost et al. found a slight decrease in respiratory frequencies with sensory stimulation, and a gradual increase in frequency with interview questions and with success and failure on the memory tasks that followed (657). Increased respiration has been reported with sexual orgasm (740), with breathing becoming deeper and faster in the early stages of sexual arousal and becoming interrupted with prolonged gasps and expiration as the orgasm is approached (705).

Irregular, slow, sighing respiration was early associated with fainting spells (252), and Shock (1144) cited studies in which anxious subjects show frequent respiratory irregularity, increased depth of breathing, and sighing (60, 1081, 1192). On the other hand, ulcer patients in states of tension, anxiety, resentment, anger, guilt, obsequiousness, and desperation showed rapid and shallow respiration with frequent sighs (923). Such variations in findings may be aspects of complex interrelationships, as suggested by the measurements on one of the patients studied by Stevenson et al. (1202). An increase in respiration was seen during moderate anxiety; however, with great anxiety, "bordering on panic," breathing became extremely shallow and not more rapid.

GENERAL RESPIRATORY SYMPTOMS

The frequently noted symptom of hyperventilation was observed in cases of anxiety neurosis by Kerr et al. (698). Schimmenti's survey of 500 people revealed 27 per cent of the females to show hyperventilation symptoms as compared to 9 per cent of the males; however, a condition of hypoventilation associated with a "so-called phlegmatic temperament" was seen more often in males (1097). Hyperventilation was described as involving accentuation of intercostal breathing, which is more characteristic of exertion and excitement than is the more usual emphasis on diaphragmatic breathing. Schimmenti reported that hyperventilation resulted in alkalosis of the blood, with the carbon dioxide increasing beyond 55 volumes per cent, as well as in an increase in alkalinity of vaginal secretion, which reportedly contributes to reduced sexual sensation and predisposes the vagina to excoriation or chafing and infection. Schimmenti also listed other physical and physiological consequences of hyperventilation, as well as various associated symptoms such as dizziness, muscle-tension pains, and increased heart rate. The "cause and core" of this syndrome he asserted to be anxiety that is "cathected," or "bound by the hyperventilation habit." Hyperventilation at fasting blood levels has been found by others to result in blood alkalosis that was associated with electroencephalographic delta activity, but these "abnormal" waves were prevented in some types of cases by raising of the blood sugar levels (285, 555, 689).

Many studies exist concerning symptoms or disorders of the respiratory tract. In the observations by Faulkner of esophageal spasms, parallel bronchial widening and narrowing occurred with pleasant and unpleasant suggestions, respectively (347). In a case of nocturnal dyspnea, anger and hostility were found to result in an exaggerated pressor response, hyperventilation, and decreased ventilatory efficiency (1342); another case of hypnoanalytically treated dyspnea and fatigue was seen to be based on intense, long-standing conflicts (1101). Wolf found the diaphragmatic muscle to play an important role in the respiratory distress and dyspnea produced in 17 patients by discussion of situational conflicts (1345). Willard,

Swan, and Wolf described various observations relating to the mechanics of respiration and of dyspnea, and these indicated that impairment of the ventilatory mechanism of respiration may occur under stressful circumstances (1326). "Almost universal" breathing difficulties have been said to be seen with neurocirculatory asthenia (242). The amount of sputum secretion of a patient with a lifelong bronchitis was reported by Stevenson and Wolff to be closely correlated with his feelings of conflict, anxiety, and resentment (1206). The amount secreted increased sometimes as much as eightfold under stress conditions and then diminished again when the stress had passed.

ASTHMA

Studies associating asthma symptoms with psychological stress are relatively numerous. In another paper, Stevenson reported a bronchitis case similar to the one just noted and a case of bronchial asthma in which the secretion was associated with feelings of anxiety and resentment (1198). A relatively early study by Ziegler and Elliott related attacks of bronchial asthma in nonprotein-sensitive patients to "psychic stimuli" (1383). Halliday presented his observations and abstracts concerning 30 consecutive, uncomplicated cases of persons disabled by bronchial asthma who were studied methodically in one to four sessions, 24 of them being seen two times, and he emphasized the importance of understanding the psychological factors involved (516).

In a psychiatric survey of 50 randomly selected cases of bronchial asthma taken from an allergy clinic by McDermott and Cobb, 37 patients seemed to show an emotional component related to the condition, and 20 of these patients associated this with the onset of their condition (827). The remaining 13 patients predominantly were young males. Neurotic traits, usually of a compulsive character, were found in 30 of the patients studied. Of the "emotional group," only 20 per cent benefited by somatic therapy as compared to 54 per cent of the "nonemotional group." Also in the "neurotic" and "nonneurotic" groups, those benefiting from treatment with drugs and biological products were 20 per cent and 50 per cent respectively.

Brown and Goitein compared 40 asthmatic patients with 40 patients having allergy and with a healthy control group, finding both patient groups to be more maladjusted than the control subjects and defining a "respiratory personality" for the asthmatic patients that included cyclothymic dispositions, paranoid features, repressed hostility, and self-punitiveness (157).

The complexity of these studies is exemplified by a study by Treuting and Ripley involving 28 females and 23 males in which the following information was elicited: from skin tests with extracts of six common allergic substances; detailed personal and family histories; physical examinations revealing primarily the characteristic rales, rhonchi, and wheezes of asthma at some time of observation; laboratory studies revealing an eosinophilia above 3 per cent in 34 cases, and X-ray films indicating pulmonary abnormality for 30 patients and sinusitis for 33 patients of whom only 3 complained of nasal congestion (1266). These experimenters established a definite relationship between skin reaction and the occurrence of symptoms in only 2 of 51 cases, and seasonal variation of symptoms seemed definite with only 2 cases. Conversely, 36 cases associated symptoms with situations that were followed by certain emotional reactions for the patient. Another patient refused to discuss her problems, and in 12 cases no apparent correlation between the symptoms and emotional factors was seen. Intense fear and rage were frequently accompanied or followed by asthma attacks, and depression "was almost universal in all patients" during these attacks. Much evidence suggested that asthma attacks may be an alternative to crying. Poor heterosexual relationships and marked dependency on the mother figure were characteristic of most patients; these are also frequently reported in psychoanalytic literature (321, 377, 434a, 827, 910, 1083, 1297).

Similarly, an intensive clinical study of 27 asthma patients by French et al. suggested that emotional conflicts associated with separation from a rejecting mother figure constitute the central problem of these patients and that conflictual sexual impulses are most significant in precipitating the asthmatic attacks (377). The threshold of allergic sensitivity was seen by these investigators to be dependent upon the patient's emotional state, and with psychotherapeutic diminution of the conflicts associated with the mother figure, the patients became more resistant to allergens. Other studies also have emphasized the importance of conflicts that concern the mother in regard to bronchial-asthma attacks (906). Still other clinical studies have simply placed emphasis on the emotional and symptomatic aspects of this condition (981) as contrasted to an emphasis on its psychosomatic etiology (164, 287a, 321, 819, 1077, 1091, 1336). Many writers have taken a conservative attitude in questioning the emotional etiology of asthma, but at the same time cognizance is usually taken of the importance of emotional factors in the asthmatic attacks (38, 1152). Asthma and eczema are found relatively more frequently in young children than are other psychosomatic conditions (1170).

Employing psychological instruments and clinical interviews to study 45 female allergy patients, Saltzman found some differentiating features between asthma, hay fever, and urticaria patients (1078). He related the onset of asthma and urticaria to "emotional life situations," and reported repressed aggressive feelings for hay-fever subjects.

Stevenson and Ripley reported the following pneumographic respiratory findings with 15 bronchial-asthma patients and 7 anxiety-neurotic patients while discussing life situations that were associated with different feelings, as judged by the patients' reports and by the experimenters' clinical observations (1205, p. 489):

> 2. Increased rate or depth or both and sighing were found chiefly with anxiety but sometimes during anger and resentment. Decreased rate or depth or both were found when the patients felt tense and on guard with feelings of anxiety or anger and when feeling sad or dejected.
> 3. Irregularity of respiration was commonly associated with anger, particularly when this was suppressed. It was also associated with feelings of guilt and occurred during weeping.

Asthma patients were observed to prolong expiration more markedly during emotional disturbances, and it was associated with wheezing and dyspnea in some patients. The discussion of attitudes and conflicts known to be associated with the respiratory symptoms of given patients evoked these symptoms in over half of the patients.

Lovett Doust and Leigh noted the use of the classification "intrinsic" asthma, which implies endocrine, psychogenic, metabolic, or nervous mechanisms, and the classification "extrinsic" asthma, which implies the predominant mechanism of allergens such as dust, drugs, and pollens; however, the relative weight given to these two types of factors by experimenters with different opinions concerning etiology was thought to rest more frequently on prejudice than on strictly scientific criteria (817). These experimenters undertook an extensive study of 30 bronchial-asthma patients, employing clinical, pathological, radiological, spectroscopic, oximetric, and psychotherapeutic techniques and a number of therapy sessions ranging from 8 to 120 per patient. They found "pent-up emotional tension" to be accompanied by anoxemia that can be inhibited by asthmatic dyspnea or that can be overcome by motor expression of emotion in "weeping, laughing, the acting out of anger, confession . . . or by asthma" (817, p. 304). Depression and rage were seen to be predominantly associated with this condition, and bronchial asthma alternated in some cases with clinical depression under stress conditions.

OTHER SYMPTOMS AND PERSONALITY TYPES

More controversial and complex is the possible relationship of psychogenic factors to pulmonary tuberculosis (296, 894). A study of 100 consecutive tuberculosis admissions revealed these patients to be "sensitive, anxious, rigid, and emotionally labile," and a disintegration of their generally marginal psychosocial adjustment "almost invariably" had occurred in the two-year period preceding onset or relapse of their illness (593a). The findings also included alteration of adrenocortical activity as indicated by 17-ketosteroid excretion. From a detailed examination of 300 such patients, Wittkower discerned no specific prevalent personality type, but in all patients appeared an "inordinate need for affection together with conflicts over aggression" (1339a). Other personality factors related to tuberculosis have been elaborated by other authors (1170a).

A neurogenic breathing defect of patients with functional cardiovascular disease, or neurocirculatory asthenia, which favors the intercostal muscles rather than the normally used diaphragmatic muscles, has already been described (393).

Studies of respiratory changes in neurotic conditions have been noted by Altschule to include: normal or slightly increased respiratory minute volume for neurotic and neurocirculatory-asthenia patients when relaxed; irregularities in respiratory rate and rhythm for neurocirculatory-asthenia and for some other neurotic patients both at rest and when upset; increased respiratory rates to 60 or more per minute with the emotional upset of hysterical attacks; and similar increases with stress and with recall of stress, especially for hysteria and anxiety states (38). Wishner reported that 11 psychoneurotic patients with predominant anxiety tended to have a greater respiratory rate than 10 normal control subjects (1332).

Finesinger took respiratory tracings for 24 control subjects and 64 psychoneurotic patients, which included a group (No. I) of 43 anxiety, hysteria, and reactive-depression patients, and a group (No. II) of 21 hypochondriacs and compulsive neurotics, with 3 questionable schizophrenic patients (355). Tracings were taken while these subjects were instructed to think of pleasant and of unpleasant ideas, and their statements were recorded. Comparisons were made of 4 types of changes, namely, sighing respiration, minor fluctuations, major fluctuations, and deviant tracings going beyond the top and bottom modal reference lines on the spirogram. Significant changes occurred in all of the measures for Group I, whereas only 2 measures showed significant changes with Group II. The later were less reactive than control subjects on rate and depth of respiration, producing therefore less total respiration. Pleasant ideas were associated with an increase in sighing respiration with both groups and with the control group. For Group I, unpleasant ideas produced significant increases on the spirogram in upper minor fluctuations, upper major fluctuations, points off the upper reference line, and lower minor fluctuations.

The experiment of Malmo and Shagass employing different patient groups, and using the Hardy-Wolff thermal pain stimulation for stress, showed breaks in the respiratory pattern to be characteristic of patients with high anxiety levels (860, 861). This respiratory disturbance was not found to be closely associated with heart complaints, though patients with heart complaints did show an over-all respiratory variability in terms of deviation of rate and amplitude from the subject's own average.

With mixed groups of predominantly neurotic children compared to normal groups during frustration, Jost (656) and Sherman and Jost (1137) found significant differences between the groups both with and without the frustration stimulus. The emotionally disturbed groups produced more deviant respiratory movements; however, such deviations increased in both groups with frustration (656).

Altschule reported that respiration measures with the functional psychoses reveal little of significance, although irregularity of rhythm has been observed (38). Also, sighing respirations were found to be common with endogenous depression, and lying was differentiated from hallucinations in producing hyperventilation.

A very interesting inverse relationship of asthma with psychosis has frequently been reported and has been summarized by Funkenstein (409, p. 566). Funkenstein observed symptoms of asthma and urticaria to disappear during psychotic episodes. He also administered the drug Mecholyl, which is known to precipitate attacks in asthmatics (261), to 5 psychotic patients with histories of asthmatic attacks before mental illness (409). Mecholyl precipitated a fall in systolic blood pressure and precipitated severe asthmatic attacks in all cases, which subsided only when the blood pressure reached preinjection levels. During the depressive state of one patient, at which time the blood pressure was elevated, the Mecholyl failed to produce the usual reaction. With a sixth case, in which urticaria ("hives") occurred for the first time accompanying the intense anxiety of early schizophrenia, it was found that Mecholyl would precipitate attacks of urticaria only during psychotic states. Treuting's and Ripley's series included one patient whose asthma alternated with urticaria and another whose asthma alternated with psychosis (1266).

Leigh and Lovett Doust cited controversial findings in the literature concerning a possible close relationship between bronchial asthma and psychosis, but they believed that no such relationship exists (764). From a study of 28 psychotic patients with bronchial asthma, in which 26 of these patients reported that chest infections had preceded this condition and in which only 10 per cent of the patients showed allergic manifestations, Leigh and Lovett Doust found no intimate relationship between the asthmatic attacks and the psychoses of these patients, of which the types were 16 manic-depressive, 11 schizophrenic, and 1 senile-paranoid. As one of several examples supporting the thesis that a reciprocal relationship does exist between the physical manifestation of a psychosomatic illness generally and the psychological manifestation of a psychotic illness, Appel and Rosen reported a case with paranoid reaction occurring at the times of the patient's asthma attacks (50).

OTHER REACTIONS

In the considering of reactions in the upper-lateral-chest areas, one should recall Wolff's observation of similar, though differentiated, reactions in the mucous membranes of the stomach, the vagina, the bladder, the large bowel, the nose, and the bronchi (1358). Also, the reports of the suppression of lactation by emotion should be noted (38).

LOWER CHEST AREAS (Areas No. 11a and 11b)

The literature reveals little data on distinctive physiological changes with psychological reactions for the area of the lower left chest, Area No. 11b; however, the spleen is known to contract in sudden emergency reactions as well as in times of strong physical exertion, and thereby releases a reserve blood supply. The stomach, which is usually partially in this area, will be considered under the section on the lower left epigastrium (Area No. 10) that will follow; and similarly, the kidneys will be considered with the back (Area No. 23).

There are a few studies relating to hepatic functioning, which concerns Area No. 11a, the lower-right-chest area. Wittkower observed that most emotions, such as joy, sorrow, and anxiety, stimulate bile secretion with twofold to sixfold increases occurring; however, bile secretion was entirely or almost entirely inhibited during anger (1335). Stimulation by hypnotic suggestions resulted in an "especially light" type of bile with the affect of joy (321, 1333). He also believed that spasms of the bile ducts occurring with annoyance might be a contributing factor in icterus and in gallstone formation.

Stresses have been reported to influence the hippuric acid test (987), and hepatic circulation was seen to decrease with fainting and to remain depressed long thereafter (38, 90), indicating an apparent initial splanchnic vasodilatation that was followed by a period of vasoconstriction (90). Also with this, Bearn et al. found increased hepatic glucose output with a rise in capillary blood glucose concentration and increased concentrations of peripheral and hepatic venous blood lactic acid. Cannon had early observed that the epinephrine secreted with stress precipitates the release of sugar stores in the liver (195), which Bondy believed may partly account for the very great variations in hepatic blood glucose (137). Similarly, increases in the blood ketone bodies, which are produced in the liver, were seen to result from threats to the security of both diabetic and nondiabetic persons (568). This was discussed in some detail under the section dealing with endocrine-gland functions.

Sham rage in decorticate animals has been reported to produce sympathin from the liver, as well as from other organs, apparently by way of direct central-nervous-system innervation (136, 426).

Generally, normal hepatic functioning is reported with neurosis (38). Although disturbed hepatic function is frequently reported in functional psychoses, a probable nutritional basis for this has been suggested (38, 1092).

EPIGASTRIC AREA IN GENERAL (Areas No. 8 and 9)

General reference has already been made in this book to the muscles of the diaphragm, and with stress it is reported that the diaphragm is flattened by increased muscular contraction and shortening (1326, 1345). Wolf made fluoroscopic observations on 17 patients with respiratory complaints while discussing situational conflicts, and he described a characteristic disorder of diaphragmatic function with the attacks that were thus stimulated (1345). The diaphragmatic muscle assumed a progressively lower position, and its contractile state increased to prohibit adequate inspiratory excursion, producing dyspnea with a feeling of inability to take a breath. In 7 of the subjects, occlusion of the cardiac end of the esophagus was observed during diaphragmatic spasm, and this occurred at times even without the degree of diaphragmatic contraction necessary to produce breathing difficulty. Diaphragmatic flutter has also been associated with emotional factors (528). Patients with the symptoms associated with functional cardiovascular disease (neurocirculatory asthenia) tend to de-emphasize the use of the diaphragmatic muscle, which is used predominantly in normal breathing, as was noted under the section on the central chest (393).

The material that will be considered under the upper-central-chest area, Area No. 4, relating to the esophagus is also pertinent to this area, since proximal to the apex of the diaphragm, the esophagus joins the stomach at the cardia. Wolf and Almy studied 20 asymptomatic controls and 14 patients who had complaints that swallowed food seemed to stick in the retrosternal region (1347). Irregular contractual activity of the lower two thirds of the esophagus and a localized obstruction just above the cardia were seen in the patients with "cardiospasm" in connection with their life conflicts and stressful feelings and also in the control group when under the following experimental stresses: compression of the head, examinations, hands in ice water, and discussions. These findings will be described in detail on p. 292.

STOMACH AREA OF THE EPIGASTRIUM (Area No. 10)

GASTRIC REACTIONS IN GENERAL

The inhibition of gatsrointestinal functioning by fear or anger was early demonstrated by Cannon (187, 188, 189, 195, 200) and was observed later by Rogers (1054, 1055) and by Todd and Rowlands, who noted prolonged emptying and decreases in tone and in amplitude of contraction with anxiety and tension (1253). Also in the early 1900s, Brunswick reported a differentiated tonus response in the stomach and rectum occurring with pleasant and unpleasant emotions, the former showing increased tonus and the latter relaxation (170). He suggested a possible specific effect of increased tonus in the stomach occurring with disgust. Changes in gastric motility were also observed by Landis under conditions of severe "emotional upset" (745).

In 1937, Wittkower reported "all possible variations" of disturbed gastric functions to occur with emotional reactions, including changes in the quantity and acidity of gastric secretions and in the emptying time of the stomach (1335). In the majority of cases there was increased tonus with emotion, and It was observed that emotions could cause extreme hyperacidity. The same emotion seemed to produce uniform changes in a given subject, but different subjects reacted differently.

Alvarez also reported "psychic secretion" of digestive juices, including gastric, pancreatic, and bile, and he observed the stopping of secretions, as well as changes in gastric motility, with emotions and fatigue (39).

Altschule cited several studies showing gastric hypofunction in startle, in a variety of strong feelings and emotions, and in fatigue (38, p. 84). Also, a great variety of changes in the volume and acidity of gastric secretion was reported to occur with moderate emotional changes. Gellhorn noted an early report of increased gastric secretion in sexual excitement (317, 426).

A study of gastric acidity of 8 male undergraduate students by Mahl during academic examinations and during control periods showed significantly greater acidity during the former, and the increase was very closely related to the degree of conscious "anxiety" of these subjects (854). Whereas Mahl's results were based upon single fractional samples for each of three periods, Heller et al. later studied gastric acidity by means of hourly samples over a twelve-hour period from 10 hospitalized patients, 5 with and 5 without gastrointestinal symptoms (548). First, a study of a routine nature was made, but the process of the second study appeared to produce anxiety in the subjects, and with this, all the subjects showed elevated gastric acidity over the twelve-hour "anxious" period; however, no significant differences in this respect were found between the two groups of patients. Similarly, 2 patients under psychoanalysis were reported to secrete more hydrochloric acid during the relatively more anxiety-arousing therapy sessions, and these investigators emphasized the view that the hydrochloric acid increase was not dependent on oral-passive wishes nor on any symbolic or other origin except the association with increased anxiety. Mahl and Brody found increased gastric hydrochloric acid with apprehensive anxiety in both a group of 6 psychoneurotic patients who showed evidence of chronic "free-floating" anxiety, and in a group of 7 control subjects who were clinically free of such symptoms; however, the results were only "suggestive" that the hydrochloric acid secretion was significantly greater for the former than for the latter (856). Other studies have also reported increased hydrochloric acid secretion with fear or anxiety (587, 915). An animal study by Mahl had suggested a possible differential effect on gastric acidity between acute and chronic fear because hydrochloric acid was secreted only with the latter (853, 855). Hypnotically induced emotional states in 24 subjects, divided into three groups on the basis of (Taylor) "anxiety" scores, revealed differences in gastric secretions between "low" and "high" anxiety groups, which might partially explain earlier contradictory findings (330a). The "high" group secreted more free and total hydrochloric acid than the "low" group under conditions of "fear," whereas the reverse was true for "anger" conditions;

and under the condition of "contentment" there were rises in free and total acid and in pepsin in all groups, with the free-acid secretion for both "low" and "high" groups equaling the level of the "high" group under the fear condition.

GASTRIC FISTULA AND OPERATIVE STUDIES

Some of the most significant findings in regard to gastric functioning have come from studies of people with gastric fistulas, which enabled a section of the gastric mucosa to be observed. Early observations were made by Beaumont (92). One of the best known is the case of Tom, who was observed by Wolf and Wolff over a period of five years (1351). Pleasant food associations for this subject resulted in increased gastric motility, marked increases in acidity, and a slightly darker color of the mucosa. Quite different was his fear reaction to an irate doctor, described as follows (1351, p. 2):

> The mucous membrane of his stomach also [as his face] blanched from 90 to 20 on the color scale and remained so for 5 minutes until the doctor had located the object of his search and left the room. Then the gastric mucosa gradually resumed its former color.

Other emotions that implied a feeling of being overwhelmed and dejected similarly inhibited gastric secretion and at times were accompanied by anorexia, "sinking in the stomach," and nausea. Also, the gastric hypofunction was regularly associated with diminution in the flow of saliva. A differentiated type of gastric hypofunctioning was seen, however, in settings of disgust or guilt occurring with feelings of rejection. At such times along with the pallor, inactivity, and diminished acid secretion in the stomach, there occurred an increase in salivary flow and an apparent acceleration of secretion of the gastric mucosa. It was emphasized that these were not Tom's habitual ways of reacting, nor was gastric hypofunction his usual reaction to threat. He usually dealt directly with a stress situation or quickly forgot it, and his gastric disturbances were usually never sustained except during periods of special stress. Great anger, including feelings of humiliation and resentment, produced hyperemic and engorged gastric mucosa (as well as a red face), the acid production more than doubled, and vigorous contractions began. These reactions presented a general appearance of overactivity comparable to but less intense than that encountered in experimentally induced gastritis. A similar reaction was observed when withdrawal of partial support by a benefactor was threatened and produced feelings of resentment and anxiety, which resulted in an increased basal secretion of acid over the previous two weeks and continual engorgement and reddening of the mucous membranes. With solution of the problem, acid production and vascularity returned to former levels. Wolf and Wolff believed that the basis of gastritis and peptic ulcer may lie in this reaction of hyperactivity. Exposure of the collar of mucosa to gastric juice for four days resulted in an experimental ulcer. Also, "the degree of response in the stomach to stimuli arising out of situational stress was found to be great enough to modify or even cancel out the effects of ingestion of various foods or drugs"; these observations were supported by other studies (1358). On occasions when Tom felt thoroughly defeated or overwhelmed by a situation, he displayed gastric hypofunction, which, in one instance, was sustained for two months, and was associated with anorexia, taciturnity, and loss of drive and weight.

Individual differences in reactivity as well as the problem of semantics in the delineating of psychological states are again emphasized by the observations of Crider and Walker on a Negro woman with a gastric fistula (258). As will be noted, however, a subsequent study of this patient by Margolin, Orringer, and Kaufman cast doubt on the specific conclusions of this study (871). It was believed that disgust resulted in markedly depressed motility and that in moderate fear, the color gradient of the gastric mucosa decreased from 50 to 40. Also, with an apparent sullen and defiant mood, gastric motility was reported to be cyclic with large peristaltic contractions, but after the motility subsided, the color gradient fell again and the secretion became meager. On this basis, Crider and Walker believed that their observations differed from those of Wolf and Wolff, and maintained that the "patient showed depressed secretion and motility and blanching of the mucosa not only when she was fearful but at each time she was considered to be angry, resentful and anxious as to the outcome of her treatment." (In regard to the spasm of the cardia due to apparent psychological factors noted in the previous section of this book, the finding of Crider and Walker that mechanical stimulation of the cardiac sphincter produces a reflex bile-stained secretion may be of relevant significance.) The subsequent study of Margolin, Orringer, and Kaufman, which cast doubts on the conclusions of Crider and Walker, revealed that this patient unconsciously associated conflictual sexual fantasies with the experimental procedures involved in the study of her fistula, and consequently her feeling reactions were seemingly more complex than had been previously realized (871).

Still another subject with normal gastric functioning was observed by Wolf and Andrus before and after a vagotomy (for cancer), and the pattern of gastric hypofunction in fear and dejections and the pattern of hyper-function in anger and hostility prior to vagotomy were again seen (1348). During three extensive observation periods following the vagotomy after seventeen, nineteen, and twenty-one days respectively, no spontaneous waves of forceful gastric contraction were recorded, and one observation of overt anger resulted in no detectable changes in the appearance of the gastric mucosa.

FINDINGS REGARDING GASTRIC ULCER

Many studies more directly relate peptic-ulcer and gastric-ulcer etiology and aggravation of ulcer symptoms to psychological factors. Reference has already been made to the 1937 report of Draper et al., which differentiated ulcer patients from patients with gall-bladder disease on the basis of EKG findings and hypothesized constitutional character differences on this basis (307). Mittelmann and Wolff conducted a two-part study in which the first part included 25 duodenal-ulcer patients, 5 gastric-ulcer cases, and 13 normal subjects without complaints (923). "Exhaustive clinical person-ality studies" were made on all of these subjects, with the following conclu-sion concerning the ulcer patients (923, p. 15):

> The personality features of these patients were variable and the incidents precipitating the emotional reactions numerous. However, the reactions of anxiety, insecurity, resentment, guilt and frustration obtained in all. Also, compensating efforts to bolster the self-esteem by assertions of independence, self-sufficiency and perfectionism were common. It was evident from the time of onset of the personality disturbances that the ulcer itself was not responsible for the major emotional conflicts or the reactions.

In the second part of this study, 9 duodenal-ulcer, 1 gastric-ulcer, and 3 gastroduodenal-ulcer patients, and 13 control subjects were studied during "relaxed" states and during emotionally charged interview conditions. The aim was first to arouse the particular emotional reactions that the individual subject displayed in his everyday experiences and then to eliminate the stress and presumably reverse the subject's reactions toward normal. Tension, anxiety, resentment, anger, guilt, obsequiousness, and desperation were accompanied by increased hydrochloric acid, mucus, and pepsin secretions, and increased magnitude of contractions with continuous peristaltic activity; at the same time respiration became more rapid and shallow with frequent sighs, a drop in finger temperature usually occurred, and ulcer symptoms were often exacerbated. With emotional security, functional overactivity decreased and approached normal. Normal subjects showed patterns similar to those of patients with ulcer, gastritis, and duodenitis except for the greater magnitude and duration of change in the patients.

Wolff (1357, p. 1079) noted observations by Groen (501, 502) on patients whose peptic-ulcer symptoms disappeared with overt expression of anxiety and hostility in concentration camps and reappeared later under normal conditions of active, competitive, career striving. Many other reports also support the relatedness of peptic ulcers to the emotional factors just described above (18, 39, 151, 262, 295, 310, 321, 544a, 672, 682, 783, 1048, 1121, 1216, 1227, 1346, 1352, 1357).

After a review of the literature and clinical study of 200 peptic-ulcer patients, Sullivan described the personality characteristics of these patients as follows: tense, anxious, driving, active, mildly agitated, versatile, restless, pleasant and likable, self-reliant, responsible, successful, sexually well adjusted, determined, striving for superiority, over-extended in activities, and insecure (1216). He subscribed to a theory of multiple etiology (or "factors"), and he made a four-group classification in analyzing 200 cases, of which: (1) 72 per cent had "typical ulcer personality"; (2) 11 per cent had "definite psychoneurosis"; (3) 5 per cent had "striking external precipitating situations"; (4) 10 per cent revealed no associated personality or situational factors; and 2 per cent were eliminated due to incomplete observations. Conflictual oral dependency needs have frequently been suggested as etiological factors in peptic ulcer (20, 21, 22, 222a, 434a, 546, 672, 701, 820a, 994a, 1085, 1296a).

Duodenal-ulcer patients have been significantly differentiated from a group of patients with various somatic disorders by analysis of the results of psychological measures that reflected personality variables (159). The ulcer patients were reported to have more unfavorable M:FM and FC:CF Rorschach scorings and to show indications of an "overly extratensive" personality orientation that is "superimposed on a basically introversive personality structure." Similarly, Poser found positive results in differentiating 30 duodenal-ulcer patients and 30 ulcerative-colitis patients from each other and from 30 healthy control subjects by means of suggestibility, pain reactions, and galvanic-skin-resistance tests (1002). Thereby, Poser claimed support for Alexander's theory (19) that different emotional tensions produce varied physiological responses with the result that psychosomatic, or vegetative, disorders are associated with specific emotional constellations.

On the other hand, Krasner, in employing a psychological instrument, the Guilford-Martin Factor Inventory, did not find significant differences in personality constellation between 30 duodenal-ulcer patients and 27 ulcerative-colitis patients, although each of these patient groups was significantly differentiated from 44 hospital patients with "nonpsychosomatic disorders" (725). As compared to this last group and in terms of this psychological instrument, the ulcer patients were described as being more shy, withdrawn, seclusive, fluctuating emotionally, flighty, socially passive, and easily irritated. Also, the colitis patients were found to show a significantly "more inhibited disposition" than the ulcer patients.

Browning and Houseworth tested the suggestive finding of Szasz (1225) and others that indicated that the removal of ulcer symptoms by surgery or by means other than psychotherapeutic modifications of the patient's basic conflicts may be followed by the development of other symptoms (160). Twelve-month to eighteen-month follow-up studies were made on 30 duodenal-ulcer patients who had been treated by successful surgical removal of the ulcer, and on 30 duodenal-ulcer patients who had been "treated by conservative medical measures" without complete remission or reduction of ulcer symptoms. They found that a parallel increase in other psychosomatic and psychoneurotic symptoms occurred. After twelve to eighteen months, the medically treated group showed no redistribution of symptoms, and all were still able to work, whereas in the surgically treated group, 11 were totally incapacitated, and, in addition to them, 4 subjects had recurrence of ulcer symptoms, 2 subjects (making a total of 4 having these symptoms) showed moderately severe sustained hypertension and another showed reactive hypertension, 6 subjects (making a total of 7 having these symptoms) developed an incapacitating degree of musculoskeletal symptoms, 5 others (making a total of 6 having these symptoms) developed migraine headaches, 2 (making a total of 5 having these symptoms) developed asthma, 3 (making a total of 7 having these symptoms) showed psychocutaneous disorders, 16 (making a total of 20 having these symptoms) complained of rather severe neurasthenic symptoms, and 2 (making a total of 17 having these symptoms) manifested troublesome anxiety.

From a review of the literature, Scodel hypothesized two different etiological types of ulcer patients: one type seemingly derives from an upper-middle-class or upper-class background where behavior favoring socioeconomic achievement is emphasized, and these patients refuse to accept their dependency needs, conceiving of themselves as being "active, efficient, and masculine" and maintaining levels of aspiration so high that they are unable to attain their goals (1115). The other type of ulcer patient that was hypothesized, and called "attitudinally counteractive and overtly passive," was said to be of "lower or lower-middle class background," where satis-factions of nonstriving occupational types are encouraged. Although these patients also deny their dependency needs, their overt behavior is inhibited, conforming, and unassertive even though they perceive themselves to be active, productive persons. Comparing 34 of the latter type, who had active or benign duodenal-ulcer conditions except for two cases of gastric ulcer, with 38 predominantly psychoneurotic patients, Scodel found etiologically significant differentiated personality features of the two types that he hypoth-esized by means of interpretation of psychological instruments and tech-niques that included: a "level-of-aspiration" experiment, a "memory for completed versus interrupted tasks" experiment, a "perseveration of inade-quate hypothesis" experiment, and the Hysteria, Masculinity-Femininity, and Psychopathic Deviate scales of the Minnesota Multiphasic Personality Inventory. The ulcer patients scored significantly higher on the first two MMPI scales.

A study of 30 patients with benign gastric or duodenal ulcers showed uropepsin excretion to be twice as great as normal, and these patients, as well as nonpatients with excessive uropepsin excretion, were found by clin-ical and psychological study to have the "so-called oral receptive, dependent personality" (918). Also, nightly uropepsin studies, along with daily nota-tions of emotional reactions, were made on 3 patients in psychotherapy and on 18 "normal" subjects and other subjects for long periods ranging up to two years. Increases in uropepsin excretion were found to occur primarily in response to life situations that threatened or mobilized the individual's unconscious wishes for love and wishes to be taken care of. Thus, a mech-anism involved in the occurrence of peptic ulcer was implied.

Mirsky noted that a number of neonates also have high pepsinogen secre-tion, and he suggested a constitutional factor for the development of both the gastric symptom (or ulcer) and the dependent (or "oral-demanding") personality type, which engenders a strained relationship with the mother figure that may foster hostility and rejection (917).

It has been reported that about 50 per cent of patients with gastric ulcer characteristically show hyperacidity and that all factors involved in the rate of production of gastric acid are not known (38). Nevertheless, it is known that in general the gastrointestinal processes are facilitated by para-sympathetic (vagus) innervation, and are inhibited by the sympathetic. Babkin has found, by stimulating all parts of the cerebral cortex of dogs, that only the orbital surface and the anterior end of the cingulate gyrus affect gastric motility; the stimulation generally arrested or diminished the

antral waves except in one experiment when stimulation of the orbital surface produced increased motility (56). Babkin believed this effect was
probably the result of depression of the activity of the lower gastric vagal
centers, though several other possibilities exist. In any case, a mechanism
whereby cortical functioning acts on gastric activity was suggested.

Also in similar experimentation, electrical stimulation of very localized
areas in the frontal-lobe cortex were seen to result in twofold to fourfold
increases of gastric secretions (287). Other writers have reported variable
and poorly integrated autonomic activity in peptic-ulcer patients, as well as
abnormal personality constellations (1045, 1073). The abnormal EEG findings with peptic-ulcer patients that were discussed in the cephalic section
(p. 151) were also thought to be associated with disturbance in the autonomic nervous system (706).

OTHER GASTRIC REACTIONS

Vomiting has also been frequently associated with psychological states
(995, 1344, 1352, 1357). The Rorschach performances and the results of
clinical studies of 20 pregnant women with symptoms of persistent vomiting
were compared to those of 14 nausea-free pregnant women by Harvey and
Sherfey (535). It was found that the former group showed: a life history
of gastrointestinal disturbances in response to emotional stress, marked im-
maturity of personality, serious disorders of sexual adjustment including
consistent frigidity, and markedly increased anxiety and tension associated
with their pregnancy, especially during periods of vomiting.

Altschule cited a number of studies of gastric activity with neurosis and
psychosis that indicate generally normal reactions except that gastric motor
activity may be increased in neurotics and normals or decreased in schizophrenics (38). He believed that the reported normal incidence of peptic
ulcer in psychotic patients is evidence against somatization of conflict as the
etiology of this condition.

CENTRAL ABDOMINAL AREA (Area No. 14)

The literature reveals little concerning the effect of psychological factors
on the small intestine; however, reference has already been made to similarities of functioning throughout the gastrointestinal tract, and, for example,
the effect of Banthine in diminishing upper-small-intestine motility is seen
to have similar effect on the rest of the gastrointestinal tract (696). Nevertheless, by direct observation of a case, Weeks noted marked differential
reactions to chemicals between the colon and the small intestine (1295).

He reported also that excitement resulted in marked peristalsis of the small intestine and evacuation of feces from a transverse colostomy. Dunbar (321) reported Alkan's observations that psychic influences that modify small-intestine secretion are rare; however, the motor activity of the small intestine has been seen to be affected by psychological states, and the motor activity is even more affected in the colon (large intestine) (27).

MIDRIFF AREAS (Areas No. 12a, 12b, and 12c) AND LATERAL MID-ABDOMINAL AREAS (Areas No. 15a and 15b)

FUNCTIONS OF THE DUODENUM AND LIVER

First, it should be noted that the duodenum is situated in the midriff area to the right of center. The studies that have just been described above, relating to duodenal ulcer, should be considered in terms of the possibility that duodenal ulcer may have a somewhat different etiology than gastric ulcer, and their etiologies might be related to differences in emotional reactivities between the duodenum and the stomach.

In connection with liver functioning, Wittkower's report was also mentioned, stating that bile secretion taken from the duodenum was increased by joy, sorrow, and anxiety and was inhibited by "annoyance" and that the bile accompanying joy was especially light (321, 1333). Others have emphasized neurotic, psychosomatic factors in biliary-tract disorders (186a).

TRANSVERSE, DESCENDING, AND ASCENDING COLON SECTIONS

The several sections of the colon underlie a large area of the body surface; however, most reports fail to make specific reference to which section of the colon has been studied, and the results are usually generalized as being applicable to the whole colon. Because of the relative ease of observation, it is probable that most such generalized reports are based on studies of the sigmoid colon, therefore all references to unspecified colon findings will be presented in the body-area classification that will follow, namely, Area No. 13a. Specific references to the transverse (Area No. 12), ascending (Area No. 15a), or descending (Area No. 15b) colon are rare. There is, of course, some good basis for the generalizing of colonic functioning since Weeks made direct observations that the ileum and the transverse and sigmoid colon were often active at the same time. Also, Alvarez noted cases of increased activity of the jejunum and bowel with appetite associations (39).

FISTULA STUDIES

Similarly, Wolff, Grace, and Wolf made generalizations concerning colonic reactions on the basis of observations of 4 patients with different colonic fistulas that included the ascending, transverse, descending, and sigmoid colon (1362). Reactions of "conflict, anger, resentment and hostility, or anxiety and apprehension" were associated with colonic hyperfunction, which included hyperemia, hypermotility, and increased enzyme and lysozyme secretion. Reactions of persons being "overwhelmed" with "abject fear and dejection" were associated with colonic hypofunctioning, which included pallor, relaxation, lack of contractile activity, and relatively low concentrations of lysozyme secretion, which subjects with ulcerative colitis displayed more frequently and sustainedly than did subjects apparently free of colonic disease. Also, colonic mucosal erosion and ulceration correlated with phases of sustained conflict and anger and receded with relative calm and security. The reaction of 2 of these 4 subjects will be described in more detail in the following paragraphs.

Grace et al. observed one subject with a fistula, who had had a large area of colonic mucosa evaginated, before and after a bilateral supradiaphragmatic vagotomy for the purpose of relieving ulcerative colitis (475). The condition was of six years' duration. The patient had been treated by a cecostomy two years after onset and an ileostomy two years later, and a loop of ascending colon and cecum and a small section of ileum on the abdomen were left. Measures of motor activity, blood flow, lysozyme concentration in the mucosa, mucus secretion, and fragility were made, and special note was taken of changes in color, which varied from a pale yellow red to a brilliant cardinal, because the color has been shown to reflect changes in blood flow (1037). After referring to a similar study (476, 477) the authors stated (475, p. 541):

In brief, this type of experiment consisted of measuring colonic function as above, before, during and after discussion of topics of personal concern to the patient which were associated with conflict and resentment. . . Control observations showed a relatively hyperactive bowel. The membrane was moderately engorged and red (60). The subject had been humiliated over the way he had been treated in the hospital and he felt angry and resentful. He was allowed to ventilate his hostile feelings and in twenty minutes felt calm and relaxed, the bowel was less active, the color had fallen to 30, and the bowel became less contracted. The topic of his attitude towards his sister-in-law was abruptly introduced into the conversation. Within a few seconds the bowel became redder (70), and more contracted.

After about three minutes, neutral and diverting topics were again introduced and the colon again blanched to a color of 30 and became less contracted. During the interviews these effects were repeatedly observed, and following the vagotomy, the effects were still the same. The patient was resentful because the chief surgeon had not himself performed the operation and in addition felt anxiety, resentment, and helplessness over home problems, and he became grim and taciturn. Within two days the exposed area of colon contracted from 7″ by 2¾″ to 3¼″ by 2¼″ showing: no peristaltic movements, engorged membrane of scarlet red, numerous petechiae and small fresh ulcerations, extreme fragility, profuse gray-white, thick, foul-smelling discharge from the stoma, and a sustained rectal temperature of from 100° F. to 102° F. This condition lasted for two weeks and was accompanied by severe cramping abdominal pains, and the authors stated as follows (475, p. 539):

> It was of special interest that the intensity of the nausea, epigastric fullness and vomiting varied considerably from day to day. On days of relatively good spirits, feelings of security and calm, he was able to eat and retain three small meals without undue discomfort. On days of anger, resentment and hostility, his dysphagia was very severe and he vomited after each effort at food taking, as well as during the night. . .
>
> The rectal discharge of muco-pus subsided at the end of 2 weeks. He had finally utilized his opportunity to express freely his hostile and resentful feelings. Suggestions were made for improving his home situation, and he was given a great deal of reassurance and encouragement. Within 48 hours of this free unburdening of his conflicts, the colon elongated to its former size of 7 by 2¾ inches.

Also, the color faded to 50, the petechiae disappeared, the fragility lessened, and the purulent discharge from the stoma and rectum ceased. For the purposes of this discussion, this subject shall be called subject A.

Another case of fistula involved the descending colon (Area No. 15b) and the sigmoid colon (Area No. 13a), which were studied continuously for three weeks. The pain of ice water resulted in blanching of the mucosa (476, 1358). There was apparent fright at the prospect of head-screw pain, and after five minutes of such pain a pronounced blanching of the mucosa from 40 to 15 on the color scale occurred along with diminution of motor activity and decreased lysozyme concentrations; the effects persisted for five minutes until the head screw was released (476). In an interview situation, this subject, who shall be called subject B, showed little change in the colon when relatively neutral topics were involved, but discussion of difficult periods of his life induced blushing and hyperemia of the mucous membrane and accelerated contractions, which appeared to be associated with anger, resentment, and humiliation. Subject A, described in the preceding paragraph, reacted differently than subject B to the ice water and head-screw pain stimuli: i.e., with engorgement and hypermotility, though lysozyme concentration was decreased slightly.

This appears to be a good example of individual personality differences, in which two people probably reacted to the same stimuli in two different ways. This might be classified as basic "feeling" (or "emotional reactivity") since the blanching and associated changes seemed to be related to something like a "fear" reaction, and engorgement and associated changes seemed to be related to something like "anger." This difference was also exemplified by the subsequent attitudes of the subjects: the subject with engorgement (subject A) said that he would be willing to repeat the experiment any time despite conflicting feelings, and the subject with blanching (subject B) said that he would not repeat the experiment because he was fearful of suffering permanent damage to his head or his arms. Even the subject who was agreeable to repetition (subject A) showed differential colonic changes during a four-week period of low spirits, dejection, and mild depression, at which time the colon was constantly at about a color scale of 40 and was almost motionless, with only slight changes even in interview situations aimed at stimulation. Conversely, subject B, who was usually easygoing and showed a relatively normal functioning, also showed a hyperemic, hyperactive, engorged, and fragile colon with high lysozyme concentration in circumstances of anger, humiliation, and resentment. In an instance of very intense and persistent anger, a sudden onset of spasm reduced the exposed colon to approximately half its former size. The subject with ulcerative colitis (subject A), noted in the preceding paragraph, had suppressed feelings of anger and humiliation for more than 50 per cent of the time, as contrasted to the one period of anger for subject B, and the associated colonic reactions were appropriate in respect to those already described in this book.

LOWER ABDOMINAL AREA (Area No. 13a) AND ANAL AREA (Area No. 26)

SIGMOID-COLON REACTIONS IN GENERAL

Large rosettes of evented colonic mucous membrane, which was obtained after colostomies for surgical correction of anorectal deformities in 3 healthy children (ages 4, 9, and 10 years), were observed by Friedman and Snape to: (1) blanch with mildly painful stimuli applied to the nearby abdomen, the color returning within ten minutes although reddening followed blanching in some instances; (2) blanch with the verbal suggestion of pain; (3) redden and engorge with the sight or smell of appetizing food and with eating, returning to normal after the meal was eaten, although distasteful food for one subject had only a slight effect on the color; and (4) remain pale during stool extrusion but thereafter become markedly engorged (395).

Almy and Tulin did proctoscopic observations on 7 healthy male medical students under the painful stress of head screws and observed the following results concerning the sigmoid colon: with the application of painful stimuli for 3 subjects (nos. 1, 3, and 5), a slight blanching of the colonic mucosa occurred, followed in one to nine minutes by a return to normal or flushing; with headache, an increased contractile state occurred, occluding the lumen, and marked hyperemia and spasms occurred in 3 subjects (nos. 2, 6, and 7), and markedly increased secretion occurred for 2 subjects (nos. 3, and 5); and with the instrumentation, mucosal damage and small hemorrhage occurred in only 1 subject (no. 7) when his distress was great and his mucosa very engorged (36). The disturbed functions reverted almost completely to basal levels within one to five minutes after removal of the head screws. The behavior and affective responses for subjects 1, 2, 3, 5, and 6 were similar, and were characterized as "passive," "resigned," or "loose (relaxed)," and although they showed little or no resentment toward the experimenters, they reproached themselves for volunteering and recognized a conflict between their desire for self-preservation and their desire to comply with the situation and to appear brave. Almy and Tulin stated that healthy men under stress can develop changes usually seen only in cases of irritable colon or organic disease of the colon.

Later, Almy, Kern, and Tulin employed the conditions of hypoglycemia and of discussing troublesome life situations in addition to the cold stimuli and the head compression in 45 experiments on 39 subjects who had no clinical disorder of the colon (35). About half of the subjects exhibited marked increases in the contractile state of the sigmoid colon, and with all of these reactions there were indications of stress. By contrast, only 2 of those whose colon did not so react gave evidence of a general stress reaction. With all of these stimuli, the colonic response of each subject seemed to depend on whether the stimulus was regarded as a threat to his security. Employing the same stimuli with 39 patients having spastic constipation or colonic pain, Almy et al. reported the same general results and conclusions, and in the discussing of stressful life situations with 29 of these patients, similar markedly increased colonic motility was frequently seen (33).

Also, in another study, Almy included 50 healthy persons and 100 patients with irritable colon (32). The lower sigmoid colon was viewed through a proctoscope, and kymographic measures of motility were taken while known emotionally charged life situations were discussed. Results consistent with the findings just described were obtained. An increase in over-all activity of the colon seemed to be associated with anger or resentment; and, in two cases involving depressive feelings, colonic hypofunctioning was seen, with major wavelike movements reappearing when the feelings of one patient changed. In other experiments on patients without organic disease of the colon and on subjects with irritable colon, Banthine was seen to inhibit sigmoid contractions except when emotional stress was marked (696). Thus, the experimental studies of Almy et al. involved more than 100 subjects over a period of four years and induced "emotional tension" by interview techniques (34). The following differentiated reactions were described: (1) heightened motility with "emotional tension," including hostility and defensiveness; (2) decreased motility with feelings of helplessness, self-reproach, and defeat; and (3) the association of constipation symptoms with the former and diarrhea symptoms with the latter, with rapid alternation between the two patterns a frequent finding. Psychotherapeutic studies of Karush et al. with 6 ulcerative-colitis patients associated colonic motility with fear and with fearful inhibition of rage toward parental figures, and lower-gastrointestinal-tract activity was accompanied by inhibition of salivary activity (678a). In 23 consecutively admitted ulcerative-colitis patients, Engel found these patients to show bowel bleeding when feeling "helpless, hopeless, or despairing," and 20 of these patients suffered headaches generally when they "felt in control, had taken an active or aggressive stand, made a decision, or thought something through," and this was followed by conscious or unconscious guilt (334a, p. 345).

From a study employing balloon tracings of 300 healthy colons, Kern, Almy and Stolk observed almost continuous wavelike activity of a nonpropulsive type that appeared to represent contractions of circular muscles and fell into three types of wave classifications (697).

OTHER FINDINGS WITH PATHOGENIC CONDITIONS

Attention to the psychological variables in colonic functioning first came from the noting of emotional factors in abnormal functioning. In 1928, Bockus, Bank, and Wilkinson reported the findings of nervous manifestations in each of 30 mucous-colitis cases studied (135). Emotional factors were emphasized in a 1939 report covering a ten-year study; the investigators pointed out that the irritable-colon syndrome usually occurs in a setting of emotional tension (1314). Wolff has described these patients and their condition as follows (1357, p. 1065) :

> The patient with ulcerative colitis is characteristically an outwardly calm, superficially peaceful individual of more than usual dependency [474, 790, 1007]. On going beneath this calm exterior it becomes apparent that this outwardly placid person is "sitting on a powder keg" of intense hostility, resentment and guilt. These long-standing unrelieved feelings are associated with hyperfunction of the colon, with increased motility, increased vascularity, turgescence and small hemorrhagic lesions. Increased concentrations of lysozyme are capable of damaging the mucosa and of exposing it to the corroding effects of the myriad organisms present in the bowel [474]. The combination of hypermotility, hypervascularity, hemorrhages, increased amounts of lysozyme, increased fragility of the mucous membranes and great numbers of organisms in the large intestines may lead to the ulceration, characteristic of the syndrome of ulcerative colitis.

Chambers et al. presented a case summary of an ulcerative-colitis patient who was treated successfully by means of psychotherapy (222), and similar improvement in this condition after changes in the personality or life situation has been reported by others (255, 263, 320, 678, 790).

Poser's differential comparison of ulcerative-colitis patients, duodenal-ulcer patients, and control subjects in their responses to psychological instruments has already been discussed in the section dealing with gastric functions (p. 232) (1002). Of these groups, the colitis patients were seen to show the greatest "suggestibility," "pain reactions," and galvanic-skin-resistance responses so significantly that they were thought to be on the unfavorable end of a reaction continuum (517a, p. 84; 1002). The Thematic Apperception Test stories of colitis patients reflected "persistent avoidance of the 30 antisocial themes, submission to authority, lack of aggression, and need for emotional support by the family" (1002). On the Rorschach protocol, they tended to emphasize color form (CF) and even pure color (C), although the productivity of both patient groups was consistently low. Greater goal striving on "level-of-aspiration tests" was indicated for ulcerative-colitis patients than for peptic-ulcer patients (544a). As has been noted, Krasner did not find the ulcerative-colitis and peptic-ulcer patients significantly differentiated from each other on the Guilford-Martin Factor Inventory, although they were significantly differentiated from control subjects; however, the results tended to confirm that the 27 ulcerative-colitis patients were passive, insecure, shy, sensitive, and moody (725).

From a study of 45 ulcerative-colitis patients, sigmoid-colon abnormalities of reduced phasic activity, associated with severe diarrhea, and of unusually large, apparently propulsive waves were frequently seen (695). In six of seven experiments on 6 patients who showed reduced spontaneous colonic activity, emotional conflicts aroused by personal interviews resulted in increased amplitude and frequency of wavelike contractions, and it was postulated that "continued autonomic bombardment" of the colon might be the initial event in the pathogenesis of ulcerative colitis.

It should be noted that the injection of acetylcholine, a parasympathetic stimulant, produces spasm, congestion, and oversecretion in the colon (38, 1315), and prolonged cholinergic stimulation has been seen to produce colonic ulceration in experimental animals (805, 1302). It has also been stated elsewhere that ulcers and lesions occur experimentally in the colon as well as in other parts of the gastrointestinal tract as a result of apparent overstimulation of parasympathetic nerves (64, 1315) and of lesions in the region of the hypothalamus (684, 1287).

In introducing the vagotomy as a therapeutic procedure for ulcerative colitis, Dennis et al. reported that all 4 cases had improved (292). They reported on a later group of 25 patients of whom 14 showed improvement; however, the direct-observation study of 1 case by Grace et al. revealed that vagotomy effected no changes in the influence of psychological states on colonic functioning (475).

White, Cobb, and Jones stated that the lesions resulting from the administration of drugs that stimulate the action of the parasympathetic nervous system failed to produce lesions exactly like those of mucous colitis; however, with the oral administration of acetyl-beta-methyl-choline, chloride lesions of a similar type were seen; moreover the lesions resulting from locally applied drugs were similar to those of mucous colitis (1314).

Other parasympathetic effects that have been observed in animals during "emotional excitement" include bladder contraction, defecation, and erection of the penis (616).

COLONIC FINDINGS WITH PSYCHOSES

Altschule reported no findings of consistent changes in colonic motility for manic psychosis, but cited findings of common colonic stasis for depressive and schizophrenic psychoses (38). Weiss told of a patient who had

had ulcerative colitis and diarrhea for several years, whose symptoms were relieved with the onset of depression when he became constipated (409). After electroshock and recovery from depression, this patient's ulcerative colitis appeared again. Development of ulcerative colitis was also noted in a case upon remission of a schizophrenic psychosis (50).

RECTAL REACTIONS

It was found in 1924 by Brunswick that changes in tonus of the rectum occurred with a variety of emotionally charged stimuli and that pleasant reactions generally resulted in increased tonus whereas unpleasant ones showed relaxation of tonus (170). Wolff stated that it was well known that the urge to defecate did not usually occur during violent exercise or competitive sports, and he attributed this to the consequences of the psychological state (1357, 1360). A drop in the temperature of the rectum during fainting, apparently reflecting decrease in blood flow, was seen (488), and the stoppage of rectal contractions with remote electrical stimulation during states of marked fatigue and fasting has been reported (748).

Wolff differentiated the functioning of the internal and external sphincters, and he elaborated the mechanism of differentiated colonic and rectal functioning with different psychological states as follows (1357, p. 1067):

> The external sphincter, made up principally of skeletal muscle, and innervated by somatic nerves, may participate in a pattern of widespread skeletal muscle contraction involving especially the neck, back, peri-anal region and parts of the extremities. The internal sphincter, innervated by adrenergic fibers, operates reciprocally with the sigmoid and colon and its cholinergic fibers. Thus, it is likely that when the contractions of the sigmoid are intense, the muscles of the external and internal sphincters relax. The feces deposited and compressed in the rectum are dehydrated, and there remain for longer than the usual period.

Patients with constipation showed the large bowel to be slack and elongated and colonic contraction waves were absent or minimal except for the sigmoid colon where these were of a nonpropulsive type. Also, spasm of the rectal sphincter with or without widespread muscle tension was seen. This "hypodynamic state" was associated with feelings of dejection, futility, and discouraged striving. With diarrhea, on the other hand, the bowel was narrowed and shortened and contraction waves were conspicuous. This was associated with situations of fear, panic, and feelings "of being suddenly confronted by more than could be managed."

Groen's observations in a concentration camp, which was "an over-whelming situation," revealed an increase in diarrhea, and in contradistinc-tion to some other conditions, few patients with ulcerative colitis improved and one became worse and died (501, 502).

Almy described patients with spastic constipation as being "usually tense, with ill-concealed hostility and an air of rigid determination to solve his problem" (32). In contrast, patients with functional diarrhea are "usually soft spoken with a superficial attitude of guilt and countercurrents of deeply buried resentment with a sense of personal inadequacy to deal with his prob-lems." For the diarrhea patients, expressed feelings of hopelessness appeared to be correlated with reduced wavelike motility in the sigmoid colon. The relatedness of functional diarrhea to regressive, infantile attitudes, with dependency desires and with feelings of helplessness is commonly seen in clinical literature.

The relationship of pruritus ani (itching of the anus) to personality factors has been presented in this book under the section dealing with skin conditions (p. 200).

BLADDER FUNCTIONING

Bladder functioning is, of course, dependent somewhat upon that of the kidney, which shall be discussed under the back (Area No. 23). In turn, kidney functioning is dependent in part upon the antidiuretic hormone of the posterior pituitary that was discussed in the section concerning endocrine glands (p. 173). Nevertheless, changes in the tonus of the bladder itself have frequently been associated with psychological states. Thus, relative frequency or infrequency of urination may be due either to the rate of filling the bladder from the kidney or to the tonus of the bladder itself.

Clinical observations of frequent urination with feelings of anxiety and apprehension (569) or with "stress" (570) or "nervousness" (242, 1098) are common; however, such changes are perhaps most commonly associated with kidney functioning. Freeman reported increased bladder tension to heighten the general level of postural tension (371).

By psychiatric and psychological studies, Straub, Ripley, and Wolf found, in the investigating of bladder function of 26 patients, that both urinary frequency and retention correlated with variations in the emotional state and life situation of the individual (1212). Such changes were demonstrated experimentally by the taking of measurements during discussions of relevant conflicts. These findings are exemplified by Wolff's description of bladder changes in a patient who was extremely tense, insecure, and complained of frequency and urgency of urination and who showed (1) with relative tranquillity and reassurance, pale-pink mucosa of the bladder, which would accommodate 300 cc. of fluid without discomfort, and (2) with apprehension, a blushing, turgid, and intensely hyperemic mucosa of the bladder, which would accommodate no more than 50 cc. of fluid and then with pain (1358).

Abnormal bladder functioning with schizophrenia involving a capacity for greatly increased vesical pressure has been reported; water retention particularly at the onset of depression or schizophrenia has been noted by Altschule, as well as a similar effect in normal subjects with the administration of adrenocorticotropic hormone (38).

SEX ORGANS

In the lower abdominal area (Area No. 13a) are also located several of the sex organs, including the ovaries, which were discussed under the section dealing with the endocrine glands (see p. 183). References have been made to the emotional factors associated with pseudocyesis, dysmenorrhea, amenorrhea, leucorrhea, and sterility. Kroger indicated that sterility in endocrinologically normal women may result from chronic anxieties, including fear of pregnancy, accompanied by tubal spasm (735a). Similarly, emotional upset is frequently associated with pregnancy, producing vomiting and other symptoms (1058a). Leucorrhea was most frequently associated with frigidity, and resulted from these psychopathological changes: "After strong sexual excitement the blood vessels around the vulva, vagina and uterus are congested; the smooth muscles of the pelvic organs are contracted and form a kind of erection. After the onset of orgasm, all the overfilled blood vessels usually empty at once, thus resulting in a copious mucoid discharge" (735a, p. 422). Related findings of these types are presented in Chapter 17 in association with internal sensations. Altschule stated that the effect of violent emotion in causing miscarriages and in arresting uterine contractions in labor is well known clinically (38). Finally, studies of rabbits in coitus show activity of the uterus that furthers the movements of the spermatozoa (1034).

GENITAL AREA (Area No. 13b)

Psychological factors related to the functioning of the testes, and including castration studies and studies of the relationships between psychological states and secretion of sex hormones, were discussed under the section on the endocrine glands (p. 183). Relatively little information is reported concerning the penis except the well-known fact of engorgement with the feeling of sexual excitement. The fact that psychological factors can inhibit or distort normal sexual functioning and genital reactions is well known clinically (1, 86, 111, 704, 705, 735a, 752).

Kuntz listed the following localized physiological reactions incidental to male orgasm: peristaltic contraction of the ducti deferentia preceding the urethral expulsion of seminal fluid, and contraction of the compressor urethrae, and of the ischiocavernosus and bulbocavernosus muscles (740). Kuntz stated that the reactions involved in female orgasm are less definitely known but include: peristaltic contractions in the Fallopian tubes that are propagated to the uterus and vagina and are followed by rhythmic contractions of the striated sphincter vaginae muscles. Kinsey et al. referred to various glandular secretions in the genitals of both males and females occurring with sexual stimulation (705). Glandular secretion into the vagina with sexual excitement is also well known, but studies in this connection are generally lacking.

Wolff reported changes in the vagina during resentment and anger apparently not directly related to sexual conflict (1358). By interviews and by the correlating of vaginal changes with life situations over relatively long periods of time for 7 women, tension and conflict with frustration and anxiety were seen to produce hyperemic vaginal mucosas, mostly labial, and increased mucus secretion, which are changes characteristic of patients with complaints of leucorrhea. Two subjects manifested a different type of condition with depressive circumstances: one showed pallor of the labial mucosa; the other showed pallor and friability of the vaginal mucosa; and both showed minimal vaginal secretion.

The occurrence of pelvic congestion was found to be consistently related to stressful life situations, and particularly to times when these patients, who had difficulty in identifying with a mother figure, were in situations that required them to function as women, such as being pregnant (324). In such situations, these patients were seen to react with increased blood flow in the vaginal walls and sustained pelvic hyperemia that led to congestion, edema, at times "cystic" enlargement of one or both ovaries and of the uterine fundus, and hypertrophy and hypersecretion of the cervix.

In a "hyperventilating" type of female described by Schimmenti, increased alkalinity (pH) of vaginal secretion was said to "reduce voluptuous sensation in the vagina" and to predispose the vagina to excoriation and chafing with consequent leucorrhea and to possible infection (1097).

Dunbar cited German studies reporting dysmenorrhea to be frequently psychogenic in origin (944, 954), and leucorrhea, vaginismus, frigidity, dyspareunia, *grossesse nerveuse,* menstrual difficulties, marked labor pains, and spontaneous abortions were all noted to relate at times to emotional factors (321). Concerning these observations, Wolff's finding of similarity in the mucous membranes of the stomach, the vagina, the bladder, the large bowel, the nose, and the bronchi should again be recalled (1358). Levy reported a positive relationship between the length of menstrual periods and the individual's proneness to maternal behavior (773).

POSTERIOR HEAD AND NECK AREAS *(Areas No. 19 and 20)*

Much of the literature relating to the posterior head and neck areas pertains to headaches and sensations of various sorts that shall be considered in Part IV. Also, since psychological states have been studied primarily in connection with the muscles of these areas, some reference has been made to them under the section dealing with muscles, and of course related neurophysiological findings have been presented as a separate section. In summary, it may be recalled that muscle potentials in these areas show a positive relationship to anxiety, stress reactions, and functional complaints that involve these regions (860, 865, 866). In this respect, head movements were differentiated from muscle tension; the tension itself is more pathological. Similarly, psychoneurotics and acute psychotics showed more neck-muscle reaction to various stresses than did normal control subjects, even though no initial difference in the level of neck tension was found (866).

BACK AREAS *(Areas No. 21, 22, 23, and 24)* AND HIP AREA *(Area No. 25)*

Muscle changes in these areas have also been found to have significant relationships to anxiety, stress, and functional complaints, and those findings have been treated here in the same manner as those described in the preceding paragraph (595).

KIDNEY CHANGES

Part of the kidneys underlie Area No. 23, and renal function has been related to psychological states in complex ways. Kidney function in regard to functional hypertension has been elaborated in the section on the circulatory system (p. 166). During World War II, Anderson was able to make direct observations of a urinary fistula, and found that the mention of pleasant foods and drinks resulted in a "definite measurable increase" in the rate of flow of the urine and that the membrane of the kidney became redder (from 40 to 70 per cent), indicating increased mucosal vascularity; however, tasting of the foods added little to these effects (44). With similar stimuli, Rooke obtained increased flow from urethral catheters (1058). It was proposed by Anderson that the mechanism of this effect parallels the parasympathetic activity in the stomach and elsewhere; it involves dilatation of the renal capillaries and activation of "quiescent" glomeruli because the renal nerve supply is joined by the lowest splanchnic nerve and by branches from the vagus, and these have a vasomotor function. Sympathetic innervation is also involved, as was shown by Wolff's finding that bilateral lumbo-dorsal sympathectomy abolished the vasoconstriction of the efferent arterioles when hypertensive subjects reacted to emotional stress, although the afferent arterioles were not affected; it was suggested that the latter might be governed by a humoral mechanism (991, 1358). With a decrease in renal blood flow the filtration fraction was seen to rise. Suggestive evidence was also presented by Chalmers and Lewis to the effect that emotional factors may affect the release of the antidiuretic hormone by the posterior pituitary gland (221). Similarly, Verney reported an antidiuretic effect with faradic stimulation by needle electrodes in the flanks of a dog (1271).

In the study of 27 well-adjusted healthy males and females, Chalmers et al. found statistically significant changes in renal plasma flow with the discussion of emotionally charged topics; positive as well as negative deviations from basal values were found (220). Several authors have reported decreased renal blood flow during psychological stress as well as during physical discomfort or pain (1229, 1341). Other studies indicated that the injection of epinephrine or one of the more powerful sympathomimetic drugs has a similar effect (38, 1011). The adrenaline action has been found directly to influence the efferent glomerular arterioles rather than the afferent ones, and also has the result of engorging and expanding the latter due to the consequent increased blood pressure (230, 1036, 1159). It should be noted also that renal blood flow is autonomous in remaining constant, irrespective of rises and falls in arterial pressure (1159). Smith observed two cases wherein marked renal vasoconstriction accompanied instances of apprehension on the part of patients (1159).

Pfeiffer and Wolff induced emotional conflict in 35 subjects and studied another subject during relaxation only; 13 of these subjects had "normotensive" blood pressure (140/90 or less) and 23 of them had higher blood pressure, which was classified as "hypertensive" (991). The elevation of systolic and diastolic blood pressure that occurred during discussions of personally threatening topics was accompanied by a fall in effective renal blood flow and a rise in filtration fraction, indicating increased renal arteriole resistance. The direction of these changes was the same for both normotensive and hypertensive groups, but "the increase in renal vascular resistance was unequivocally greater in the hypertensive group." Lumbodorsal sympathectomy and splanchnicectomy of 6 hypertensive patients were seen to result in a reversal of the renal pattern just described at the time of the emotionally induced elevation of systemic arterial pressure, and was interpreted as a failure of the efferent glomerular arterioles to participate in the reaction whereas the afferent arterioles remained responsive. Thus, a sympathetic control of efferent glomerular arterioles of the kidney was postulated along with an intrinsic, or an intrarenal humoral, control of afferent glomerular arterioles. These effects contrast with those of ACTH and cortisone administration which, as has been noted earlier, produce an increase in renal blood flow (620) and a progressive increase in glomerular filtration fraction (772) as well as a reduction in tubular reabsorption capacity for glucose (248).

It has been said that the changes in water secretion cannot be attributed to changes in glomerular filtration (570, 1161); hence the effects noted above of adrenaline and parasympathetic stimulation and of probable changes in the posterior pituitary antidiuretic hormone are implicated in the diuretic reaction, which has been associated particularly with "apprehension" and "anxiety." Hinkle et al. noted the common clinical observation of frequent urination with feelings of anxiety and apprehension (569, 576), and they cited reports of diuresis with experimentation (321, 569), with hypnosis (547, 588, 875), and with the expectation of going into combat (569). In the experiment of Hinkle et al., diuresis occurred in 11 of 12 subjects who were experiencing intense conflicts during discussion of personal topics, and the periods of increased urine flow appeared to be related to specific personal conflicts only in the degree to which such conflicts aroused anxiety (569). The one subject who showed no diuresis expressed feelings of depression and anger, but there was no evidence of anxiety, whereas all the other subjects were anxious during their interview. The diuresis was characterized by a 200 to 500 per cent increase in urine volume, a fall in specific gravity of the urine, and a fall in the concentration of chlorides.

Hinkle and Wolf also observed that diuresis usually occurred in a setting of anxiety in a nondiabetic woman as well as in diabetic patients, 64 of whom were included in their study (576). In the comparing of experimental and control groups of 14 patients with diabetes mellitus in each group, Hinkle, Edwards and Wolf injected stressful personal topics in their interviews with the experimental group (570). They found this to result in diuresis with a rise in the excretion of chlorides and ketone bodies; in the diabetic patients with glycosuria, the glucose excretion paralleled the rate of water excretion and was considered to be an important factor in the development of diabetic acidosis and coma. Stress diuresis was seen not to be dependent on osmotic changes related to the excretion of glucose nor on changes in the concentration of glucose in the blood. It was also seen that diabetic patients could tolerate ingestion of concentrated glucose solutions in the absence of stress, but that with stress, the loss of water and chlorides might be accentuated.

No studies have been found in the literature relating directly to the hip area (Area No. 25).

SHOULDER AREAS (Area No. 5) AND EXTREMITY AREAS
(Areas No. 16, 17, 18, 27 and 28)

Most of the reports that present physiological correlates of psychological changes for these areas have been elaborated under the section dealing with the skin (p. 195), because such studies generally have employed psychogalvanic skin measurements. Conversely, most of the studies employing the psychogalvanometer and measures of skin temperature have restricted their measurements to these areas, and particularly to the palm of the hand.

The study of Malmo et al. of 21 controls and 75 psychoneurotic and psychotic patients under three stress conditions showed that the mean arm-muscle tension of psychotic patients was reliably higher than that of the controls, although it was approximately equal to that of the other patient group (866). A slight negative correlation was found between finger movement and the muscle tension of the arm, which is particularly significant in that in earlier studies these authors had differentiated anxiety patients from other psychiatric patients and from controls on the basis of finger movement (861, 864, 867). In some cases the maximum increase of tension in the arm, as shown by the electromyogram (EMG), was just prior to the starting signal and was interpreted as reflecting anticipation. Individual consistency in muscle tension was seen with the three different stress situations, which included a pain-stress (of the Hardy-Wolff thermal stimulator), a speed-discrimination test, and a mirror-drawing task.

Psychoneurotic tremors, which are frequently seen clinically, have been found to have characteristics different from tremors of organic origin (145). The study of finger movements by Malmo et al., referred to above, included 75 neuropsychiatric patients divided into three groups of anxiety, early schizophrenic, and other types, and finger movements were measured under the stress of the thermal stimulator (860, 861). The greatest finger movement was found in the anxiety group; the early schizophrenic group most resembled the anxiety group in terms of their responsiveness in terms of several different physiological measurements. By comparison with the clinical status of the case, these measurements showed that, in general, the severity of the anxiety appeared to be related to the degree of reaction to the physiological disturbance, i.e., the more severe the anxiety, the greater the overreaction to the pain stimulation. Jost also found a mixed group of emotionally disturbed children to show more hand tremors both before and after frustration tests than well-adjusted children, although gross movement was not significantly different (656). As early as 1932, Luria recorded tremor and stated that emotional conflict resulted in tremor and in disorganization of motor response (823). Berrien concluded that of nine variables considered in finger oscillations, three were more indicative of emotional reactions, namely, average length per cycle, variability of the wave trough, and "T units" (115). "T units" refer to the average number of time units elapsing between the moment that the upstroke on the kymograph was almost completed and the moment that the downstroke was definitely under way. The stimulus consisted of emotionally significant questions relating to the patient's past experiences. In this study 16 psychotic subjects were employed.

Observations on 47 patients with complaints of "cold hand" or Raynaud's syndrome showed that a drop in skin temperature of the finger occurred in all but three instances with 2 subjects when they were under the stress of having their histories taken and of discussion of bodily complaints and difficulties in life situations (922). In a later study with 30 ulcer patients, they also found a usual drop in finger temperature with tension, anxiety, resentment, anger, and guilt (923). Ulcerative-colitis patients, however, have shown finger vasodilatation with "anxiety and fear" that led to no effective action and relief (678a). Changes in finger-skin temperature have also been observed during stressful interviews with 27 healthy, well-adjusted males (220).

Now that the physiological and psychological correlates have been considered in this section, discussion of the integrated and interrelated functioning of the various body systems in different psychological (feeling) states will be presented in Part V. The internal sensations will be discussed in Part IV.

CHAPTER 14

Constitutional Factors

THEORETICAL AND HISTORICAL CONSIDERATIONS

In the consideration of all the physiological changes that have been presented in the preceding chapters, there remains the problem of ascertaining the degree to which changes of these types are constitutionally inherited or environmentally established, or both. Human physical appearance and behavior traits seem to be influenced by both physical constitution and past experiences, and the question is still open as to what extent these are determined by inheritance or by the individual's adjustment to his environment. Also, in a given set of constitutional characteristics, what are the limitations and the alternatives for subsequent changes that may be effected by either the individual himself or by his environment? Needless to say, all physiological reactions have a constitutional basis in the physical make-up of the human species. However, the fact is that within given limitations, individual variations in the functioning of given body parts and processes are seen, and, here too, the question is presented as to whether such differences arise primarily from heredity or from the individual's functional mode of adjustment to his environment.

Actually, this problem is seen to be somewhat more complicated than the statement implies when one considers detailed factors involving both psychological states and physiological functioning. For example, a given individual might be found to have a higher blood pressure than most other people, and his blood pressure might even be a characteristic of his immediate family and of his predecessors; however, if increased blood pressure is found to be a characteristic of anger feelings (suppressed, repressed or otherwise), the question occurs as to whether the increased blood pressure or whether the anger may be etiologically primary and which, if either, is inherited or culturally transmitted (learned) by the family. The same type of question can be presented for all of those physiological reactions, described in the preceding sections, that were seen to vary with different psychological states and personality constellations. Such factors need to be closely evaluated in longitudinal studies over several generations; however, this type of study is particularly difficult to accomplish. An opinion has been expressed that the necessary longitudinal studies of genetic, psychological, and physiological types that may completely evaluate the relative influence of nature and nurture in personality development and human functioning will probably not be accomplished within this generation (404). Some progress concerning inheritance-environment relationships has been made by horizontal studies, which compare the characteristics of different individuals, groups, and family members as measured at a given time. Primarily, only the few available studies of the last type will be presented here.

The history of attempts to associate human physical types with given temperamental or personality characteristics extends at least back to the time of Hippocrates (814, 1028). In more recent times, attempts to elaborate on relationships between body structure and personality type have been made by Viola (1272) in Italy, by Carus (211) and Beneke (103) in Germany, and by several investigators in the United States and England (1028). These studies were criticized by Rees and Eysenck, when they referred to the sampling methods employed in their own work of this type, as follows (1028, p. 8):

> The number of persons measured had sometimes been rather small; the number of measurements taken had not always been sufficient; and the samples studied (students, psychotics, adolescent boys and girls) bore little resemblance to the material with which we had to deal.

MORPHOLOGY-PERSONALITY CLASSIFICATIONS

There have been many contributors to the investigations and theories of morphology-personality classifications (1129), but the best known is Kretschmer. He described the following types: (1) an "asthenic" (or "leptosomic") type, which referred to a relatively thin bony physique and which he reported to be predisposed toward schizoid psychopathology; (2) a "pyknic" type, which referred to a relatively fatty, massive physique and which he reported to be predisposed to more vigorously expressive psychopathologies, such as manic-depressive psychosis; (3) an "athletic" type, which referred to a relatively muscular physique; and (4) a "dysplastic" type, which he conceived to include incompatible mixtures of the other types in physique and in temperamental characteristics (732).

Well known also is the work of W. H. Sheldon and associates who employed extensive statistical techniques to study the relative relationships between the degree of physical type and the degree of associated personality characteristics (1129, 1130, 1131, 1132). It might be expected from what has already been presented concerning body processes and their interrelationships that varying kinds and degrees of predominant psychological states ("feeling and emotion") might be associated with characteristic body structures, which in turn could be classified in terms of personality types. Sheldon classified human morphology in terms of varying degrees of the following types of structural characteristics: (1) "endomorphy," in which the emphasis in structure is on the digestive viscera; (2) "mesomorphy," in which the emphasis in structure is on the bone, muscle, and connective tissues; and (3) "ectomorphy," in which the emphasis in structure is on fragility, linearity, flatness of chest, and delicacy throughout (1132).

In a separate study, a classification of 60 personality traits was made (1131). The traits that correlated positively with each other and that negatively correlated with all the other traits were grouped together. This resulted in three clusters of closely associated traits; no fourth cluster could be determined by statistical analysis. The three constellations of personality characteristics were named as follows: (1) "viscerotonia," characterized by general relaxation, love of comfort, sociability, and gluttony for food, for people and for affection; (2) "somatotonia," characterized by a predominance of muscular activity and vigorous bodily assertiveness; and (3) "cerebrotonia," characterized by restraint, inhibition, and the desire for concealment. A correlation of body types with personality types in terms of these classifications was undertaken. This study produced a positive correlation of +.80 between the morphological and temperamental characteristics that were just listed above; endomorphy was associated with viscerotonia, mesomorphy with somatotonia, and ectomorphy with cerebrotonia. It should be kept in mind, however, that these correlations of traits and physical characteristics represent constellations. Thus, the questions remain as to what more basic or fundamental physiological processes underlie these constellations and what relationships these processes have to personality formation and, more specifically, to psychological states.

Many studies pertain strictly to classification and nosology of body characteristics, but only a few of these will be presented here. Using an obverse-factor-analysis technique for the analysis of photographs of hospitalized male psychotic patients, which included 5 subjects for each of Sheldon's three body types selected from a sample of 90, Lorr and Fields found morphological-trait patterns similar to the three described by Sheldon, even though the variables defining these patterns were not restricted to Sheldon's three components (814). It was suggested, however, that the 76 somatotypes identified by Sheldon could be more simply defined in terms of two factor types, namely: (1) a bipolar factor defined at either end of the continuum by the endomorphs and ectomorphs, with muscularity relatively absent in this type, and (2) a factor defined by mesomorphs, with muscularity highly predominant.

Howells also conducted a separate morphological analysis, and compared the results to those of Sheldon (606). He did a factor-analysis study of 15 individuals who were extremely dominant in either endomorphy, mesomorphy, or ectomorphy, and employed thirty-four different measurements for intercorrelation. Three factor groupings were reported: the first expressed "mass," and opposed endomorphy directly to ectomorphy; the second opposed "top heaviness" to "bottom heaviness" (which was thought not to be the equivalent of androgyny); and the third opposed "trunk-face development" to "limb development." Although Howells added that these groupings would not necessarily apply outside the sample used, he thought that questions were raised, applicable to Sheldon's components, as to whether endomorphy and ectomorphy are relatively independent, or are basically only one continuum, and whether there may exist other components not covered by Sheldon's system.

Morphological variations among different races were seen in Kraus's comparison of Sheldon's seventy-six somatotypes with those for 544 adult Japanese male office workers in northern Japan (726). Only twenty-five somatotypes were revealed for this population, and two of these types accounted for more than 37 per cent of the sample. No somatotypes were found among the Japanese that were not reported by Sheldon for the Americans; conversely, the somatotypes that comprised 75 per cent of the American sample were not found among the Japanese.

Employing statistical methods, Burt reported clearly differentiated "eurymorphic" and "leptomorphic" types among adults and children; however, in the study of several groups, including various ages and normal and psychoneurotic types, only low positive correlations, "too small to be of any practical value," were found between physical type and "temperamental type" (181, p. 542). He added, however, that there were "numerous minor indications suggesting that the correlations of temperamental characteristics with physiological types, or what perhaps may be called the individual's biochemical pattern, may prove much larger."

More positive findings were reported by Rees and Eysenck, who employed Kretschmer's leptosomatic-pyknic scales to make somatoscopic gradings and employed factor analysis of various anthropomorphic measurements in a study of 389 successive hospital admissions, which included 200 neurotic patients and 100 nonneurotic soldiers (1028). A correlation of $+.962$ was found between the two methods employed. Three main body types were designated, which were similar to Kretschmer's classifications but were in a continuum in relation to preponderant growth in breadth and length: (1) leptomorph, which was defined as having an index of body type of more than one standard deviation (SD) above the mean; (2) eurymorph, which was defined as having an index of more than one SD below the mean; and (3) mesomorph, which was defined as being intermediate between these two. The body-type index was calculated for 400 neurotic soldiers and was correlated with 200 psychiatric-trait ratings. This revealed leptomorphs to have tendencies toward the "affective group of symptoms," including anxiety, depression, and obsession, and it revealed eurymorphs to show tendencies toward "the hysterical group of symptoms," which were considered much less psychopathological than the former. The neurotic soldiers appeared to be slightly more leptomorphic than the nonneurotic soldiers; however, the difference was not statistically significant. The neurotic group included a significantly higher number of leptomorphs and eurymorphs, as well as a significantly smaller number of mesomorphs, than did the nonneurotic group. These findings supported earlier ones of Eysenck based on a study of 700 neurotic soldiers (345). An association of "frank aggression" with a high degree of somatotonia has been suggested (888a).

STUDIES OF SPECIFIC FUNCTIONS AND CHARACTERISTICS

Environmental influences affecting morphology can be exemplified by the emphasis of Deutsch and others (298, 434a, 1255) on functional factors in obesity (see p. 396). Similarly, Fry compared 39 "fat" children to 50 control children in terms of medical, anthropometric, and psychosocial variables (401). No evidence of constitutional factors was found, but it was noted that a large percentage of the "fat" children had been treated as the "baby" of the family.

Both the physical and the psychosocial environments are, of course, factors to be considered in the evaluating of variations in morphology. For example, McFarland suggested that the ease of adaptation to high altitude is inversely related to body weight (831). In this connection, Andean native children were found to be significantly of less weight than children of similar racial stock at sea level. Similarly, it was reported that obesity was rarely found among the adult natives.

Nothwithstanding such findings, constitutional factors are more frequently emphasized in reports that relate to body type and personality characteristics, since it is common knowledge that physical body characteristics and appearance are inherited to a considerable degree. Similarly, findings and expressed opinions that variations in characteristics of some physiological functions are constitutional or inherited or both are frequently seen. Nielsen and Roth thought that six of nine types of spirograms, which they classified from 20,000 readings, were hereditary (953). Mirsky inferred from the findings of a high quantity of pepsinogen in a "significant number" of neonates that a consequent pattern of excessive hunger and "oral demanding" characteristics might affect the infant's relationship to his mother and result in the type of personality problems seen commonly in peptic-ulcer patients (917). It had appeared to Draper et al. that "within limits persons afflicted with the same illness exhibit a characteristic morphology," suggesting that "the nature of the anatomic panel may often indicate a relationship between total personality and disease" (307, 308). In investigating this, electrocardiographic components were compared for 107 ulcer patients, 37 gall-bladder patients, and 578 general hospital patients with normal records in these respects. Significant differences between the EKG curve patterns for persons with ulcers and persons with gall-bladder disease appeared to exist within certain age groups, and these differences were also reported to vary significantly from the records of the general hospital patients. In another study, the similarities of the pressor and other cardiovascular reactions in a pair of girl twins were presented as evidence that certain stocks possess proclivities for the development of specific disorders (362, 1128, 1357). Some suggestions of heredity in types of electroencephalographic-wave patterns have also been reported (472, 688, 689). The basis for considering inborn discharge thresholds in psychoanalytic theory has been presented by Rapaport, who stated (1022, p. 185) :

These considerations are not pure theoretical niceties: there are clinical phenomena necessitating some such assumption. (a) The psychosomatic symptoms appearing in the first days of life, such as infantile exemata, inclination to colics, and also the early manifested individual differences, e.g. of hypo- and hyper-motility, suggest the crucial role of differential thresholds in channelling the discharge of tensions into specific individually varying directions [340].

STUDIES OF TWINS

A somewhat different approach in the study of relationships of constitutional structure to personality characteristics is the evaluation of relative personality features of twins and other family members on the presumption that degrees of genealogical constitutional relatedness exist. The major shortcoming of this method is the virtual impossibility of eliminating or isolating common environmental variables that may account for findings of similarity among the family members. Studies of twins have usually revealed similarities that the investigators frequently attribute to constitutional factors; however, environmental influences have also been given emphasis (368, 951).

Kallman reported studies based on twin-index cases that included co-twins and siblings and parents of 1252 psychotic cases and over 2500 senescent cases (669, 670, 671). He, like others (1157a), found a relatively high familial incidence for specific types of various psychoses, with a higher incidence for more closely related family-member classifications. It was also stated that "affective instability and biochemical dysfunction produced by the manic-depressive genotype" appeared to be correlated with "genetic factors" for gout, diabetes, and, especially, an obesity tendency. A study of one identical twin with duodenal ulcer, and the other without it related the former's ulcer to a bad marital situation whereas the latter's marriage satisfied his dependency and other needs (994a).

Shields studied 36 identical and 26 fraternal same-sex twins, who were school children twelve to fifteen years of age, in order to assess their liability to psychiatric disorder (1142). Although the genetic factor in individual differences and in similarities of the twins' personalities was recognized, it was seen that identical twins did not always suffer from the same complaint in the same degree, and the case histories suggested environmental explanations for such differences.

Other experimenters have felt that constitutional factors should be emphasized on the basis of clinical observation of the frequent occurrence of given diagnostic personality constellations in different patients, on the presumption that common factors must be sought in the specific or nonspecific genes of the individual that manifest themselves in the individual anatomy, physiology and chemistry of the human body (753) Clinical observations were thought to be related to the finding of closer similarity in autonomic reactions of twin children in comparison to nontwin siblings who, in turn, showed greater similarity in reaction than did unrelated children (655).

BREEDING

The observation of different temperamental characteristics in different breeds of a given species of animal, as well as the breeding of given strains to produce desired characteristics, lends support to the hypothesis that different human ingroups may possess constitutionally different personality tendencies (1074). Standard tests have been experimentally developed whereby "emotional" rats and "fearless" rats could be distinguished (513, 1376). Rats with these different characteristics were kept apart, and by means of selective inbreeding, it was seen that the descendants of the original groupings came to reproduce animals with the characteristics designated. Anatomical analysis of these rats showed that the "emotional" rats possessed much larger adrenal, thyroid, and pituitary glands than did the "fearless" rats. Presumably, the internal environment of these two types was considerably different in respect to physiological functioning and reactivity. Many similar studies have been reported (513). On the other hand, Scott concluded, in assessing the relative importance of social and hereditary factors that produce disturbances in life adjustment during periods of stress for laboratory animals, that social factors are more important than hereditary factors, but hereditary factors were also considered to be important; consequently, there was thought to be "little point" in trying to determine the actual relative importance of these factors except in specific situations (1117).

It seems to me, however, that the determination of constitutional characteristics and the determination of the limitations of variability and of malleability of physiological-psychological relationships are of the utmost importance in the development of the science of psychology and in the understanding and treatment of human behavior. Some reference has been made to environmental factors in human development in Parts I and II, but no attempt has been made to elaborate the nurture-nature problem beyond the presenting of studies that specifically relate physiological functioning and noncognitive psychological functioning.

Part IV

Physiological Changes Associated with Internal Sensations

CHAPTER 15

Theoretical Developments Concerning

Internal Sensations

EARLY VIEWS

The studies considered in Part III, which related noncognitive psychological states to physiological functioning, stemmed for the most part from medical research; contributions from psychology were of secondary significance. Internal sensations have been given major consideration by the medical profession, though the concern has been primarily of a diagnostic and physiological nature. Actually, very little has been done in the direction of the considering of the relationship of internal sensations to noncognitive inner experiences, even though some limited steps were made in this direction in the investigations of Wundt's three-dimensional theory of feeling.

As discussed in Chapter 5, Wundt's theory proposed that feeling is the subjective aspect of "pure sensation" and postulated the polar feeling dimensions of "pleasantness-unpleasantness," "arousing (exciting)-subduing (depressing)," and "strain-relaxing" in addition to the characteristics of quality and intensity (591, 1373). Wundt attempted to support his theory by reinterpreting the results of physiological measures taken by Lehmann under various psychological conditions, but Shepard disputed the validity of this and of other theoretical assertions on the basis of his own early experimental study of "organic changes and feelings" (1134). Shepard took various physiological measurements while his subjects made empirical introspective judgments in terms of Wundt's classification categories. Another type of early experimentation involved empirical introspective reports of sensations experienced during hunger, thirst, nausea, "call to defecation," and urination as investigated by Boring (138)

Already presented in Chapter 10 was the experimental work concerning Wundt's theory, which came under the influence of Titchener and his psychological school. It will suffice here to recall that Titchener used the so-called method of impressionism, which was principally the technique of paired comparisons, in asking his subjects to analyze their affective experiences as they made choices between simple stimuli, such as colored pieces of paper. In rebutting Titchener's criticisms of his theory, Wundt asserted that such techniques would produce a "complex" or a "fusion" of feeling and could not constitute disproof of the dimensions of feeling as postulated by him.

There were in addition a few other observations concerning Wundt's theory. Vogt reported that the qualities of "pleasantness-unpleasantness" and of "elevation-depression" were differentiated by a woman under hypnosis (95, p. 60). Alechsieff became the first to support Wundt's theory experimentally at a time when most psychologists supported the Titchenerian view, but he too submitted to the views of Titchener and Orth to the extent of trying to prove that Wundt's feeling dimensions were of a nonsensory nature (95, p. 63). These investigators sought a criterion of feeling as differentiated from external sensation, namely, something "indefinable and unanalyzable" and consequently something to be classed as an elementary psychical process. Beebe-Center stated that Wundt dominated the psychology of the 1900s in this field and that the first systematic issue dealt with experimentally was this minor issue of his "qualities" and not the more important issue of the relationship between "feelings" and the other psychical classifications (95). Titchener's attack on Wundt's effective qualities began a tradition for approach to the problems of affective experience that limited the scope of psychological perspective to a narrow aspect of the larger problem concerning the nature of inner experience, and that tradition still exerts an influence. With this approach, "affective experience" came to be considered synonymous with judgments of relative pleasantness; however, only in relatively recent times has this implication of the tradition become clearly recognized (988, 989). Nevertheless, a striking aspect of the experiments by the Titchenerian group—which was considered to be incidental and even an interference at the time—were the almost invariable reports of internal sensations.

Gradually, the hypothesis that internal sensations might have a bearing on the problems of affective experience began to receive recognition by members of this group. Still, the academic consideration of these sensations has usually been narrowed to their meaning according to the Titchenerian tradition. About the same time as internal sensations began to be considered in this respect, another new approach to the understanding of the broader nature of affective life was in the making. By the 1920s, Watson, Cannon, and others had made progress in the understanding of noncognitive inner experience by means of expressive experimental techniques, and approaches embodying external, "objective" techniques soon came to dominate research relating to the nature of "feeling and emotion."

Ruckmick dated the concept that considers "affectivity" to be based on sensory experience to 1893, when Burbon identified pleasantness with tickling, and to 1894, when von Frey considered unpleasantness to be the same as pain and pleasantness to be the avoidance of pain (95, 1071). Stumpf was also included in the early history of this concept, since in 1907 he set forth a classification of affective sensations that labeled tickle, itch, euphoria, and sexual, and other "coanesthetic" sensations as pleasurable and identified unpleasantness with pain. In 1917, Titchener stated that Stumpf's position maintained that the term "emotion" should be used to refer to actual functions, or "acts" (1248). Stumpf asserted that "elementary feelings" are in fact sensory phenomena and that there is no justification for the use of the term "feeling." Nevertheless, it was not until some doubt began to be cast on the then-dominant Titchenerian tradition that a theory postulating a sensory basis of feeling—a sensory theory—really began to evolve in experimental psychology.

CRYSTALLIZATION OF THE SENSORY THEORY

The first person to cast this doubt on the Titchenerian theory was Nakoshima in 1909 (95). He employed tones and colors as stimuli for affective experience and observed that practically all subjects described internal sensations (947). He also found that the subjects required a longer time to make judgments concerning Titchener's postulated "affective quality" than to report their sensory experiences. Nevertheless, he favored the Titchenerian view. Koch, of Germany, asserted in 1914 that the prerequisite to the testing of Wundt's three-dimensional theory would be an experimental determination of the criteria of "pleasantness" (P) and "unpleasantness" (U) (95, p. 69). He experimented with eleven criteria and reported that: (1) subjects invariably reported organic sensations as concomitants of P and U; (2) P and U are independent of objective stimuli, but so are organic sensations; (3) P and U are sometimes weakened by attention and sometimes strengthened; and (4) observers reported imaginal P and U independent of objective stimulation. He concluded that the problem of whether Wundt's qualities should be classed with pleasant and unpleasant feelings or with sensation no longer existed because all these must be sensory.

It was about 1921, however, with Yokoyama's experiment, which employed colored paper as stimulation for affective experience, that the new movement really began to break away from the Titchenerian tradition (1377). Yokoyama concluded that P and U judgments as meanings are made by all observers and that evidence for these as "non-sensory existential processes" is weaker than evidence for them as sensory mental processes. The loss of P and U concomitants with the diminution of sensory organic content of consciousness was also noted. Yokoyama asserted that "P and U, whether sensory or non-sensory, are to be thought of as integral to the total organic complex," and he concluded that "organic sensory content is the *sine qua non* of P and U." In the same year P. T. Young reported a similar experiment to determine the relationship between P and U and organic responses (1379). Each observation was scored for the intensity of P, U, and I (indifference) and for the presence or absence of organic sensations. Many organic sensations were reported that included warmth, cold, and pressures that were referred to the chest, heart, and trunk. Yet, 38 per cent of the reports of P and U were made without reference to organic sensations. Young considered the possibility of subliminal physiological changes since he found that the average organic score for reports of I was less than scores for P or U and that as the intensity of P and U decreased, the organic scores approached that of I. He concluded that "there is no *sine qua non* of P and U." Nevertheless, Young's findings strongly supported the view that internal sensory experience is an important aspect of affective experience.

In 1922, Warren contended that "a feeling is an experience in which systemic sensations are the main element" and that these are made up of organic or pain sensations or both (1280). He observed that when systemic sensations combine into feelings, their special qualities usually fade away and the prominent feature is their pleasantness or unpleasantness.

"BRIGHT" AND "DULL" PRESSURES

With Nafe's work in 1924 a sensory theory really began to receive some recognition. He, as all experimenters in this field, employed simple sensory stimuli in the tradition of Titchener. Also, the problem considered was the one of the Titchenerian tradition. The issue was still the nature of "feeling," as pleasantness and unpleasantness, and not the broader problems of inner experience. Nafe helped to clarify the issue, however, by asserting that the nature of the term "affective quality" is an assumption. At that time, the concept that any term is a mere symbol of a phenomenon, *as defined or approximately set forth,* was not generally emphasized. Then, as very frequently now, terms such as "affect" were assumed to possess an innateness in themselves. Scientists and writers attempted to define such terms by referring to other more or less vague terms and phenomena. They did not recognize the need for setting forth all terms as being reducible to specific aspects of the given phenomenon or phenomena. Nevertheless, Nafe broke with the Titchenerian tradition in asserting that (945, p. 507): "The presence of the impalpables in scientific subject matter is, indeed, . . . anomalous, if not contradictory. We decided, therefore, to show the courage of our scientific convictions and to assume that the affective qualities are palpable." He also believed that previous experiments had made an "error of transcendence" because the experimental subjects had been asked to divide their attention by doing two things at once—namely, to observe the experiment and at the same time to apply logic concerning it. Nafe emphasized the importance of not overburdening the observer in a way that would make him timid or anxious. He maintained that a stimulus of moderate intensity was required for these experiments so that the feeling would not reach the proportions of an "emotion." Nafe employed visual, auditory, olfactory, gustatory, and tactual stimuli, and asked his subjects to "attend exclusively to the affection" in order to determine whether it is "so loose as to have no reference to the sensation" or whether it was "tied to the sensation." The subjects used many terms of a sensory nature to describe their subjective experience. Since this work was done at Cornell, however, and since all the subjects were familiar with Titchener's "touch pyramid," all of them finally agreed on the terms "bright pressure" and "dull pressure" as adequate descriptions for their sensory experiences of pleasantness (P) and unpleasantness (U), respectively. These observers also reported that an experience might be neither P nor U.

By 1927, Nafe had come to the conclusion that the terms "bright" and "dull" pressure were not descriptive of affective experience as such, and that these terms had meaning for his subjects only because of their familiarity with Titchenerian terminology (945). He indicated that by "bright pressure" Titchener meant not tactual pressure but rather a feeling of well-being and that "dull pressure" referred to a heavier feeling. Both of these terms appeared to represent a fusion of experience comparable to the simultaneous application of hot and cold stimuli to the skin. Nafe concluded that affection is palpable and stands up under observation and that it has an independent variable of intensity. He stated (946, p. 387) that psychologically "an emotion and an affection must be defined alike and both are complexes of sensory experiences."

In 1927, Young performed an experiment similar to those of Nafe, but he used three subjects who each had different psychological training back-grounds (1380). He obtained varied results and concluded that the matter of description and localization of P and U depends on one's concept of the terms. That is, those who think of P and U as sensory can describe and localize them, whereas those who think of them as nonsensory and nonclear affective processes cannot.

Hunt employed a different technique to test the reality of "bright and dull pressures" (611). His subjects first made judgments in terms of bright and dull pressures in regard to the experience produced by stimuli of colored paper. Later the subjects were presented with the same stimuli and asked to make judgments concerning the P or U of their experiences. The correlation found was $+.90$. He concluded that these findings supported Nafe's conten-tion but did not prove it. Three alternative interpretations of the results were suggested: (1) affection is bright and dull pressure; (2) affection and bright and dull pressures depend upon identical processes but also upon different attitudes (awareness); or (3) affection is accompanied by bright and dull pressures. Hunt favored the last alternative.

A year later, Converse repeated Hunt's experiment but used tones and different types of music as stimuli (250). She obtained only a $+.39$ correla-tion and concluded that these results did not support Hunt. She asserted that his high correlation might be due to "laboratory atmosphere" or other "unspecified and unspecific" conditions, and she maintained that the terms "bright" and "dull" are themselves very suggestive of P and U experience. This opinion was supported to some extent by Ruckmick's 1935 study based on questionnaires that requested judgments relative to the localization of "bright and dull" pressures (1072). It should be recalled, however, that Nafe had already recognized the problem of terminology.

OTHER FORMULATIONS OF THE SENSORY THEORY

Subsequently, an article by W. A. Hunt brought focus on the broader aspects of research concerning affective experience (613). Hunt "proposed that the terms 'Pleasantness' and 'Unpleasantness' be viewed as broad generic concepts covering a multitude of related, but by no means identical, phenomena" (613, p. 815). These concepts were thought to develop by "verbal conditioning" that associated bodily experiences with the elements of the affective situation, but once established, verbal responses were thought to be independent of immediate bodily involvements. Hunt also asserted that he "confirmed Nafe in a sceptical atmosphere," and he even confirmed the localization of "bright pressure" in the upper chest and of "dull pressure" in the abdomen and lower trunk (611a). This last finding referred to the experimental findings of Horiguchis in 1927, which were also supported by the work of Hoisington (589).

With an approach apparently independent of the types of experiments noted above, H. C. Warren localized sensations of his own that he identified with feeling experiences (1280). Sensations of "fear" were localized in the lower viscera and in the region of the lungs and heart; sensations of "anger" were localized in the upper digestive tract, heart and lungs, and circulatory system; and sensations of "love" were localized in the lungs and generative organs. He also felt "anger" to be less unpleasant than "fear."

GEMELLI'S CONCEPTS

In 1949, Gemelli, of Italy, reported experiments that covered three years and employed simple stimuli similar to the earlier experimentation described above, and he also employed musical selections and poems to produce "more pronounced feelings" (433). His subjects described numerous "psychic processes," including "perceptions, representations, tendencies, volitional acts, etc." that accompanied affective states. At the same time, they described a variety of specific internal (organic) sensations that were localized in various parts of the body. The "vast variety" of these sensations proved difficult to classify, but affective states were reported only with concomitant internal sensations. Gemelli formulated the following concerning his research (433, pp. 213, 299, 302):

> Thus our findings indicate that at the very core, so to speak, of what the organism *feels,* there is a special manner of being and feeling of the organism itself. . .
> Now between the feelings and the tendencies there is a close connection, as has been pointed out already. Each group of feelings shows that underlying it there is a group of tendencies. . . Thus we see that tendencies unite with the affective resonance set up by them to form a biological complex—the feeling and impulse being only two different aspects of the same endothymic life. . . We are, therefore, dealing with a fluid matter, as it were, and it is vain to hope that feelings can be actually fixed and formulated.

Gemelli favored a functional approach in psychology, and he proposed recourse to introspection for the interpreting of the difference in affective behavior. He equated biological and psychological homeostatic functioning, and in this he emphasized the unconscious aspects of basic tendencies as being "a part of life itself" and "an orientation of energies." Feelings were conceived of as having a basis in internal sensation and as functioning in the regulation of action, such as "at times stimulating it (as in joy) and at other times restraining it (as in depression)" and such as modifying behavior in the continuous interchange between self and environment, with feeling being directed toward persons and things and being the basis of values.

Gemelli believed that a complete enumeration of types of feeling is impossible because they are vague and there are no terms to describe them and because they are an elementary and primitive state of consciousness. Therefore, feelings were thought to be named either by referring to the organ in which they are localized, or by referring to the external and internal causes that produce them, or by referring to the inclinations and the instincts that they express.

MASON'S RESEARCH

In 1941, I formulated concepts of inner experiences and feelings somewhat similar to those of Gemelli (876), and in recent years I have undertaken three experiments employing stimuli designed to engender common feeling experiences in order to determine relative emphasis on differential bodily locations of internal sensations with different feeling experiences (877, 878, 879, 879a). In the first, a small number of graduate-student subjects observed and rated any internal sensations noticed according to body localization while imagining themselves in situations of interest that had occurred earlier in the day (877). This procedure was repeated by each subject over a series of 129 observations at the rate of approximately 3 per day. In the second experiment, standard stimuli consisting of pictures and corresponding emotionally toned stories were presented to 36 college-student subjects in groups of approximately 6 each who rated ten body areas for the presence or absence, the intensity, and the depth of sensation (if any) and who rated the type of feeling reaction produced by the stimulus (if any) (878). A third study employed 178 relatively healthy army subjects and 139 army patients of various diagnostic types who rated the ten body areas for the presence or absence of internal sensation and for its intensity (if any) during seven short motion-picture scenes (879). These scenes were themselves rated for the feeling reactions they produced by 94 additional healthy army subjects. The group sizes averaged 16.1 subjects per session for the sensation ratings and 31.3 subjects per session for the feeling-reaction ratings. The results of these studies will be presented under the appropriate body-area classifications that will follow and especially under the section pertaining to the sensations that accompany different psychological states. It may be noted here, however, that in the last, more extensive study, 91.5 per cent of the subjects reported internal sensations during the experimental observations and an additional 3.6 per cent reported internal sensations only during the practice observations. Also, statistical analysis of variance showed that the over-all differences in the ratings between the ten anatomical areas, between the seven situations, and between the areas and situations each were significantly different at less than the .1 per cent level of probability.

OTHER CONCEPTS INVOLVING SENSATION

In recent years there has been a gradually increasing recognition of the role of feelings and of internal sensations in human experience, but the theoretical approaches in the attributing of roles to internal sensations have been varied and frequently limited in scope. Werner and Wapner presented a theory of perception in which emphasis was placed on "sensory-tonic" experience as follows (1306, p. 91):

> This means that the factors contributing to perception are tonic as well as sensory. Tonus is used in its wide connotation. It includes the state of the organismic tension as evidenced by the visceral as well as by the somatic (muscular-skeletal) reactivity. It refers to the dynamic (motion) and the static (posture) state of the organism.

Perception was conceived of in terms of various levels, of which the "sensory-tonic" level was considered to be the most basic and primary, although the concept of the organism as a whole was also embodied.

Many concepts concerning internal sensations were presented at the Mooseheart Symposium in 1948 (1033), including the views of Piéron (994), Michotte (901), and Shock (1144), as well as of others who have been cited earlier in connection with the James—Cannon controversy. Similarly, other writers have recently emphasized the afferent sensory component of feeling or emotions, as well as the implications of such functioning in emotional maladjustment (17, 358, 1331). The importance of realistic bodily awareness and "self-concept," which involve cognitive factors, have also been reported (461, 1100). A somewhat different type of sensory awareness in relation to noncognitive inner experience is emphasized in Indian psychology, which was discussed in Chapter 5 (57, 1124).

The work of Burrow (175, 176, 177, 178), the late director of the Lifwynn Foundation, and of Ødegaard (959, 960) represents a rather unique approach in respect to internal sensations. These writers placed primary emphasis on broad generalities; however, Burrow stated that "the immediate business of the phylobiologist, therefore, is with internally perceptible behavior patterns and with a concrete appreciation of a differentiation in internal systems of tension—a differentiation through which man may determine what is homeostasis or cotentive behavior and what is conflict or ditentive behavior" (178, p. 479). He added that many years were required to produce these findings and concepts. Cotention, it was said, implies integration, co-ordination or health, whereas ditention implies disintegration, disorder or disease. Cotention was considered to be the primary or natural state. Finally, physiological measurements were employed to some extent to support these concepts, and their findings will be presented in the appropriate sections of this book.

Deutsch has emphasized that the "psychological implications of psychosomatic processes can be fully understood only if the interaction of the sensory perceptions and their related psychic elements can be traced back to their earliest sources and shown as an entity" (299b, p. 293). Early cathected sense perceptions were considered as forming a body ego, and in different phases of development, sensory constellations are hierarchically built up and differently grouped. He believed, like Schilder (1093a), that no isolated sense impression exists, that synesthesia is a basic principle of perception and that specificity is determined structurally and by time level. Changes in emotional attitudes toward objects were found to depend upon constellations of ego-governed, instinctual-sensory patterns and on the dominance of one or another sensory feeling within the total sensory awareness. Citing studies by Hornbostel (597a), a construct of "unity of the senses" was postulated that included a common-suprasensory factor known as "brightness in opposition to darkness" common to all organs. Deutsch maintained that "if primitive instinctual drives become evident, the unity of the perceptual components is dissolved and the emphasis shifts from one sense-modality to another" (299b, p. 298), and the threshold is lowered for specific sensory perceptions from the unconscious into the preconscious. Such sensory stimuli are conceived to be abstract precursors of recollections of objects with which they are associated, and they disappear when the corresponding instinctual conflicts are settled.

STUDIES OF INTERNAL SENSATION PER SE

Since only very limited studies have been made that relate internal sensations to psychological states generally, it will be appropriate in this chapter to present information concerning internal sensations *per se* so that (1) some idea of the potential for the experiencing of internal sensations may be achieved, and (2) some hypotheses may be postulated concerning the physiological organs or processes involved in those body areas where internal sensations have been (or may be) observed by subjects.

Boring noted that except for the muscular sense, very little reference was made concerning internal sensibility until this century (140). Needless to say, medical men have long used certain internal sensations as bases for diagnostic reference, which will be considered shortly. In the nineteenth century great strides were made in the understanding of exteroceptive sensations and related physiological functioning. In addition to the traditional five senses of vision, hearing, touch, smell, and taste, there was added a "muscle sense" by Bell (140). The general sense modality of touch was subclassified into pressure sensations, pain sensations, and temperature sensations of warmth and cold (1369). Much research has gone into the study of cutaneous sensations, yet in many respects the basic mechanism of their physiological functioning remains a mystery. Even in regard to the most completely studied sense modality, which is vision, Morgan has pointed up the weakness of the prevailing theory of duplicity of receptors, for which there are numerous alternative possibilities (929). Concerning the commonly hypothesized skin receptors he stated that "one cannot tell much about perception from the anatomy of receptors in the skin" (929, p. 30). Similarly, Ruch noted that the "number of senses and just what constitutes a separate sense are by no means fixed," and he made reference to still another sense, namely, equilibrium (1069, p. 292).

Jenkins, too, described the indefiniteness of sense modalities (644, 645) and emphasized that the problems of the conceptualizing of internal sensations are even more complex, as follows (643, p. 1188):

> In summary then, it seems that we actually know little or nothing about what simple qualities are *both sufficient and necessary* for the various complex somesthetic perceptions. This does not imply that the complex phenomena are unique and unanalyzable, or that there are additional sense organs remaining to be discovered. It does mean that the complex somesthetic perceptions are a rich and almost untouched field calling for further research.

Actually, more has been accomplished along this line in medical studies than is commonly realized by psychologists. The numbers, extent, and origins of internal sensations have yet to be thoroughly explored. In addition, studies need to be made concerning the relative interaction of groupings of internal sensations; such relationships have so far been only slightly studied even in regard to exteroceptive sensations (809, 1093a). It has been reported, however, in some studies that the perception of exteroceptive sensations is affected by the presence of certain internal sensations.

CHAPTER 16

Neurophysiological Considerations

NEURAL IMPULSE AND TRANSMISSION

General neurophysiological functioning has been presented in Chapter 11, and only specific references to internal sensory functioning will be made here.

Much material concerning the neurophysiology of sensory experience was presented by Ruch, who noted that there were many different sorts of classifications for types of sensation in medical and physiological use (1069, p. 293). None of these classifications, he added, has a distinctive physiological basis that justifies it over other classifications. Even the concept of "specific nerve energies," which proposes that only given types of energy or energies constitute an adequate stimulus for a given sense receptor, is limited by the fact that relatively artificial stimuli (such as electricity) may be an adequate stimulus for known receptors (such as the retina). It is also limited by the fact that relatively few specific types of receptors have been definitely isolated. Increasing evidence indicates that much of the functioning that has been conceptualized in terms of receptors and in terms of specific energies may take on conscious significance only near the central terminus of the nerve tract involved. This, however, does not deny the importance of the stimulus or of the functioning of the nerve fibers in response to the stimulus, whether they are internal or external to the body surface. An example of the importance of central functioning in this respect is seen in the experiencing of various sensations, such as visual and somatic ones, by direct stimulation of appropriate brain areas.

Another point to be considered is that sensory stimulation in given areas of the body and for given types of sensations have relatively different sensitivities and rates of adaptation, or duration. Thus, in regard to sensations stimulated by the internal organs or processes themselves, it might be expected that areas constantly contiguous and processes that have regular rhythms might not ordinarily be consciously noticeable; however, with expansion or displacement of organ contacts, with spasms (as of the esophagus), or with abnormal rhythm, such as with heart fibrillation, awareness at some level of consciousness may be involved. The limited knowledge at hand concerning these factors will be presented under the different body-area classifications in the next chapter, and it will also be summarized under the data pertaining to different types of sensations that will be presented in Chapter 18.

Three types of nerve fibers have been identified by their characteristic spike-potential waves; types A and C relate to somatic sensations and type B consists of sympathetic and preganglionic fibers. Type A has the fastest conduction rate and subdivides into four subtypes of fibers with progressively slower conduction rates and smaller diameters. Evidence indicates that the slow-conducting C fibers transmit pain impulses, though some of the slower fibers of the fast-conducting A group also are related to pain sensations (1067, 1385). This supports other evidence of a dual system of pain (418, 782, 1067, 1355). Moreover, there are indications that sensations of light touch, position, and vibration are transmitted by the same A fibers (1069).

The various types of somatic and visceral sensory impulses traverse either the posterior spinal tracts or the anterolateral spinal columns, or both. The anterolateral columns contain three ascending tracts: the spinothalamic, the spinotectal, and the spinobulbar (1067). The sensations that are known to be conducted over the spinothalamic tract are: pressure and touch, pain, warmth, cold, sexual sensations, tickle, itch, and feelings of muscular fatigue. At the spinal level the fibers serving the same quality of sensation become grouped together. Pain fibers for the cutaneous, muscle and visceral sensations are grouped in the anterolateral tract, and muscle sense fibers are grouped in the posterior column; the ventral tract appears to contain relatively few pressure fibers, and the lateral tract appears to contain pain and temperature fibers. Needless to say, the joining of these tracts by the cranial nerves and their ascent into the brain stem is extremely complex and includes junctures with several nuclei and ganglia.

All sensory tracts except the olfactory tract synapse in the thalamus before continuing to the cerebral cortex. Ruch stated that the main function of the thalamus is clearly to relay impulses to the cerebral cortex, while at the same time it integrates them in some way via the association nuclei, and the final expression of the activity of the association nuclei comes through the cerebral cortex via an elaborate system of corticothalamic fibers, which

form circuits with potentialities of interplay (326), thus making an insep-
arable functional relationship (1067).

The relief of pain (95a) or anxiety (53a), which can follow a prefrontal
lobotomy, is usually attributed to changes in frontal-lobe functioning; according to Arnold, however, this anxiety reduction may be due to the complete
degeneration of the dorsomedial nucleus of the thalamus, thus preventing
excitation of sympathetic effectors that may prolong and intensify "emotion"
(53a). Direct removal of the dorsomedial nuclei (thalamotomy) is claimed
to have the same effect in reducing anxiety without producing the defect
in initiative and integrated thinking that are the consequences of lobotomy
(53a, 1179a).

Delgado has presented evidence supporting the idea that nociceptive
sensory impulses may be relayed in the posteroventral nuclei of the thalamus
and integrated in the hippocampus, which may thus assume a role more
generally attributed to the postcentral gyrus (289a).

By the time the thalamus is reached, nerve tracts no longer serve separate
sensory modalities, though a capacity for topographical organization is pre-
served. Ruch stated that (1067, p. 337):

> Thus, in so far as anatomy can discover, the body surface is projected
> upon the postcentral gyrus, with spatial relations preserved, much as a
> lantern slide is projected upon a screen. This point-to-point relationship
> is unquestionably of significance in the localization of stimuli, in distin-
> guishing two points from one, and in other functions having a strong
> spatial element. The degree to which the thalmocortical projection systems
> to areas 4 and 6 and to areas 5 and 7 are spatially organized is not certain
> and is not easy to discover. . .
>
> The extent of the cerebral cortex involved in somatosensory function
> has never been settled. A *potential somatosensory area,* as delineated ana-
> tomically, may be defined as that region which receives projection fibers
> from the thalamus exclusive of the geniculate bodies. It includes the whole
> of the prefrontal lobe, the motor area, and the whole of the parietal lobe.

More recently, the functioning of the reticular formation of the brain
and of the limbic system (see pp. 136-137) in respect to sensory impulses
have been elaborated. Some afferent systems have been found (in cats) to
effect extensive connections with units of the reticular formation whereas
other systems made few or perhaps no such connections, which led some
observers to the conclusion that corticoreticular relations appear to mirror
only to a slight extent the bulboreticular-formation organization (1091a).

Electrical stimulation of the septal area, anterior to the thalamus, in 23 patients resulted in sensations such as "warmth, faintness, a glowing feeling, anxiety, and a queer feeling" (541a, 962a). It has been suggested that with the afferent integration in these brain parts "a triple linkage may occur involving the 'I' or self, and the 'Non-I' or non-self, and the intermediate or the communicating worlds" (460a, p. 341).

SENSORY IDENTIFICATION

Sensations appear to be topographically identified cortically, and, when identified, they are projected to the peripheral point of stimulation as though the localization itself took place there; this phenomenon is called *the law of projection*. This mechanism of localization is well exemplified by the common clinical "phantom-limb" phenomenon, wherein amputees report perceptions of sensations in parts of the body that no longer exist (329, 344, 426, 607, 719, 806, 992, 1043, 1093a). The immediate stimuli for this perception in most instances are nociceptive impulses from the limb stump.

Studies relating to localization of the functions of different brain parts have been discussed earlier (p. 146). Of particular relevance here is the fact that direct stimulation of brain sections in conscious subjects can produce sensations that effect or project sensations in peripheral body areas (legs, arms, vocal cords, and retina) and can be employed clinically (708) and experimentally (982, 983, 984). In this connection, it should also be recalled that lesions in the cerebral cortex do not abolish consciousness, whereas lesions in the area of the third ventricle and higher brain stem do produce unconsciousness (983). This latter area has been termed the "centrencephalic system" by Penfield, who, on the basis of the type of exploration just noted, attributed to this hypothalamic area the "functional integration" of the various functional areas of the cerebral cortex (983).

Another important finding that concerns cortical localization, which has been reported in studies involving electrical stimulation of brain parts, was elaborated by Ruch as follows (1067, p. 338):

> The second fact which emerges from these studies is that sensations can be elicited from stimulation of the motor areas (4 and 6), and, according to some, they are indistinguishable in quality and frequency of occurrence from the responses of the classic sensory area of the postcentral gyrus. The map showing the distribution of responses forms a striking parallel with the map of the density of the thalamocortical projection fibers, though the sensory excitable area falls somewhat short both anteriorly

and posteriorly. Sensations of the spinothalamic category—pain, warmth and cold—were rarely reported, the usual response being a sense of numbness, tingling, and especially a sense of movement unaccompanied by actual movement. No evidence of zonal localization of modalities was obtained.

The projection of the body surface upon the postcentral gyrus appears to be in terms of body regions, such as the head, arms, or legs, but the projection in the cerebral cortex appears to be in terms of dermatomal regions.

A dermatome is an area of the skin supplied with afferent fibers by a single posterior spinal root; these regions are delineated by uniform contours, which are horizontal across the trunk but vary in form over the extremities and overlap in such a way that two or three spinal roots may supply a single point on the skin. The dermatomes are sensory root fields as differentiated from peripheral nerve fields.

In a study of referred muscle pain, Travell, Berry, and Bigelow concurred with earlier findings that showed that the distribution of referred somatic pain is constant for the structures that are stimulated and that pain referred from different sites may fall entirely within a given dermatome attributed to one segment (622, 685, 1261). They took issue, however, with the "prevailing concept" that states that referred somatic pain follows a simple "segmental" or nerve-root distribution since they found (1) that the pains usually were perceived respectively in different portions of a given area, (2) that the reference from a single site may comprise fragments of several "segmental pain areas" rather than any one, and (3) that the referred pain may include a whole "segmental area," skip the adjacent one and reappear distally (1261). From these findings it was concluded that referred somatic pain involves special spinal pathways.

It is to the dermatome areas that the phenomenon of *referred* sensations from visceral organs relates. That is, sometimes sensations in a given dermatome area are stimulated within visceral organs that are considerably removed from the pain site either (1) because the particular organ possibly has a phylogenetic relationship with the particular nerve root concerned, or (2) because of transfer of nerve impulses to adjacent nerves at the spinal root juncture, or (3) because the visceral afferent nerves converge with cutaneous afferent nerves; neural impulses under these conditions are transmitted by the same spinothalamic tract and are interpreted in the same way at the cortical level.

The importance of topographical distribution in sensory perception places primary emphasis on cortical functioning since the thalamus seemingly does not possess the capacity for fine discrimination and accurate localization, and therefore theoretical elaborations on thalamic functioning must be limited to quantitative rather than topographical differences (1067). Actually, relatively little is known concerning the pathways and thalamic or cortical representation of many internal sensations (1068, p. 374).

AUTONOMIC FUNCTIONS

In addition to the nerve tracts already mentioned, the sympathetic and parasympathetic nerves and the white rami were noted to possess afferent sensory neurones from the viscera (1068). Afferent impulses from the structures of the body cavity are carried over these tracts as well as by the somatic nerves from the body wall and diaphragm. Visceral reflexes of vital functions, such as cardiac regulation and micturition, are parasympathetic, and although sympathetic stimulation affects these reflex functions, the afferent sympathetic fibers do not appear to be essential for them. Probably, there are some exceptions to this rule, particularly in regard to responses to pressure in the circulatory system. Thus, the sympathetic afferent nerves would appear generally to serve a function that is apart from the elementary level of reflex regulation. Most, if not all, of the internal sensations of the so-called "organic" type, such as sensations arising from hunger contractions or from bladder fullness, are believed to be carried by the parasympathetic nerves.

Ruch also delineated the stimuli considered to be adequate for visceral pain, which, he noted, is not produced by many of the stimuli (such as cutting) adequate for cutaneous pain. These stimuli include: (1) dilatation or distention, (2) spasm or strong contraction, and (3) chemical irritants. Generally, these pain impulses are conducted by the sympathetic nerves, and, since regulatory reflexes are usually not involved, sympathectomies are often performed for the relief of pain. In some instances pain impulses are conducted by parasympathetic nerves, particularly in the pelvic region. Also, there is evidence that some pain impulses may be conducted by the vagus nerves of the esophagus and respiratory tracts (1068, 1317). However, no pain impulses are believed to be carried by the thoracic and abdominal vagus nerves.

OTHER AFFERENT NERVE FINDINGS

The phrenic somatic nerve transmits afferent sensations for the following thoracic and abdominal areas: central zone of the diaphragm, portions of the pericardium, and the biliary tract. The thoracic and upper lumbar spinal nerves transmit sensations from the parietal pleura, the parietal peritoneum, borders of the diaphragm, and roots of the mesentery.

The interaction of visceral and somatic structures is also seen in the fact that visceral afferent impulses not only excite referred sensations in somatic structures, but such impulses also inhibit certain reflexes, as, for example, the inhibition of the knee-jerk reflex by bladder distention. Similarly, a "form of intermodal integration between different types of sensations" at the cortical level has been indicated by findings that the magnitude and form of local electroencephalographic response to a visual stimulus may be modified by a concurrent auditory stimulus (435, 633), and that the electrical pattern of the sensory receiving area may be modified by factors that affect the level of consciousness (633). Moreover, convulsive activity and its associated electroencephalographic correlates are closely associated with the presence of afferent neural impulses of proprioceptive and cutaneous, particularly nociceptive, types (426).

Gellhorn described differentiated effects of nociceptive and proprioceptive impulses on the central nervous system, the latter influencing quantitative changes of reflexes and movements by acting on the motor cortex apparently via an unmodifying facilitatory process within the spinal cord, whereas the nociceptive impulses result in quantitative and qualitative modification of the effects of motor-cortex stimulation via alterations at spinal and supraspinal levels (426, 432, 1240). He also noted an "intimate interrelation" between afferent sensory impulses and voluntary movements. An intact afferent system is, of course, required for adequate motor functioning.

The fact that impulses from the lower brain stem are largely responsible for normal cortical activity is shown by the occurrence of a great reduction in this electrical activity after the isolation of the cortex (426). Three groupings of such afferent impulses are made: (1) the long-tract systems such as the medial lemniscus and spinothalamic system, which carry afferent impulses to specific projection areas; (2) the facilitatory system, which activates the posterior hypothalamus and then leads to the cortex via the ventromedial group of thalamic nuclei; (3) the diffuse afferent system of Morison and Dempsey, which involves the dorsal medial thalamic nuclei and particularly affects the areas around the suppressor areas (426). Gellhorn also designated the following order for the effectiveness of afferent impulses in producing a generalized cortical encephalographic reaction, which parallels a general level of awareness, or consciousness: nociceptive, proprioceptive, acoustic, and, lastly, optic. Such responses to nociceptive stimuli were not abolished by anterior hypothalamic lesions, but they were abolished by lesions in the posterior hypothalamus and by lesions in the ventral medial thalamic nuclei and the subthalamus (above the posterior hypothalamus) (426, 716). Thus, these afferent impulses, at least, appeared to activate the hypothalamic-cortical system, being relayed chiefly via the ventromedial part of the thalamus (426, 1191). It was concluded that cortical activity is influenced by this system as well as by the spinothalamic system that involves the diffuse thalamic system.

All of these facts support the possibility that higher cognitive functions, or psychological states, may be directly affected or determined by internal sensory experiences that in turn may be subject in varying degrees to direct awareness. The facts also refute or detract from many of Cannon's arguments against this hypothesis that were noted in Chapter 10.

It is common clinical knowledge that some internal sensations, for example, heart palpitation, may be interpreted differently at the cognitive level by different individuals, since some persons relate such sensations to displaced fears and to familial incidents of related types (1144). Nevertheless, a theoretical distinction should be made between what may be "normal" or constitutionally determined relationships between physiological functioning and internal sensations and psychological states (or "feeling") in contrast to deviant or personalized interpretation, or perception, of internal sensations (1093a).

CHAPTER 17

Internal Sensory Experience in Terms

of Body-Area Location

METHOD OF PRESENTATION

The body-area classifications (Figure 1, p. 145) and major physiological systems, which were considered in Part III in terms of the relationship between physiological functioning and psychological states, will now be considered in terms of internal sensory experiences. First, data will be presented concerning generalized physiological functions. Next, sensory data concerning the different body-area classifications that are shown in Figure 1 will be presented, first in terms of the types of sensation reported for the areas and then in terms of the relationship of sensations to other psychological states reported, such as "feelings and emotions." With each body area will be listed most of the major organs that are to some considerable degree located below the area diagrammed in Figure 1, except that data concerning a given organ will usually be considered only for that area under which the major or most central part of the organ(s) is situated. The decision as to whether to present a given organ under the front or the back body-area classification was resolved in favor of the direction that the related sensations are most frequently reported. In each area, all organs for which some sensations have been reported in a standard medical text, *Cabot and Adams Physical Diagnosis* (5), or elsewhere will be noted at the beginning of each section.

It should be added here that pain sensations appear with pathology in all nerves; and apart from the neurophysiological considerations just noted, there remains to be presented little additional material concerning the general nervous system. No data relating sensations directly to the circulatory system or to the general endocrine-gland system have been noted; in fact, there have been few reports relating sensations to the more general physiological processes. Changes in body chemistry and particularly the administration of given drugs, including alcohol, may have widespread effects on sensory experience. Jellinek and McFarland found that alcohol in strong solutions with even medium doses has a prompt and considerable effect on the nervous system, such as in increasing the two-point threshold by 90 per cent (642). This book, however, is primarily concerned with internally stimulated sensory experiences, and the little-known data that relate internally produced chemical changes to sensation will be considered under the body areas affected, since such changes are relatively localized in nature.

MUSCLE, BONE, AND SKIN

It appears that pathology in all muscles and in most bones produces pain sensations (5), except that no pain is found in the cartilage or compact bone (1230). Sensations of "tapping" or "pressing" have been produced in cartilage; diffuse pain is usually felt in cancellous bone (782, 1230). Most of these pain characteristics are presented by Tarsy, and he described muscle pain as "aching" and "diffuse," being experienced in distant parts of the body in proportion to the strength of the stimulus, as contrasted with the brief and superficial characteristics of skin pain. Fascial pain is well localized, whereas subcutaneous tendon and periosteal pain is always dull, disagreeable, and diffuse, with tendon pain being intermediate between fascial and muscle pain. Subcutaneous ligaments yield localized pain, but pain may be diffuse and referred with the deeper ligaments when they are severely involved. Interspinous ligaments produce pain similar to muscle pain.

Pressure on localized muscle areas, called "trigger points," have been found to result in localized areas of referred pain, which arise from responses of skeletal muscles and arteries, such as pain over the front of the shoulder induced by pressure on an irritable infraspinatus muscle and such as pain in the forehead and temple induced by neck-muscle stimulation (1262).

Pains stimulated in the esophagus, in the colon, and in the abdominal wall (556) have been attributed by some writers to muscle tension or distention, and headaches stemming from muscle tension, which is associated with emotional conflicts, are commonly seen (860, 1356). Also, the awareness of conflictual "ditention" by the Lifwynn group was thought to be based to a large extent on muscular tension in the eyes and throughout the body (174, 175, 176, 177, 178, 959, 960).

Skeletal-muscle hyperfunctioning in the back area has been found in subjects complaining of backaches under conditions engendering apprehension, conflict, anxiety, hostility, and guilt (595). A similar finding has been related to "tension headaches" (390, 391, 1356) and somewhat less definitely to arthritic pains (461). Also, several studies were discussed earlier in this book (p. 226) that showed that functionally induced tension of the diaphragmatic muscles results in pain, discomfort, and dyspnea. Similarly, as will be described subsequently (p. 324), pains in the right shoulder associated with muscle tension have been related to life situations and emotional stress (813). With increased neuromuscular self-awareness and control, relief for muscular tension is reported (624a).

In the early introspective experiments of Shepard, the psychological state of "strain" was described as "composed of sensations from the muscles, the backflow from the active muscles, particularly those of accommodation of a sense organ," and these sensations were also found to be involved in the state of "excitement" (1134, p. 555).

Internal sensations reported by 36 subjects for ten body areas under conditions of mild, emotionally toned projective stimuli of various types were classified according to the following rough estimates of depth: "skin," "muscle," "intermediate," and "deep" (878). The "muscle" classification was the most frequently employed for the ten body areas rated (namely, Areas 5a, 6, 10, 11, 11a, 12a at the juncture of 12b, 13b, 14 along with part of 13a, 21, 23, and 27c of Figure 1, p. 145). The "intermediate" classification was next most frequently used, and the "deep" classification was the least frequently reported.

Skin pain was described as having a brief and distinct quality of "prickling" when produced by a brief stimulus and a "burning" quality when produced by a more prolonged stimulus, and it was well localized and never referred (1230). Lewis has described skin and muscle pain to be respectively distinctive and "impossible to confuse" once one has learned to distinguish them (782). Skin temperature was seen to fall generally with subjects under stress, presumably as an aspect of vasoconstriction; however, only in the subjects with Raynaud's syndrome did pain, cyanosis, and pallor result (922). Low environmental temperature alone did not produce these symptoms. Skin sensations, stemming from "coldness and sweating of the hands, axillary sweating, warmth of the face," and so forth have been noted during pre-examination tension (560). Pruritus ani and some other skin conditions that involve itching, "crawling," and similar cutaneous sensations have already been noted in an earlier chapter (p. 195) to involve functional factors. Montagu presented evidence that adequate cutaneous stimulation of the skin, particularly for the infant, is necessary for healthy physiological and psychological functioning (926).

CEPHALIC AREA (Area No. 1)

SENSATIONS EXPERIENCED IN GENERAL

This area extends from the frontal skull to the eyes. Pain sensations are reported from pathology of the brain, cranial nerves, and spinal tracts that produces headaches of various kinds; pain also arises from eye strain and from frontal and sphenoid-sinus disturbances (5).

Cerebral vasoconstriction, which may result from the hyperventilation associated with emotional reactions and results in dissociation of oxyhemoglobin and cerebral anoxia, produces sensations of giddiness and faintness (1097, 1143, 1342). A similar syncope reaction of faintness and weakness may result from a transient failure of the peripheral circulatory bed (173, 1342) and from "cerebral anemia arising from the retardation of the forward flow of the blood" in patients with "functional cardiovascular disease" (neurocirculatory asthenia) who manifest arterial and arteriolar constriction, apparently due to an exaggerated reflex reaction to a normally decreased venous blood flow (393, p. 63).

The "giddiness and faintness" sensations referred to above would seem to me to be one type of experience that differs from most sensations in respect to the type of localization involved, and it would seem to relate very closely to the cognitive area of inner experience. The whole question of what kinds of sensations, other than headaches, may be stimulated within brain matter is very nebulous. The Lifwynn group reported sensations in connection with the stress of tension "situated within the anterior cephalic zone" (174, 178, 959, 1224).

HEADACHES

In addition to tension (279, 391, 658, 1149, 1354, 1356), headaches may arise functionally from vasoconstriction or from vasodilatation of the brain arteries and veins, as well as from other pressures on the brain arteries or veins, on the cranial or cervical nerves, or on the dura at the base of the brain (38, 1355, 1356). Wolff's experimentation indicated that "dilation and not contraction of arteries" causes vascular pain, and headaches resulting from dilatation of the cerebral arteries have a pulsatile throbbing quality (1355, 1356). Although arterial contraction was ordinarily not found to cause pain directly, the muscle ischemia resulting from vasoconstriction may produce pain, as may possibly also nerve-root ischemia (1356). The quality of intracranial head pain was found to be the same when stimulated in different ways.

Also described by Wolff was extracranial pain, which may arise from the scalp and periosteum and relates primarily to the arteries of the scalp, the veins being much less pain sensitive or not at all so.

The frequent clinical symptom of tension headache (the functional etiology of which has been discussed earlier, pp. 248, 284), was studied by Friedman et al. in 400 cases and they stated as follows (391, p. 174):

> We believe that the term tension headache should be limited to head pain occurring in relation to constant or periodic emotional conflicts, which may be conscious or unconscious. Such an emotional state may induce headache by producing changes in the caliber of the cranial vessels and spasm of the skeletal muscles of the head and neck. Tension headaches have no prodroma, are usually bilateral, occipital or frontal, and may be accompanied by a variety of associated signs, including anxiety, nausea, and vomiting. Frequency and duration are variable.

This type of headache was differentiated from conversion and migraine types, the latter being usually "brief, paroxysmal, unilateral, and throbbing in character" and frequently associated with gastrointestinal symptoms.

Migraine headaches are caused by dilatation and distention of relaxed cranial arteries, which are usually the branches of the external carotid artery. These attacks have been described as "but one aspect of a diffuse disturbance in function occurring periodically during or immediately after a period of stress" (1354, 1356). In the studying of personality and life-situation reactions of 46 migraine patients, Wolff found as follows (1356, p. 348):

> Personality features and reactions dominant in individuals with migraine are feelings of insecurity with tension, manifested as inflexibility, conscientiousness, meticulousness, perfectionism, and resentment. These temperamental features lead to frustration; to dissatisfactions about family, financial, or personal status; and to intolerance of periods of low energy in themselves, or of relaxed standards in themselves and others.

Migraine attacks were found to be directly related to the patient's level of blood pressure, which is a precipitating factor when the smooth-muscle tone of the cranial arterial walls is low. Also, there is evidence of a locally active noxious agent (962b).

Sustained painful distention of cerebral arteries results in contraction of head and neck vessels that thereby may become painful (1335). Similarly, sustained painful conditions in the sinuses may result in the spread of pain and aching widely over face and head regions (1354, 1356). In addition, it should be noted that headaches occur by means of indirect stimulation in association with dysfunction or diseases in many parts of the body, such as the chest (538), the bladder (1356) and the colon (334a, 1354).

From surgical experimentation on 45 patients, Wolff outlined six basic physical mechanisms within the cranial cavity that produce headache as follows (1356, p. 95):

> Headache may result from (1) traction on the veins that pass to the venous sinuses from the surface of the brain and displacement of the great venous sinuses; (2) traction on the middle meningeal arteries; (3) traction on the large arteries at the base of the brain and their main branches; (4) distention and dilation of intracranial arteries; (5) inflammation in or about any of the pain-sensitive structures of the head; and (6) direct pressure by tumors or adjacent tissue on the cranial and cervical nerves containing many pain-afferent fibers from the head.

Though headaches are commonly associated with conflictual feelings, the physiological basis for such headaches will vary in different cases (390, 1356, 1358). In one study, the symptom of headache was not seen to run a parallel course with "feelings of poor health," but rather seemed to relate to the degree of repression or suppression of anger feelings (527).

FACIAL AREA (Area No. 2)

Local pains involving all parts of the face are known, and pain in this area at times accompanies heart ailments (angina pectoris and myocardial infarction) (5). Pain from the face, nasal structures, nasopharynx, and mouth are mediated by the ophthalmic, maxillary, and mandibular branches of the trigeminal, or fifth, cranial nerve (1364). The mouth cavity reacts to stimuli in a manner similar to that of the external skin, having in addition taste receptors on the tongue (643); pain stimulated here, such as with the "ice-cream headache," may result in a frontal headache via the fifth cranial nerve (737, 1356).

Contraction of the masseter muscle, sustained over days or months, produces sensations of tightness and aches in the jaws, the zygoma, and the temporal region (1356). Also, these muscles were said to be among the first to contract with states of tension, determination, or desperation, remaining so for long periods.

The eye sensations observed by the Lifwynn group in connection with "ditention" have been related to the finding of a reduced number of eye movements in "cotention" under a wide variety of stimulus conditions (959). Also, eye dysfunction and muscle strain may result in headaches (1354, 1356), as may also swelling and engorgement of the mucous membranes in the nose and adjacent spaces, which may be an aspect of reactions to life stresses (1354).

THROAT AREA (Area No. 3)

Local pathology produces pain in the structures of the throat, namely, the pharynx, upper esophagus, larynx, epiglottis, thyroid gland, and parathyroid gland (5). It is to be noted that this area classification does not include the muscle and bone parts of the throat and neck, which are considered separately under Area No. 20. Noxious sensations from the pharynx, tonsillar pillars and fossae are mediated by the glossopharyngeal, or ninth cranial nerve (1364).

Payne and Poulton reported that painful stimulation of the upper esophagus may at times produce sensations in the throat as well as elsewhere (976). These authors defined the "sensation of nausea" as a sensation felt at the back and lower part of the throat, not being usually associated with pain, although it was noted that nausea is often accompanied by "uneasiness in the pit of the stomach" (978). The common sensation of "lump in the throat" has been associated with localized contractures and wide dilatations above them (348). Also, sensations of "choking" and of "constriction in the throat" were reported by hypertensive patients in connection with other symptoms precipitated by disturbing life situations (1358).

It is common knowledge that vocal-cord changes occur with changing psychological states. Although many patterns of vocal inflections are culturally determined, it seems that some may be constitutionally universal. A high-pitched voice occurring with fear or tension has been noted (1326).

UPPER-CENTRAL CHEST AREA (Area No. 4)

SENSATIONS EXPERIENCED IN GENERAL

This area extends from the collar bone to the second rib at the sternum and includes as major parts the alimentary canal, trachea, sternum, and thymus gland. Noxious sensations from the esophagus are believed to be mediated by the sympathetic fibers and to enter the spinal cord at any point between the lowest cervical segment and the thoracic segments; there is also some possibility that the vagus nerve may carry afferent fibers (1364).

Findings concerning the whole esophagus will, for the sake of convenience, be presented here even though the esophagus extends to the epigastric area; for the same reason the trachea will be considered in connection with the upper-lateral chest area (Area No. 7), which includes the lungs.

Local pain is reported for the esophagus, trachea, and sternum, and secondary pain in this area is stimulated by heart and lung conditions (5). A sensation of dullness is reported with thymus involvement, and from the esophagus originate sensations of burning and of fullness or distention, extending down the length of the esophagus to include the precordial area and the upper epigastrium.

ESOPHAGEAL STIMULATION

A study of the alimentary canal by Hertz in 1911 revealed that no sensation was felt from the swallowing of liquid at room temperature, from which it was concluded that no tactile sensibility existed (556) and similar conclusions were drawn by Boring a few years later (139). Cold sensations were produced by Hertz with 0°C. liquid and warmth from 40°C. to 50°C. temperatures. Sensations were usually localized easily in the esophagus when using a balloon or large bolus of food as stimuli (556, p. 1054):

> This [balloon] was often associated with an increase in the local sensation of fullness, and occasionally a sensation of uncomfortable fullness was also felt behind the cricoid cartilage, from which it passed rapidly down to the position of the balloon, where it reached its greatest intensity.

Similar localizations were reported for clinical cases of food obstruction and for four fifths of 134 cases of cancer of the esophagus; the other fifth of the cases referred sensations of obstruction or fullness to the upper third of the esophagus whereas the stenosis was in the lower third. When distention was rapidly produced by the balloon, pain resulted, and this was slowly replaced by sensations of fullness. Sensations of pain and fullness were equally well localized on the anterior of the body. They were felt to be deeply situated in the mid-line, and pain "was invariably associated with a sensation of pain at the same level behind, this sensation feeling as if it were less deep than the anterior pain." Painful fullness was felt in the anterior of the body, whereas the posterior sensation "resembled a stitch."

In the comparing of sensations stimulated in the esophagus by a water-filled balloon with clinical reports of patients, Payne and Poulton and others found the sensations of "heartburn" to be associated with peristaltic movements of the esophagus and also often associated with increased tonus that contracts the lumen (976). These investigators found the tonus that contracted the esophageal lumen to vary even during states of relaxation when no "subjective sensation" was experienced by the subjects observed, but greater variability in tonus was seen when the subjects complained of pain or discomfort. Using an air-filled balloon as a stimulus in the normal esophagus of 2 subjects, two types of pain were differentiated as follows (977, p. 236):

> The character of the pain produced in our experiments varied according as it was continuous or intermittent. In the former case it had a burning character, and was reminiscent of heartburn. An unpleasant sensation referred to the throat, but also situated deeply at about the level of the suprasternal notch, was present if the bag was high up in the esophagus. If it was lower down the pain was usually referred to the costal angle, and the lower part of the sternum in the mid-line. When the pain was intermittent it had what was best described as a gripping character.

Payne and Poulton experimented upon themselves, using the air-filled balloon, and reported a sensation of nausea to result from tension on the esophagus and, especially, on the upper part of it (978). This was felt to resemble a sensation of "globus" but of different quality. Also, a sensation of tingling was usually associated with a phase of esophageal activity.

The sensation of "heartburn," which was subsequently followed by nausea, has also been reported with the introduction of 95 per cent alcohol directly into the cardiac end of the esophagus of a subject (1355, 1363). Similarly, Wolf and Wolff in studying Tom, the subject with the fistula, found nausea to occur with direct application of alcohol, acid, and mustard to the lower end of the esophagus, but this did not occur when these were applied to folds of gastric mucosa (1363). A concentration of these substances in the stomach resulted in "heartburn" localized beneath the xiphoid, which was attributed to a reflex constriction of the cardiac end of the esophagus.

The findings of Bloomfield and Polland differed from those of Hertz in that sensations, produced by an inflated bag in the esophagus of 39 ward patients, most of whom were free of gastrointestinal complaints, were usually referred to either the lower end of the sternum or to the neck area just above the suprasternal notch (133b). They added, however, that "other situations at various levels of the sternum to the right and in back were frequently indicated," and "sometimes the subject pointed to two perhaps widely separated areas or first to one spot and then to another." The diagram presented by these authors shows eighty-seven indications just above the sternum and forty-eight just below it, with other indications extending down the front of the sternum and fanning out from the lower cluster to cover about two thirds of the front body area. In addition, twenty-one indications were shown on the back, around the thoracic region just below and between the shoulder blades, and six of these were in the center. It was reported that most subjects repeatedly referred sensations to the same, or to nearby, locations on their bodies irrespective of the position of the balloon. Pain was generally felt after 15 to 25 cc. of air had been introduced under a pressure of from 80 to 150 mm. Hg. Though these subjects had great difficulty in describing the character of the sensations, they usually described them as being inside. The descriptions varied from "a deep burning," "pain like a lump—not very severe," "a stretch, a tight feeling," "pain," "a pressure, no pain but it hurt," "sharp little pain," "like gas pains," "contraction," and so forth.

Kling noted sensations similar to "tightness" with esophageal spasms (710). Jones also related the common pain of "heartburn" to esophageal spasms that were fairly well localized over the site of stimulation and usually stemmed from spasm of the cardiac end of the esophagus (648).

Chapman compared the esophageal and cutaneous sensitivity of 29 normal subjects by balloon distention of the lower esophagus that elicited sensations of substernal fullness (227). The subjects were "taught to point to the location where a sensation of substernal fullness first occurred." Threshold values ranged from 15 cm. of water pressure to 89 cm., with a mean average value of 37 cm. for the esophageal balloon. The rank coefficient correlation of visceral sensory threshold to cutaneous pain perception for these subjects was +.57 with a probable error of .9. Only one subject was reported to show a gross discrepancy in thresholds, with the cutaneous threshold very high and the esophageal low.

More recently, Wolf and Almy compared 20 asymptomatic control subjects with 14 patients who had complaints that food seemed to stick in the retrosternal region; they found that when the patients swallowed barium, it was pinched off at the level of the epigastrium (1347). When healthy subjects swallowed barium cooled to 6.5°C., sensations of cold were noted in the retrosternal region as well as a slight delay in the emptying of the esophagus and an increase in its motor activity. With a second swallow of the cooled barium, these characteristics were increased, and with the third swallow, a substernal sensation of tightness was produced along with a relatively long delay in emptying and marked contractual activity in the lower two thirds of the esophagus. Hot barium at 63°C. produced sensations of "burning in the esophagus and marked increase in motor activity," and Tabasco sauce in the barium produced a "painful sensation of burning" that after the fourth swallow was supplemented by dyspnea and "pinching off" of the barium at the diaphragmatic level with much pain, which was thought to be the equivalent of "cardiospasm." Similarly, several stress situations, including the putting of hands in ice water, compressing of the head in a metal device, examination periods, and discussions of disturbing life situations, revealed two primary mechanisms of reaction. The primary reaction to stress was irregular contractual activity of the lower two thirds of the esophagus. The secondary stress was localized obstruction just above the cardia, presumably from forceful contraction of the diaphragm, and reduced activity in the lower half of the esophagus. These reactions occurred both in patients with complaints of cardiospasm and in healthy subjects under stress. The cardiospasm reaction was believed to be defensive in that it would be appropriate against ingested irritants, and it was related to the following personality characteristics of the patients (1347, p. 416):

> As a group, they are dour, humorless, wary, suspicious, non-committal and defensive rather than aggressive in their dealings with day to day problems. Moreover, they are given to suppressing rather than expressing their conflicts and feelings. They are circumstantial, bear grudges and brood unusually over minor slights and humiliations. In short, in their attitudes and behavior, they are ruminative, and rumination is suggested by their esophageal dysfunction.

It was therefore believed that the "entity" designated as "diffuse spasm of the esophagus," or "esophagitis," may represent an early or mild phase of the "cardiospasm" or "megaesophagus" symptoms, which are biological patterns of defense with stress.

Sensations of warmth and cold, stimulated directly in the lower end of the esophagus, have been found to overshadow similar sensations from within the stomach and to be localized beneath the xiphoid (1352).

CENTRAL-CHEST AREA (Area No. 6)

SENSATIONS EXPERIENCED IN GENERAL

This area is situated just over the heart and overlies the lower sternum and a very limited rib area as well as the esophagus. Pain in this area can result from heart ailments, which may produce secondary sensations in the entire upper torso, face, upper extremities, abdomen, and thighs; also, different heart diseases have different extensities (5). Other sensations occurring are "smothering sensations" and consciousness of abnormal heart actions (fibrillation, "turning over," feelings that the heart is about to stop, and weakness) (5). Also in this area are pains from deltoid-muscle infection and from the precordium (precorditis), as well as from the esophagus, which was mentioned in the preceding section. Similarly, secondary pain in this area derives from the gall bladder (cholecystitis), from the cervical or thoracic spine (arthritis), from the stomach, and from the lungs (which will be covered in the next section).

NEURAL PATHWAYS AND REFERENCE

Noxious impulses from the heart are carried along with the sympathetic nerves, entering the sympathetic chain anywhere from the middle cervical to the fifth thoracic ganglion, which in turn enter the upper five thoracic segments of the spinal cord (1364). Characteristically, heart pain is correctly localized beneath the sternum, whereas referred pain is localized mainly in the anterior portion of the third to sixth thoracic segments with hyperesthesia over the precordial area, but it may also be localized along the medial aspect of the left shoulder and arm, involving the first and second thoracic segments and possibly even including paths of reference from the third cervical to the tenth thoracic segments (647, 648, 1317, 1364). In angina pectoris (cited as a classic example of referred pain), there is an unreferred deep substernal, agonizing pain as well as the referred pain that extends through the first thoracic dermatome over the chest wall with a characteristic extension along the underside of the arm (1068). The referred pain with coronary occlusion or angina of effort seems to emanate from one or more of the anterior portions of the first four or five thoracic segments, and it spreads headward, appearing to arise within the structures supplied by the cervical segments even to include the lower jaw and teeth (1355, 1356).

CARDIAC SYMPTOMS

The pain of angina pectoris has been associated with increased heart work to a degree that is not paralleled by increased flow of blood through diseased coronary arteries (38). Although Wolf and Wolff (1342) have cited a case in which this pain seemed to be precipitated by lowered cardiac output due to emotional factors, Altschule suggested the possibility that anginal attacks may be precipitated by strong emotional reactions that usually cause cooling of the skin over the acral areas, which is known to favor such attacks (38). The same mechanism, he stated, applies to myocardial infarction. On the other hand, anginal pain has been specifically associated with thoughts and feelings related to repressed anger or hostility, and this pain, as well as the pain of coronary occlusion, has been thought to reduce feelings of guilt and thereby relieve anxiety (51, 461).

Burchell reported that precordial pain as a symptom of anxiety is one of the most difficult diagnoses with which the cardiac consultant is most often confronted, and he described such pain as characteristically located below the left nipple, although it is sometimes bilateral, often in a circumscribed area, needlelike in quality or simply a dull ache, lasting minutes, hours or days and having no definite relationship to exercise (173).

CARDIAC SENSATIONS AND REACTIONS TO STIMULATION

In general, the experiencing of pain has been seen to alter heart functioning (463, 806, 1356). As early as 1929, sensation experiments were made on the exposed heart of man by Alexander, Macleod, and Barker with the following findings: light touch was perceived; rubbing was interpreted as pressure; heavy pressure and pricking with a needle were interpreted as touch; tension on the left ventricle produced no pain; heat of 130 to 140°F. and cold of 40 to 50°F. could not be identified; vibration from tuning forks was not sensed; electrical stimulation produced pain only when extrasystoles occurred; two-point discrimination could be made with one fork each on the right and left ventricles but not with both forks on the right ventricle (25). Also, no distant reference of sensation was produced by any of the stimuli applied to the heart or pericardium (the membranous sac enveloping the heart) except that pressure against the anterior pericardium resulted in two "reflex" disturbances: (1) "squirming" of the body and extremities on painful stimulation of the heart or pericardium that may have been wholly or partially voluntary; and (2) activation of coughing on irritating of the pericardial cavity. Using the same stimuli on the diaphragmatic pericardium produced only sensations of "pressure" and once "slight pain" with heavy pressure. Similarly, for the parietal pericardium, only pain sensations occurred, which were stimulated by sweeping of the finger around the pericardial cavity, by pinching, pricking, and scratching of the inner surface of the pericardium, and by pressure against the anterior pericardium and thoracic wall, resulting in severe local and referred pain.

A few years later, sensations of the pericardium and of the pleural membranes were investigated by Capps and Coleman in so far as possible by the inserting of an exploring wire in the thorax of 35 patients following thoracentesis (202). Seemingly, contact was made with the pericardium of 9 subjects, and 4 gave no evidence of sensibility, whereas 5 reported pain in the neck, which was similar to that stimulated by irritation of the central diaphragm. This pain occurred around the trapezius ridge and apparently was transmitted by the phrenic nerve. Similar experiments on patients and observations of a variety of conditions revealed the following (202, p. 66):

> 2. Exploration of the inner surface of the pericardium with a silver wire failed to induce any response of pain in the serous membrane.
> 3. Pressure on, and scratching of, the pericardial investment of the heart itself did not produce pain, although "tripping" of the apex with the wire induced a peculiar feeling of distress and apprehension.

Traction on a ligature of the descending branch of the left coronary artery resulted in indication of pain in a dog (782).

A ten-month study of 2 healthy, trained observers, male and female, and a series of experiments on selected patients with palpitation symptoms led Wolf and Wolff to the following conclusions (1342, p. 300):

> Palpitation may be defined as sensations, usually painless, experienced in the chest or over the heart and presumably arising from the heart or its adjacent tissues. There is no evidence to suggest that the sensory threshold in the periphery is lowered during the period of palpitation. Changes in the intensity or frequency of stimuli caused by the beat of the heart may be associated with (a) increased stroke volume; (b) displacement of the heart or tissues around it so that tissues ordinarily not stimulated by the beating heart are in a position to be stimulated; (c) occurrence of a beat out of phase with preceding and succeeding beats; and (d) rapid beating of the heart.

The emotional components of such reactions were determined by clinical and case-history material, including the verbal reports of the patients.

OTHER INTERNAL PERCEPTIVE RELATIONSHIPS

A year of "day-to-day" studies of the cardiovascular and respiratory functions of healthy subjects, and also short-term observations on selected patients by these same investigators revealed that the persistent low-grade stresses and strains of "everyday" living produce the following heart symptoms at times: palpitation associated with increased stroke volume in connection with anxiety, anger, guilt, rage, frustration, and tension; and heart pain with narrowing of the arteries due to a fall in cardiac output and coronary blood flow (1342).

Gemelli's long-term observations associated the "state-of-disgust," or "repugnance," with "tightening of the heart and the whole chest" and associated the state of "anxiety, fear, etc." with such reports as "the feeling of fear gripped my heart, it seemed to beat harder and faster," and the like (433, p. 213). Altschule referred to "well-known" reports of clutching discomfort about the heart occasioned by fear that has been differentiated from angina-pectoris sensations by subjects who have experienced both, and he added that "heavy sensations" in this area in association with sadness are commonly experienced (38). "Cardiac neurosis," involving somatic complaints referred to the heart or cardiac fixation without somatic symptoms, have been described as being possibly one special type of anxiety neurosis and as having a central underlying theme of anxiety and fear (680). Cardiac sensations are also frequently reported by patients diagnosed as having neurocirculatory asthenia, or "functional cardiovascular disease," or simply "anxiety reaction" (242, 1097).

The association of "cardiospasm" sensations in this area with a defensive type of esophageal hyperactivity was presented in the previous section (1347), and in this connection should be added the finding of "heartburn" with mechanical stimulation of the cardiac sphincter (258). A case having symptoms of "heart attack" that related to diaphragmatic flutter should also be noted (528). Friedman observed that the precordial pain of "functional cardiovascular disease," or neurocirculatory asthenia, apparently arises from cardiac impact against unusually fatigued intercostal muscles that the patients employ excessively for breathing instead of the more normally predominant diaphragmatic musculature (393).

Uncomplicated, or functional, paroxysmal auricular fibrillation, wherein no evidence of organic cardiac disease is found, has been frequently observed (886, 962, 970). With this condition, the patient complains primarily of "palpitation" or "pounding" of the heart, and only rarely observes the irregular beating of his own heart; these symptoms involved premature ventricular systoles, which are primarily associated with "psychogenic or nervous" factors that act on a neurogenic mechanism (886). This condition was thought to be disabling for military service.

Hypnoanalytic treatment of a patient who was for many years aware of extrasystoles was reported, and a direct relationship was seen to exist between the extrasystoles and "states of tension" (1101). A study of auricular arrhythmias indicated that patients were at times aware of heart acceleration (sinus tachycardia) before the onset of paroxysmal tachycardia; in patients observed during emotional disturbance, there occurred "first a racing of the heart (sinus tachycardia) and then the abrupt onset of the paroxysmal tachycardia" (323). Malmo found heart complaints (such as palpitation) in psychiatric patients to correlate specifically with increases in heart rate and with a high degree of variability in both heart rate and respiration (860).

Wolff noted that the diaphragm may participate in defense reactions and produce sensations in the substernal region (1358). Subjects with essential hypertension and complaints of precordial pain, palpitation, and dyspnea were then described as having strong conflicts with repression of hostility and as reacting with a defensive mobilization pattern. He exemplified this by a patient with precordial sensations who showed increased blood pressure and cardiac output and a cardiographic elevation of ST segments and of T waves (indicative of coronary insufficiency) during a period of "aggravation." Sinus arrhythmias and also tachycardia may be caused by hyperventilation—which is frequently associated with emotional reactions—and this may contribute to the palpitation reported with emotional upset (38).

FEELING REACTIONS

A series of experiments studying reports of internal sensations with different reactions in different emotionally toned situations was undertaken by myself (see p. 270), and in all three of these studies, the central-chest area was given greatest emphasis (879a). In the first study, the "central-chest area" employed for ratings was so extensive that it included the epigastrium, in addition to the central-chest area (Area No. 6) shown in Figure 1 (877). All subjects reported sensations of a "unitary" nature in this area. "Unitary sensations" were defined as occurring consistently and being meaningfully related to given psychological states or reactions; however, almost all types of combinations of associated reactions were listed by the subjects from a wide variety of rating classifications that were provided, including ratings of relative pleasantness and of several specific feeling-reaction associations. Also, sensations in this area were frequently reported to be noticed simultaneously with sensations in other areas. For example, "pleasant" sensations with rated "reaction association" of "going toward" were reported to occur in this area at times simultaneously with "pleasant sensations" having a reaction association of "sexual association" in the lowest front trunk area, which included the genitals. Of the fifty-three body areas available for rating, encompassing the whole body, this "central-chest area" was one of the eleven areas in which focal points of "unitary sensations" were reported. For example, in this large area that overlies many vital organs, subject A observed the "unitary sensation" of "pleasant" sensations with the reaction association of "going toward" and "attraction or possessiveness," which he labeled "romance"; however, in the same area was observed also a unitary sensation with an "unpleasant" rating and with the reaction association of "going from, aversion or avoidance" and "going against, struggling for or against," which, along with simultaneous sensations in other areas, was labeled "embarrassment . . . including feelings of insecurity." In this experiment, the sensations reported represented only the most noticeable locus of sensation occurring, and it was apparent that many of the internal sensations did not seem to be of a unitary nature since the "unitary sensations" described did not include all of the sensations reported.

Of 36 male subjects in the second experiment, 14 reported the greatest frequency of sensations in the central-chest area, and their ratings of these sensations were relatively intense (878). In rating of the depth of the sensations in this area, the classifications "muscle" and "intermediate" were employed by the subjects more frequently than the other two categories available, namely, "skin" and "deep." The subjects as a whole placed greatest emphasis on this area in all situations except the "sexual" one, for which the central-chest area was somewhat less noticeable than the genital-pubic areas (Areas No. 13b and 13a). Included as stimuli were situations involving feeling reactions of "significance," "enjoyment," "love," "depression," "fear," and "anger." Of these situations, sensations in the central chest were most noticeable in the "love" and the "anger" feeling-reaction types.

In the more extensive third experiment, an analysis of variance including the Tukey statistical process revealed the central-chest area to be in the significantly most highly rated grouping of areas, which also included the right midriff (Areas No. 12a near 12b), the central abdomen (Area No. 14), and the lower left epigastrium (Area No. 10). The central-chest area was given major emphasis in all seven situations, with first ranking in all but two of them and with second and third ranking in these; nevertheless, the percentages of ratings for this area revealed variations in sensation pattern for the different situations. Relative to the other situations, the central-chest area was strongly rated in the situation with a predominant loading of "love" and in the situation with a predominant loading of "friendliness," this last one having also a marked loading of a feeling of "significance" or "importance." The central-chest area was rated least, as compared to other situations, in the situation having a predominant "sexual" loading. It should be noted, however, that the central-chest area ranked second to the genital-pubic area (Area No. 13b and part of 13a) (with the lower-left-diaphragm area and the right-midriff area tying for a close third ranking), for the quartile of the nonpatient group, which appeared to be the healthiest on the basis of the Harrower Multiple Choice (Rorschach) Test.

In this last experiment, the subjects were asked to describe the nature of the sensations experienced. In the various chest sensations mentioned by the subjects two sensations of "flutter" were associated with the "heart," and most of the thirteen sensations classified as "palpitation" made some mention of the heart. Most of the other sensations described generally as "in the chest" seemed to be of a different nature: seven "fullness," six "tightness," three each of "tingling," "hollow," "pressure or heavy," and "breathing sensation," two each of "warmth," "slight," and "expansion," and one each of "wave," "twitching," "lightness," "sharp," and "excited." Sensations described as extending from the "chest to the abdomen" or vice versa were one each of "pain," "tickling," and "soothing," and described as "from the waist up" were one each of "tingling," "chills," and "wave."

UPPER-LATERAL CHEST AREA (Area No. 7)

This area extends upward from a horizontal line at the lowest juncture of the ribs and the sternum to the collar bone and shoulder area, and it extends laterally over the rib area to a vertical line from the shoulder blades, but excludes the heart area. The area overlies the lungs and bronchi, pleura, bone, muscle, and breasts, and all of these are capable of pain sensation with adequate stimulation (5, 1364). Nevertheless, like most visceral organs, the lung is insensitive to such usual direct pain stimuli as puncture by an exploratory needle (782).

TYPES OF SENSATIONS OCCURRING

Lung conditions also result in subjective dyspnea, and feelings of suffocation and of constriction; pneumonia also produces concurrent pain in the upper-central-chest area and in the central abdominal areas as well as in the central-chest (heart) area. Tingling in the nipples during pregnancy is reported. Also, tactile sensibility of the breast in association with sexual stimulation is well known (705). Secondary sensations in this area, stimulated by heart conditions, have been noted in the previous section (38, 173, 643, 1358), and those relatively few secondary sensations stimulated in this area by conditions of the esophagus (133b, 1347) and the diaphragm (1358) were described in the section pertaining to the upper-central chest area.

The lungs and bronchi, being embryologically related to the neck, are innervated by fibers from the third and fourth cervical segments that are carried in the vagal rami to the spinal cord (1317, 1364). The pain from the pleura is transmitted by the intercostal nerves and, on the diaphragmatic surface, also by the phrenic nerves (1364). Sensations of the lungs and bronchi are often correctly localized (1317, 1364). No referred pain from the lungs has been reported (1068). Not only is local pain found in the lungs (5), but closely localized sharp pain in the parietal pleura was found to occur with pressure from wire stimulation by Capps and Coleman (202). Localization of pleural pain was more exact in the anterior and axillary regions than in the posterior wall, and occasional pain in the intercostal space just below the site of irritation was seen. These investigators found the visceral (or pulmonary) pleura to be devoid of pain with this stimulation for 35 cases, and also "other forms of irritation" were tried without producing discomfort. These structures did not produce referred pain.

HYPERVENTILATION AND DYSPNEA

Hyperventilation and dyspnea have been commonly associated with emotional reactions, and Altschule stated that "the smothering sensations and the feeling of a need to take deep breaths experienced by some patients appear to be entirely sensory" (38, p. 67). Similar findings were reported by Wolf and Wolff in associating dyspnea and insufficient pulmonary ventilation with "everyday" stress-producing life situations involving anxiety, anger, guilt, rage, frustration, and tension (1342).

Willard, Swan, and Wolf observed that everyone may easily become aware of the complex sensations associated with breathing and that the act of such awareness itself may result in alteration of the rate and depth of respiration (1326). By such a mechanism, various stimuli acting on the respiratory system to produce unpleasant sensations may be interpreted by the subject as difficulty in breathing, and thereby affect breathing and produce dyspnea. Many such reactions were considered by these investigators to be a part of normal experience as exemplified by the following common associations: sighing with depression, yawning with boredom, tightening in the throat and deep breathing with fear; also, "gasping, grunting, screaming, snorting, sobbing, wailing, and moaning are all familiar" (1326, p. 583). Experimentation with some patients and normal subjects revealed that restriction of the free exit of air from the chest, either physically or functionally, may result in a lowering of the midposition of the diaphragm and limit its free movement that is necessary for normal breathing, thereby trapping air in the distended lungs (1326, 1345). A relationship between inability to expell air easily and shortness of breath, leading to dyspnea and associated sensations, was therefore postulated. Patients' complaints of difficulty in breathing were frequently characterized by a choking sensation and subsequent hyperventilation (1326). It was presumed that "anxiety associated with the globus phenomenon, produces a state of panic and hyperventilation, and not infrequently results in the diagnosis of paroxysmal dyspnea" (1326, p. 586). Such a reaction was seen in a stressful interview. Restriction of free movement of the chest wall, physically or functionally via muscle contraction, was observed to result in dyspnea, progressive inflation and distention of the lungs, and inefficient bellows action.

The following complaints have also been reported with functional hyperventilation: a tight feeling across the front and upper part of the chest, a sensation of "weight" on the chest, and a feeling of suffocation (1099). Functional hyperventilation was described as a "vicious cycle" and "a vicious habit" that occurs three times more frequently in women than men, and includes about 27 per cent of the general female population, and was attributed to anxiety. Complaints of pain in the chest have also been associated with tension of the shoulder muscles, which itself has an emotional component (813). In seeking the basis for these common findings, it was seen that with normal subjects, voluntary hyperventilation produced faintness, giddiness, and similar complaints followed by numbness and tingling about the mouth and extremities, cold hands, and possibly fainting, and with prolonged hyperventilation, there may be signs and symptoms of tetany (1192).

OTHER INTERNAL PERCEPTIONS

In connection with states of sadness and depression, Gemelli reported irregular breathing with pauses and "pain" in the whole chest, and with disgust or repugnance, one subject observed a "tightening of the heart and the whole chest" in addition to several gastrointestinal symptoms (433). Also, a Lifwynn observer first became aware of respiratory sensations and then found a markedly slower respiration in the more pleasurable and healthy "cotentive" pattern of reaction than in the opposite "ditentive" state (959). Measurements showed an increase in the thoracic and abdominal amplitudes of respiratory movements for "cotention."

LOWER CHEST AREAS (Areas No. 11a and 11b)

These areas include that part of the rib structure that lies below a line that is horizontal with the lowest end of the breastbone (the xiphoid process of the sternum) and extends laterally, on either side of the body, between the xiphoid and a line that goes down vertically from the inferior angle of the scapula. On the right side, this area partially overlies the liver and gall bladder. On the left, it overlies the spleen, part of the stomach (which will be considered separately under the epigastrium, Area No. 10), and part of the lungs (which were considered in the preceding section). All of these structures as well as the pleural membrane appear to be capable of pain sensation. Liver pain may extend to all of the epigastrium, whereas gall-bladder pain may include the right epigastric areas as well as the central-chest area and may also be referred to the central-back area (Area No. 22) (5, 1364). Liver and gall-bladder pain may also extend superficially to the right upper quadrant (Area No. 7a) (1068). In one case of pain wherein the gall bladder had been displaced from its normal position, Hertz observed that the pain seemed to be localized where the patient's gall bladder was normally located, and he cited this as evidence of his thesis that sensations from visceral organs are localized at the average point where the organ is usually located in a given subject (566).

Pain impulses from the liver and the biliary tract as well as from the stomach and pancreas are believed to be carried in the splanchnic sympathetic trunks that enter the spinal cord in the seventh to ninth thoracic segments (1364). Concerning this apparent multiple common innervation, Wolff stated as follows (1364, p. 61):

> These facts explain in part the difficulties encountered in differential diagnosis of epigastric pain. Not only may it arise from these structures named but also from retroperitoneal tissues, skeletal muscles or from lesions of the nervous system such as herpes zoster or cord tumors which involve dorsal roots. Epigastric pain may even be referred from the heart or other thoracic structures as mentioned above or from impulses arising in the lower bowel including the transverse colon and appendix.

He asserted that although the hepatic parenchyma has not been found pain sensitive, pain does arise from rapid distention of its capsule. Pain can also be stimulated in the gall bladder, and it is localized in the distribution of the ninth thoracic segment either anteriorly beneath the right costal margin or posteriorly at the angle of the scapula (1354).

Capps and Coleman stimulated the diaphragmatic peritoneum over an arc region of the upper part of the right-lower-chest area (Area No. 11a) with the results that light touch or gentle stroking of the under surface of the diaphragm produced no sensation and firmer pressure produced pain (1) diffusely over the peripheral margin, narrow anteriorly and broad posteriorly, and (2) referred to the right costal border, over the lower ribs and the right hypochondrium (202). Firm pressure on the central portion of the diaphragm elicited sharp pain over the outer third of the trapezius ridge. More limited stimulation near the lower-left-chest area (Area No. 11b) showed that just the peritoneum immediately above this area similarly referred sensations to the outer edge of the trapezius ridge on the same side, whereas stimulation just an inch below the costal border, in Area No. 12c, produced localized pain. On the other hand, it is commonly asserted that solid organs, such as the liver, the spleen and the kidney can be tightly squeezed, cut, or burned without causing pain (643, 782). The gall bladder, too, is said to be insensitive to clamping and cautery (764). Wittkower has reported sensations in the right upper abdominal region with the state of "annoyance" that he explained as resulting from spasm of the bile ducts (321, 1333).

The lower-right-chest area (Area No. 11a) was one of the ten body areas included in my more extensive studies of the relationships between internal sensory experience and reactions to situations with different feeling loadings that have been described somewhat in preceding sections. Relatively few sensations were reported for this area in all three studies. In the first rather limited study, which included rating areas for all of the body, no significant findings were apparent for this area (877). In the second study, ratings were made for the depth of sensations observed; the categories "skin," "muscle," and "intermediate" were employed frequently, but very few "deep" sensations were reported (878). In the most extensive of these studies, this area again received rather consistently moderate ratings relative to the other nine areas rated. In relation to the different types of situations presented, it was rated more strongly with the "anger" loading and rated least with the loading of "significance," or feeling of "importance" (879).

EPIGASTRIC AREA IN GENERAL (Particularly Areas No. 8 and 9)

Area 8 is to the right of the mid-line and above a line extending across the epigastrium from the sixth left rib to the tenth right rib, whereas Area 9 is to the left, above this line, and Area 10 includes the epigastrium below this line to a horizontal line connecting the lowest rib points. Sensations reported in the literature, however, do not often differentiate among these areas, but refer to the epigastrium, or diaphragm, generally. Usually underlying Area 8 are part of the liver and gall bladder and, below that, the upper part of the right kidney and the right adrenal cortex. Usually underlying Area 9 are part of the liver, the esophagus where it enters the stomach, and part of the left kidney and part of the suprarenal gland. Area 10 primarily overlies the stomach, although part of the left kidney is deep beneath it. Also, to the lower right is the duodenum, and the pancreas stretches deeply across this area.

The following sensations and organs referring pain have been reported for the epigastrium, and the additional areas in which sensations may occur are shown in parentheses with the additional areas of primary involvement in italics (5): (a) variations of pain in the alimentary tract (*4, 6*); (b) pain, cramps, gripping, colicky sensations in the stomach (11b; and hiatus hernia: 5a, & b, 17a & b, 21, 6, 4); (c) secondary pain, cecum (*15a*); (d) gall bladder (*11a*; 7a, 22); (e) secondary heart pain (*6*); (f) abdominal lining tissue (peritonitis); (g) duodenum (ulcer: burning or boring pain, 21, 22); (h) pleura (diaphragmatic; 12, 20, 5a & b); (i) liver (11a; 7a, 5a); (j) pancreas ("deep" pain; 10, 12 and 22 at 23). In the previous section it was noted that noxious impulses from the pancreas were carried by the same pathways as those from the liver, biliary tract, and stomach (1364). The perineal tissue overlying the pancreas has been found to be very sensitive to pain (782, 932).

Pain stimulated in the central zone of the diaphragmatic pleura or peritoneum is referred to the shoulder at the neck, whereas stimulation of the margins of the diaphragm refers pain to the posterior abdominal wall (1068) or other abdominal areas, including at times the lower epigastric area (202). Capps and Coleman have stated as follows that referred pain involves phrenic innervation of the neck (202, p. 22):

> The phrenic nerve supplies the anterior two-thirds of the diaphragmatic pleura, with the exception of a peripheral band of varying width. The nerve fibers spread out from the central nerve trunk toward the border, where they come in contact with the sensory fibers of the last six intercostal nerves. Although the transition from phrenic to intercostal pain is usually abrupt, still there is evidence that the fibers interlace. Occasionally along this intermediate zone moderate pressure produced pain in the abdomen while stronger pressure set up pain of phrenic origin in the neck.

The fact that pain sensation that is stimulated in the esophagus is frequently referred to the epigastric area below the sternum has been noted under the upper-central-chest area (Area No. 4) (133b, 227, 258, 556, 1347). Pain, as well as other sensations relating to changes in the diaphragmatic musculature, was also noted under that area and under the central-chest area. Similarly, some localization in this same region for sensations stimulated in the stomach and in the duodenum will be presented in the next section (133b). In addition to the symptoms listed with cases of "hysterical" diaphragmatic flutter, "abdominal fullness, belching, and epigastric pain described as 'burning' in type," were reported but these more probably stemmed from a coexisting duodenal ulcer (528).

Limited associations of the state of joy with "expansion of the chest and the diaphragm" (433) and the association of the Lifwynn group's state of "cotention" with decreased respiration and increased amplitude of thoracic and abdominal respiratory movements have been presented in preceding sections (959). These reports are consistent with Kling's notation of sensations of tightness in the epigastrium with fear states (710). Similarly, in an experiment of mine, there were frequent associations of various feeling reactions with sensations in a large classification area that combined the epigastrium with the central chest, and these were described in connection with the latter area (877).

STOMACH AREA OF THE EPIGASTRIUM (Area No. 10)

SENSATION STIMULATION AND REFERENCE

Ruch stated that the epigastrium is the superficial area wherein stomach pain is localized and that stomach sensations are transmitted via the visceral afferent axon that enters the spinal cord at the seventh and eighth thoracic segments (and possibly also via the sixth and ninth segments) and via the peripheral visceral pathway, which is the major splanchnic nerve (1068).

Wire stimulation of the peripheral rim of the 2-inch or 3-inch wide diaphragmatic pleura and of the posterior third of the membrane (which are innervated by sensory fibers of the intercostal nerve) gave rise to pain in the lower thorax, in the lumbar region, or in the abdomen (202). It was observed in an early study that the stomach (as well as the esophagus) has specific warm and cold sensations, but touch sensations were not experienced when the subjects swallowed (138).

In 1921, Payne and Poulton reported studies of the upper intestinal tract in which pressure from a water-filled balloon was measured, and they noted that normal pressure within the stomach of a resting subject varies very little (976). It was seen that when the patient felt an epigastric pain, the pressure within the body of the stomach rose slightly, and within the pylorus very strong contractions were seen to correspond closely to the periods when the pain was worse; a similar relationship with the lower esophagus was also observed (see p. 289). Other observations revealed that pain subsequent to strong stomach contractions was followed by duodenal contraction. It was concluded that pain in the upper abdomen might be associated with movements in the pylorus, in the duodenum, or in the jejunum (as seen in one case after gastrojejunostomy), and that these parts could probably be affected alone or simultaneously and with or without simultaneous movements in the esophagus, which might produce "heartburn." Subsequently, these experimenters performed studies using each other as subjects; they employed an air-filled balloon, which, when inflated in the cardiac part of the stomach, produced a "sensation of sinking" that was thought to be due to the events taking place in the lower part of the stomach since the observations revealed that only the pyloric section contracted (978). This sensation of sinking lasted about a second and was experienced repeatedly. It was thought to be due to a slight increase in the tonus of the stomach wall that might stretch specific sensory end organs and would be eliminated by a peristaltic wave acting to abolish the stretch. The sinking sensation was said to be "analogous in every way to nausea," which, as already described, these authors related to tensions in the esophagus. At the same time, a desire to eructate was felt, and the associated sensation was localized deep in the mid-line about the level of the clavicle, and had the quality of a "lump" or "globus" that aroused the urge to eructate for its elimination, although eructation was not necessary.

Bloomfield and Polland found that with balloon inflation in the stomach there were much less sharply localized sensations than with inflation in the esophagus or duodenum (133b). The sensations were usually described as deep and not occurring on the surface, and the subject usually placed his whole hand over the general area affected. Most of the localizations of sensation were in the epigastrium just below the sternum and tended slightly to the left, but a few were below the stomach level in the mid-line area, and one was situated in the left lower chest approximating the outer upper edge of the stomach. In several instances the induced sensations were said by patients to resemble spontaneous discomforts. Two subjects found the stomach sensations to resemble those of the esophagus, and others also reported a resemblance between esophageal and duodenal pain. Reported sensations of the stomach included those of fullness, "gas pain," painful tight feeling, pressure, "burning, gassy pain," and ache. Almost all of 12 subjects localized pain from inflation of the duodenum over that organ, at and below the line horizontal with the lowest point on the area of the body to which the ribs extend, with about half of the localizations of pain well into the epigastrium and usually centered, but also tending toward the right. The sensations that were produced included: "sharp, dull, and hot sticking" pains; "a burning cramp," producing nausea; ache; "full cramp-like feeling"; and "dull pressure."

Hertz attempted to establish the basis of hunger sensation (to be described subsequently) by balloon inflation of the stomach, which produced a "sensation of fullness or tightness in the upper part of the abdomen" with desire to eructate in 2 cases after pressure of 12 and 14 mm. Hg respectively. After 20 seconds, the pressure fell 2 mm., apparently due to relaxation of the stomach wall, and simultaneously the sensation of fullness disappeared. Increased pressure produced repetition of this cycle for five times. The sensation was felt deeply beneath the upper part of the anterior abdominal wall in the mid-line. Rapid inflation of the balloon produced pain; however, Hertz found that it is much more common for pain to result from distention of a part of the stomach than from distention of the whole. Localization was the same as for distention, varying with the individual, but extending from near the sternum to near the umbilicus. When, as in clinical cases, only part of the stomach was subjected to abnormal tension, pain was felt in the upper or lower sections of this area, corresponding to the location of the stimulus between the cardiac and pyloric divisions of the stomach. Thus, pain was occasionally to the left in gastric cases and sometimes to the right in cases of duodenal ulcers. Although Hertz found alcohol to produce a sensation of warmth, 4 ounces of 0.5 hydrochloric acid solution produced no sensation in the stomach. He also stated that peristalsis by itself cannot cause pain.

More recently, the sensations of a normal stomach were studied before and after vagotomy by Wolf and Andrus, who found that induced sensations were essentially the same nineteen and twenty-one days after vagotomy as before the vagotomy (1348). The tactile stimulation of slight pressure with a blunt glass rod (5 mm. in diameter) in the stomach was not felt; however, a pressure of 40 gm./sq.cm. was felt as such and localized, while 125 gm./sq.cm. produced slight aching pain and, after 30 seconds, nausea, the former disappearing first upon removal of the rod. Water at 40°C.

produced warmth that was localized just below and slightly to the left of the umbilical region within 7 seconds, and water at $13\frac{1}{2}°$C. produced cold in the same area within 15 seconds. This particular localization was thought to relate to the effects of an earlier operative procedure. Wolf and Wolff found that in Tom, the subject with a fistula, temperatures between 18 and 40°C. produced no sensation in the stomach, but warmth and cold were felt above and below these ranges, respectively, and deep in the epigastrium in a fist-sized area (1352). Also, pressure sensations were reported with pressure of approximately 30 gm./sq.cm. from a glass rod in the stomach, but the localization was only rough. With intragastric pressure at 15 mm. Hg in a manometer 7 mm. in diameter, a feeling of fullness was reported by this subject; with pressure of 35 mm. and 1500 c.c. of air, pain was felt throughout the entire epigastrium and occasionally in the flanks and back at that level and was associated with a dull, aching, and "sickening" sensation. Wolff reported that experimentation with a healthy mucosa of the fundus of the stomach produced no pain (1) upon squeezing with forceps, (2) upon faradic stimulation that was intense enough to produce pain on the tongue, (3) or upon contact with 50 or 59 per cent alcohol solution, 1.0 NHCl, .1 N sodium hydroxide, or 1:30 suspension of mustard (1355). On the other hand, with inflamed, congested, and edematous gastric mucosa, pain of considerable intensity was produced by all of these procedures. Two series of experiments undertaken by this group indicated also that pain may be experienced directly from the muscularis or serosa, and revealed: (1) stomach contractions with a force of pressure of 30 mg. Hg against an indwelling balloon usually produced pain, although when the gastric mucosa was inflamed, pressure of only 20 to 25 mg. was required; (2) stretching of the stomach directly by glass rods usually required 100 gm./sq.cm. to produce pain, but when the stomach wall was strongly contracted, pain resulted from pressure of 50 gm., and when the stomach was relatively relaxed, pressure of 150 gm. was required to elicit pain (1352, 1355). Gloyne asserted that the normal gastric mucosa is insensitive to cutting, pinching, tearing, or exposure to varying hydrogen ion concentrations; however, if the mucosa becomes inflamed, it may be sensitive, presumably because of a lowered pain threshold (461).

ULCER SENSATIONS

Palmer reported from experiments of his own and others that peptic ulcer occurs only in the presence of acid gastric juice and that this gastric acid produces inflammation, necrosis, and pain (967). This pain can be relieved by emesis, by aspiration of the stomach, or by any procedure that neutralizes the acid, including ingestion of food or alkali (965, 966, 967). The similar findings of Wolf and Wolff with their gastric-fistula patient, Tom, have already been noted (1350, 1352).

Gloyne stated the belief that the pain of peptic ulcer depends primarily upon the degree of inflammation present in or about the lesion; an acutely inflamed ulcer is highly sensitive to mechanical or chemical changes, including those of peristalsis, spasm, and hydrogen ion concentration, and the acid gastric juice is critical for evoking the inflammation (461). On the other hand, he noted clinical cases where there was typical peptic-ulcer pain without demonstrable roentgenographic or gastroscopic evidence of ulcer, and this pain pattern lasted several months or more in some patients before an ulcer could be demonstrated. Also, it was reported that typical ulcer pain may persist after surgical removal of an ulcer. Gloyne stated as follows (461, p. 142):

> [the associated] continual gastric hyperacidity represents a physiologic expression of the psychologic intense longing for rest, security, help and love. And the pain becomes a psychological cry for help. It also may represent an aggressive demand for help and if this need is not met the pain may persist. Since the pain is characteristically relieved by vomiting, one can infer that the pain may represent in this instance a physiological expression of disgust and resentment which develops into nausea and vomiting.

Similarly, epigastric pain typical of the "ulcer" type occurred in peptic-ulcer patients in situations involving significant personal conflicts wherein gastric hyperfunctioning, via vagus innervation, was associated with lowering of the pain threshold and increased fragility of the stomach membranes (652). Statistical analysis of a psychotherapy record revealed an association of gastric peptic-ulcer pains with "the product of a conflict of dependent strivings and defenses" and with a "surgent syndrome" (820a).

HUNGER SENSATIONS

Some time ago, Cannon described hunger sensations as "a very disagreeable ache or pang or sense of gnawing or pressure which is referred to the epigastrium" (194). Hertz associated hunger with "the sensation of emptiness in the upper part of the abdomen," which, with eating, is succeeded by a "feeling of fullness" (556). Boring reported the following "primary" hunger sensations (as distinguished from such secondary sensations as "weakness and faintness, headache," etc.) for 9 subjects who were observed during states of hunger induced by fasting (138, p. 312):

[1] dull pressure of considerable intensity in area above umbilicus. With this also pain, an achy, gnawing pain. Or else a muscular tension, a feeling of muscular contraction in this region, gives the meaning of "gnawing." I think I sometimes have mere "emptiness". . . [2] On the sensory side hunger is composed of temperature and muscular sensations. . . The localization is in the stomach. . . [3] A dull, yet insistent ache—very diffuse. It seems to cover an area of about 20 cm. in diameter, fairly deep, and extending upward from a point of the sternum. . .

Many introspective elaborations were made by all the subjects. Boring noted a case of similar "hunger sensations" induced by the introduction of HCl into the subject's stomach. Sensations in the stomach and elsewhere were also observed: almost painful "contractions," "a dull heavy ache," "a gnawing, sinking pressure-like quality in the stomach region, extending up a little under sternum," and "vague moving pressures, localized in stomach."

Wolf and Wolff stated concerning the subject with the fistula, Tom, that vigorous stomach contractions produced "the familiar pangs of hunger," cramping, intermittent, deep, moderate, and lasting ten to forty seconds. Although these were localized in the left lower quadrant, it was thought that this localization might have been due to a peritoneal adhesion from an old operation (1352). Tom was able to localize pain stimulated on the collar of the mucosa of the fistula within 3 to 4 cm. of stimulation. These observations were generally confirmed later on another subject with fistula; in still another subject, such sensory experiences were seen not to be altered by a vagotomy. On the other hand, Crider and Walker reported that a subject complained of a cramping pain during an exceptionally strong stomach contraction (258), and the pain was followed by a feeling of hunger. This subject was also observed to report hunger pangs at a time when no contractions occurred, which led them to agree with Wolf and Wolff (1352) in the denying of Carlson's early thesis that stomach contractions always accompany the sensation of hunger (204). In a subsequent study of the patient reported by Crider and Walker, however, some doubt was cast on the reliability of her anamnestic reports (871). Other observers have reported that the gastric hypomotility resulting from bilateral transthoracic vagectomy and extensive thoracic sympathectomy, with a predominant vagotropic effect, did not reduce sensations of appetite, hunger, nausea, or gastrocolic reflex in patients with duodenal ulcers or essential hypertension (120, 1279). Weiss observed that "a nagging intolerable sensation in the epigastrium often referred to as 'nervous hunger' is symbolic of the emptiness of the emotional life" of obese persons who overeat to allay anxiety or to gratify pleasure cravings that should be satisfied in other ways (1299, p. 143).

OTHER INTERNAL PERCEPTIVE RELATIONSHIPS

Many reports associate stomach sensations with various psychological states. Kling, for example, related the sensation of "sickening" or sinking, to gastric contractions that occurred with fear in reaction to a sudden loud voice (710). Wolf and Wolff also associated the "sinking feeling" in the stomach with fear in describing the reactions of their subject with a fistula, Tom (1353). However, their primary emphasis was on the association of anorexia,, "sinking in the stomach," and nausea with a feeling of being overwhelmed and dejected that was accompanied by stomach hypoactivity (1358). Similarly, "epigastric uneasiness" and anorexia were found among students with pre-examination tension, but disappeared after successful completion of the examination (560). Gastric hyperfunctioning in some individuals, as noted in Chapter 13 (p. 227), has been associated with feelings of anger and with unconscious longing for dependency supports when threatened with deprivation or unacceptance in dependency relationships, and symptoms of "heartburn" and localized epigastric pain occurred, which could be relieved by food or soda whether or not ulceration had taken place (1357). As one of the symptoms of the emotionally based "hyperventilating type" of personality, Schimmenti reported for the stomach area "a sensation of a void or emptiness in the pit of the stomach" or "butterflies in the stomach"; these patients generally also showed a relative hypochlorhydria, or reduced hydrochloric acid content, in the stomach, with indigestion frequently occurring, especially after the eating of foods with a heavy protein content (1097).

FEELING REACTIONS

My research with 36 subjects, in which the stomach area (Area No. 10) was rated for internal sensations in situations with different feeling loadings, revealed that this area was one of the most strongly emphasized, ranking usually second only to the central-chest area (878). The occurrence of sensations in this area was more prominent with feeling reactions of "love" and with situations having feeling loadings of "fear" and of "anger" than with the other four main feeling reactions and loadings. The absence of sensations in this area relative to other areas and situations was seen most in situations and feelings with ratings of "significance" or "importance." Of the 36 subjects, 10 placed primary emphasis on this area. In rating of the depth of sensations experienced here, the "muscle" and "intermediate" classifications predominated; "deep" ratings were relatively absent; and the "skin" classification held an intermediate place.

In the more extensive research project of the same type, the stomach area was in the statistically significant, most highly rated grouping of areas that included three other of the ten areas (Areas No. 6, 12a, 14) (879). The stomach area was given less emphasis by the quartile of normal subjects rated least healthy on the basis of Harrower Multiple Choice Rorschach. The total nonpatient group of 178 emphasized this area in the situations with loadings of "love" and in the situation with loadings of "anger," where "enjoyment" was also a secondary loading. The area received relatively little emphasis in situations with the "significance" loadings.

In the subjects' optional descriptions of the sensations, it was not clear exactly what area they had in mind when referring to "the stomach" or to the "abdomen" since lay concepts of these terms may include anything from the chest to the genital areas. A few of their sensation descriptions, however, were more specifically localized. In Area No. 10, the stomach area, were reported four sensations of "tightness" and one each of "fullness," "sickness," "pulsing," and "hit in stomach." In Area No. 14, the central abdominal area, were two "pit-of-the-stomach" sensations, and one each of "hollow," and "swelling." Also six other sensations of "pit of the stomach" and one of "sinking in the stomach" were reported without localization. These more specifically localized sensations may provide a clue as to the possible location of the following sensations, which were described as "in the stomach" or "in the abdominal area": fourteen "tightness," six "sickness," five "hollow," three "funny feeling," two each of "tingling," "fluttering" and "weakness," and one each of "pressure or heavy," "ache," "wave," "slight," "warmth," "good," "tickling," "breathing," "prickly," "quick-like," "excited," "as hungry," "murmuring," "turning," "sinking," and "cold." My own early association of differentially predominant sensations in this area was with a feeling called "companionship," which included differentiated patterns of sensations for feelings called "love," "humor," and "thrill" (876).

MIDRIFF AND HYPOCHONDRIAC AREAS
(Areas No. 12, 12b, and 12c)

This area includes the hypochondrium (Areas No. 12a, 12c) and the intermediate section above the navel (Area No. 12b), extending between horizontal lines at the top of the navel and at the lowest point on the area of the body to which the ribs extend, and goes around to a line that goes vertically through the inferior angle of the shoulder blades. The areas are divided by allowing of approximately 4 inches (or one third of the frontal width) for the central area (Area No. 12b). These areas overlie the transverse colon and the lower part of the kidney on either side, and the right part of the duodenum. Pains in these areas may arise directly from the duodenum, jejunum, transverse colon, and peritoneum, and pain may be secondary to conditions in the heart, pleura, lungs, or stomach (which may also produce direct pain in Area No. 12c) (5, 202).

With regard to possible differential functioning or internal perception of the various sections of the colon, it has been reported that the section of the colon above the sigmoid (which is located in the lower abdominal area) has afferent innervation by sympathetic trunks, and the innervation of the sigmoid colon and rectum is supplied mainly by other fibers (1364). Also, pain from the spermatic cords and testicular structure may at times be referred to the hypogastric region in addition to being felt *in situ* (1364).

The wire exploration of Capps and Coleman revealed that the parietal peritoneum and its underlying serosa showed pain localized within one inch from strong pressure of a smooth point or from light pressure or movement of a rough point of wire, but no pressure sensations were reported (202). Correct localizations with limited inflammations were also seen. Pain stimulation of the diaphragmatic peritoneum always referred pain to some distant part, and stimulation of the outer margin produced diffuse pain over the lower costal region, over the hypochondrium, and, at times, over the lower abdominal quadrant on the same side. Also, with relatively intense stimulation of the diaphragmatic pleura, diffuse pain will spread down into the midriff area. In a very early study of the parietal peritoneum, Ramström found no sensation with light pressure or temperature change, cramplike pain with strong pressure, and a stitchlike pain with cutting (202, 1008).

From what has been seen in the previous section, it would seem that sensations in the right midriff might differentiate duodenal activity from the gastric activity of the left epigastrium, although some sensations from either source, as well as from other organs may be reflected in the epigastrium generally.

In the first limited research to compare different feeling reactions and bodily sensations, 3 of the 5 observers reported that sensations in the area above the navel had consistent feeling associations, and 2 observers, including myself, associated sensations in this area with "going against" or "struggling" (877) or "anger." The third observer reported frequent pleasant sensations in this area concurrently with sensations in the adjacent epigastrium and central-chest area. In the next two internal-sensation studies, one of the ten body areas rated was to the right of the mid-line, approximately at the juncture of Areas No. 12a and 12b. In the earlier, more limited study, little of significance was found concerning this area, although sensations were relatively absent in situations and feeling reactions of "enjoyment" (878). Also, in rating of the depth of the sensations that were observed, the "muscle" classification was used more frequently than the others in this area, and this was true also for the central abdominal area and the genital area. In the more extensive study, this area at Areas No. 12a and 12b was one of the four significantly highly rated areas (879). This area was rated as relatively high in the occurrence of sensation throughout the seven situations with different types of feeling loadings, with less variation in the different situations than occurred in many other body areas. A relatively marked decrease of ratings occurred with the "sexual" loadings, which contrasted especially with the intense ratings in the nearby central abdominal area (Area No. 14) for that loading. Also, relatively strong ratings of sensations were seen with "fear," "anger," and "significance" loadings. The possibility that internal sensations in this area are indicative of some "emergency type" of reaction, such as anger or aggressive feelings, is suggested. (In this connection it was noted that the area of by far the greatest emphasis with the "sexual" loading, namely, the genital area, was rated relatively slightly with the "anger" loading.) Also, there was a relative absence of sensations in this area, as well as in the central abdominal area (Area No. 14), for different patient groups who were diagnosed as neuropsychiatric or related types.

CENTRAL ABDOMINAL AREA (Area No. 14)

This area is approximately 4 inches wide, and includes approximately one third of the frontal width extending from the top of the navel to a horizontal line connecting the lower tip of the iliac crest and overlying primarily the small intestine. Direct pain may derive from the small intestine and from the peritoneum, and secondary pain may derive from heart or colon conditions (5, 202, 1068). In this area, as elsewhere, experimental stimulation of pain in the peritoneum was sharply localized.

Visceral afferent pathway axones enter the spinal cord at the ninth and tenth, and possibly also the eleventh, thoracic segments, and the major splanchnic nerve is the peripheral visceral pathway for the small intenstine (1068).

Relatively few internal sensations were reported in this area with the initial study of feeling reactions in which the subjects usually only rated the most noticeable area of sensation for a given reaction (877). I observed, however, sensations that had relatively unpleasant associations with feelings called "yearning," or "longing" (which are of a somewhat depressive type); these sensations were located in the lower part of this area and just below it (or in the "pit" of the abdomen) (876). In the first study, which included ratings of ten body areas, Area No. 14 was rated rather strongly with "sexual" feelings (being near the pubic-genital area, in which sensory rating were by far the most intense with "sexual" feelings) (878).

In the more extensive study of this type, the central abdominal area was among the four significantly highly rated areas, and it was relatively intensely rated for all situations, showing very little variation (879). Its greatest ratings were with the situation having a "mixed" feeling loading, in which feelings of "depression" or "inadequacy" predominated. Its least ratings were with the situation having a predominant "significance" loading. Since these two types of feeling would seem to be somewhat opposite, the possibility is suggested that the respective extremes of sensation in this area are indicative of these feelings. The quartile of the nonpatient group who scored healthiest on the Harrower Multiple Choice Rorschach gave their strongest ratings in this area; however, it was also the second strongest area rated with the quartile group who scored least healthy on this measure.

LATERAL MID-ABDOMINAL AREAS (Areas No. 15a and 15b)

These areas are lateral to the central abdominal area (Area No. 14) and extend around to lines that go vertically through the inferior angles of the shoulder blades. Pain may derive directly from the cecum, ascending colon, descending colon, peritoneum, and the kidney (which extends primarily from the central-back areas) (5, 1068).

The eleventh, and possibly the tenth, thoracic, the first lumbar, and the second, third, and fourth sacral segments receive the visceral afferent pathway axones from the ascending and sigmoid colons and from the rectum, and the lumbar chains and preaortic plexus and the pelvic nerves and plexuses are the peripheral visceral pathway (1068). Of course, referred pain to the abdominal dermatomes may derive from spinal lesions in the lower thoracic segments (1230).

It has already been noted that the swallowing of warm and cold water, after delays of seven and fifteen seconds respectively, resulted in corresponding sensations just below and slightly to the left of the umbilical region (1348). In 1931 Bloomfield and Polland inflated a balloon in the descending and sigmoid colons (involving Areas No. 15b and 13a respectively) in 9 patients who had miscellaneous disorders without bowel disease with the following results (133b, p. 471):

> Referred sensations of the same general sort as those originating in the stomach or duodenum were obtained . . . more or less indescribable deep discomforts involving elements of fullness, pressure or colic and obviously related to sensations normally experienced in connection with movements of the bowel. . . . In some instances pain was sharply localized as regards surface distribution as in Case 5; in others there was a wide indefinite area as in Cases 1 and 6. . . . It is seen that the whole area from umbilicus to pubis is implicated and that there was no definite relation between the situation of the stimulus and the site of referred pain.

Symptoms in these areas were seen with the emotionally based "hyperventilating" personality syndrome as follows (1097, p. 233):

> Proceeding to the lower abdomen, the patient is apt to complain of pain over the region of the appendix and, inasmuch as she is likely to be tender on palpation over this point and may even show an increase in white cell count, the examining physician will suspect an appendicitis and may be influenced, by the patient's anxiety and psychic complicity in preferring relief from the organic approach, to recommend an unnecessary appendectomy. This lower quadrant tenderness is due to congestion and distention of the cecum and ascending colon which the hyperventilator has in a periodic form on a purely functional basis. A delay of several days with reassurance and sedation would have revealed the functional nature of the symptoms. Another subjective symptom in the lower abdomen is pain in the iliac region, usually on one side, more often on the right. This region is likewise generally tender on palpation and sometimes also leads to an unnecessary abdominal operation. This condition is due to nothing more than a functional congestion of the ovary which is periodical and which clears up spontaneously in the intermission between attacks.

LOWER ABDOMINAL AREA (Area No. 13a) AND ANAL AREA (Area No. 20)

ORGANS, SENSORY INNERVATION, AND REFERENCE

The lower abdominal area includes the part of the pelvic cavity that is below a horizontal line that connects the lower tips of the iliac crests, and it overlies the bladder, cecum, ileum, segments of the small intestine and of the peritoneum, prostate gland, seminal vesicles, and a segment of the ureter, ovaries and Fallopian tubes, uterus, sigmoid colon, and rectum. The vagina will be considered separately under the genital area (Area No. 13b). Local pain may derive from the colon, rectum, peritoneum, bladder, prostate gland, uterus and uterine tubes, ovaries and Fallopian tubes, and the pelvic girdle; a secondary pain may derive from heart conditions (5).

As has been noted previously, the afferent innervation of the upper colon sections differs from that of the sigmoid colon, which appears to be mainly supplied by afferent fibers through its mesentery from the lower thoracic and upper lumbar segmental nerves without involvement of sympathetic or parasympathetic pathways (1364). However, the rectum was said to be innervated by afferent fibers through the parasympathetic rami from the second to fourth sacral segments. Also, ureteral pain was said to be carried by the lower splanchnic trunks, which enter the lower two thoracic and the first lumbar segments, and noxious impulses from the trigone and structures below the bladder are carried by parasympathetic rami from the second to fourth sacral segments (1317, 1364). The afferent fibers from the pelvic organs of the male are said to reach the spinal cord via the parasympathetic plexus and the hypogastric plexus; from the testes the afferent fibers travel along the tenth thoracic nerve; from the epididymis the afferent fibers are carried by the eleventh and twelfth thoracic and first lumbar nerves (1089).

In the female, (1) noxious impulses from the fundus uteri are carried via the hypogastric plexus and enter the spinal segments from the tenth thoracic to the first lumbar segments; (2) the noxious impulses from the cervix are carried by the second and fourth sacral nerves along with those from the bladder neck; (3) the noxious impulses from the Fallopian tubes and ovaries travel along the nerve plexus entering the tenth thoracic segment; (4) and, finally, noxious impulses from the closely contiguous structures including the broad ligaments, other mesentery and retroperitoneal structures are transmitted by branches of the lumbosacral plexus and segmental nerves (1364).

Wolff and Wolf indicated the following pain references: (1) noxious stimulation of the structures below the bladder was noted to refer pain to the distal tip of the urethra; (2) prostatic pain was reported in the perineum or referred to the lower lumbar region; (3) noxious stimulation of the spermatic cords and testicular structure produced pain *in situ* and also at times in the hypogastric region; and (4) renal-colic pains were found to be referred to the testes and referred along the groin and inner aspect of the thighs

(1364). Other pain references and innervations were elaborated by Ruch as follows: (1) from the ureter, pain is referred superfically to the loin and groin, and the visceral afferent pathway axones enter the spinal cord at the first and second lumbar segments; (2) from the bladder fundus and bladder neck, superficial pain is referred to the suprapubic area and perineum and penis, and the visceral afferent pathway axones enter the spinal cord at the eleventh and twelfth thoracic, first lumbar, and second, third, and fourth sacral segments; and (3) pain from the fundus and cervix of the uterus is referred superficially to the lower back and perineum, and the visceral afferent pathway axones enter the eleventh and twelfth thoracic, first lumbar, and second, third, and fourth sacral segments (1068). It has been reported that the spinothalamic tract carries the sensations of a full bladder, of pain from the bladder and urethra, and of temperature from the urethra, whereas the posterior column carries sensations of touch and pressure from the urethra (948, 1279).

EXPERIMENTAL AND CLINICAL STIMULATIONS

As early as 1911 Hertz observed experimentally that rapid inflation produced pain in the colon and also in the rectum that slowly disappeared with deflation (556). Slower inflation produced sensations of "fullness" or "wind," which Hertz attributed to the muscular coat, as he did also the sensations produced by instruments in the colon. He reported that these sensations were always felt at a lower level than those due to gastric distention, but the character of the sensations was similar. He believed that he had experimentally "ruled out" the possibility that the sensations derived from the peritoneal attachments. The distention of the pelvic colon produced sensations at a level below the umbilicus, but in several patients finger pressure on the anterior abdominal wall, via a colostomy opening, produced no sensation in most cases. Similarly, distention of the colon just above the sphincter produced the same sensations just above the pubis, but no rectal sensations were involved. Also, he reported that squeezing of the abdominal wall between the fingers usually resulted in only local sensations in the muscle and skin; however, in two cases sensations of fullness and pain occurred, possibly due to tension on the muscular coat. Slow inflation just above the rectal flexure also resulted in sensations of fullness in the mid-line a little above the pubes, but never in the back. Hertz observed that the accumulation of fecal material in the pelvic colon is normally unaccompanied by sensation, but if an excessive quantity collects, owing to obstruction, discomfort and subsequent pain result just above the pubes. This filling usually produces a desire to defecate. Sensations arising from balloon distention of the bowel are usually localized at the mid-line, because the bowel has been noted as embryologically a mid-line structure.

Boring also reported that balloon inflation within the rectum induced "all degrees of intensity" of the call to defecation. He found that with injection of 50 cc. of warm water at 50 to 70°C. the desire to defecate was very intense, whereas with an equal amount of cold water at 0°C. this reaction did not occur; 10 cc. of 5 per cent HCl also produced the urge to defecate (138). These sensations were described predominantly as "pressure," but muscular movement and "a dull ache" were included. The localization varied with the intensity of the experience and included dull, diffuse, and vaguely localized sensations, as well as clearly defined sensations having the following course as intensity became increased: "(1) muscular pressure in the rectum; (2) rectal pressure became intense and achy, general abdominal pressures develop; (3) dull pain introduced; (4) sharp, piercing pains, of uncertain and ranging reference, appear" (138, p. 325). These sensations were usually localized in the lower abdominal and anal area, but at times extended to various body parts. With defecation, similar sensations of "strain," "pressure," and even painfulness of various types were seen. With urination and its call, sensations of "fullness," "pressure," "strain," and also "warmth" in the region of the bladder were reported as well as a considerable variety of local sensations in passage of the urine and the subsequent relaxation and relief of the tension and strain.

Much pain and discomfort are seen in the lower abdominal area with cases of "irritable colon," or "mucous colon," which has long been associated with emotional tension (595, 1315). Pain stimulated in the ureter from a descending renal stone was seen to have a fixed reference to the groin (1068). Brief, low-intensity electrical stimulation or inflation of an inlying balloon in the ureter produced severe pain along the medial border of the rectus abdominis muscle, extending from the genital area up to either side of the umbilicus. This pain was localized at the level of stimulation except that with prolonged or intense electrical stimulation, the pain spread to other parts of the segment and ultimately also occurred in the back over the kidney area (845, 1355, 1356). With this pain, muscle-contraction effects soon masked the ureteral pain so that the entire flank became tender. Also, a disturbed bladder in paraplegic patients has been seen to result in throbbing and diffuse bifrontal and bitemporal headaches that could be relieved by draining of the bladder (1356). Internal sensations arising from ureteral expansion and from distention of the bladder have been found to have an adverse effect on external sensory perception (809).

FEMALE ORGANS AND CONDITIONS

There is a report (265) of a sharp pain arising from the rupture of the mature follicle at ovulation, which was followed by a discharge of sexual energy with strong erotic sensations in the genital area, which was said to be followed in turn by tension and erotization of "the whole surface of the body."

The occurrence of abdominal pain with dysmenorrhea should be noted; this pain may arise from various conditions, including the sudden and severe uterine contractions that also produce the labor pain of child bearing (1364). Dysmenorrhea, which is said to be generally psychogenic in origin (321, 735a, 944, 954), has been given a fourfold classification by Novak and Harnik: (1) intermittent pains resembling those of labor with discharge of blood clots; (2) pains from hyperemia or distention of the capsule occurring shortly before the onset of menstruation and subsiding with its onset; (3) menstrual colic, which is the type of dysmenorrhea most frequently seen; and (4) membranous dysmenorrhea (321, 954). Dysmenorrhea and labor pains were said to be the most common pain involving the female genital structure. Most dysmenorrheic pains were related to contractions of the uterine musculature; however, some may also occur from traction on adherent structures involving inflammatory fibrotic or neoplastic processes (1364). "Labor pains" are reported with pseudocyesis, along with nausea and other bodily changes (735a).

Similarly, pelvic congestion was noted in Chapter 13 (p. 246) to have a relationship to life stress and emotional reactions that involve resentment and result in sustained pelvic hyperemia leading to congestion, edema, and pain (324, 1360). The sensations and mechanics involved were described by Wolff as follows (1360, p. 111):

Pelvic congestion results in lower abdominal pain, located in the suprapubic region or in either or both lower quadrants. Pain is often also experienced in the sacral area, and may radiate into the antero-medial parts of the thighs. It is characteristically a dull, heavy ache, sometimes with a burning component. On this more constant pain may be superimposed more intense or cramplike pain, of brief duration, usually in response to a jolt or sudden movement. Pain is commonly increased in the premenstrual phase of the cycle, and is often augmented by coitus. . . . Frequently there is often tenderness of the parametrium, "cystic" enlargement of one or both ovaries, diffuse enlargement of the uterine fundus, and congestion, hypertrophy and hypersecretion of the cervix.

ANAL AREA

The anal area (Area No. 26) includes the anus itself and extends to the testes or vagina. Local pain results from muscle, bone, and nerve involvement; secondary pain may arise from conditions of the bladder, prostate gland, or the vestibular glands of the vagina (5). Hertz reported that a rod having temperatures of 10 to 50°C. in the rectum produced warmth sensations, whereas one at 0°C. produced no sensation (556). When he inflated the lower part, or ampulla, of the rectum, sensation was felt in the rectum itself, and inflation in this area resulted in the desire to defecate, which, he added, was never experienced after excision of the rectum. Inflation of the sphincter ani produced "the same sensation as when the bowels began to open." Functional and emotional factors associated with the itching of pruritus ani were noted in Chapter 12 (p. 201), and with this, sensations of heat were also reported (850).

GENITAL AREA (Area No. 13b)

ORGANS AND SENSATIONS

This area includes the testes, penis, vagina and vulva, all of which are capable of local pain, and it includes also the vestibular glands of the vagina. Secondary pain in the genital area may derive from the kidney or bladder (5, 1066). A relative lack of touch and pain sensibility has been reported for the vagina; however, the outer and inner surfaces of the labia minora appear to be richly supplied with nerves and are very sensitive to touch, as are also the clitoris of the female and the embryonically corresponding phallus of the male (705). Anterolateral chordotomy usually results in the loss of sexual sensations (618, 1068); however, tumescence and ejaculation are possible without sensation in paraplegics, indicating that such functioning can be achieved at the reflex level without cerebral intervention, although the sympathetic and parasympathetic nervous systems, as well as the cerebrum, are normally involved (705, 1042).

SENSATION STIMULATION

Already noted in Chapter 13 (p. 247) was the association of the organismic ejaculation sensations with the peristaltic contraction of the ducti deferentia, although the origin of the specific sensations that constitute the sexual orgasm are not definitely known (705). Kinsey et al. reported that in the sexual arousal of the female, the tactile stimulation of the clitoris, the labia minora, and the contiguous funnel-shaped vestibule leading to the orifice is important (705). He added that the female may also be very conscious of pressure on the ring of levator muscles just within the vaginal entrance, which may respond reflexly with pressure stimulation. Kinsey reported erotic responsiveness of the vagina notwithstanding its poor tactile sensibility, and he noted that perhaps a majority of females find with coitus involving deep vaginal penetration, a type of satisfaction that differs from that provided by the stimulation of the labia or clitoris alone. He believed the mechanics involved to be primarily "psychological" but related also to body contact. The latter includes increased pressure on the whole genital area and stimulation of the nerves of the perineal muscle mass (or the pelvic sling), as well as some direct stimuli of the vagina itself, which shows some sensitivity in some women, mostly in the upper (anterior) walls just inside the vaginal entrance (705). Also in this area were noted various glandular secretions with sexual arousal in both the male and female.

Genital symptoms of the emotionally based "hyperventilating type" of female were reported by Schimmenti (1097, p. 233):

> These are vaginal and cervical tenderness experienced usually during the act of intercourse and confirmed by the physician on vaginal examination. The hyperventilator has muscular and mucosal congestion. These, together with the lowered vaginal acidity discussed previously, combine to produce a peculiar paradox of genital symptoms. She has at the same time deep sensitiveness to the distention, impacts, thrusts, and friction necessarily characteristic of the sexual act, but has a hyposensitiveness to the superficial sensation especially of the specific sexual voluptuous order. The superficial sensation may be so recessive that she is unable to perceive tactually the presence of the penis in the act of intercourse.

In general, "pain and revulsion" with intercourse are reported by frigid women, and it has been asserted "that the majority of women derive little or no pleasure from the sex act" (735a, p. 294). For some, pruritus vulvae, involving itching, reflects genital tensions stemming from psychosexual conflicts (735a)

FEELING REACTIONS

In my three studies relating internal sensations and feeling reactions, the genital area was rated along with the pubis, and in the first rather limited study, the central section of the lower abdominal area was also included within the area diagrammed for rating. Nevertheless, even in this first study, 4 of the 5 subjects consistently associated sexual feelings with sensations in this area (877). I specifically noted sensations to occur in the pubic area as well as in the genitals with sexual feelings along with sensations that were somewhat different qualitatively and deeper within the pelvis (876, 877). Sensations in this area were also rated as frequently occurring with "pleasant" associations and with reaction associations of "going toward, attraction or possessiveness" (877). In the first study of this type, which set forth ten body areas to be rated by all subjects, the "suprapubic and genital area" was included (878). By far the most prominent sensations in this area were reported with feelings and situations having a "sexual" loading. There was a marked absence of sensations in this area with feelings and situations having an "anger" loading. Relatively strong sensations in this area were also seen in situations with a "love" feeling loading. In the rating of the depth of sensations in the suprapubic and genital area, the "muscle" classification predominated over the "skin," "deep," and "intermediate" classifications.

In the last, more extensive study of this type, the corresponding area rated was called the "genital-pubic" area, and again it received relatively little sensory-rating emphasis except in the situation with a "sexual" loading, where the sensation ratings were very strong (879). Relative to the other types of situations, strong sensory ratings also occurred in the genital-pubic region with the "love" loading. A relative absence of sensation occurred in the situations with loadings of "anger" and in the situation with a feeling loading of "friendliness," which were situations that also included a pronounced feeling loading of "significance." Also, the analysis of variance interaction was significantly low in this area with the situation having a "fear" loading. The optional sensation descriptions included: seven "genital sensations" and one sensation each of warmth, excited, and relaxing.

SHOULDER AREAS (Areas No. 5a and 5b)
AND UPPER-EXTREMITY AREAS (Areas No. 17 and 18)

SHOULDER AREA IN GENERAL

The shoulder area extends from the arm at the level of the arm pit to the clavicle, or collar bone, and pain arises directly from local pathology and indirectly from the stomach and from the liver along with diaphragmatic surface involvement (5, 202). Referred pain over the front of the shoulder has been produced by pressure on irritable infraspinatus muscle even though the subject was able to relax completely as shown by the absence of electro-myogram potentials from over muscles (biceps and triceps) not in the reference zone, whereas action potentials were shown from the deltoid muscles within the referred-pain area (1261). On the other hand, referred pain in the shoulder direct from phrenic-nerve stimulation was not influenced by surface anesthesia of the area (1371).

In a study of 300 medical patients with various psychosomatic disorders, Lorenz and Musser reported that 20 per cent complained, upon inquiry, of pain and stiffness in the shoulder region, which were of long duration in the majority, and this symptom was found to be intimately related to the patients' emotional reactions and to stressful life situations (813). Approximately two thirds of the patients with such shoulder pain presented a chief complaint of pain in the shoulder, chest, or neck. Lorenz and Musser noted the mechanism of "emotional" stress resulting in sustained increases in muscle tension, and related these findings to the large percentage of clinical patients having a painful stiff shoulder or subacromial bursitis that is usually classified as being of "obscure etiology." Medically induced relaxation of shoulder muscles has been reported to relieve this pain (998, 1263).

FEELING REACTIONS

In my initial limited study of feeling reactions and internal sensations, rated optionally for any body area, very few focal points of sensation were reported for the upper extremities. One subject, however, reported "unitary sensations" that were concurrent in this area with those of other areas and that had reaction associations of "going away from" or of "going against" and were labeled "determination" (877). With the first internal-sensation study, the right-shoulder area was rated by all subjects along with nine other areas and received relatively low ratings throughout the seven different types of situations; however, the ratings were relatively low in situations with "enjoyment" and "significance" loadings, and they were relatively high in situations with "fear" and "anger" loadings (878). Also, there was relatively little variability in ratings between the classifications for the depth of sensations that occurred except that "deep" sensations were at a relative and an absolute minimum as compared to other areas of the body, and the "skin" and "muscle" classifications were most frequently employed.

With the more extensive study of this type, the right-shoulder area, along with two other areas, was found statistically in the next to least intensely rated grouping (879). The internal-sensation ratings in the right-shoulder area showed very little variation in the different situations; however, in the two situations with feeling loadings of "significance," increased ratings were seen, which possibly could have been related to the relatively increased ratings in the upper-middle-back area (Area No. 21) at these times. Descriptions of the sensations that occurred included two each of "tightness" and "ache" and one each of "chills," "pressure or heavy," "slight," "twitching," "pain," "tired," and "quiver," and "a tingling" sensation was reported for the arms.

EXTREMITIES

In addition to local pains in the upper-extremity areas, secondary pain may derive from heart or stomach conditions (5, 1068). The referral of pain from one finger to another has been reported to have a central basis and not to be dependent upon afferent innervation within the reference zone (1356).

Sensations of coldness and sweating of the hands are common aspects of clinical anxiety, and these have been noted experimentally, particularly in experiments involving pre-examination tension and so forth (560). In the emotionally based "hyperventilation type" of personality, symptoms of numbness, or a feeling of "going to sleep," were noted in the arms, hands, and fingers, as well as a "tingling" at the fingertips, and these sensations could be accentuated by the applying of compression lightly about the arms so as to reduce blood circulation (1097). Elsewhere also, psychogenic symptoms of "uncomfortable sensations" in the hands and arms were thought to relate to hyperventilation (242).

POSTERIOR HEAD AND NECK AREAS (Areas No. 19 and 20)

Pathology involving the brain, cranial nerves and vessels, and the spinal tract produces headaches of various kinds in Area No. 19, as has been discussed in regard to the cephalic area (p. 286) (5, 1230, 1356). Area No. 20 includes the bone and muscle parts of the neck and the cervical vertebrae, from which nerves go to muscle structures in the neck and back regions. Pain in this area may arise directly from cervical disks and from muscle tension or, as has been noted, may be referred from the diaphragmatic pleura and diaphragmatic peritoneum (to the trapezius ridge), and from the heart (and pericardium) (52, 1230).

It should be added that in contrast to direct stimulation of pain-sensitive intracranial structures on or above the superior surface of the tentorium cerebelli, which results in pain in the frontal area forward from a line that goes vertically to the ears, stimulation of such structures on or below the inferior surface of the tentorium cerebelli produced pain posterior to this plane, which was associated with pathways in the ninth and tenth cranial nerves and in the upper three cervical nerves (1364). The third and fourth cervical segments innervate the lungs and bronchi via the vagal rami, and the lowest cervical segment participates in thoracic sympathetic innervation, which is said to carry noxious afferent impulses from the esophagus (1317, 1364). Forehead and temple pain may be referred from "trigger points" in the neck muscles on which pressure results in vasoconstriction of the temporal artery (1261). Tarsy pointed out that pain from cervical-spine conditions may extend over the scapula, under the clavicle, and from the shoulder to the hand, but he added that tenderness is most commonly localized at the seventh cervical-nerve area and most frequently the pathology derives from mechanical stress because the first to sixth vertebrae are poorly supported as compared to the seventh cervical vertebra, which is attached to the thoracic cage (1230).

Under the stress of the Hardy-Wolff thermal stimulator, Malmo, Shagass, and Davis found that patients with a history of head and neck complaints had reliably higher muscle-potential scores taken from the neck than the patients with a history of cardiovascular complaints (860, 865). Similarly, Wolff reported increased potentials during resentment, frustration, dissatisfaction, and apprehension from head and neck muscles with a series of persons complaining of headaches and feelings of tension, whereas during periods of asymptomatic relaxation the muscle potentials were minimal or absent (595, 1356, 1358). He added also that the muscle-contraction headache of anxiety and tension may be coupled with other headaches, such as the vascular headache of migraine or those from infection, inflammation, trauma, or noxious stimulation.

In this book it has already been noted (p. 324) that in some patients with psychogenic shoulder pain there was a chief complaint of neck pain (813). Also, "neck pain," neck tension, and neck pressure, especially in the back of the neck and lower-head area were reported frequently in the psychogenic "hyperventilating" personality type (1097). The sensations that Wolff described included "tightness," "bands," "head-in-a-vise," "caps," "crawling sensations," "tender lumps," or "cramplike aches," with any section or combination of head sections being involved and with variable duration, although the muscle-contraction type generally is the most sustained, lasting from days to years. Stevenson referred to a case of muscle tension producing pain in the back of the neck in "excitement" (1199).

BACK AREAS (Areas No. 21, 22, 23 and 24) AND HIP AREA (Area No. 25)

BACK AREAS IN GENERAL AND AREA NO. 21

The back areas are situated between lines that go perpendicularly through the inferior angles of the shoulder blades, and the uppermost back area (Area No. 21) includes the first four thoracic vertebrae from which nerves lead to the heart, larynx, trachea, bronchi, and lungs. Secondary pain in this area may derive from the heart (5) and possibly from the esophagus (556). Noxious impulses from the esophagus are thought to be carried by sympathetic nerves that enter the spinal cord by all thoracic segments, as well as by the lowest cervical segment (1317, 1364). The upper three or four thoracic ganglia and the corresponding posterior root ganglion transmit afferent impulses from the pulmonary pleura and large blood vessels to the spinal cord, whereas the first and second thoracic chain ganglia and the corresponding posterior root ganglion carry afferent impulses from the heart to the spinal cord (1089). Also, some evidence suggests that there exist a few afferent fibers in the cardiac nerve that joins the third to fifth thoracic ganglion, and that similar fibers are also present in the hypogastric plexus, which enters the spinal cord in the lumbar and lower thoracic sympathetic chain ganglia. The thoracic nerves also innervate the parietes of the thorax and abdomen, with the first five nerves limited to innervation of the first five intercostal spaces (1230).

From one to six times weekly for periods of from one week to two years, Holmes and Wolff measured the potentials bilaterally over the back and extremities and rated the pain of 75 subjects, all but 10 of whom had a backache syndrome (595). In addition, extensive clinical and social-history studies were compared with the measurements taken. The comparison revealed a significant relationship between life stress and hyperfunctioning of these muscles, with the hyperfunctioning occurring as a pattern of reaction to situations "engendering conflict, anxiety, and other strong emotions," and resulting in pain in the back, neck, and extremities (595, p. 32). The pain was characteristically of a dull, aching quality, experienced "deep" in the skin and poorly localized. In some patients it involved a limited area, and in others it involved the greater part of the back. Also seen was referred pain, which at times involved the abdomen, buttocks, perineum, or extremities, and which at times was more disturbing to the patient than the back pain itself. For some patients, strenuous activity or trauma in the setting of a threatening life situation took on enhanced etiologic significance. The postulated mechanism of pain involved (1) intense and sustained skeletal-muscle activity with the elaboration of a noxious tissue metabolite ("Factor P") and (2) a state of relative ischemia of these muscles, engendering the gradual accumulation of the noxious metabolite sufficient to exceed the pain threshold. It should be noted, however, that this study refers to the back generally and may or may not be of particular significance as regards the uppermost-back area (Area No. 21), particularly since the backache syndrome usually involves primarily the lower back.

FEELING REACTIONS IN GENERAL AND IN THE UPPER BACK

In the initial study relating feeling reactions to internal sensations in various areas of the body, relatively few sensations in the back areas were reported; however, most of them were reported as having unpleasant associations (877). The upper-back area rated in that study encompassed both Areas No. 22 and 23. I reported sensations in this area to be associated with a feeling of "significance" or "importance," which may occur independently or along with other feelings in pleasant, unpleasant, or "neutral" situations, and therefore the last classification appears to be most appropriate for such sensations. Also, concurrent predominant sensations with the association of "significance" are most prominent through the upper-back, neck, head, and shoulder regions, and may even be present in the upper-chest and extremity areas, as well as throughout the whole body, as "tonus" or "tension," in relatively intense states.

In the first study, wherein the uppermost-back area (Area No. 21), the lower-middle-back area (Area No. 23), and the calf of the left leg (Area No. 27c) were rated for sensation in different situations by all subjects, a relative absence of sensations was seen, but with situations and feelings involving "fear" and "anger," sensations in these areas as well as in the shoulder area were much more prominent (878). Relative to other types of situations, sensations in the uppermost-back area and in the shoulder area were more predominant with the "anger" loading, and sensations in the lower-middle-back and the calf areas were more predominant with the "fear" loading. In the classifying of the depth of the sensations observed in the back areas, the subjects employed about equally all the nomenclature, namely, "deep," "intermediate," "muscle," and "skin," although the latter two predominated slightly.

With the more extensive study of this type, relatively low intensity ratings for sensations in the back areas were again seen; however, the uppermost-back area (Area No. 21) was revealed to be in the second statistically significant grouping, which placed it in a tie for the ranking of 5½ in intensity of occurrence among the ten areas rated (879). Sensations in this area were relatively strong in situations with a loading for the feeling of "significance," particularly in relation to other situations and also to other areas. Secondary to the emphasis with "significance," the upper-back area (Area No. 21) also received relatively strong ratings with the "fear" and "anger" loadings. A relative absence of sensation in this area was seen with the "sexual" loading. The optional description of sensation revealed the following for the back areas: "chills" in the lower-middle-back area (Area No. 23); two "tingling" sensations, two "chills" sensations and one "funny feeling" reported as running up or down the back or spine; and for the back generally, five "tingling," two "chills," two "waves," two "excited," and one each of "tightness," "pull," "tired," and "tactile." Also, a "pull" sensation was reported in the back of the neck.

UPPER-MIDDLE BACK AREA (Area No. 22)

The upper-middle-back area (Area No. 22) includes the fifth through twelfth thoracic vertebrae from which sympathetic nerves lead to the celiac ganglion, which in turn connects with the esophagus, stomach, viscera, blood vessels, liver, pancreas, suprarenal glands, colon, jejunum, ileum, and rectum. The fifth thoracic segment, in addition to the first four, receives afferent fibers carrying noxious impulses from the heart; however, the area of reference for cardiac pain may extend over a wide path from the third cervical segment to the tenth thoracic segmental distributions (648, 1317, 1364). Thoracic innervation of the esophagus has been described (p. 289), and also the seventh to ninth thoracic segments receive splanchnic sympathetic trunks, which are believed to carry pain impulses from the stomach, pancreas, liver, and biliary tracts (1364). It has already been seen that gallbladder pain is localized in the distribution of the ninth thoracic segment (1317, 1364), and that splanchnic sympathetic pathways, carrying noxious impulses from the small intestine, enter the spinal cord from the ninth to eleventh thoracic segments (1364). Also noted was that sympathectomy affects innervation of the colon above the sigmoid level. The lower two thoracic segments and the first lumbar segment receive the lower splanchnic trunks, over which pain impulses from the kidney and ureter are carried (1317, 1364). The tenth thoracic nerve carries afferent nerves from the testes, and afferent fibers from the epididymis reach the spinal cord via the eleventh and twelfth thoracic and first lumbar nerves (1089). From the tenth thoracic to the first lumbar segments, the superior hypogastric plexus enters the spinal cord and carries noxious impulses from the fundus uteri of the female, and at the tenth thoracic level, noxious impulses from the Fallopian tubes and ovaries reach the spinal cord via the plexus of nerves that accompanies the ovarian vessels (1364). Also, the broad ligaments, mesentery, and retroperitoneal structure receive afferent innervation from the lumbosacral plexus and segmental nerves. In addition to pain from the muscle, bone, and nerve parts in this area, pain may be referred from the kidney, the stomach, the duodenum (5), and the esophagus (133b). As already described (p. 320), prolonged or intense direct electrical stimulation of the ureter resulted in the spread of pain from frontal sites to a posterior reference over the kidney, where pain was also localized with brief, low-intensity faradic stimulation of the kidney pelvis (846, 1355, 1356). The following dermatome innervation stems from these thoracic segments: the fifth innervates the fifth intercostal space; the seventh through eleventh innervate the lower chest and abdomen; and the twelfth innervates the lower part of the abdomen along an area parallel to Poupart's ligaments (1230).

Specifically, this area was not rated in the internal-sensation studies noted earlier; however, following the initial study, one of the subjects and I independently noted a relatively increased occurrence of sensations in this area during states of fatigue or sleepiness.

LOWER-MIDDLE BACK AREA IN GENERAL

The lower-middle back area (Area No. 23) includes the lumbar vertebrae, from which sympathetic nerves lead to the inferior mesenteric ganglion and then connect with the sigmoid colon, rectum, kidney, bladder, gonads, and external genitalia. The first lumbar vertebra also receives nerve fibers, which, like the nerves listed for the upper-middle back area (Area No. 22), lead to the celiac ganglion. Afferent fibers from the pelvic organs, other than those described in the preceding section, pass to the spinal cord through the lumbar nerves (1089). In this area, direct pain frequently arises from lumbosacral strain and from protrusion of vertebral disks (5). Also, referred pain may arise from the pancreas, ovary, uterus or uterine tube, adrenal glands, and especially the kidneys. Thus, strain frequently occurs at the twelfth thoracic and first lumbar segments, producing low-back tenderness and pain that extends to the lower quadrant and upper thighs, including the iliac crest and the upper portion of the buttocks (38, 1230). A relationship of the "back-pain" syndrome to emotional tension was presented at the beginning of this section (595). It has also been noted that wire stimulation of

the diaphragmatic pleura at the lateral and anterior margins and the posterior third of the diaphragm produced referred pain in segmental distribution
over the lower thorax, back, and abdomen, which includes this area (Area
No. 23), as well as a lower segment of Area No. 22 (202).

FEELING REACTIONS

I reported early a relative increase of internal sensations in this area with
feelings of "anxiety," or "fear" (876, 877). As was described above, in the
first study in which this area was rated by all subjects for internal sensations
in different situations, the lower-middle-back area, along with the calf area,
showed relatively more sensations in the situations and with the feelings that
involved "fear" than in other types of situations (878).

In the more extensive study, statistical analysis revealed this area to be
in the next to the last grouping in terms of intensity of sensations reported
with the situations presented (879). The lower-middle-back area was
strongly rated in the two situations with "significance" loadings, but was less
strongly rated than the uppermost-back area (Area No. 21). Apart from
these situations, relatively strong ratings for sensations in this area occurred
with the situation having a "fear" loading, and with this there was also a
relative spread of emphasis throughout the back body areas rated. Perhaps
it is most characteristic with this loading that, with all back body areas
being emphasized, the sensations in this area (Area No. 23) approximate or
exceed those of the upper-back area (Area No. 21), which differs from the
pattern with most other feeling loadings. The lower-middle-back area was
also rated relatively strongly with the situation having a "sexual" loading,
and this emphasis was specific relative to the other back areas; however, it
was also associated with absolute and characteristic predominance of sensations in the genitals and lower abdominal areas. Thus, relatively strong sensations in this area seem to be given relative emphasis in at least three
distinct patterns involving "fear," "significance," and "sexual" feelings, respectively. In comparing of the healthiest quartile of nonpatient subjects
with the quartile rated least healthy in terms of psychological adjustment,
it was seen that among the back areas the healthy group placed major emphasis on the upper-back area (Area No. 21), whereas the least healthy
group made relatively much stronger ratings in the lower-middle-back areas
(Area No. 23) so that its absolute ratings equaled those for the upper back.
Also, the sum total of frequencies of sensations in the back body areas that
were rated (Areas No. 21, 23, 17c), was greater for the least healthy quartile
than for the other three groups, and it was particularly greater than that of

the healthiest quartile group. Similarly, in practically all the patient groups, there was a relatively great emphasis on the three back body areas, and particularly on the lower-middle-back and the calf areas.

SACRAL AND HIP AREAS

The sacral area (Area No. 24) includes the sacral vertebrae from which parasympathetic nerves lead to the same organs that the sympathetic nerves of Area No. 23 do. Pain here may arise from lumbosacral strain at the junction with Area No. 23, from sacroiliac-joint disorder (5), from the prostate gland, and from the ovary, uterus or uterine tube (5, 1360). The second to fourth sacral segments receive afferent nerves through the parasympathetic rami, which innervate the rectum and the trigone and the structures below the bladder (1317, 1364). The involvement of the lower lumbar and upper sacral segments in the innervation of female organs has already been noted above; in addition, the second and fourth sacral nerves provide innervation for noxious impulses from the cervix and the bladder neck (1364).

Hertz reported that balloon inflation immediately below the flexure in the rectum produced sensations in the rectum or, with some subjects, in the area of the sacrum (556). Similarly, Bloomfield and Polland found that inflation in the rectum produced a sensation of "pain in the low back similar to that experienced when the bowels are about to move" (133b).

The hip area (Area No. 25) includes the rear pelvis and attachments, and pain here frequently derives from sacroiliac-joint disorders (5).

LOWER-EXTREMITY AREAS (Areas No. 16, 27, 28)

In addition to local pains, pain in this area may arise from the kidney, the ovary, uterus, or uterine tubes (5), as well as extend from the "low-back-pain" syndrome (595).

Gemelli reported that states of anxiety, fear, and so forth were associated with a sensation in the legs of wanting "to get up" and "run away" (433). In the psychogenic "hyperventilating type" of personality, lower-extremity symptoms included: aching and pain in the thighs and calves, pains in the joints of the knees and ankles, coldness of the lower limbs, especially the feet, and numbness of the legs, and "going to sleep" easily with sensations of "pins and needles" and of crawling on the skin (1097).

Few sensations were reported for these areas in my first study that related feeling reactions and internal sensations that were specifically rated (877). The calf area of the left leg (Area No. 27c) was included in my two studies that had ratings by all subjects for ten areas of the body, and in both studies the sensations that were reported were at a minimum for this area on the average. Statistically, this area constituted a significantly separate "grouping" or division in the more extensive study (879). In the first of these two studies, sensations in the lower-extremity area were at an absolute minimum in comparison to other areas and at a relative minimum (in terms of occurrence in the experimental situations) for the situations and feeling reactions with "love" and "sexual" loadings (878). Sensations were comparatively more intense in the "fear"-loaded situation than in other ones. Also, a relative absence of sensations in this appeared to be one of the differentiating features for the distinguishing of the internal-sensation reaction pattern with "anger" from that with "fear"-loaded situations. In the ratings of the depth of sensations, the "muscle" classification predominated greatly here, although there were also "skin"-classification ratings, but relatively few "intermediate" or "deep" ratings.

In the third and more extensive study, the sensation ratings in this area showed relatively little variation among different situations; however, the lower-extremity area was more intensely rated with the "fear" and "significance" loadings and was rated little with the "anger" loading (879). In comparison to the other body areas, the lower-extremity area was the least intensely rated in all situations except those in which loadings of "fear" and of "significance" predominated. Descriptions of the sensations that occurred included five "tightness," three "tingling," two "twitching," and one of "ache" and of "quiver." One sensation each of "tightness" and "weakness" were also described as "in the legs."

CHAPTER 18

Types of Internal Sensations

FACTORS IN THE PERCEPTION OF INTERNAL SENSATIONS

Separate consideration should be given to the different types of sensations that are reported by subjects for several reasons: (1) to determine the breadth of human internal sensory experience as contrasted to the limited traditional classifications of sensations, (2) to determine normative frequencies for the experiencing of given sensations under various circumstances, and (3) to study the possible relationship of types of sensations with types of internal body structures or functions. It has already been noted that the types of internal sensation that are reported are far more numerous than the classifications of sensation that are considered traditional in experimental psychology, namely, visual, auditory, taste, olfactory, cutaneous (including touch, cold, warmth, and pain), and kinesthetic. The exact determination as to which sensory terms employed in this chapter represent basically distinct sensations, which represent variations of a type of sensation, and which represent a combination of basic sensation types or a combination of perceptual artifacts must of course be determined by experimentation. The type of experimentation that is required will doubtless entail the statistical evaluation of differential introspective judgments and impressions.

Although no truly normative data are available for the experiencing of internal sensations, the more extensive research study by myself (see pp. 298-300) relating internal sensations to feeling reactions provides some data that may be helpful in the understanding of this type of perception (879, 879a). The stimuli that were employed consisted of three practice situations, including one of a mild "startle" type, and seven experimental situations, each involving a short motion-picture scene, which stimulated predominant feeling reactions of significance, enjoyment, love, sexual passion, fear, anger, and depression or inadequacy. With these stimuli and under closely controlled, but nonsuggestive, conditions, 91.5 per cent of all 317 patients and

335

nonpatient subjects reported internal sensations in the experimental observations, and an additional 3.6 per cent reported sensations only in the practice observations, comprising a total of 95.1 per cent. The mean frequency of total sensations reported by the nonpatients for ten body areas in the seven experimental situations was 16.8 per subject. Two major factors influencing the perception of internal sensations should be considered: one factor is the individual's relative focus of habitual awareness or nonawareness in regard to the various areas of experience such as his external environment, his cognition, and his noncognitive internal environment, and the other is the strength, or effectiveness, of the stimulus employed. The first factor and other psychological influences have been discussed in Part I and will be considered to some extent in the next section. Some idea of the second factor may be obtained by the contrasting of the average total frequency of 16.8 sensation reports for the seven situations that employed motion-picture stimuli with a comparable approximate average of eleven sensation reports obtained when employing still pictures and recorded-voice stimuli of similar types for 36 subjects (these subjects were of higher socioeconomic and educational level, however) in the earlier study (878). Similarly, the comparable frequencies in the third and more extensive study ranged from 5.10 sensation reports per subject for the fear-loaded situation to 1.25 for the depression-loaded or inadequacy-loaded situation, which resulted in the least amount of internal-sensation ratings (879).

In the experimental situations the types of sensations that were noticed and reported most frequently by far were "tightness" and "tingling." Also frequently described were : "chills," "palpitation," "warmth," "sickness," "hollow" and "pressure or heavy." The subjects frequently expressed their difficulty in the describing of internal sensations, and a rather wide variety of descriptions were given. The normative sensation reactions for patterns of sensory reactions with given types of feeling loadings will be considered in the next section.

The possible relationships of given types of internal sensations to given body structures will become apparent within the limited extent that such information is available as each type is considered. Most available information concerning such relationships comes from clinical and experimental medical studies that are primarily concerned with pain and variations of pain for reasons of diagnosis and treatment. More information is particularly needed concerning other types of sensations. This can be exemplified by the considering of my more extensive study that related internal sensations and feeling reactions (879). When two persons reported experiences of sensation predominantly in the same body area, it could be questioned whether the sensation arose from the same anatomical structures or processes. The qualitative descriptions of sensations for the different body areas suggested that different types of sensation are involved in various areas. There were also indications that different anatomical structures were involved in the given areas of classification that were used in this study, as exemplified by the references to "in the chest," "in the heart," and "in the lungs" made by subjects for the central-chest area (Area No. 6). There was also some evidence that in given body areas certain types of sensation, or sensations, tend to predominate, which differentiate one body area from another. Thus, more complete studies are needed to differentiate these types of sensation.

PAIN

CLASSIFICATION AND INNERVATION

Some authors have expressed the view that no dichotomy should exist between the conception of sensory-stimulated pain and the "pain" of unpleasant feeling states (46). The following discussion, however, relates primarily to the former, more common conception of pain sensation as being sensory stimulated.

Although all fields of medicine are greatly concerned with pain, primary emphasis on its study is found in connection with neurological and muscular-skeletal (especially orthopedic) considerations.

A dual system of pain fibers, one fast and one slow, was described at the beginning of Part IV (1067, 1385). All parts of the nervous system are capable of some variation in pain, and neurological disorders, particularly those involving the spinal column, may be productive of pain in almost any part of the body. Similarly, by means of the nervous system, somatic pain in skeletal muscle or skin may be referred from stimuli acting on various visceral organs. As presented in the beginning of Part IV, referred pain usually assumes dermatomal distribution and is specific for various organs. Referred pain, however, constitutes a relatively small proportion of all pain that is reported by patients or by experimental subjects.

A threefold classification of pain origin is commonly employed, including (1) superficial or cutaneous pain, (2) deep pain from muscles, tendons, joints, and fascia, and (3) visceral pain (1068). For gross classification of pain, "superficial" and "deep" are generally employed to distinguish the quality of pain perceived, since "superficial" has been described as having a pricking, bright, burning, itching quality, which is highly localized, and "deep" has been described as having an aching quality, which is deep, diffuse, and less precise in localization (1355). Dual qualities of cutaneous pain have also been described, including a pricking quality of immediate perception upon stimulation and a burning quality, which is more slowly aroused and appears to be intermediate between superficial and deep pain (522, 1355).

Ruch noted that the so-called receptor endings for somatic pain (involving the skin, muscles, tendons, joints, and fascia) are relatively nonspecific in not generally requiring a particular "adequate stimulus"; instead, they respond to extreme degrees of several kinds of stimulation in contrast to most visceral organs for which only certain types of stimulation are adequate to produce pain (1068). As shall be described, adequate stimuli for the visceral organs are closely related to the environment and the activity of the given organs (1068). Visceral-pain impulses are conducted primarily by sympathetic nerves, though some parasympathetic innervation is involved in the pelvic area (1068). Thus sympathectomy of these organs for relief of pain is usually possible without severely disturbing the motor functioning.

ANATOMICAL PAIN CHARACTERISTICS

Tarsy indicated that pain of a given type was experienced consistently from a given type of tissue even though many different stimuli were employed (1230). Included as stimuli for referred pain were injection of hypertonic saline solutions into the tissues that were being investigated, and included for direct (or local) pain were these same stimuli, along with pinching, squeezing, light and deep pressure, pulling of hair, burning, electric shocks, and others (782, 1230). In regard to the skin, only a "pricking" sensation was found with a brief stimulus, but a "burning" pain was found with prolonged stimulation and these sensations were brief and well localized. In the muscles, an "aching" pain was found, and the pain was at times referred from stimulation of the fleshy belly of a muscle, of the muscle tendon, or of its fascial covering and tendon sheath. The reference area for referred sensation was variable according to the complexity of the structure, but it was always in accordance with segmental distribution. Since the classification of "local" and "referred" pain could not be applied to all cases, it was thought better to speak of pain as being either moderately well localized or as being diffuse and poorly localized. Muscle pain was always relatively "diffuse," and the more diffuse pain appeared to be projected to the vicinity of the deep structures innervated by the same spinal segment. Tenderness was also frequently associated with muscle pain. Similarly, joint pain was diffuse or referred in accordance with the strength of the stimulus. Pain stimulation of the interspinous ligaments, situated deeply in the trunk, shoulders and pelvic girdle, also gave rise to referred pain of segmental distribution as well as to pain exactly similar in character to muscle pain, with the aching lasting for three to five minutes and felt deeply in the limbs and trunk. The characteristics described for subcutaneous (web of finger and toes), tendon, and periosteal pain were always "dull," "disagreeable," and "diffuse," and it endures at the peak for an appreciable time (1230). From subcutaneous periosteum, pain was found to be confined to the neighborhood of the point of stimulation, whereas from deeply situated periosteum, it was felt diffusely and was at times referred. Tendon pain was reported as being intermediate between fascial and muscle pain, and involving local pain that at times was felt over a large area when it was severe (1230). Simple local pain derived from the fascia covering the trunk and limbs and from sub-cutaneous ligaments, but deeper ligaments, when severely involved, produced diffuse and referred pain. The lining of the suprapatellar pouch produced severe pain localized as "somewhere in the knee," but only sensations of "tapping" or "pressing" derived from a needle inserted in the knee joint or patella. Similarly, cancellous bone was found capable of diffuse pain, but no pain was produced in cartilage or compact bone.

Pain referred from the viscera to somatic areas could frequently be distin-guished from pain of somatic origin by the continuity of the "pain curve," since the somatic pain was more constant and the pain of visceral origin more frequently occurred in "attacks."

Although normal contractions and relaxations of visceral organs appar-ently do not result in pain, they may do so if the blood supply is inadequate, and also the following stimuli are generally recognized as adequate to induce visceral pain: "(i) dilation or distention, (ii) spasms or strong contractions, especially when accompanied by ischemia, (iii) chemical irritants" (1068, p. 365). Pain from the organs of the viscera should be distinguished from pain stimulated in the inner surface of the body wall, though both of these may produce either local or referred pain. It should be noted that referred pain can arise from somatic structures; also, the concept of referred pain is somewhat ambiguous as it does not clearly distinguish between superficial diffuseness and remote neural transmission of impulses. The reference of visceral pain is not due to any unique properties of the visceral-pain path-ways; the common denominator of referred visceral pain and referred mus-cular pain is that they both originate deep in the skin (1068, p. 371). Faulty projection of such pain was thought to be due to the infrequency of occurrence and the inability to use vision to verify the source of stimulation and to develop a superficial projection. Thus, the factors of learning and of individual relative awareness must be considered.

PAIN TYPES AND STIMULATION

"Burning pain" has been reported in the esophagus with the swallowing of Tabasco sauce (1347), with some peristaltic movements, and with distention (133b, 977). Similarly, burning pain has been reported in the stomach and the duodenum with distention (133b), with ulcer (923), and with the mechanical stimulation of the cardiac sphincter, called "heartburn" (258). An achy, gnawing pain has been reported in the stomach region in connection with hunger (see p. 310), and aches or slight pains have been reported in the esophageal region with nausea (138). Similarly, with the call to defecation, pressure sensations were followed by a dull ache and then by painful sensations in the lower abdomen as well as by an ache in the anus, which became "hot" and "burning" (138). With urination, a sharp burning pain in the glans penis was reported by one subject (138), and such a sensation was also reported frequently with genitourinary diseases. Lower abdominal pain from pelvic congestion has been described characteristically as a dull heavy ache, sometimes occurring with a burning component (1360). Also, protracted twinges of "darting pain" or of a "burning sensation" in the left-chest area have been differentiated from cardiac pain (680).

"Gripping pain" has been reported in the esophagus (977). "Cramplike" pain has been reported with exceptionally strong contraction of the stomach (258), but very vigorous contractions without pain have been observed in the rectum and sigmoid colon (36). Cramping pain in the muscles is well known, and occasionally pains associated somewhat vaguely with "a kind of cramps," "a full cramplike feeling," and the like were reported with distention of the stomach and of the sigmoid colon (133b). One similar reference was noted with wire pressure on the parietal peritoneum and with an instance of the wire's rubbing on the intestines (202). Severe cramping abdominal pains were reported when observations on a loop of ascending colon and cecum and a small section of the ileum (all prolapsed onto the surface of the abdomen) revealed the following physiological changes, which were associated with a reaction of anxiety including very strong resentment and feelings of helplessness: marked and prolonged contraction, no peristaltic waves, membranes engorged, numerous petechiae and small fresh ulcerations, fragility, a gray-white discharge, and increased rectal temperature

(475). The reference to "abdominal cramps" is of course common, and a "gripping pain" of the heart has been reported (5). The terms "gas pain" and "painful tightness" and similar terms were frequently given during the distention experiments involving the gastrointestinal tract that included the esophagus, stomach, duodenum, sigmoid colon, and rectum; these sensations faded at times into the sensation of "fullness" (133b, 556).

"Sharp pain" has been produced by thermal stimulation of the forehead ("sharp, jabbing pain") (227), by distention of the esophagus ("a sharp little pain" and "a sharp burning pain"), and by distention of the duodenum ("severe sharp pain") (133b). Such "sharp" pain was reported more consistently with the pressing of the end of a wire against the parietal peritoneum, and it was well localized; however, with the stimulation of the diaphragmatic peritoneum, the "sharp pain" was referred along the trapezius ridge of the neck (202).

"Aches" of various kinds have been reported in regard to head and neck muscles (595, 782, 860, 866, 998, 1356), back muscles (595, 998), and the duodenum (133b). In addition to muscle tension, headaches may arise from vasoconstriction, vasodilatation, or other pressure on the arteries and veins of the brain as well as from pressure on the cranial and cervical nerves or on the dura at the base of the brain (38, 782, 1356). Extracranially, pain may arise from the scalp and periosteum. The vascular and muscle-tension headache types are clinically the most common by far. Aching has been seen in the facial area innervated by the first to third divisions of the fifth cranial nerve (1356). Also, aching with psychogenic contraction of the masseter muscles and of the muscles of the pharynx was reported.

INTERNAL PAIN THRESHOLD

A few studies deal with the threshold of perception of internal pain. In this regard, a distinction should be made between pain perception and pain reaction, since the former is measured by introspective report and the latter is measured physically or physiologically in many ways. This distinction would seem to be pertinent to the reports of patients with lobotomies for the relief of intractable pain, wherein the pain stimulation is still perceived but no longer is "felt" as being painful to various degrees (375, 514, 515, 658, 1275, 1355, 1356). With such patients, the cutaneous-pain threshold has been found to be lowered bilaterally even with a unilateral prefrontal lobotomy (703). The reaction patterns of the organism to pain include so many components, both psychological and physiological, that a distinction between perception and reaction for pain cannot be so clearly delineated as in other sensations (45, 234, 1355, 1356, 1361).

Chapman and Jones compared the threshold for perception of "substernal fullness" (which was considered to be the "only recognizable end-pain") caused by distention of the lower esophagus, with the cutaneous-pain threshold for thermal stimulation of the forehead from the Wolff-Hardy apparatus (227). The esophageal sensory threshold for 29 normal subjects ranged from —60 per cent to +58 per cent of mean average value of 37 cm. of pressure with a standard error of 3 cm. Individual variations were from ±5 per cent to ±18 per cent. The rank coefficient of correlation of esophageal sensory threshold to cutaneous pain perception was +.57 with a probable error of .9, which indicated a fairly significant correlation. One subject, however, had an extremely high cutaneous-pain-perception threshold but showed a low threshold for visceral perception. The cutaneous pain perception for 200 subjects ranged from —40 per cent to +50 per cent of the mean average value, and individual variations were from ±2 per cent to ±6 per cent.

It has been found that patients with psychoneurotic and some psychosomatic conditions generally show a lower threshold for pain reaction than do normal controls (223, 224, 226, 514, 551, 590, 785, 1094, 1095, 1096, 1356). With psychoneurotic patients, pain-perception thresholds tend to have a bimodal distribution and a greater range than for normal subjects, with the low thresholds seen primarily with anxiety and hysterical patients (226) and with patients complaining of general "nervousness" (224). Also, a bimodal tendency with the schizophrenic diagnoses should be noted, with early-schizophrenic patients approaching anxiety patients in having a relatively low threshold of reactivity (515, 862) and chronic-schizophrenic patients showing high thresholds of reactivity in comparison to normal, neurotic, and acute-psychotic subjects (515, 866, 868). Studies on cutaneous pain perception alone, employing the Wolff-Hardy thermal stimulator, have, however, revealed little difference in pain perception between normal and psychoneurotic subjects (226, 521). With increased age in healthy, neurotic, and depressive subjects, the pain-perception and reaction thresholds are found increased, and although depressive patients show uniformly high threshold levels, a shifting to lower, more normal threshold levels was seen with those patients who showed clinical improvement after electroshock therapy (515). Neither direct suggestion nor placebos were found to alter pain thresholds for normal subjects or for psychoneurotic patients (225); however, variations in the experimental instructions may affect the thresholds that are found (226). Differences in threshold for different types of pain apparently can result from pathological changes in the nervous system because patients with surface hyperesthesia and hyperalgesia in association with deep pain showed no significant lowering of threshold for either pricking or burning pain; however, when experienced, these pains were perceived as being more intense and more lasting than normally (1356).

TIGHTNESS, CONTRACTION, CONSTRICTION, CRAMP, AND THE LIKE

Reference has just been made to "cramping pain" and "gripping pain," which may represent an extreme degree of tightness. Again, the problem of semantics in the communicating of internal sensations should be recalled, as there is great variation among individuals and also the likelihood of possible "incorrect" reports.

A fear type of reaction has frequently been associated with sensations of tightness in the substernal region (with contraction of the muscular sheath of the diaphragm, see p. 306), in the throat (433, 710) (with spastic esophagus, 710), about the heart ("clutching") (38), and in "tightening of the heart and the whole chest" (433). Tightness has also been reported in the stomach with hunger at times (138, 1352) and in the lower abdomen with the "call to defecation" (138). The last two types of sensory experience suggest that the contracting muscles also produce "pressure" sensations in these areas (138).

The tightness type of sensation was the one most frequently described in my most extensive study that related internal sensations and feeling reactions, and in that study, the "fear"-reaction situation was by far the most strongly rated (879). "Tightness" sensations were reported specifically for the following areas: five for the calf, one for the leg, one for the back, two for the shoulder, five for the chest, one for the upper body, fourteen for the lower-left diaphragm, twelve for the "stomach", two for the right midriff, two for the abdominal area, one for "over various," one for "of nerve," and one for "of muscle."

Esophageal changes have been observed to produce "a substernal sensation of tightness" (1347), and, with distention, "a stretch, a tight feeling" (133b). Also, a "cramp-like" feeling was noticed with stomach distention (133b). Sensation reports include "constriction in the throat" (1358), epigastric cramps and gripping, neck tenseness, and, finally, feelings of suffocation and constriction from lung and bronchial conditions (5).

TOUCH AND RELATED SENSATIONS

Clinically and experimentally, a distinction is frequently made between sensations of "touch," relating to light contact, and of "pressure," relating to increased application of force. With light contact no sensations were found in the esophagus (556), stomach (1348), or parietal peritoneum (202), and relatively little sensitivity of this type was found in the vagina (705). However, in parts of the heart, "touch" sensations were reported even with heavy pressure and with pricking as well as with light contact (25, 1342).

Palpitation may be considered a touch type of sensation that is frequently reported in the heart area (5, 1203, 1342). The sensation of "pulsing" would also seem to be a touch sensation related to vascular rhythms. Similarly a "pulsing" variation of pain and of headaches is commonly reported.

"HEAVY," PRESSURE, FULLNESS

Internal sensations of these types are usually vaguely described and frequently are difficult to identify or classify. Possibly sensations of "distention" and of "swelling" are the same as "fullness" (or a degree thereof), and these may hold a relationship to "tightness," yet, "pressure" may represent an entirely different sensation.

"Substernal pressure" and choking sensations have been described in emotional reactions (1358). Direct physical stimulations have produced sensations of pressure in parts of the heart (25, 1342) and in the stomach (138, 1348, 1352). Sensations of fullness with pressure were frequently reported in the lower abdomen occurring with the call to defecation (138). Fullness sensations were most frequently obtained with gentle balloon dilatation of the gastrointestinal tract as exemplified in reports concerning the stomach (133b, 556, 1352), the colon (133b, 556), and the rectum (138); in the esophagus, however, one study emphasized the experiencing of pressure sensations (133b) whereas another emphasized fullness sesnsations (556) with this stimulation. Pressure with a glass rod in the stomach has produced the common sensation of "pressure" (1352). In the duodenum, painlike sensations were emphasized, and there was only one report of "dull pressure"; frequent painlike sensations were also reported for the stomach (133b). "Gaslike" (or "gassy distortion") sensations, which involved "elements of fullness," were reported frequently for the colon, and one "pressure-pain" report was noted (133b). Sensations of fullness and of muscular pressure in the genital and suprapubic abdominal areas were observed with the call to urination, which apparently related to distortion of the bladder (138). Hertz concluded from his early study that "the ill-defined sensations which occur in all parts of the alimentary canal, and which may be grouped together as 'the sensations of fullness', are due to stretching of its muscular coat and constitute a form of muscle-sense which is probably shared by all hollow viscera" (556, p. 1121).

Arnold associated sensations of "tension and fullness" with aggressive movements, as contrasted to fear reactions (52). Altschule indicated a "heavy sensation" about the heart associated with sadness (38). In association with disgust, Gemelli reported "oppressive (heaviness, contraction) of the abdomen" (433). The extensive feeling-reaction study that I conducted resulted in the description of the following sensations in the areas noted: for "fullness," seven chest, one lower left diaphragm; for "pressure" or "heavy," one right shoulder, three chest, one stomach; and for "expansion," two chest, and one "swelling" in lower abdomen (879).

"HOLLOW," "EMPTY"

"A local sensation of emptiness in the abdomen" (556) and "in the area above umbilicus" (138) has been noted in connection with hunger. "Hollow" sensations were reported for the following areas in the feeling-reaction research: three chest, four stomach, one abdominal area, and one lower abdomen (879).

"SINKING," "SICKNESS," NAUSEA

"Sinking" sensations would seem to relate either to the preceding category or to nausea, or both. Thus, Wolf and Wolff reported a "sinking feeling" in the stomach that accompanied a reaction of fear or a feeling of being overwhelmed and dejected, and anorexia was associated with this feeling in the case cited (1351). Similarly, Kling noted "sickening" or "sinking" sensations, which were attributed to the stomach, with fear reactions (710). In the feeling-reaction studies that I conducted, the following sensations were reported: two "pit-of-the-stomach" sensations, for which localization was given in the lower abdomen, and six sensations for which no localization was given; a "sinking" sensation in the stomach and another one in the lower abdominal area; and a "hit-in-the-stomach" sensation in the lower left diaphragmatic area (879).

Boring's 1915 study of experimentally induced nausea revealed it to be very complex, including sensory reactions in many parts of the body and including the following alimentary-tract sensations: "pressure-complexes referred to the stomach, or pressure-waves localized in the esophagus" indicating incipient vomiting; the "sinking feeling" and the dull "sickishness" described as "purely pressure"; the "gnawing pressure" and the "ache" described as "partly pressure"; and, for almost all subjects, a dull ache or pain in the stomach region (138, p. 320).

Payne and Poulton, in the study of nausea by means of balloon distention of the esophagus and stomach, defined nausea as a sensation felt at the back and bottom of the throat due to tension on specific end organs in the esophagus, especially in the upper esophagus; however, they also postulated that a "sinking" sensation, felt in the abdomen, is "analogous in every way to nausea" (977). In association with nausea, these investigators described reports of "feeling of sickness." It appeared that the sensation of "sinking" was due to a slight increase in the tone of the walls of the stomach, so that the sensation was felt with relaxation of the stomach wall, and this reaction was frequently accompanied by a desire to eructate.

Sensations of nausea have been reported with disgust (433, 1344, 1358), with despondency and dejection (1344, 1358), with induced "emotional upset" during extreme fatigue (745), with pre-examination tension (560), with migraine headaches (1356), and with psychogenic emotional reactions (681, 1299). Such reactions have been observed to be accompanied by depressed digestive functioning and gastric hypoactivity (1343, 1351, 1358). Almy and Tulin found nausea reactions to be accompanied by increased sigmoid colonic spasms under physical stress involving conflictual feelings (36). Direct contact has produced nausea by stimulation of the cardiac sphincter (258), by pressure of 125 gm./sq.cm. on the stomach membrane (1348), and by inflation of the esophagus; however, nausea from inflation of the esophagus was much less frequent than with inflation of the stomach or duodenum (133b). Most evidence suggests that nausea sensations relate to esophageal activity that is either directly or reflexly stimulated (976, 977, 1358).

With my feeling-reactions studies, the "fear" situation was the most pronounced one, and "sickness" sensations were reported as localized: one in the lower-left diaphragm, five "in stomach," and one in "abdominal area" (879).

COLD, WARMTH, AND RELATED SENSATIONS

Cooling of the hands is commonly reported with anxiety and tension (38, 560). Direct cold stimuli have been perceived as such from the esophagus (being felt in the retrosternal region) (1347) and from the stomach (1348), but such stimuli were not perceived from the ventricles, the diaphragmatic pericardium, or the parietal pericardium of the heart (25), from the parietal peritoneum (202), or from the rectum (556).

The well-known sensation of "chills," such as those usually associated with "running up and down the spine" as contrasted to those associated with "chills and fever," would seem to represent a separate type of sensation. Flashes of "heat" and "chill" sensations have been reported to occur for long periods following castration (1232). Chilly sensations are reported at times by neurocirculatory-asthenia patients (242). Similarly, patients with the functional-hyperventilation syndrome were seen to complain of coldness in the lower limbs, especially the feet (1097). In the feeling-reaction research that I conducted, where the reaction to the "fear" situation was most intensely rated, "chill" sensations were reported as follows: seven in back areas, one in the right shoulder, and one "from waist up" (879).

Warmth in the face was noticed during pre-examination tension (560). Warmth in the genital area has been associated at times with the call to urination and with urination (138). Warmth sensations in my feeling-reaction study were localized as: two in the chest, one in the stomach, and one in the genital-pubic area (879). Alcohol produced warmth sensations in the stomach (556, 1358), and direct-heat stimuli have resulted in such sensations from the esophagus (556), from the stomach (556, 1348), and from the rectum (556), but not from the ventricles, diaphragmatic pericardium or parietal pericardium of the heart (25) or from the parietal peritoneum (202).

"Burning pain" has already been discussed under pain. For most of the same body parts for which this sensation was reported, just "burning" sensations were reported: in the esophagus with heated barium (1347) and with distention or spasms ("heartburn") (5, 133b); in the stomach and the duodenum with distention (133b) (and with ulcer the usual "burning pain") (5, 923); and in the nose with allergic stimuli (215).

OTHER INTERNAL SENSATIONS

In the feeling-reaction research that I conducted, "prickly" sensations were reported once "in stomach" and once "over various parts" (879). Similarly, a sensation like "prickly pear" was noted in the distention of the esophagus (133b).

"Tingling" was one of the most frequent sensations reported in my feeling-reaction study, possibly due to the fact that the "fear"-loaded situation was the most effective stimulus or that a mild "startle" stimulus of a sudden whistle blast was used in the practice observations (879). The following localizations were reported for this sensation: three in the calf, seven in the back areas, three in the chest, one in the "waist up," two in the abdominal area, three "over various parts," and one "on skin." Shepard's early study revealed the following types of related sensations associated with "excitement": "tingling all over," and "shiver seemed to rush" (1134). Tingling of the breast during pregnancy has been noted (5). The sensation of tingling was also reported to be "usually associated" with a phase of esophageal activity (978). Hyperventilation has been seen to result in tingling and numbness of the mouth and extremities (1192).

With the functional-hyperventilation syndrome, numbness of the leg and "going to sleep" easily, accompanied by sensations of "pins and needles" or "ants crawling on the skin" have been reported, and these sensations also occurred in the upper extremities at times (1097). Similarly, electrical stimulation of the cerebral cortex of conscious patients has at times resulted in reports of "electricity," or a "sticking," sensation (982), "a tingling feeling," "an absence of feeling called numbness," "a sense of movement," "a pricking sensation," and "a funny feeling" in various parts of the body (983).

The common sensation of itch has been reported to be of functional, or internally aroused, origin at times (850, 1059). Other sensations reported in my more extensive feeling-reaction study included: "quiver": one in the calf and one in the right-shoulder area; "twitching": two in the calf, and one each in the shoulder and chest; "sting": one in the back; "shocks": one "over parts except stomach"; "wave": two in the back, one each "in the chest", "waist up," and "stomach"; "tickling": one "chest to abdomen" and one "in stomach"; "dullness": one in the back; "weakness": two "in stomach", one "in legs"; and "tired": one each in the upper back and right shoulder (879).

A "muscle sense," or kinesthesis, is conventionally associated with presumed receptors in the muscles, tendons, and joints. Most of the studies that refer to "muscle sense," however, simply involve the perception of spatial relationships without the use of certain sense modalities, such as vision. In an experiment in which the subject is blindfolded, for example, he may be asked to perform certain tasks with his hands that will involve spatial relationships, and the results are interpreted in terms of "muscle sense." In the light of what has been presented in the preceding chapters, it seems clear that numerous sensory and perceptual factors may be involved, and must include all internal sensations in the region of the body concerned. Also, the fact that spatial localization in, and of, body parts is related to specific brain areas, which are apparently organized on the basis of learning, was presented in Chapter 16. It may well be that these areas, involving what can be considered essentially cognitive functioning, are of primary importance in so-called "muscle-sense" functioning. Thus, whether this "sense" constitutes a separate category of internal sensation can be questioned. On the other hand, reference has been made in the preceding section to the association of various sensations with relative states of muscle contraction and relaxation. Fatigue sensations, which are often associated with muscle activity, will be discussed in Chapter 20.

Sensations of giddiness, dizziness, faintness, and so forth, which may be produced by cerebral anoxia (1342) and by failure of the peripheral circulation bed (173), are experiences that would also seem to relate more closely to cognitive functioning, or failure thereof, than to specific modalities of internal sensation, although possibly both types of experience may be involved.

Part v

Differentiation of Noncognitive Psychological States by Means of Physiological Reactions and Internal Sensations

CHAPTER 19

Considerations in the Differentiation

of Psychological States

Some attempts to differentiate various psychological states by means of physiological functioning were presented in the beginning of Part III along with several theories stating the basis for such distinctions. Similar concepts concerning internal sensations were elaborated in the beginning of Part IV. In this part some further evidence along this line will be developed and will be followed by a consolidation of the differential distinctions reported heretofore.

PERSONALITY DIFFERENCES

There is some evidence that the patterns of internal sensations reported by groups of people having different types of adjustment—personalities or predominant feelings—may differ, and thereby may possibly reflect their predominant psychological state or states. In my own rather extensive study already described (pp. 298-300), which related internal sensations and feeling reactions, 100 per cent of the quartile of nonpatient subjects, judged to be emotionally the healthiest on the basis of the Harrower Multiple Choice (Rorschach) Test, reported some internal sensations in the experimental situations as compared to 91.5 per cent of the total nonpatient group (879). Analysis of variance for the total nonpatient group also revealed that the over-all differences in the ratings among the ten anatomical areas employed, among the seven experimental situations, and between the areas and situations were each significantly different at less than the 0.1 per cent level of probability.

In the comparing of the total nonpatient group with various groupings of patients, predominantly of neuropsychiatric and psychosomatic types, the means and more particularly the variability of sensation ratings were found to be significantly different. The mean frequency of ratings per subject was somewhat higher for the patient group (20.3) than for the nonpatient group (16.8); however, the patient group showed a markedly bimodal distribution of frequencies when compared by diagnostic type, with only three of the twenty-five diagnostic groupings having means between 15 and 20. It was inferred from this that at least two general factors were probably operating that would distinguish the various diagnostic groups, and these were hypersensitivity (or hyperresponsiveness) and hyposensitivity (or hyporesponsiveness) either in responding to the stimuli or in the awareness (or the reporting) of internal sensations. It was suggested that deviant mean frequencies of internal-sensation reports might be indicative of the habitual direction of the focusing of awareness by the individual subject and by the patient groupings.

Although the qualitative descriptions of internal sensations were generally similar for patients and nonpatients, marked differences were seen in the responses to the question as to whether they had noticed such internal sensations before the experiment, as for example (879, p. 73):

> Certain groups are relatively low in reports of prior introceptive sensations, such as Neurotic Depressive 33.3 per cent, Schizophrenic general w/o Sub-diagnosis and Dermatitis 55 per cent each, as compared to over 70 per cent for the nonpatient group. Other patient groups were relatively high in this respect, such as Hysteria general, Blackout, and Passive-Aggressive each with 100 per cent.

The following variables studied were found to have little relationship to frequencies of reports of internal sensations for the nonpatient subjects: Army General Classification Test scores or their equivalent; educational level; age; and the Harrower Multiple Choice (Rorschach) Test scores, in which, however, some relevant tendencies have already been noted. In addition, the lower cut-off point of intelligence of the subjects studied might be considered as being in the "Borderline" intelligence category, and a slight but very consistent increase of sensation reports along with higher Classification Test scores (which presumably reflected relative intelligence over all) was seen. The choice of the "Nothing at All" category on the Harrower Multiple Choice Test was seen to correspond to very low reports of internal sensations. This choice was classified by Harrower as the least healthy response (531), and it would seem that it may indicate in many cases a negative attitude toward the situation.

MEANINGFULNESS OF SENSATION PATTERNS

If one is to interpret the patterns of internal sensations that are found in this study as being normative for different feeling reactions, some limitations must be considered (879, p. 82) :

> Even if introceptive sensation is closely related (or corresponds) to the dimensions of feeling experience, the question remains as to what extent the patterns suggested by this study can be expected to recur with the feeling reactions indicated. The final answer is unknown even though certain consistent findings are evident throughout the two earlier studies of a similar nature and the present one. Nevertheless, with the stimulus situations here used and with relatively naïve untrained subjects, as here employed, individual patterns differentiating situations according to different feeling loadings are not likely to be clear cut. This can most easily be demonstrated by again recalling that the mean sensation frequency for the nonpatient group was 16.8 ratings whereas 70 area ratings were made. It is true, of course, that there was a relative concentration of sensation ratings in a few situations, which were therefore presumed to be more effective stimuli. Therefore, a higher percentage of sensation ratings would result either from limiting the analysis to the more intensely rated situations or, probably also, from presenting only the relatively more effective stimulus situations to the subjects. For the present, however, the introceptive sensation patterns suggested for situations with different feeling loadings can better be accepted in terms of tentative group norms and in terms of tendencies which may (or may not) be found applicable for differentiating individual patterns on the basis of future research.

In the individual's perception of his own internal sensations, the nature of his *differential awareness* is of crucial importance if he is to distinguish the meaningfulness of such reactions in terms of "feelings," or of other psychological states. The studies of internal sensation indicate that, generally, sensations in given body areas, such as the central chest, are perceived as relatively intense in comparison to certain other body areas, such as the lower back. Thus, differentiating reactions to different types of situations involves differentiating the relative intensity of sensations in various areas of the body, rather than simply noticing the most pronounced area of sensation at a given time.

CHAPTER 20

Types of Noncognitive Psychological States

EXCITEMENT-RELAXATION AND THE "FEELING OF SIGNIFICANCE"

CONCEPT OF EXCITEMENT

Stratton designated "excitement" as a separate psychological state that sharpens perceptions and heightens endurance (1211). Excitement has also been presented as an early developmental state (150), and it has been viewed as a basic psychological dimension involving "activation," or "arousal," and individual differences, as well as temporal fluctuation, are manifested (316a). Excitement is common to intense emotional reactions of both pleasant and unpleasant types. This state might also be reflected in different physiological findings for different degrees of "motivation" (758a). It would seem to be this aspect of intense emotional reactions that at times results in symptoms and even in death, as was exemplified by the "not infrequent occurrence of sudden death" in persons with the joy of seeing a Red Cross bus coming to a concentration camp (38, 1199). A concept of this type was presented as early as 1930 by Skaggs, who postulated a continuum of "attention states," which, with "exceedingly high attention" involve diffuse bodily sensations and may be considered independent of superimposed emotions (1153, p. 375).

EARLY EXPERIMENTAL FINDINGS

Skaggs found progressive degrees of increases in the amplitude of breathing in mental work, mental relaxation, excited anticipation of electric shock, and reactions following electric shock. On the other hand, the regularity of breathing, which in Skaggs's experiment showed an inverse relationship to pulse rate, was greatest in relaxation, was less in mental work, and was least in the emotional conditions of anticipation and reactions. Also, breathing was more rapid with mental multiplication than with the other conditions. In addition, the "physiological substrata of startledness" were said to consist of a violent contraction of the diaphragm and a sudden contraction of the chest muscles, which are involved in an inspiratory movement.

As early as 1906, Shepard reviewed the findings that related physiological changes to changes in attention, and he reported from his own experiments on a subject (who was lacking a section of the skull) that with sensory attention, with attention to arithmetical problems, and with all agreeably exciting light or music stimuli employed, there occurred a fall in the volume of the hand, suggesting vasoconstriction, a smaller pulse, and a rise in volume in the brain and in brain pulse, suggesting vasodilatation (1134). With relaxation, there was often found first a fall in hand volume and a rise in "brain volume," suggesting an adjustment period, followed by a gradual increase of hand volume and a decrease of "brain volume" to normal. Also from other subjects, descriptions of "excitement" included sensations of "an indefinite uncertain muscular strain" and also of "tingling all over," with muscular sensations predominating. Relaxation seemed to be the release from either strain or excitement.

In another early study, Landis reported that with "sudden, unexpected stimulation (surprise)," there was a pattern of sharp rise in systolic blood pressure followed by an immediate fall (748). Mild startle might be considered to involve a form of excitement, although with stronger reactions fear or other feelings are frequently involved.

RELEVANT ELECTROENCEPHALOGRAPHIC FINDINGS

Much neurophysiological evidence specifying changes relating to degrees of the "wakefulness-sleep" dimension has been gathered (see p. 136), and most such findings have involved EEG or other electrical measurements.

"Startle" has been seen to block the alpha rhythm of the EEG for 15 to 20 seconds whereas the beta waves were only momentarily blocked (108, 634, 794). EEG changes involving the more common dimension of relative excitation, namely, wakefulness-sleep, were summarized by Gellhorn, who observed the following: with drowsiness, the alpha potentials become temporarily interrupted and their amplitudes diminish; with light sleep, delta potentials (of about 5 per second) replace alpha potentials and groups of waves with a frequency of 14 per second (spindles) appear; with deeper sleep, delta potentials increase in amplitude and duration and more spindles occur; and with more sleep, delta potentials decrease in frequency (to about 0.5 per second) and increase in amplitude (to about 200 microvolts) (426, p. 184). The spindles are more distinct in the parietal cortex. In reviewing the experimental evidence available, Gellhorn postulated that the anterior hypothalamic sleep center produces sleep by inhibiting the posterior hypothalamic center of wakefulness.

Electroencephalographic changes have been seen in arousal, showing fast waves superimposed on slow ones as a generalized reaction over all the skull but more pronounced in the frontal and central areas, which suggested activation via the hypothalamic wakefulness center (426, p. 196). An increased delta index, as well as an increased heart rate, has been recorded following strong emotional stimulation by questions related to significant events in the individual's history (581, 1188). Similarly, with induction of states of awareness, attention, and readiness, Williams found facilitation of alpha with bursts of high amplitude, regular alpha activity as well as increased beta activity, though alpha was depressed with attention to stimulation (1327). The beta low-potential fast activity from 18 to 40 per second, which is more predominant in frontal regions, has been found to displace waking alpha activity during increased "tension" or excitation (271). Concerning such EEG findings, Darrow postulated that (274, p. 298):

> The alpha-like and theta rhythms of precentral areas may indicate release of effects of subcortical springs of action [272]. These effects may be "blocked," suppressed, or controlled in alert states by processes of attention or "activation" [632, 934]. In mature and well-adjusted individuals they may be regulated and released in the presence of an adequately sustained and appropriately *phased* parietal-occipital alpha rhythm. It is suggested that this may be part of the neuromotor mechanism involved in establishing an appropriate defensive anticipatory postural "set." Mechanisms contributing to this integration and regulation are probably the specific elaborative and diffuse thalamic reticular systems described by Jasper [632] which project both to the precentral and to the postcentral areas.

Darrow cited many EEG studies on "alerting effects" that support his formulation. Gellhorn also observed that in the isolated cortex, electroencephalographic activity is greatly reduced in comparison to normal, which he believed indicates that impulses from the brain stem are largely responsible for normal cortical activity (426).

VARIOUS PHYSIOLOGICAL CHANGES

Shock noted that parasympathetic innervation is involved not only in severe emotional disturbances but also in "mild psychic excitation," including reactions of blushing, lacrimation, fainting, vomiting, involuntary urination or defecation (1144). Arnold asserted that startle was a parasympathetic phenomenon and distinguished it as one type of excitatory state in which "functional decortication" seems to occur, another such state being an "explosive or epileptoid reaction"; however, a mild form of "excitement or elation, with moderate parasympathetic activity," was considered to be one of three basic psychophysiological states (the other two being fear and anger) (52).

Increased palmar sweating has been found with a wide variety of stimuli (821), as well as with reactions of "anticipation, apprehension and ideation," and Darrow thought this to be one of the best indicators of "facilitative, preparatory, or emergency functions mediated predominantly by the sympathetic system" (270, 796). On the other hand, Altschule cited references that indicated that vasoconstriction occurred in the extremities during concentration that was not obviously emotionally toned, as well as with "simple startle" and with anticipation (38). Similarly, a fall in the skin temperature of the extremities was seen in a wide variety of eighteen "types" of pleasurable and nonpleasurable emotional reactions, which would seem to have involved excitement (922).

Though some studies suggest hormone secretion during "excitement," the reactions involved in these studies would seem to relate more specifically to fear, "anger," or other states (424, 431). After reviewing the literature and after observing the effects of ACTH and cortisone administration on 80 patients with a wide variety of clinical conditions, Goolker and Schein concluded that the primary mental change was the production of a state of cerebral excitability, called the "ready state," which precipitated "affect perturbation with lability" and which resulted in ideational stimuli that seemed of much greater temporary importance to the subject than previously, thereby influencing the direction of affect change (471). Fox and Gifford have described similar reactions, in which ACTH and cortisone appeared to them to accelerate the rate of biochemical interchange and to promote mobilization of energy for cellular work (365). This led to the hypothesis that these metabolic changes constitute physiological sources of "instinctual tension," having the effect of an increased drive to discharge energy or an increased need to obtain instinctual satisfactions.

The problem of separating the variables of "excitement" from the variables of other types of psychological states, as indicated before, is also involved in many studies that showed increased blood pressure (270, 748) and heart rate (464, 503, 560, 1188) and respiratory changes (9, 129, 214, 754, 1153) when startle stimuli were employed. A somewhat less extreme degree of "excitement" involved the following physiological changes in a study of 10 subjects during relative degrees of relaxation and "mental work," or states of attention and awareness: (1) average rates of respiration and heart beat were significantly greater during "color-naming work" than during mental repose, or rest, before or after the work, and were significantly greater than during either continuous work of random pressing of psychergometer keyboard or gazing at serially presented colors; (2) significant increases in blood pressure during color naming but significant decreases during keyboard operating and during the passive color presentations were seen; (3) greater palmar skin conductance occurred during color naming than during any of the other conditions listed above, and the level of palmar conductance was found to be related to the difficulty of the task, to the degree of alertness, to the amount of bodily tension, and to the amount of energy mobilized for responding; (4) a true control base line for physiological activities of minimal mental alertness was difficult for the young adults to maintain for more than ten minutes without falling asleep, and all physiological reactions measured showed continuous decline for the first half hour of mental response before establishing a base line, which was then maintained for the next half hour (520). With startle (1252) as well as with a great variety of strong feelings and emotions (38), there has been reported in regard to gastric motor functioning, a cessation of peristalsis, a decrease in tone, and delayed emptying. Also, gastric peristalsis ceased in animals with apparent excitement, and it returned to normal with their apparent relaxation (1253). On the other hand, "excitement" has been seen to result in marked peristalsis of the small intestine and in evacuation of feces from a transverse colostomy (1295).

Thus, the term "excitement" may relate to studies involving strong startle and heightened emotional reactions; however, in these reactions there would seem to be other psychological states involved, including especially some type of "emergency reaction," and it would seem that at least initially this term could best be employed for the relatively mild excitement described by Arnold.

RELAXATION

The psychological state of "excitement" may be considered to have a *somewhat* polar relationship with that of "relaxation," and with this in mind, physiological changes under conditions of relaxation will be considered briefly, some having already been noted in the above paragraphs. Excessive vasoconstriction in emotionally unstable subjects has been reported to disappear during sleep (286). Uninhibited action and emotional security, as well as relaxed states, were seen to result in vasodilatation and increased skin temperatures; however, conflict states had the opposite effect (920, 922). During periods of tranquility, the sebum secretion on the face was generally found to be uniform and stable (812, 1363).

The stimulus condition of music produced no change in blood pressure (748). Exercise under conditions of security and relaxation resulted in a lower heart rate and cardiac index than under conditions of anxiety and resentment (323). Similarly, emotional tachycardia was reported to subside with sleep (38, 134). Lower electrocardiographic potentials occurred in the "gradual adaptation," or relaxation, of 20 subjects to experimental apparatus; with the mental work of arithmetic, higher frequencies with shallow potentials for each heartbeat were seen (364).

With relaxation and rest, the respiratory minute volume was usually normal or only slightly increased in patients who otherwise had high values, and this was also true of esophageal motor functioning (38). Similarly, a patient with marked bladder tension was relieved when strong efforts that were made to reassure her produced a period of relative tranquility (1358).

INTERNAL SENSORY PERCEPTION

The literature reveals no specific internal sensory changes associated with the term "excitement"; however, the internal-sensation studies conducted by me included a feeling reaction of "significance," which perhaps represents a less ambiguous term for states of excitement uncomplicated by other feeling reactions. This reaction was rated under the following definition to determine the feeling loadings of the motion-picture stimuli in my most extensive feeling-reaction study: "a feeling that the subject matter is significant or important" (879). The subjects were encouraged, in the rating of their feeling reactions, to list as many types of reaction for a given situation as they felt, and had the choice of eight categories in addition to categories of "none" and "other." The reaction of "significance," or importance, was listed last in an effort to obtain ratings of this type in situations in which it was not combined with other feeling reactions.

My early observations suggested that a differential, relative increase of sensations in the upper-back area (extending to the neck area) and to some extent in the whole upper torso, occurred with the feeling reaction of "significance" (876, 877). In my more limited internal-sensation study, the predominant stimulus of this type produced feeling reactions of "significance" 40 per cent of the time (878). With this reaction, there was a relatively low occurrence of sensations in all body areas rated, including even the central-chest area (Area No. 6), in comparison to other situations.

In my more extensive internal-sensation study, one stimulus situation resulted in feeling reactions of "significance" in approximately 43 per cent of the frequency (and in approximately 60 per cent of the intensity) of the ratings, and there was also approximately 22 per cent in the frequency of "friendliness" ratings (879). The absolute rankings of occurrence of internal sensation for the ten body areas that were rated placed the right-midriff area first, the central chest second, the "central" abdomen (with a slightly lower rating) third, and the genital-pubic area last; however, in comparison to the other situations, the percentages of ratings for the lower abdomen were least and the sum ratings of the back body areas (including the upper-back, the lower-back, and the calf areas) were high, and particularly so for the upper-back area (Area No. 21), which seemed to be the most differential feature of the internal-sensation reaction pattern.

A synthesis of the findings for physiological functioning and for internal-sensation patterns is not readily apparent. The differential occurrence of sensations in the upper-back area may have some relationship to the frequent occurrence of muscle tension in this area or to the location of thoracic nerves leading to the heart, larynx, trachea, bronchi, and lungs (see p. 326). Also, the apparent vasoconstriction in the extremities with this reaction may in some way be related to the shift of relative awareness to the upper-torso area; however, there remains the possibility of much more complex vaso-motor and other reactions in different body areas than have as yet been studied.

PLEASANTNESS AND UNPLEASANTNESS

As has been discussed in Part II, this classification of pleasantness and unpleasantness represents not so much a noncognitive psychological state (or feeling) as a type of judgment that may of course be a higher-order generalization deriving basically from types of psychological states. Nevertheless, these terms were employed so much, particularly in the early literature, that the findings relating to them should be considered. Much confusion as to the feeling components actually involved in many of the studies concerning pleasantness and unpleasantness exists.

PHYSIOLOGICAL CHANGES

Morgan has advised hesitancy in expecting simple correlations between pleasantness-unpleasantness and the two autonomic divisions respectively (928). Vasoconstriction and fall in skin temperature have been related to "conflict" (920, 922), and unpleasant dreams have been seen to increase blood pressure (849). Altschule (38), however, cited references indicating that similar peripheral vascular changes also result from "strong pleasurable emotions" (119), including "pleasurable excitement" reported by Mittelmann and Wolff (922).

In the measuring of the amplitudes of breathing and of gross bodily movements during emotion-producing motion pictures, Cason and Cason found that the effects of unpleasant feelings were of longer duration than those for pleasant ones, and a positive correlation was found between the two measures (212). Increased basal metabolic rates have been reported for hypnotized subjects under the suggestion of impending misfortune (821). Also, unpleasant "emotions," including anxiety, depression, and rage, posthypnotically induced as dreams, have been associated with relative anoxemia, whereas pleasant ones, similarly induced and including euphoria and ecstasy, were associated with raised blood oxygen saturation (816, 818). Altschule's review indicated that "stresses of various types" may produce either increases or decreases in respiratory rate, with the finding of increase being more common (38). Finesinger found that induced unpleasant ideas were associated with increased sighing respiration in normal controls and in a group of patients having diagnoses of hysteria, anxiety neurosis, and reactive depression (355). In the last group, significant respiratory fluctuation was observed with induced unpleasant thoughts. With this stimulus, Finesinger found no significant respiratory changes for the diagnoses of hypochondriasis, compulsive neurosis, or questionable schizophrenia. Faulkner reported a case wherein pleasant ideas were associated with bronchial dilatation, unpleasant ideas were associated with bronchial narrowing, and inconsequential ideas produced no change (347).

Brunswick felt that "pleasant and unpleasant emotions" were distinguished by tonus changes of the stomach and rectum, and found generally a loss of gastrointestinal tone with unpleasant states and increased tone with pleasant states except that "disgust" was also associated with increased stomach tone (170).

INTERNAL SENSORY PERCEPTION

The earliest studies concerning internal sensation related these only to pleasant and unpleasant reactions, as was discussed in Chapters 5 and 15. Pleasantness was associated with "bright pressure" in the upper-chest region as contrasted to the association of unpleasantness with "dull pressure" in the lower abdominal and trunk region (589, 945, 946). However, more variable reports were also seen (259).

On the basis of free association, subjects of my first internal-sensation study associated internal sensations with pleasant reactions in 89 per cent of the observations; however, predominant sensations in the lower-back areas had frequent unpleasant associations or associations with avoidance (877).

ELATION OR ENJOYMENT

Some of the findings that were just presented in association with "pleasantness and unpleasantness" might well apply to this category of elation or enjoyment. Unfortunately, there are relatively few reports of physiological findings in connection with a specific reaction of elation or enjoyment. Henry found an increased basal metabolic rate in states of elation, overactivity, tension, and agitation (921). A finding of increased blood oxygen with suggested "euphoria and ecstasy" was just mentioned (816). Bekhterev reported that a state of gladness produced faster and stronger heartbeats (710). A moderately active, secreting stomach with relatively red mucosa was observed under conditions of a happy and co-operative mood (258). Wittkower reported that joy, as well as sorrow and anxiety, increased bile secretion, though the secretion accompanying joy was said to be especially light (321, 1333). Associations of manic psychosis with a relatively high frequency of alpha rhythm and of depressed phases of this psychosis with a low alpha frequency have been revealed, but no shifts in alpha frequency to correspond to changes, or to degrees of change, in these psychotic phases were seen (617).

Gemelli reported various sensory associations with the "state of joy": "more rapid and deeper breathing"; " 'expansion' of the chest and the diaphragm"; "a feeling of strength in my whole being"; and "organic—my whole organism" (433). One stimulus situation in my more limited feeling-reaction, internal-sensation study resulted in 58 per cent of feeling reactions of "enjoyment" (878). The most distinguishing feature of this reaction in comparison to those of other situations was the relative absence of internal sensations in the right-midriff area (Areas No. 12a, 12b), and also the right-shoulder area (Area No. 5a) received relatively low ratings. In my more extensive internal-sensation study none of the experimental stimulus situations produced a majority of ratings for the elation or enjoyment reaction, although this reaction did occur in two of the practice observations that were not analyzed (879). The relative absence of sensations in the right-midriff area may possibly be indicative of comparatively normal functioning of the transverse colon or duodenum, each of which has been noted to show marked changes under stress conditions and with "excitement" (see pp. 227, 236).

FRIENDLINESS AND LOVE

PHYSIOLOGICAL CHANGES

The feeling reactions of friendliness and love will be considered separately here, though they appear to have much in common with, and a close relationship to, the feeling of elation or enjoyment. No physiological findings have been specifically related to friendliness reactions and few have been reported for love. Dysinger and Ruckmick found that movies about love and sex, among other things, were the most effective in producing galvanic skin reactions with subjects sixteen years of age and least effective in producing responses in subjects below twelve years of age, but the responses were similar for both sexes (328). Thus, such reactivity relates in part to sexual maturation. Another study reported that during the postovulative phase of the human female's menstrual cycle, the desire to be loved on an infantile level is at its height (100).

INTERNAL SENSORY PERCEPTION

I early associated increased differential internal sensations in the epigastric area, tending toward the lower left area (Area No. 10), with a feeling reaction called "companionship," or "friendship" (876). Associated with the "companionship" reaction and occurring in this area were still more specific differential sensations that qualitatively distinguished among feeling reactions of "love," "humor," and "thrill" respectively (876, 877).

A secondary feeling loading of "friendliness" has already been noted with the analysis of the "significance" reaction in my more extensive internal-sensation experiment (879). The reverse proportion, with primary loading of "friendliness" (approximately 54 per cent) and a secondary loading of "significance" (approximately 24 per cent), was obtained in another stimulus situation. The following sensation pattern was found: the central-chest area (Area No. 6) was strongly rated, ranking first, and was rated high compared to the other types of reactions; the right-midriff area (at Areas No. 12a, 12b) and the "central" abdominal area (Area No. 14) tied for second ranking, being only slightly stronger rated than the upper-back area (Area No. 21); the genital-pubic area (Area No. 13b) was rated little compared to the other areas and to the other situations; the lower left epigastric area was rated low compared to the other situations; and the back body areas were rated strongly in the manner already noted for "significance" reactions. In both of these types of feeling reactions, the "healthiest" quartile of the nonpatient subjects placed greater emphasis on the lower left epigastric area than did the subjects as a whole.

The feeling-reaction proportions and the internal-sensation patterns were found to be somewhat more definitive for "love." In my limited sensation experiment the proportion of these reactions for a given situation was 52 per cent, and the most consistent differential internal-sensation pattern included the most prominent sensations in the central-chest area with the second most prominent sensations in the genital-pubic area and a relative absence of sensations in the back body areas compared to other types of reactions (878). In my more extensive study, the feeling reactions of "love" for a given situation ranged in frequency from 81 per cent for the "healthiest" quartile of nonpatients to 74 per cent for the "least healthy" quartile group, and for the total nonpatient group the following internal-sensation pattern was obtained with the ten body areas rated: sensations in the central chest, the lower left epigastrium, and the "central" abdominal areas predominated. As already noted, sensations in the genital-pubic area were rated strong compared to all other situations except the sexually loaded one, and sensations in the lower-back area were more strongly rated than usual compared to those for the upper-back area (879).

Some synthesis of these various pleasant feeling reactions with physiological functioning will be attempted in the next section.

SEXUAL FEELING

GENERAL DISCUSSION

Much has been written about the role of sexual feeling or drive, but there remains a great hiatus of knowledge concerning related physiological and sensory functioning. Wenger refers to "three or four visceral patterns" occurring with behavior that is termed "sexual excitement" including initial inhibition of overt activity, response and tumescence with sustained stimulation, the orgasm, and "relief" after orgasm (1304). The vasodilatation and certain muscular responses that lead up to the orgasm are parasympathetic in origin, though other sexual responses involve sympathetic innervation (878). Some evidence has been presented that the functioning of the anterior hypothalamus may be an integral factor in sexual responsiveness (1194); and lateral preoptic stimulation was associated with sexual behavior whereas medial preoptic stimulation was associated with maternal behavior (see p. 138). The assertion by Kinsey et al. (705) that male and female humans possess a different capacity to reach an orgasm has been disputed, but it is commonly recognized that a generally longer foreplay period is usually required for female orgasm.

HORMONAL FINDINGS

Beach's studies have emphasized the interaction of sensory and central factors in sexual arousal, with the higher mammals being relatively nondependent upon hormones or other specific stimuli for arousal. Similarly, the presence of gonadal hormones in the blood stream does not in itself result in sexual excitement nor does gonadectomy necessarily prevent successful copulation (86, 87, 88, 89). Nevertheless, male androgen and female estrogen hormones, as well as the gonadotropic hormones of the anterior pituitary, usually accompany sexual arousal (424, 1310).

One group of observers has placed great emphasis on hormonal variations within the sexual cycle of the female, believing that the following stages produce specific psychodynamic manifestations of the sexual drive: estrogen production was associated with active psychodynamic tendencies directed toward an externalized object; high progesterone levels were associated with passive receptive psychodynamic tendencies, and, conversely, low hormone levels were associated with "destructive hostility, negative narcissism, infantile demanding dependency, depressive, and eliminative tendencies" (99, 100, 265).

OTHER PHYSIOLOGICAL CHANGES

The report of galvanic-skin-response changes in adolescents, but none in children below twelve years of age, occurring while observing movies concerning love and sex has been noted (328). With gratifying sexual performance, a rise in "electrical potential" has been reported by Reich as contrasted to a fall in the absence of gratification, as well as in the presence of anxiety (1232).

With motion pictures of nude dancing girls, Scott found a rise in systolic blood pressure for men subjects (1116). Increased basal metabolic rate occurring with thoughts of members of the opposite sex as well as with other stimuli, was found by Totten in contrast to negative findings with less "drastic" stimulations (821, 1259). More definite findings were those of Boas and Goldschmidt, who obtained a complete cardiotachographic record of heart rate during intercourse and found peaks of 143 to 146 beats per minute during the orgasm (134). The review of Kinsey et al. revealed that the normal pulse rate of 70 to 80 per minute may be increased to over 150 with sexual arousal, and, similarly, normal diastolic and systolic blood pressure of 65 and 120, respectively, may be increased to 160 and 250, respectively, with orgasm (705). Also, a peripheral blood shift was postulated with the tumescence of all distensible parts of the body and increased surface temperature.

Kinsey et al. described the breathing as being deeper and faster in the early stages of arousal and as becoming interrupted with the approach of orgasm, with prolonged gasps on inspiration followed by forceful collapse of the lungs on expiration. Also various genital glandular secretions were described for sexual arousal and, especially, orgasm. Individual gastric reactions to stimuli that may, or may not be sexually stimulating have been seen to vary greatly according to the interpretation of the stimuli by the individual (871). Increased gastric secretion with sexual excitement has been observed (317, 426). Clinical reports have frequently associated disturbances of the bladder with sexual conflicts, but such functional disturbances have also been observed when conflicts of other types appeared to be predominant (1213). Emotionally based increases in alkalinity of the vaginal secretion have been said to contribute to reduced "voluptuous sensations" in the vagina, predisposing it to excoriation or chafing and consequent leucorrhea (1097). This, combined with muscular and mucosal congestion, also functionally based, was seen to increase deep sensitiveness of painful types and to reduce superficial sensations of voluptuous types in the vagina.

INTERNAL SENSORY PERCEPTION

All internal-sensation studies have related predominant sensation in the genital-pubic area with sexual feelings (876, 877, 878, 879). In the limited study that I conducted, one stimulus situation produced 82 per cent of rating of sexual feeling reaction (878). With this stimulus, sensations in the genital-pubic area were most intense, and sensations in the central-chest area were the second most prominent compared to all other types of situations, and sensations in the "central" abdominal area were also highly rated compared to the other situations. Similar findings were seen in the more extensive study with a frequency of approximately 67 per cent of "sexual passion or desire" reactions for a given situation: the genital-pubic area was rated very strongly for first ranking; the "central" abdominal area received second ranking; and the lower left epigastric area was third; the central-chest and the right-midriff areas ranked very close in ratings to the lower left epigastrium, but they were rated the least compared to the other situations; the lower-back area was rated most intensely of the three back body areas rated, being rated strongly compared to the other situations except those with high "significance" (and "friendliness") loadings (879). The calf area received the least ratings, and the lower-chest area was rated low compared to the other situations. The "healthiest" quartile of nonpatient subjects placed still relatively greater emphasis on the genital-pubic area, the "central" abdominal area, and the lower left epigastric area in comparison to all the nonpatient subjects.

SYNTHESIS OF SENSORY AND PHYSIOLOGICAL FINDINGS

First of all in attempting a synthesis of the physiological and sensory findings for the relatively pleasant types of psychological reactions, it would seem apparent that the marked increase in sensation in the genital-pubic area occurring with sexual feeling reactions relates to the relatively well-known physiological changes that take place in that area with such feelings. This is exemplified by Kuntz's assertion that sensations, which are immediately associated with ejaculation and which arise simultaneously with the initiation of peristaltic contractions of the ducti deferentia, constitute the sexual orgasm (740). He added that although the details concerning such sensations are not known, the neural excitation involves widespread reactions including: (1) for both sexes, augmentation of the rate and force of cardiac contractions, stimulation of respiration, frequent occurrence of perspiration, and at times spastic contractions of the extensor muscles of the lower extremities; (2) for the male, contraction of the compressor urethrae, the ischiocavernosus and the bulbocavernosus muscles, which act to expel the seminal fluid; and (3) for the female, peristaltic contractions in the Fallopian tubes at the height of excitation, and then the contractions are propagated to the uterus and vagina and are followed by rhythmic contractions of the striated sphincter vaginae muscles (740). The increased sensations in the "central" abdominal area may relate to glandular, vascular, intestinal, and muscular changes in or near that area, and particularly may relate to its close proximity to the lower abdomen. The muscular changes as well as possibly the increase of sacral innervation may be the basis of the relative increase of sensations in the lower-back area as compared to the upper back.

As might be expected, the "love" reaction showed a similar, though less pronounced, pattern for these areas. The strong sensations in the lower left epigastric area with both of these reactions may relate to gastric changes. The most distinguishing differential feature between the "love" and "sexual" reactions is the reversal in emphasis on the central-chest and genital-pubic areas, the latter being so strong with "sexual" feeling that it overshadows the usually pronounced sensations in the central chest. These central-chest sensations would seem to relate to heart function at least in part, and since esophageal sensations are also localized in and around this area, its functioning may also be involved. In these feeling reactions, particularly the "sexual" one, also was seen a relative de-emphasis on sensations in the right-shoulder and right-midriff areas, as was also seen with the "enjoyment" reaction of the more limited study. These may be indicative of a lack of muscle tension in the shoulder area and of relative inactivity or "normal" activity of the duodenum and transverse colon in the right-midriff area.

The available analysis for the feeling reaction of "friendliness" includes such a large proportion of "significance" feeling that it is difficult to evaluate in relationship to these other relatively pleasurable feeling reactions. However, this may in itself be indicative of a relative shift of sensory reactivity to upper body areas, particularly the central chest in the front and the upper-back area in the back of the body with this type of reaction as compared to "love" and "sexual" feeling reactions.

TENSION

GENERAL USAGE OF TERMINOLOGY

Tension is a somewhat generalized term that is most frequently used ambiguously in the literature; however, at times it implies a state of general muscle tension that is usually an aspect of an unpleasant feeling state. The term has also been used to include unspecified or general reactions to "frustration" or "stress" (710, 936b). More specifically "neuromuscular tension" has been employed by one group of observers to indicate postulated basic reaction types, or "tensional patterns," with "cotention" representing a comfortable adjustive type and "ditention" representing an uncomfortable nonadjusting type (178, 959, 1224). Very often the use of this term embodies mixed feeling states, such as "anxious, depressive, or restrained aggressive attitudes," which are reactions to stress or conflict. Also, so-called tension (or "nervous energy," or simply "conflict") has been conceptualized by some as being channelized within the nervous system into hysterical (383) or psychosomatic symptomatology (858).

PHYSIOLOGICAL FINDINGS

An intercorrelation of personality traits and physiological measures by Darling suggested two groupings of subjects on the basis of high positive intercorrelations among systolic blood pressure, pulse pressure, and diastolic blood pressure that were negatively related to the high intercorrelation between galvanic reactivity and conductance level (267). The reactivity of one group of subjects appeared to be based on a high level of tone, or "tension," in the sympathetic nerves or on a low level of opposing tone in the parasympathetic nerves; whereas the other group of subjects tended toward a high degree of parasympathetic, or possibly toward a "balanced" reaction of both the parasympathetic and sympathetic systems. The latter group was more alert, more excitable or noninhibited, and more active physically than the former, whose responses were interpreted to involve possible inhibition of parasympathetic activity.

Excessively fast encephalographic activity in the cerebral cortex has been described as being more or less typical of conditions of anxiety or "tension" (271). Some concepts relating ACTH and cortisone levels to "instinctual tensions" have already been noted (see pp. 175, 359). The amount and duration of elevation in body temperature in response to a given amount of work was found to be greater during periods of long-lasting "emotional tension and conflict" than during relatively tranquil periods (469). Also, periodic fever episodes have been observed in some persons at times of sustained "stress" (1360). Kuno found sweating palms characteristic of "mental strain" (738), and this is also a common sign of clinical (38) and experimental (748a) "tension" or "anxiety." A similar reaction was seen in the fall in skin temperature of the extremities, and involved complex emotional factors including "various degrees of tension" (922, 923). Somatic tension has been referred to as a common symptom of anxiety, involving varying degrees of generalized muscular tension (796). Head and neck muscles were found to have increased potential on the electroencephalogram when subjects felt tension punctuated by headaches whereas the muscle potentials were minimal or absent during relaxed states without discomfort (1358).

An attempt to study Lewin's conceptualized "tension systems" was made by taking electromyographic measurements of five muscle groups, including the forehead, the back of the neck, the chin, and the extensor surfaces of both arms, during the administration of four drawing tasks (1158). It was found that: the activity produced a steady rise in muscle tone; muscle tension fell more after completion of a task than after interruption; and the subjects with the greatest rise in muscle tension during the drawings tended most to maintain this tension when interrupted. These results were attributed to central neural processes capable of self-maintained activity.

Arrhythmias were observed to occur in patients mostly during periods of "sustained and mounting tension, whatever its dynamics," but occasionally the "let-down" period following such "anxiety, resentment, or striving furnished the setting for an attack" (322). The extrasystoles of a patient studied by hypnoanalysis were seen to be proportional to his "states of tension" (1101). In "tension" states, respiration was seen to become more rapid and shallow, with frequent sighs, and an increase in hydrochloric acid, mucosa, and pepsin secretions were found in the stomach, as well as more continuous peristaltic activity and increased magnitude of contractions (923).

Irritable-colon patients under "emotional tension" exhibited two types of disturbances in colonic functioning, one being an over-all increase in activity of the sigmoid colon and the other being a decrease in activity, and colonic disorder seemed to be a normal accompaniment of "emotional tension" (32). This was supported by reactions of healthy subjects experiencing "emotional tension" from the stress of head screws or painful immersion of the arms into cold water (36). Regardless of the coloring of their emotional reactions, vascularity, motility, and secretion of the sigmoid colon were all increased under the stress, and there were only transient blanching and no instances of relaxation of the colon at these times. Thus, it would seem that the prior finding of decrease in colonic activity at times in patients would relate to some psychological state different from the type of "tension" produced by this latter study. "Tension" associated with premenstrual states has already been noted (p. 184).

I have already discussed the association of headaches with tension, particularly that of the head and neck muscles (1353, 1356). Also presented was the vague sensory awareness of patterns of "ditention" and "cotention" within the body, the latter reportedly representing man's biologically normal reaction and the former representing "an internal pattern of tension" (960). Common types of reactions involving sensory awareness are exemplified by healthy medical students under pre-examination "tension" and are: warmth of the face, coldness and sweating of the hands, axillary sweating, palpitation, general shakiness, epigastric uneasiness, anorexia, diarrhea, and frequent urination, with disappearance of these symptoms with subsequent "relief and satisfaction" (560). More specifically, reactions involving "rage, resentment, anxiety, fear and tension" have resulted in narrowing of the coronary arteries and heart pain resulting from prolonged elevation of blood pressure and cardiac output (1342) as well as palpitation, dyspnea, fatigue, giddiness, and faintness. In another report, "anxiety and tension" produced palpitation and diarrhea in a subject (1199).

ANGER, "EMERGENCY REACTION," OR "STRUGGLE"

CONCEPTUAL USAGES

This category is intended to be broad enough to include any feeling of "struggle," including anger, resentment, determination, and so forth. It also embodies an element of "emergency reaction" in that the organism may appear in some way to be reacting *against* a disturbing stimulus. One concept is that "the emotion of anger is teleological in that it results in the stimulus being removed from the receptor" (499). Another study has generalized that a "feeling of good health is dependent both upon a gratification of basic needs and upon an ability to discharge anger externally and rather completely when the needs are not gratified" (527). Thus in considering related studies, it may be well to note not only physiological functioning with the psychological state of anger but also the way that the anger is being handled or directed.

NEURAL FINDINGS

Several authors have emphasized the relative increase in sympathetic innervation in anger as compared to fear (424, 812). This innervation includes such reactions as increased heart rate and output, increased peripheral resistance with an elevation of diastolic and systolic blood pressure, and reduced renal blood flow that may be eliminated by sympathectomy (426). However, a more recent view has reversed this emphasis on the basis of reactions to physical stimuli applied to parts of the brain (53, 53a). The first view is supported somewhat by Darrow's findings concerning the occurrence of 7-per-second, alphalike bursts of EEG activity in frontal and motor areas during a boy's frequent uncontrolled outbursts of rage (273). Both reactions were eliminated by daily doses of the parasympathetic drug, Prostigmin Bromide, but with subsequent administration of the anticholinergic (antiparasympathetic), atrophine, the original EEG pattern reappeared.

Other studies have related aggressive paroxysmal rage patterns, or a low frustration level, to findings of theta activity in the temporal region (562, 563, 564, 1001, 1031, 1184). There remains the good possibility that the two divisions of the autonomic nervous system have different, differential innervation in different parts of the body.

Increased facial sebum, presumably from vasodilatation, was seen on the face with anger (812, 1363), but caution was urged in interpreting this finding since on a number of occasions the sebum-spreading effect was equally great or small without deviation in mood that could be detected (812). Nevertheless, in a study of 30 acne-vulgaris patients, increased facial sebum was seen with anger, and the day-to-day fluctuation of such secretion was no greater than with nonacne subjects (811). The acne patients revealed a characteristic emotional pattern consisting of episodes of "anger" followed by periods of "remorse," which were accompanied by hyposecretion of facial sebum. There was a close correlation between life situations resulting in these reactions and the increase in the patient's acne pustules. Repressed hostility has also been reported for patients with atopic eczema (320).

Wechsler and Jones distinguished fear and anger reactions on the basis of the galvanic skin reaction (1294), but Hunt's findings were negative in this respect (612). Arnold believes that the increased level of general activity (1269) and muscular tension accompanying anger may differentiate this feeling from that of fear (52). Other observers have noted that excitation of striated skeletal muscles is associated with rage (424, 426) and with unexpressed strong hostile feelings (1298). Increased back-muscle activity occurred with unpleasant feeling reactions that included "resentment" and "hostility"; however, from the description it would appear possible that such feelings as insecurity or anxiety may predominate in these reactions (595). A greater than normal degree of muscular response and tension in rheumatoid patients has been associated with a chronic state of inhibited rebellious hostility, with the sustained muscular contractions also resulting in pain (461).

In 30 cases of chronic urticaria studied, the attacks were "almost exclusively" related to life situations in which the patient developed resentment because he felt unjustly treated and without recourse (479). The attacks were thought to be secondary to extreme dilatation of both arterioles and minute vessels in the skin at these times. Other observers have also emphasized repressed aggression and masochism as being psychopathological mechanisms in urticaria (1337). Constriction of arterioles and increased tone of minute vessels of the forearm have been associated with "an attitude of hostility" (479a).

Although Scott found no characteristic vascular reactions with anger or fear (1116), feelings of anger have long been associated with increased blood pressure (38, 1349). Similarly, during periods of resentment (and anxiety), greater and more prolonged increases in heart rate or cardiac index were seen with exercise than during security and relaxation (323).

In a relatively well-controlled study of 43 healthy subjects, Ax found that the reactions that were significantly greater for anger than for fear included diastolic-blood-pressure rises, heart-rate falls, the number of rises in skin conductance (taken from the fingers), and muscle-potential increases (taken from the frontalis muscle); skin-conductance increases, the number of muscle-potential increases, and respiration-rate increases were greater for fear than for anger (55). These results were interpreted as refuting Arnold's proposal that anger involves a strong reaction of both the sympathetic and parasympathetic systems, whereas fear involves only the former. It should also be noted that the intercorrelation of the various physiological measures taken by Ax was significantly higher for anger than for fear, which was taken as an indication of greater integration during anger. A study associating the directing of "anger out" with noradrenaline secretion and the directing of "anger in" with adrenaline secretion based the former on findings of increase in systolic blood pressure, more marked increase in diastolic blood pressure, mild pulse increase, and decrease in cardiac activity, whereas the latter was based on findings of a mild to moderate increase in diastolic pressure, a moderate to marked increase in pulse rate, and a moderate to marked increase in cardiac activity (410a, 411a). Those subjects showing "anxiety" also reacted as the latter group. This study serves to illustrate the possible sequences and "layers" of feeling reactivity, with associated cognitive mechanisms and behavioral expressions, that need to be differentiated and specified in studies involving "emotional" reactivity.

An increase in heart rate, along with electrocardiographic changes, has been seen to accompany expression of anger with a mixed group of patients (1202). Resentment and hostility of subjects with early labile essential hypertension was associated with hypertensive blood-pressure levels, chronically shortened blood-clotting times, and elevated blood viscosities (1104). Also, day-to-day emotional changes of patients with essential hypertension revealed that during periods of tranquillity, violent exercise, or the frank expression of hostility, their blood pressure was lower, whereas with "repressed hostility and tension" it was higher, and this increased blood pressure was also associated with increased viscosity and shortened clotting time of the blood (1103, 1104, 1105, 1360). General agreement has been reported concerning the fact that unexpressed hostility plays a major role in essential hypertension (888). With this hostility, blood-pressure elevations of 160/100 to 200/130 were related to an increase in peripheral resistance with normal stroke volume and heart rate (935a). Hostility was found to be the outstanding feature of patients with paroxysmal auricular arrhythmias, who were generally unable to express their hostile feelings and who, instead, maintained a superficially pleasant and agreeable attitude in which the attacks most frequently occurred (322, 680). Increase in ketonemia of the blood has been associated particularly with anger and also with dejection (568, 569, 576). Also, the major fluctuations in symptoms and in insulin requirements of diabetic persons were seen to coincide with periods of conflicts that were reported to involve "anxious and resentful" reactions; however, in these studies the descriptions seem to put primary emphasis on feelings of insecurity or anxiety.

In a patient with bronchiectasis, the secretion of bronchial mucus was found to increase as much as six to eight times over the normal during periods of life stress (1198). Increased bronchial secretion with a bronchial-asthma patient was also seen with "feelings of anxiety and resentment." Increased alkalinity of the saliva in "fear, anger, or other strong emotions," presumably from the lowering of blood carbon dioxide by hyperventilation, has been reported (38). Lowered blood oxygen levels were reported with feelings of anger during dreams induced by posthypnotic suggestion, with the level returning to normal with rehypnosis and abolition of the subject's rage reaction (818).

In a study of 15 asthmatic and 7 anxiety-state patients during stressful interviews, anger was found to involve irregularity of respiration, especially when suppressed, and to involve increased rate or depth of respiration with sighing; however, the latter reactions were associated primarily with anxiety (1205).

With anger the following changes were seen in the stomach: the gastric mucosa became hyperemic and engorged, acid production was greatly increased, vigorous contractions began, and general overactivity was noted (258, 923, 1351). Similar, but more pronounced, patterns of reaction were seen in patients with ulcer, gastritis, or duodenitis, and a greater magnitude and duration of change were found (923). A case of a woman, whose gastric secretion seemed to be inhibited by "anger, resentment or fright" (258), was revealed to have another basis in unconscious thought content (871). These consistent findings would appear to refute the assertion that anger results in immobility of the smooth muscle of the stomach (710). During anger, bile flow is reported to be entirely or almost entirely inhibited (1335), and certain sensations in the right upper abdomen associated with "annoyance" were explained by spasms of the bile ducts (321, 1333).

Many studies of the colon, mostly based on the sigmoid colon, have found that in anger, resentment, or the like, it becomes hyperactive, hypermotile, hyperemic, turgid, and more fragile, and lysozyme concentrations are high (32, 33, 34, 475, 1358, 1362). One study emphasized the fearful inhibition of "rage" as being associated with autonomic excitation of the colon in ulcerative-colitis patients (678a). Vesical hyperfunction and small bladder capacity "were accompanied by anxiety and resentments" (1116); however, it seems probable that the former feeling state may have been predominant in these reactions. Also, the vaginal mucosa has been seen to become reddened, turgid, and hyperemic during resentment and anger that were apparently unrelated to sexual conflict (1358). Wolff integrated this finding with his thesis that all mucous membranes of the body react in this manner with feeling states of the anger type. Finally, when women showed "destructive hostility, negative narcissism, infantile demanding dependence, depressive, and eliminative tendencies," low estrogen and progesterone hormone levels were found (99, 100).

INTERNAL SENSORY PERCEPTION

Internal sensations were reported occasionally in the studies cited above, as exemplified by the report of a patient's complaint of precordial pain while circulatory changes were observed during strong anger; in the same study, palpitation was associated with increased stroke volume during various reactions (including "anger") to low-grade stresses of "everyday" living (1342). Dyspnea was also reported. Similarly, essential-hypertension patients, having repressed hostility as a "characteristic feature," complained of precordial pain, palpitation, and dyspnea (1358). Also, with various feeling states involved, aching and hyperactivity of back muscles have been reported (595); however, the predominant state does not seem to have been of the "anger" type. Sensations of tightness or aching in the jaws, the zygoma, and the temporal region have resulted from sustained contraction of the masseter muscles over periods of days or months (1356). These muscles were said to be among the first to contract with "states of tension, determination, or desperation," and to remain contracted at times for long periods.

The findings of Almy and Tulin indicate a negative relationship of anger, or "resentment," to nausea since, in contrast to the reports of other subjects, this sensation did not occur in one subject who was resentful throughout an experiment, and in another subject the nausea sensation disappeared as he became resentful (36). Pains in "the abdomen" were reported to occur with strong rebellion against a situation to which the patient had to acquiesce, and the pains disappeared with realization of what had taken place (39). Also, it was noted that similar pains occur in persons who become very tense.

In my first limited study of internal sensations with areas for rating that included the whole body, several observers associated sensations in the area just above the navel (Area No. 12b) with reactions of "going against" or "struggling" or with "anger" (877). In the limited feeling-reaction experiment involving the rating of ten body areas, the intensity of sensations with the "anger"-producing stimulus was somewhat less than with that for "fear," and only slightly greater than that for the "love" situation, and the internal-sensation patterns with the "anger" and the "fear" reactions were somewhat similar (878). The pattern for "anger" could be differentiated, however, by a relative absence of sensations in the calf area and by an absolute minimum of sensations in the genital-pubic area in comparison to all types of situations presented. Also, the "anger" pattern was differentiated from the "fear" pattern by its relatively greater magnitude of sensations in the central-chest area (Area No. 6) as compared to other body areas simultaneously, although for both reaction patterns the sensations in this area were stronger than in any other area. In general, the internal-sensation reaction pattern with "anger" was characterized by a predominance of sensations in the upper-back area (Area No. 21) and in the shoulder area (Area No. 5) in comparison to other types of reactions (except "fear"); by an absence of sensations in the genital-pubic area absolutely and relatively; and by a strength of sensations in the central chest in comparison to other body areas that could be likened only to that with the "love" reaction. A frequency of 79 per cent of feeling reactions of "anger" for the "anger" stimulus situation was obtained in this study.

In the more extensive study a given stimulus produced a frequency of approximately 64 per cent (but intensity ratings of 78 per cent) for this type of reaction (879). The findings in the more extensive study were further complicated by a rather high percentage of "enjoyment" reactions to this stimulus (frequencies of 22 per cent for the healthy quartile and 11 per cent for the "least healthy" quartile of nonpatient subjects). The following internal-sensation pattern was found for all nonpatient subjects: a spread of strong ratings over the areas of the central chest, the lower left epigastrium, the right midriff, and the central abdomen, with the ratings for the central chest and the right midriff slightly the stronger; sensations in the areas of the lower left epigastrium and the lower right chest were strong in comparison to the other situations; and sensations in the calf area and in the genital-pubic area were of low intensity in comparison to other areas and to other situations. The "healthiest" quartile rated the central abdominal area strongly for first ranking and the right-midriff area for second ranking and placed less emphasis on the lower-right-chest area. I shall attempt to synthesize these sensations with physiological functioning in the next section.

FEAR AND ANXIETY

CONCEPTUAL USAGE

Some studies relating to the differentiation between fear and anger types of psychological states have already been considered in the previous section, and it would seem important that such a differentiation should be made since an individual's reaction to stress or to threat may embody relative proportions of both, as well as of other feeling states. Therefore, differentiation of functioning and of perception, as well as understanding of the individual's reaction, must be based on evaluation of the predominant feeling states involved in given reactions, whether in the case of an individual or in the study of groups.

Anxiety, a fearlike feeling, is probably the most frequently cited basis of neurosis and functional bodily disturbances in modern times. In primitive societies, anxiety, particularly in association with feelings of intense fear and helplessness, has frequently resulted in bodily dysfunction and even in death (1148).

Grinker pointed out that fear is teleological because of its effect of removing the receptor from the stimulus and of allowing of consequent flight from a real danger, but he stated that in anxiety the danger is not "real" but is unknown (499). With unknown danger there were noted specific unpleasurable feelings and efferent discharges and their perception, and when neither "flight nor fight" reactions occur, a frequent paralysis of higher ego functions was seen. Grinker believed that when the cerebral cortex or ego "gives up," a regression takes place and visceral expression or dysfunctions of organs occur. Such a view, however, is somewhat different from the one that emphasizes that the physiological correlates of feeling states are normal reactions and that the associated pathological conditions reflect exaggerated or sustained reactions of differential types dependent (at least in part) on given types of predominant feeling states.

The fact that an "anger," or emergency type, reaction may occur as a secondary response to fear and may be superimposed on feelings of fear or anxiety is well known clinically, and the essential difference between these two types of states may be that which was proposed in Arnold's view: that fear is innervating and forces the organism to caution, whereas anger is energizing and increases the level of somatic activity (52). Sudden fear reactions usually involve a high degree of "excitement" or startle, and (as has been noted already) this element of a person's feeling state must be considered separately in the making of differentiations. This would particularly seem to be an important differentiating factor in the more common concepts of "fear" and "anxiety."

NEURAL FINDINGS

Several studies have reported the disappearance of alpha waves on the EEG with sudden "startle" or with terrifying "fear" (108, 794, 810, 1327). A characteristic EEG record of low-amplitude, poorly developed alpha waves and occasional findings of faster rhythms of low amplitude is seen with the initial "apprehension" of subjects (796) and with conditions of anxiety or "tension," whose postulated basis was elaborated earlier (see p. 149) (271, 1236). The opposite "facilitation effects" of increased alpha and decreased beta activity with the presentation of a "fear" stimulus have been explained by Darrow as being due to the relief of the central "tension" that was generated by the anticipation of the stimulus and in which the increased cortical activity had occurred. Concerning this Lindsley stated: "Physical tension and apprehension provide a persistent source of impulses, both peripheral and central, to play upon an activation mechanism, which appears to have its principal focus in the hypothalamus" (796, p. 498).

Electrical stimulation of the hypothalamus in many subjects was seen to produce the "well-known general visceral effects on blood pressure, respiration, pupils, heart rate, sweating, vasomotor tone, bladder and body temperature" and to produce reactions of "profound anxiety" in the patients (499). Although these anxiety reactions were given different emotional expression by the patients, "in no patients were emotional expressions of anger noted; all responded with fear." Also, a distinctive EEG wave pattern was produced in this way, which, it was found, could be similarly induced by ideational stimuli associated with anxiety or fear states. Ulett and Gleser developed and crossvalidated three scales (based on basic EEG records, EEG response to photic stimulation, and subjective sensations induced by flicker), that correctly identified 59.4 per cent anxiety-prone normal subjects and 65.5 per cent anxious patients with only 11 per cent "false positives" (331a, 1269a).

Arnold (52, 53, 54) has developed the thesis that parasympathetic innervation predominates with fear, and Kling argued that fear reactions are predominantly parasympathetic (710). However, the important fact is that complex and even opposite types of reactions take place in different parts of the body with this state, as with other psychological states, and the two autonomic divisions as well as the central and peripheral nervous systems are involved.

GENERAL PHYSIOLOGICAL FINDINGS

In a study of 22 patients hospitalized because of anxiety, the degree of adrenocortical response from an injection of isotonic saline solution was found to be proportional to the degree of clinical anxiety present (238, 478). It was concluded that in a state of extreme apprehensiveness, a relatively mild stimulus can result in notable adrenocortical discharge. Similar findings with 17-hydroxycorticosteroid measurements on patients prior to operation were reported (1005a). Dilatation of the pupil with acute fright has been said to be due to the adrenaline stimulus released by shock (462).

In muscular reactions it was noted that smooth muscles (having only sympathetic innervation) cause the hairs to stand up when one is "afraid or chilly" (796). Inhibition of the striated skeletal muscles has been associated with "fear and terror" (424, 426). Also, Malmo found the following with patients having anxiety diagnosis and being under physical stress: abrupt breaks in the regularity of action potentials for neck muscles, irregularity of finger movement, and irregularity of respiration movements (860). Ax's study of 43 healthy subjects revealed that for fear reactions, as compared with anger reactions, there were greater skin-conductance increases (in the finger), a greater number of frontalis-muscle-potential increases, and more numerous increases in the respiratory rate (55). Muscle tension may be reflected in the vocal apparatus in the high-pitched voice that is heard during periods of "fear and tension," and it may also be reflected in the pharyngeal muscles in the experiencing of choking sensations and "globus" in "fright" (1326).

Acral sweating from vasomotor stimulation is a frequent clinical (38) and experimental (560) finding in "anxiety." Constriction of arterioles and increased tone of minute vessels in the forearm were observed with "an attitude of anxiety" (479a). One study differentiated two types of fear, namely, startle and apprehension, by GSR findings (84) but was not subsequently supported (612), whereas another study differentiated fear and anger reactions by GSR findings (1294). Cardiovascular changes and possible adrenaline secretion associated with the directing of "anger in" and with "anxiety" were presented on p. 166. "Fear states" have been said to involve a fall in blood pressure by dilatation of the large splanchnic vasomotor areas or by cardiac inhibition and to involve a shift in the splanchno-peripheral balance of blood supply, from somatic to visceral concentration, with compensatory peripheral vasoconstriction (710). Increased blood pressure was reported with "anxiety" (1072a). More specifically, psychoanalytic study of patients with essential hypertension associated "anxiety with minor overt expression" as the predominant psychic concomitant of minor blood-pressure elevations of 140/90 to 160/100 (related to increased peripheral resistance and normal stroke volume and heart rate); however, when the anxiety was more overtly expressed, the minor blood-pressure elevations were related to increased stroke volume and heart rate, with normal peripheral resistance (935a).

With Blatz's classic falling-chair experiment, which was reported to arouse suddenly "the emotion of fear," the following reactions were recorded: (1) changes in electrical potential of the skin; (2) respiratory changes including inspiration during the fall in all cases, an immediate retardation in respiratory rate in 9 of 11 cases, and an increase in respiratory index (I/E) in 9 of 11 cases (129). A study of 15 asthmatic and 7 anxiety-state patients during stressful "life-situation" interviews revealed increased rate or depth of respiration and sighing chiefly during anxiety, but also at times with anger and resentment (1205). Anxiety has been said to be the "cause and core" of the hyperventilation (1097). With hypnotically induced anxiety, blood oxygen saturation levels have been found to fall (818).

Cardiac changes were also revealed in Blatz's experiment for all subjects, including an immediate initial acceleration with the fall of the chair, followed by retardation, and then an acceleration phase occurred that was followed by gradual retardation (129). An initial augmentation of the force of the heart beat, with but slight decreases for longer than six minutes, and a marked irregularity of cardiac rhythm were also found. An experimental study that seemed to stimulate definite excitement and apprehension revealed marked increases in cardiac output, with the emphasis, however, placed primarily on "excitement" (1188). Similarly with pre-examination apprehension, increases in arterial pressure, heart rate, stroke volume, and cardiac index were found (560). A fall in peripheral resistance was also observed, except that in 4 out of the 23 healthy subjects slight to moderate increases in peripheral resistance were seen, which constituted the primary basis of the finding of a slight increase in blood pressure. Scott, too, found inconstant blood-pressure effects in "anger" or "fear" (1116). Feelings of "anxiety and resentment" have already been noted to result reportedly in greater and more prolonged increases in heart rate or cardiac index (323). In a study of patients with anxiety and of normal subjects, those subjects with frank, overt anxiety showed greater cardiac output before and after exercise than did less anxious subjects, the former having also a relatively high heart rate with a normal or slightly elevated stroke volume (1205).

On the basis of the comparing of electrocardiographic records taken just before surgical operations with records taken the previous day, prior to the patient's knowing of the operation, Mainzer and Krause found 24 of 53 records to be abnormal, presumably "owing to fear of the impending operation" (858). As described earlier (p. 209), three types of abnormal EKG patterns were determined. Mainzer and Krause added that myocardial damage could be induced by the vasomotor fear reaction and that one type of reaction could be due to coronary constriction of vagal origin. Stevenson, Duncan, and Ripley, in a study of 35 patients, found that reactions of anxiety and also resentment during discussion of life situations resulted in EKG changes and in relatively high heart rate and low stroke volume, impairing the heart's efficiency, shortening diastolic time, and making the heart more liable to a disproportion between cardiac work and available blood supply (1202). Such changes were significantly greater in patients with neurocirculatory asthenia than in those with arteriosclerotic heart disease. In many of the examples of marked changes that the patients presented, resentment was an apparent factor. Although Duncan, Stevenson, and Ripley found unexpressed hostility to be the major characteristic of two thirds of the 15 patients with paroxysmal auricular arrhythmia who were studied, "long-standing and pronounced anxiety was exhibited by 11 of the subjects," and in 10 patients, fear, anxiety, or apprehension provided the setting for many of the attacks of tachycardia (322). Intense fear stemming from the attack itself was frequently seen, as well as somatic manifestations of anxiety, including palmar sweating, cracked voice, purposeless movements, tremor, and exaggerated startle. Such a reaction may be related to another finding, which was that "tripping" the apex of the heart with wire induced a "peculiar feeling of distress and apprehension" (202). The "T"-wave changes on the EKG found in anxiety by Stevenson, Duncan, and

Ripley were associated with hyperventilation but not apparently caused by it (1202).

Salivary secretion has been said to cease with fear (686) and changes in the saliva with "fear, anger and other strong emotions" (1185, 1186) have been attributed to lowering of blood carbon dioxide by hyperventilation (38).

Increased bile secretion has been reported with anxiety (321, 1333). In instances of rather definite fear states, Wolf and Wolff observed marked blanching of the mucous membrane of the stomach and gastric hypofunction, which were changes regularly associated with reduced saliva flow as well as with reduction of gastric juices (1351); similar decreased motility, decreased gastric secretion, and blanching of the stomach were seen with fear-type states in a case of Crider and Walker (258) as elaborated by Margolin et al. (871). On the other hand, with mixed reactions involving "tension, anxiety, resentment, anger, guilt, obsequiousness and desperation," Mittelmann and Wolff found increased hydrochloric acid, mucus, and pepsin secretions, and continuous peristaltic activity with increased magnitude of contractions (923). These changes were more pronounced in patients with ulcer, gastritis, and duodenitis than in the other subjects. Ten patients, who were undergoing routine diagnostic work-up and who manifested anxiety concerning the need for a second gastric intubation, each showed increased gastric acidity that was maintained throughout the day of the second study (548).

It is apparent that anger, or an "emergency reaction," may differentiate these findings from those of Mittelmann and Wolff just presented, and this factor may also explain Mahl's findings of increased gastric acidity in students during pre-examination tension (854), and in 2 patients during anxiety-arousing psychoanalytic sessions (857). This is another example of how anger, or an "emergency reaction," would seem to predominate in many mixed reactions as contrasted to the more specific fear reactions. On the other hand, Eichhorn and Tracktir suggested that earlier contradictions of reports might be resolved by the considering of the subject's usual "anxiety" level (using the Taylor Personality Scale) since, with hypnotic states, they found in a "high-anxiety" group increased acid in fear and decreased acid in anger whereas the "low-anxiety" group showed the reverse but did not approach the upper level of the "high" group (330a). (All groups showed increased pepsin and free and total acid secretions in "contentment.")

In situations of "abject fear and dejection," hypofunction of the colon with pallor, relaxation, lack of contractive activity and relatively low concentration of lysozyme in the secretion were observed in 4 subjects with prolapsed colonic fistulae, and this contrasted with the marked hyperactivity in situations of "conflict, anger, resentment and hostility or anxiety and apprehension" (476). In these studies, emphasis appeared to be placed on "dejection" rather than on "fear" as associated with colonic hypofunctioning. Other observers associated colonic motility of ulcerative-colitis patients with "fear," especially since "fear" inhibited the expression of rage (678a). During pre-examination tension, or "anxiety," diarrhea and frequent urination, respectively, were noted among other things (560). Marked renal vasoconstriction was observed with fear reactions of 2 subjects under clinical study (1159).

The general association of frequent urination with "anxiety and apprehension" was noted by Hinkle et al. (569). In their study with a mixed group of patients and nonpatients, 11 of the 12 subjects who experienced intense experimental conflicts showed diuresis, accompanied by a fall in the specific gravity of the urine, a fall in the chloride concentration of the urine, a fall in blood glucose and in circulating eosinophiles, and a rise in blood ketones (569). This diuresis was specifically related to anxiety. Also, for patients with diabetes mellitus, stress diuresis occurred most often in settings of anxiety and apprehension, but intense fear was associated with oliguria (570). Similar findings were reported by Hinkle and Wolf, and subjects who were "very fearful or angry" showed increased blood sugar, apparently resulting from the action of epinephrine in releasing liver sugar stores (576), but again, anger, or an emergency reaction, appeared to be involved in this last finding. Also, more marked blood ketone changes of the type noted above have been found in diabetic patients (568). Dunbar cited the following findings: hyperglycemia in aviators was proportionate to the extent of experienced fear (870); both neurotic and normal soldiers showed glycosuria for two to three days after being under fire (902); the anxiety of patients before operations (304, 867) and of students before examination (304) resulted in an increase in blood sugar (321).

Hyperemic vaginal mucosa, with increased mucus secretion, under conditions of "tension and conflict with frustration and anxiety" (1358) has already been mentioned, as has the observation of "anxiety, fear of being attacked, extreme penis envy, and antagonism toward the male" with the rise of the female estrogen level (100). Fear and anxiety have been said to be probably the most important disturbing factors in effective sexual performance (1232).

INTERNAL PERCEPTIVE EXPERIENCE

A study by Hunt indicated that fear experiences had more internal sensory associations than pleasantness-unpleasantness, esthetic, or beauty experiences (612a). Several reports of sensations from subjects who experienced a variety of feelings, such as the "apprehension, conflict, anxiety and feelings of resentment, hostility, humiliation, frustration, and guilt" that were reported in connection with backaches (595), have already been described and the sensations also included dyspnea, palpitation, and heart pains (1342) and palpitation and diarrhea (1199).

Other general findings were those of Gemelli concerning a state of "anxiety, fear, etc." that included: "a sort of tightening of the throat; it seemed that my breath stopped"; "a wave of memories and painful impressions which I felt throughout my body, especially the chest; it seemed as if my hands were trembling"; "the feeling of fear gripped my heart; it seemed to beat harder and faster"; "I felt something in my legs as if I wanted to get up from the table and run away" (433).

Altschule stated that "the clutching discomfort" about the heart with fear "is well known" and differs from angina pectoris (38). Wolf and Wolff referred to the "familiar psychosomatic phenomenon" of the "sinking feeling in the stomach which accompanies fear" (1351), as did also Kling (710). The occurrence of nausea in situations of "sudden and abject fear" involving a feeling of being defeated or overwhelmed has also been reported as a pattern of reaction (1344). Alvarez indicated that "distress or psychic shock or fear" can cause a pain to shoot into the abdomen, as exemplified by the phrases that anxiety will tie one's "bowel into knots" and fear will hit one "in the pit of the stomach" (39).

My own experimental research study already cited, relating internal sensations and feeling reactions, revealed that sensations in the back areas were frequently associated with "unpleasant" or "going from, aversion or avoidance" reactions (877). Also, my early observations associated fear, or anxiety, with differential sensations in the lower back (876). In the limited research of this type that employed ten body areas for rating, little *within* the sensation pattern was found to differentiate the "fear" reaction from other patterns except that the lower-right-chest area was comparatively low in occurrence of sensations; however, sensations in that area were only of median occurrence in comparison to reactions in the other situations (878). Nevertheless, when the sensation pattern for this reaction was compared to those of other types of situations, it was very apparent that this reaction was characterized by a comparatively great occurrence of sensations in the back body areas, including the areas of the upper back, the lower back, the calf, and also in the right shoulder; the lower back and calf sensations were the most differentiating. The intensity of sensations with the "fear" reaction was second only to those with the "sexual" reaction, and 68 per cent of the feeling reactions to this given stimulus situation were of the "fear" type.

In my more extensive study of this type, the "fear" stimulus resulted in such feeling-reaction ratings approximately 75 per cent of the time (with the intensity percentages of 73 per cent for the "healthiest" quartile and 87 per cent for the "least healthy" quartile of nonpatient subjects). The following internal-sensation pattern was found: sensations were rated strongly in the right-midriff area (ranking barely first), the central abdomen, and the central chest, with the lower left epigastric area showing only slightly less intensity; the least sensations were rated in the genital-pubic area; the sum percentage of sensations in the back body areas that were rated, namely, the areas of the upper and lower back and the calf, was high compared to the other situations except for those with combined loadings of "significance" and "friendship," and compared to these last feeling reactions, the sensations in the lower back were slightly more prominent in comparison to the upper back in the "fear" situation (879).

SYNTHESIS OF PHYSIOLOGICAL AND SENSORY CHANGES

In attempting a synthesis of internal sensation and physiological findings, consideration should again be given to the concept that the anger type of psychological state is frequently a reaction to the fear type of state, and, of course, clinically even the reverse is frequently encountered. The internal-sensation patterns to be considered for the anger-type reactions include a generally high intensity of sensations over the upper-front-torso areas that extend down even to the central abdominal area, with particular emphasis on the areas of the central chest and right midriff and with a comparative minimum of sensations in the genital-pubic and calf areas. The patterns to be considered for the fear type of reaction include also strong sensations in most of the front-upper-torso areas, but the differential emphasis is on the back body areas, particularly the lower back. This emphasis on the back may be related to the differential finding of diuresis that stems primarily from increased kidney production, with possible secondary bladder effects, during "anxiety," and possibly may be related also to decreased urinary production in a more general stress that probably involves an anger-type, or "emergency," reaction (see p. 249).

Sensation findings concerning the epigastric and abdominal areas may be related to the differential effects of gastric and colonic turgidity and hyper-secretion and to gastric hypermotility and colonic contractility with anger-type reactions as contrasted to the reverse findings for fear-type reactions. In this connection, attention should be paid to the possible role of the duodenum since emotional factors are frequently associated with peptic ulcer and since pain localization from the duodenum is quite accurate (see pp. 226, 305, 313). Also, the types of hyperactivity that occur along the gastro-intestinal tract in anger reactions and the types of gastrointestinal changes in more "pleasant" reactions may produce sensations that would partially account for the shift of the relative emphasis of sensation to the back areas with the fear reaction.

Heart changes have been associated with both reactions, and these changes might account for the sensations experienced in the central-chest area; how-ever, sensations in this area with the anger-type reaction seem to be the more prominent, and a differential finding of increased blood pressure with anger or "struggle" was also noted. It is thus apparent that this attempt at synthesis falls far short of completeness and certainty and that the surface is only scratched in the exploring and understanding of such relationships.

DISGUST

An early study of stomach tonus changes suggested that the state of disgust should be given separate classification (170), and a complex relation-ship of this state with fear, anger, and depression has been suggested by other studies (258, 1344). Wolf observed nausea in feelings of disgust, as well as in "abject fear," but the common denominator of nausea reactions "was a feeling of defeat or of being overwhelmed accompanied by a desire to reject or eject the offending situation" (1344). In settings of disgust or guilt in feelings of rejection, Wolf and Wolff found nausea along with stomach changes that included pallor, inactivity, and diminished acid secre-tion but increased mucus secretion along with increases in salivary flow. These findings seemed to be differentiated from those pertaining to "fear or dejection" in which there occurred decreased flow of saliva and gastric juices and no nausea (1351, 1358), although another study associated nausea specifically with the absence of stomach motility and diminished acid secre-tion but increased mucus output (1343). With this reaction, subjects were seen to complain of distention, gastric fullness, belching, and "dyspepsia" (1358).

During the "state of disgust and repugnance," Gemelli's subjects reported:

"a strange sense of nausea, almost as if it were physically repugnant"; "a moment of repulsion in my whole organism"; "oppression (heaviness, contraction) of the abdomen"; and "tightening of the heart and the whole chest" (433). In a consideration of "tightening of the heart and the whole chest," the sensory findings related to the esophagus should be recalled (see p. 290). It would seem that the state of disgust represents a kind of secondary reaction (distinct from the secondary reaction of anger or the "emergency type") to other feeling states such as the fear type or more particularly the depression or inadequacy type.

DEPRESSION AND INADEQUACY

CONCEPTUAL USAGE

Depression is frequently associated with the failure to express anger type of feelings in other ways, and some experimental evidence supports such a relationship (529). However, clinically depressive feelings are seen not only to stem from the introjection of hostile aggressive impulses (which is most usually the basis of severe clinical depression), but perhaps more frequently from the feeling of loss of love or support, which involves feelings of inadequacy and of longing or yearning. It may be that the two types of clinical depression are basically different; however, it would seem that a *feeling* of depression, inadequacy or yearning, constitutes a differential psychological state.

PHYSIOLOGICAL FINDINGS

Comparatively low electroencephalographic alpha frequencies have been reported for patients with histories of a predominantly depressed type with manic-depressive psychosis, the opposite EEG characteristics being found with predominantly manic patients; however no shift in alpha frequency with changes in the psychotic phase for given patients was found (617).

Mild to moderate depression of preoperative patients was associated with lowered adrenocorticosteroid values (1005a). Sebum over the face has been reported to fall with remorse (1363) or depression (479, 812); however, vasomotor changes with this state have not been clearly differentiated (612). One study associated depression with constriction of arterioles and decreased tone of minute vessels in the forearm (479a). A fall of blood pressure in this state has long been suggested (38) and has been reported as a specific finding (1349, 1358). Similarly, a finding of cardiac hypoactivity, along with a lowered heart rate and lowered cardiac-index values, was reported with "despair and discouragement" (323), and this was seen even in hypertensive subjects when they were "utterly defeated or overwhelmed" (1201).

An increase in neutrophile content has been found, along with hyperfunction and a thick yellowish and purulent nasal secretion, during reactions involving resentment, anxiety, humiliation, and guilt, with the emphasis on the last two features (1358). With this, the mucus membrane became deep red and the turbinates swollen. Hypoglycemia has been reported in sustained "tension-depression" states with a return to normal upon disappearance of the psychic symptom (1030). Similarly, hypoglycemia was reported in patients with an asthenic syndrome including depressive features (24). Blood oxygen levels have been found to be lowered with hypnotically suggested grief states (818). Of 30 bronchial-asthma patients studied, 75 per cent showed evidence of a depressive disorder, and the resting arterial blood oxygen saturation levels of the patients were in the low normal range of 94.5 per cent (817). Also, lengthened clotting time for blood has been observed with feelings of depression (1103, 1104). Bile secretion was said to increase with "sorrow" (321, 1333). When rather specific states of dejection, including feelings of being overwhelmed and sad, occurred with Wolff's patient with a fistula, Tom, there were gastric hypofunction along with pallor of the mucosa, decreased acid secretion, as well as decreased flow of gastric juices, and also decreases in saliva (1351). Such changes have been observed in other subjects (871, 1348, 1358).

In a study by Grace, Wolf, and Wolff, a subject with "a period of low spirits, dejection and mild depression lasting four weeks" was seen to have a "monotonously constant" appearance of the colon, which remained motionless and showed decreased color varying little from day to day (476). In general, there was a finding that "abject fear and dejection" were associated with hypofunction, pallor, relaxation, lack of contractile activity and relatively low concentration of lysozyme in the colonic secretion. Other authors have reported similar findings (33, 34, 1360, 1362), and throughout most of the studies the emphasis has been on "overwhelming" and depressive states in association with colonic hypofunctioning. Diarrhea was also seen as an aspect of a defense reaction in such a state (34). These facts support other evidence suggesting that functional depression may be a primary factor in patients with anorexia nervosa, and that such patients should be considered "emotionally starved" as well as physically starved (1299).

Vesical hypofunction with retention of urine and a large bladder capacity have been found with "hysterical reactions and reactions of being overwhelmed," in contrast to the reverse findings with "anxiety and resentment"

(1213). Also, a report has been noted of a subject who failed to show diuresis when "depressed and angered" as compared to other subjects with feelings of anxiety (569). Other subjects, in contrast to the diuresis of anxiety, showed increased ketonemia with feelings of "anger, dejection, and loneliness," and this was especially pronounced with diabetes-mellitus patients (576). Some indications of a relationship between depression (91) and the suppression of emotion (24, 568) to the changes in blood glucose have also been suggested. Other subjects, feeling "overwhelmed and dejected," were seen to have decreased color of the labial mucosa, and vaginal secretion was minimal (1358).

INTERNAL SENSORY PERCEPTION

The occurrence of the following sensations or symptoms in studies that involved various feeling states, including guilt and "humiliation," among others, have already been discussed: backache (595), dyspnea, and palpitation (1342). Altschule noted that a "heavy sensation" associated with sadness is commonly experienced around the heart (38). In regard to the subject with the gastric fistula, Tom, the relationship to dejection was reported as follows: "Dejection: Other emotions besides fear which imply a feeling of being overwhelmed and dejected, may be accompanied by anorexia, 'sinking in the stomach' and 'nausea'" (1351). Also under such depressive circumstances, there was a reported sensation of feeling "funny— full." Elsewhere, nausea was seen to accompany "despondency and feelings of dejection from whatever cause" (1344).

With states of sadness and depression, Gemilli's subjects reported that grief translated "into a steady pain in my whole chest. I felt my eyes wet"; "my breathing became irregular and I had a sharp pain in the chest" (433).

In my own internal-sensation study already cited, which included all body areas, one subject reported sensations in the combined central-chest and epigastric area, along with sensations in the frontal head area, as being associated with "embarrassment . . . including feelings of insecurity" (877). I also early associated comparatively prominent sensations in the lower abdominal area with a depressive feeling called "yearning" (876, 877).

In my first limited study that rated ten body areas, it was seen that although 70 per cent of the reactions were of a "depression" feeling for the given situation, the sensations reported were of comparatively low intensity and revealed little variation among the different body areas (878). In my more extensive study of this type, a given situation resulted in a "mixed feeling" reaction that included approximately 44 per cent of the reactions of the "depression" or "inadequacy" type (the intensity percentages being 48 per cent for the "healthiest" quartile and 37 per cent for the "least healthy" quartile of nonpatients), 19 per cent "significance" and 12 per cent "friendliness" reactions (879). The occurrence of sensations with this stimulus was lowest for the experimental situations; however, the following internal-sensation pattern was found: the more prominent sensation ratings were spread over the areas of the central chest, the lower left epigastrium, the right midriff, and the central abdomen, with the central-chest area ranking first and with high percentages of ratings for all of these areas compared to the other situations, as was also the case for the lower-left-chest area; the central abdominal area was given the greatest percentage of ratings compared to the other situations; the calf and genital-pubic areas ranked lowest in occurrence of sensation, and, along with the back areas were given a low percentage of ratings compared to the other situations.

FATIGUE

CONCEPTS AND MECHANISMS

Some question has been raised concerning the semantics of the term "fatigue" (361). There can be little doubt about the existence of such a psychological state, but in some usages it would seem to refer to a type of sensation. There is relatively little in the literature concerning this state that has such important daily effects on all people. Wolf and Wolff reported that the fatigue experienced by patients was a "complex state dependent upon emotional attitudes, the absence of dominant motivation and the presence of a stress-producing life situation with accompanying inefficiency of cardio-vascular and respiratory functions" (1342).

From a neurophysiological standpoint, evidence has been presented suggesting that fatigue involves an "over-balanced catelectrotonic change" of the neural synaptic membrane, though the exact mechanics involved in the producing of such a condition in daily living are not known (963). In supporting an emphasis on the central fatigue factor, Schwab and de Lorme called attention to great individual and personality differences in fatigue reactions, as well as the great variability of fatigue depending on motivation and relaxation of a given individual (1113). Schwab and de Lorme found that subjects failed to experience any sense of general fatigue even though muscle groups were completely exhausted as indicated by ergogram readings. From a study of 65 normal subjects, 25 patients with Parkinson's disease, 50 patients with neurological conditions such as poliomyelitis, arthritis, and dystrophy, and 40 patients without structural disease but with symptoms of chronic fatigue and nervousness, Schwab concluded that fatigue in the neurological cases may arise from conditions in the muscle, the endplate, or the peripheral nerve, but that for the patient with chronic fatigue of nonneurological, nondisease nature, the source lies in the brain.

GENERAL PHYSIOLOGICAL CHANGES

Altschule stated that impaired carbohydrate metabolism leads to inefficient muscular performance in fatigue states and in neurocirculatory asthenia, which is the condition in which fatigue is a primary symptom (38). Fatigue has been seen to be the central feature of the hypoglycemic syndrome, but fatigue is also paramount in so-called neurasthenic (or neurocirculatory-asthenia) patients, who ordinarily show normal blood sugar (25, 1228). These patients, however, show a flat sugar tolerance curve, indicating an inability to raise the sugar concentration of the blood in the manner that normal persons can in response to the artificial intake of sugar and carbohydrate or in response to emotional reactivity (25, 1228). Similar findings were cited in the previous section of this book regarding so-called "tension-depression" and hypoglycemic-fatigue syndromes, wherein the glucose metabolism returned to normal upon remission of the psychical symptoms (25, 1030). Patients with the functional-cardiovascular-disease syndrome, a classification that includes neurocirculatory asthenia, show "characteristic" mental and physical fatigue, and Friedman stated that mental fatigue is probably a "result of disquietude of the personality" whereas physical fatigue is a result of the inefficiency of muscular activity of these patients (392, 393). Other writers have reported that individual differences in the fatigability of pilots are correlated with the secretion of hormones from the adrenal cortex (995.)

In my early feeling-reaction study, one subject and I noted that differential sensations associated with states of fatigue occurred in the upper-middle-back area (Area No. 22); and in my more extensive study two subjects listed "tired" sensations in the upper back and the right shoulder, respectively (877).

HUNGER AND THIRST

CONCEPTUAL USAGES

Again the semantic problem of classifying an experience as a sensation or as a feeling state is presented, and, again, it would seem that either might be used depending on the reference, since certain sensations have differential connotation in so far as these experiences are concerned. Analogous to this, it is also on the basis of the fact that sensations in given body areas may have consistent associations with given psychological states, or "feelings," that differential awareness of sensations may be meaningful in regard to the identifying of the feeling states that have just been presented.

THIRST

The "sensation" of thirst is related primarily to sensations of dryness arising locally in the mouth and throat (138), but it is necessary to distinguish between the sensation of thirst and the desire for liquid (821). Factors other than local conditions in the throat contribute to the feeling of thirst or to the desire to drink, as, for example, habit or symbolical associations. The sensations of dryness in the mouth and throat may be induced during periods of fear or excitement, at which time, among other things, there is said to be reduced salivation.

Morgan has summarized the theoretical and experimental evidence (928) showing that the experience of thirst depends upon buccal dryness (194), habit (97), and water deprivation (10, 11, 12, 97); water deprivation is in part an aspect of the functioning of the posterior lobe of the crucial pituitary gland that secretes an antidiuretic hormone (1040, 1041). At a given time, any one of these factors may not result in thirst, in animals at least (97, 274, 456); the most general factor affecting thirst over a period of time appears to be the water balance of the body (86, 97).

NEURAL FINDINGS

Several specific afferent neural tracts relating to thirst and hunger have been delineated, primarily by means of animal experimentation. Important for hunger sensations are afferent vagal impulses that reach the orbital surface of the frontal lobes (58, 426). Water-metabolism changes of the tissues result in excitation of the supra-optic nuclei (1271) and of the cortex via central thalamic nuclei (426, 536). Also, bilateral lesions on the ventromedial nucleus of the hypothalamus result in cessation of eating (41) to the point of death (426); conversely, destruction of the ventromedial nuclei leads to hyperphagia and obesity (153, 426).

Modification of food intake by means of electrical stimulation of localized areas of the hypothalamus has been reported (288). Also, two hypothalamic mechanisms for the regulating of appetite have been postulated, including a "satiety" center that was localized medially and seemed to inhibit a "feeding" center (152). The "feeding" center was localized laterally, and the possibility that alimentary sensations and metabolic factors influence these "centers" was suggested.

HUNGER MECHANISMS IN GENERAL

In the case of hunger, the relationships involved are somewhat analogous to those for thirst. Hunger pangs recur rhythmically with considerable regularity, and hunger sensations have been described as: "a very disagreeable ache or pang or sense of gnawing just below the tip of the breast bone" (194); "a general sensation of weakness and malaise in the body as a whole and a local sensation of emptiness in the abdomen"; and, with eating, "the sensation of emptiness in the upper part of the abdomen gradually disappears and if the meal is large enough is gradually succeeded by a feeling of fullness" (556). Hunger pangs have also been reported to be generally cramping, intermittent, lasting 10 to 40 seconds, deep, and moderately intense (1363). Complex and detailed descriptions involving these and other secondary sensations were reported in early investigations (138).

At one time it was thought that the experience of hunger related directly to stomach contractions since they occur with hunger and can be consciously perceived (200, 204, 205, 976); however, it is now apparent that other factors are also involved, such as habit (586, 928, 1268) and metabolic needs (928, 1063a). Morgan (929) and Ruch (1068) believed that these local contractions remain the sensory basis of the experience of hunger, although some others have questioned it (258). Concerning this experience, Cannon distinguished between "appetite" and "hunger," and regarded "appetite" as learned (194, 200). There are studies, however, that suggest the occurrence of apparently normal hunger after bilateral transthoracic vagotomy and extensive thoracic sympathectomy, resulting in gastric hypomotility, and also in the absence of the stomach itself in man (586). It was noted that increased somatic activity (1039, 1274), as well as the stomach contractions (1274) and gastric secretions (974), generally precede eating.

These findings led Morgan to hypothesize that such functions are governed by a common physiological factor in which the origin of hunger is based in some way on physiological need (928). Much experimentation has been accomplished in regard to chemical and hormonal factors in hunger. Morgan listed at least eleven specific physiological hungers, using motivational direction as criteria: carbohydrates (sugar), fat, proteins, thiamine, riboflavin, oxygen, salt, phosphorus, sodium, calcium, and water (928), but the question of exactly how these hungers function remains. It has been suggested by Richter and Young that a metabolic need may act specifically in lowering the threshold of "olfactory" and gustatory receptors (928). Also, Morgan demonstrated that various results have been obtained in the experimental correlation of the blood sugar level with gastric motility and hunger. Many of these studies, however, have overlooked or have been unable to control many of the other factors involved in hunger (544).

OTHER PHYSIOLOGICAL FINDINGS WITH HUNGER

Several studies have revealed that with hunger or preparedness to eat, there are reactions in the colon. Hertz described a "gastrocolic reflex" in which the taking of food into the stomach is followed by an increase in the rate of passage of ileal contents into the colon (476, 557, 696); however, this has often failed to occur when food was administered directly into the stomach by tube (476). Direct observation of the ascending, descending, and sigmoid colon sections with food ingestion have revealed hyperfunction that included increased blood flow with blushing of the mucosa, vigorous and frequent contractions, increased secretion with slightly increased lysozyme concentration, and slight contraction (476). In one case the engorgement was preceded by transitory blanching (395). The suggestion of food has induced defecation in a subject with an incompetent rectal sphincter (40); however, the effects described with ingestion have failed to occur under circumstances of depressive feelings (32, 409, 476). Suggestion of pleasant drinks and food has been observed directly to increase the rate of urine production in the kidney (44).

FEELING REACTIONS

Starvation studies revealed that the threshold for the feeling of hunger may be altered by various circumstances and that the felt need for nutrition is most fundamental in internal perception, taking precedence over sexual and social interests and producing marked cognitive and perceptual alterations (89, 161, 162, 367, 642a, 700, 905). Depressive feeling states, irritability, apathy, and neurotic tendencies were also found to follow in the wake of starvation (89, 161, 162, 367).

As noted in the preceding sections of this book, a lack of appetite may be associated with the presence of certain feeling states, especially depressive types; on the other hand, overeating appeared to result most frequently from a subjective "hunger" that was related to psychological, and, particularly, affective, needs (154, 186, 1299). Brosin has delineated four types of factors to which overeating responses may occur: a response to nonspecific emotional tensions; a substitute gratification in intolerable life situations; a symptom of underlying emotional illness; and an addiction to food (154). Also, emotional associations with certain foods may result in various food allergies, with the reaction to a given food at a given time depending on the emotional state of the individual (681). The following psychogenic states associated with food allergies have been reported by Kaufman: anger, anxiety, anorexia, depression, euphoria, feelings of security, guilt, hostility, passive-dependent attitudes, pleasure, syncope, and relaxation (681). He described the most common untoward idiosyncratic psychosomatic reactions to food to include nausea, vomiting, epigastric discomfort or pain, intestinal cramps, aerophagia, belching, and rarely, diarrhea, and considered them to relate to a riddance reaction.

CHAPTER 21

Differential Perception of Sensations

for Different Psychological States

Sufficient data have not yet been collected to justify detailed elaboration on the differential aspect of the sensation patterns that occur with different psychological states. Nevertheless, internal sensations can be meaningful in this respect only in so far as the relative perception of them is related by the individual to other life experiences. It was by the differential comparison, over a period of time, of only the more *relatively* prominent areas of internal sensation, both quantitatively and qualitatively, in different types of feeling states that I first became aware of some meaningful consistency in them (876). This is somewhat different from just the quantitative analyzing of different body areas at a given time, as was done in most of my internal-sensation studies (877, 878, 879); however, the results of the differential comparisons from these various studies were found to be generally similar to the sensation patterns originally noted by me.

One important factor in these various internal-sensation observations became apparent in the comparing of earlier and later findings, namely, the importance of the dimension of intensity in the ascertaining of differential internal-sensation patterns. The early observations were made by methodical projections into different types of remembered life situations, and the intensity of feeling experiences in this atmosphere of critical introspection was moderate. Casual observation in relatively intense real-life situations revealed additional differential characteristics that have not yet been analyzed in detail. For example, with strong "love" feelings, apparent heart sensations are very prominent, as are (seemingly) alimentary sensations and other sensations throughout the chest that accompany marked respiratory changes. Similarly, comparatively strong feelings of "significance" (or "importance"), when uncomplicated by the other feeling states, result in comparatively prominent sensations in the upper-back, neck, and shoulder areas, and also in the whole upper trunk. Still, another distinction can be made qualitatively for a state similar to "significance" that possibly involves an element of "awe" (and that is a rare experience for me). In this "awe" type of reaction, "wavelike" sensations seem to travel over superficial areas of parts (or even all) of the body, particularly the back areas.

The differential areas of relative quantitative perception that were emphasized in the findings presented in the preceding chapter with the major types of feeling reactions listed include: (*i*) for "significance," the upper-back area (Area No. 21); (*ii*) for "love," the central-chest area (Area No. 6) and the lower left epigastric area (Area No. 10) with secondary relative prominence in the genital-pubic and lower-back areas; (*iii*) for "sexual," the genital-pubic area and the "central" or lower abdominal areas, extending around to the lower-back areas, with secondary prominence in the lower left epigastric area; (*iv*) for "anger," a "spread" of sensations over the upper-front-torso areas, extending down even to the central abdomen but with particular emphasis on the central-chest and (right) midriff areas; (*v*) for "fear," the back body areas, particularly the lower back; (*vi*) for "depression-inadequacy," possibly the areas of the central or lower abdomen; (*vii*) for "disgust," nausea apparently along the upper alimentary canal and especially in the esophagus; (*viii*) for "thirst," dryness of the mouth and throat; and (*ix*) for "hunger," "empty" sensations in the epigastrium.

CHAPTER 22

Conclusions and Implications

The first part of this work was designed to present a somewhat "new" approach to the understanding of inner experience and to the conceptualization of personality dynamics and classification. In connection with this, a review was made of the ways in which other experimenters have conceptualized and studied that aspect, or sphere, of human experience designated as noncognitive internal perception. The last parts were designed to review medical, physiological, and psychological literature for the purpose of investigating the bases, or correlates, of internal perceptive experience and for the purpose of suggesting possible differential physiological and sensory functions with different psychological states.

As has been seen, the material available relevant to this undertaking is immense. Nevertheless, progress in these areas of study is still in an early stage of development, and, consequently, precise formulations of the relationships involved are not possible at this time. Enough data are available, however, to provide bases for more advanced experimental investigations that may relate psychological states and internal perceptions to physiological functioning. Similarly, the time is ripe for the further development of devices and techniques of physiological measurement that may more approximately identify differential psychological states and possibly also aid in personality classification. The study of internal sensations has been shown to be relevant to such undertakings.

The primary contribution was meant to be a presentation of a perspective for the considering of individual psychological functioning, placing emphasis on individual perception orientations that include relative degrees of external, cognitive, and noncognitive internal perceptive experiences. This perspective can can also be employed in the establishing of a classification of personality types (see p. 52). Particularly, an attempt has been made to direct more specific and *conscious* awareness toward the differentiating of noncognitive internal perceptive states (or psychological states). The most immediate problems that are presented in the study of such states are to identify them differentially and then to communicate them. Methods have been suggested whereby such identification and consensual classification might be established by the use of physiological measurements or reports, or both, of internal sensations (see pp. 16, 353). The ability scientifically to identify and consistently to differentiate and communicate psychological states of the human individual appears to be necessary for the ultimate progress of the social sciences generally (see p. 21). Also, the ability of the individual to permit *immediate awareness* of such noncognitive internal perceptions appears to be necessary for healthy psychological adjustment (see p. 37).

When human values are considered as ultimately having a major basis in the internal perceptive experience of each person, an increased awareness of this area of individual experience implies a more adequate adjustment on the part of all persons. Thus, goals, strivings, and interpersonal relationships can be better directed and gauged by a more realistic awareness of human needs and internal states. Finally, it should be considered, both for each person and for society, that values, goals, and behavior that can be based more on understanding and awareness of the differential aspects of internal experience might be more worth while, effective, and harmonious than those of the present, which are based to a large degree on traditions that emphasize external sensory experiences and cognitive processes.

BIBLIOGRAPHY

1. Aberle, S. D. & Corner, G. W. *Twenty-five Years of Sex Research; History of the National Research Council Committee for Research in Problems of Sex, 1922-1947.* Philadelphia: Saunders, 1953.
2. Abraham, K. *Selected Papers on Psychoanalysis.* London: Hogarth Press, 1927.
3. Abramson, D. I. & Ferris, E. B., Jr. Response of Blood Vessels in the Resting Hand and Forearm to Various Stimuli. *Am. Heart J.,* 1940, 19, 541-553.
4. Ackerly, S. Prefrontal Lobes and Social Development. *Yale J. Biol & Med.,* 1950, 22, 471-482.
5. Adams, D. F. *Cabot and Adams Physical Diagnosis,* 13th ed., Baltimore: Williams and Wilkins, 1942.
6. Adler, A. *The Neurotic Constitution.* New York: Moffat, Yard, 1917.
7. Adler, A. *A Study of Organ Inferiority and Its Psychical Compensation.* New York: Nerv. Ment. Dis. Mon. No. 24, 1917.
8. Adler, A. *Understanding Human Nature.* New York: Greenberg, 1927.
9. Adler, H. M. & Larson, J. A. Deception and Self-Deception. *J. Abnorm. Soc. Psychol.,* 1924, 22, 364-371.
10. Adolph, E. F. Rates of Adjustment of Body Water Content. *Science,* 1937, 86, 22-37.
11. Adolph, E. F. Measurement of Water Drinking in Dogs. *Am. J. Physiol.,* 1939, 125, 75-86.
12. Adolph, E. F. The Internal Environment and Behavior. *Am. J. Psychiat.,* 1941, 97, 1365-1373.
13. Adrian, E. D. Potential Changes in the Isolated Nervous System of the Dysticus Marginalis. *J. Physiol.,* 1931, 72, 132-151.
14. Adrian, E. D. & Buytendijk, F. J. J. Potential Changes in the Isolated Brainstem of the Goldfish. *J. Physiol.,* 1931, 71, 121-135.
15. Adrian, E. D. & Mathews, B. H. C. The Berger Rhythm, Potential Changes From the Occipital Lobes in Man. *Brain,* 1934, 355-384.
16. Adrian, E. D. & Yamagiwa, K. The Origin of the Berger Rhythm. *Brain,* 1935, 58, 323-351.
17. Agerberg, J. The Emotional Reactions and their Physiological Mechanisms. *Acta Pyschiat.,* 1052, 80, 143-148.
18. Alexander, F. The Influence of Psychologic Factors upon Gastrointestinal Disturbances, a Symposium. *Psychoanal. Quart.,* 1934, 3, 501-539.
19. Alexander, F. Fundamental Concepts of Psychosomatic Research: Psychosomatic Research: Psychogenesis, Conversion, Specificity. *Psychosom. Med.,* 1943, 3, 205-210.

403

20. Alexander, F. Treatment of a Case of Peptic Ulcer and Personality Disorder. *Psychosom. Med.,* 1947, 9, 321-330.

21. Alexander, F. *Psychosomatic Medicine.* New York: Norton, 1950.

22. Alexander, F., Bacon, C., Wilson, G., Levey, H. B. & Levine, M. The Influence of Psychologic Factors upon Gastro-intestinal Disturbances. *Psychoanal. Quart.,* 1934, 3, 501-539.

23. Alexander, F. & French, T. M. *Psychoanalytic Therapy.* New York: Ronald Press, 1946.

24. Alexander, F. & Portis, S. A. A Psychosomatic Study of Hypo-glycaemic Fatigue. *Psychosom. Med.,* 1944, 6, 191-206.

25. Alexander, J., Macleod, A. G. & Barker, P. S. Sensibility of the Exposed Human Heart and Pericardium. *Arch. Surg.,* 1929, 19, 1470-1483.

26. Alford, L. B. Localization of Consciousness and Emotion. *Am. J. Psychiat.,* 1933, 12, 789-799.

27. Alkan, L. *Anatomische Organkrankheiten aus seelischer Ursache.* Stuttgart: Hippokrates, 1930.

28. Allison, H. W. & Allison, S. J. Personality Changes Following Transorbital Lobotomy. *J. Abnorm. Soc. Psychol.,* 1954, 49, 219-223.

29. Allport, F. H. *Theories of Perception and Concept of Structure.* New York: John Wiley, 1955.

30. Allport, G. W. *Personality: A Psychological Interpretation.* New York: Henry Holt, 1937.

31. Allport, G. W. The Trend of Motivational Theory. *Am. J. Orthopsychiat.,* 1953, 23, 107-119.

32. Almy, T. P. Experimental Studies on the Irritable Colon. *Am. J. Med.,* 1951, 10, 60-67.

33. Almy, T. P., Hinckle, L. E., Jr., Berle, B. & Kern, F., Jr. Alterations in Colonic Function in Man under Stress. III, Experimental Production of Sigmoid Spasms in Patient with Spastic Constipation. *J. Gastroenterol.,* 1949, 12, 437-449.

34. Almy, T. P., Kern, F., Jr. & Abbot, F. K. Constipation and Diarrhea as Reactions to Life Stress. *Proc. Assn. Res. Nerv. Ment. Dis.,* 1949, 29, 724-731.

35. Almy, T. P., Kern, F., & Tulin, M. Alterations in Colonic Function in Man under Stress. *J. Gastroenterol.,* 1949, 12, 425-436.

36. Almy, T. P. & Tulin, M. Alterations in Colonic Function in Man Under Stress: Experimental Production of Changes Simulating the "Irritable Colon." *J. Gastroenterol.,* 1947, 8, 616-626.

37. Alpers, B. J. Personality and Emotional Disorders Associated with Hypothalamic Lesions. *Proc. Assn. Res. Nerv. Ment. Dis.,* 1940, 20, 725-752.

38. Altschule, M. D. *Bodily Physiology in Mental and Emotional Disorders.* New York: Grune & Stratton, 1953.

39. Alvarez, W. C. *Nervousness, Indigestion and Pain.* New York: Paul B. Hoeber, 1943.

40. Alvarez, W. C. *An Introduction to Gastroenterology.* New York: Paul B. Hoeber, 1948.

41. Anand, B. K. & Brobeck, J. R. Localization of a "Feeding Center" in the Hypothalamus of the Rat. *Proc. Soc. Exp. Biol. Med.,* 1951, 77, 323-324.

41a. Anand, B. K. & Dua, S. Circulatory and Respiratory Changes Induced by Electrical Stimulation of Limbic System (Visceral Brain). *J. Neurophysiol.,* 1956, 19, 393-400.

42. Anderson, H. N. & Anderson, G. S. (Eds.). *An Introduction to Projective Techniques.* New York: Prentice-Hall, 1951.

43. Anderson, J. E. Changes in Emotional Responses with Age. In: Reymert (1033), pp. 418-428.
44. Anderson, M. Diuresis by Suggestion. *Brit. Med. J.,* 1946, 1, 776.
45. Andrews, H. L. Skin Resistance Changes and Measurements of Pain Threshold. *J. Clin. Invest.,* 1943, 22, 517-520.
46. Angell, J. R. The Relation of Structural and Functional Psychology to Philosophy. *Univ. Chicago Decennial Publ.,* Section I, 1903, 3, 55-73. Also in *Philos. Rev.,* 1903, 12, 243-271.
47. Angell, J. R. *Psychology, an Introductory Study of the Structure and Function of Human Consciousness.* New York: Henry Holt, 1904.
48. Angell, J. R. The Province of Functional Psychology. *Psychol. Rev.,* 1907, 14, 61-91.
49. Angell, J. R. & Thompson, H. B. A Study of the Relations between Certain Organic Processes and Consciousness. *Psychol. Rev.,* 1899, 6, 32-69.
50. Appel, J. & Rosen, S. R. Psychotic Factors in Psychosomatic Illness. *Psychosom. Med.,* 1950, 12, 236-243.
51. Arlow, J. A. Identification Mechanism in Coronary Occlusion. *Psychosom. Med.,* 1945, 7, 195-209.
52. Arnold, M. B. Physiological Differentiation of Emotional States. *Psychol. Rev.,* 1945, 52, 35-48.
53. Arnold, M. B. An Excitatory Theory of Emotion. In: Reymert (1033), pp. 11-33.
53a. Arnold, M. B. The Status of Emotion in Contemporary Psychology. In: Roback (1046a), pp. 135-188.
54. Arnold, M. B. & Gosson, J. A. *The Human Person, an Approach to an Integral Theory of Personality.* New York: Ronald Press, 1954.
55. Ax, A. F. The Physiological Differentiation between Fear and Anger in Humans. *Psychosom. Med.,* 1953, 15, 433-442.
56. Babkin, B. P. The Cerebral Cortex and Gastric Motility. *J. Gastroenterol.,* 1950, 14, 479-484.
56a. Badal, D. W. Psychiatric Observations in Neurocirculatory Asthenia. *J. Am. Med. Assn.,* 1954, 154, 1054-1058.
57. Bagchi, A. Fundamentals of Feelings and Emotions in Indian Psychology. *Indian J. Psychol.,* 1952, 27, 91-108.
57a. Bagchi, A. Feelings and Emotion in Indian Psychology. *Indian J. Psychol.,* 1953, 28, 87-102.
58. Bailey, P. & Bremer, F. A Sensory Cortical Representation of the Vagus Nerve. *J. Neurophysiol.,* 1938, 1, 400-412.
59. Bakan, D. A Reconsideration of the Problem of Introspection. *Psychol. Bull.,* 1954, 51, 105-118.
60. Baker, D. M. Sighing Respiration as a Symptom. *Lancet,* 1934, 1, 174-177.
61. Baker, L. M. & Taylor, W. M. An Apparatus for recording Changes in Skin-Temperature. *Am. J. Psychol.,* 1953, 66, 124-125.
62. Baldwin, A. L. Cattell's *An Introduction to Personality Study. Psychol. Bull.,* 1952, 49, 90-92.
63. Bandler, B., Kaufman, C. & Dykens, J. W. Pregnancy Fantasies, Transference and Seizures in a Case of Epilepsy. *J. Nerv. Ment. Dis.,* 1953, 118, 376-378.
64. Banting, F. G. & Hall, G. F. Experimental Production of Myocardial and Coronary Artery Lesions. *Tr. Am. Phys.,* 1937, 52, 204-209.
65. Barcroft, H. & Konzett, H. On the Actions of Noradrenaline, Adrenaline and Isopropyl Noradrenaline on the Arterial Blood Pressure, Heart Rate and Muscle Blood Flow in Man. *J. Physiol.,* 1949, 110, 194-204.

66. Barcroft, J. *The Brain and Its Environment.* New Haven: Yale University Press, 1938.
67. Bard, P. Diencephalic Mechanism for the Expression of Rage. *Am. J. Physiol.,* 1928, 84, 490-515.
68. Bard, P. The Neuro-humoral Basis of Emotional Reactions. In: Murchison (940aa).
69. Bard, P. On Emotional Expression After Decortication with Some Remarks on Certain Theoretical Views, Parts I and II. *Psychol. Rev.,* 1934, 41, 309-329; 424-449.
70. Bard, P. Neural Mechanisms in Emotional and Sexual Behavior. *Psychosom. Med.,* 1942, 4, 171-172.
71. Bard, P. Central Nervous Mechanisms for the Expression of Anger in Animals. In: Reymert (1033), pp. 211-237.
72. Bard, P. & Mountcastle, V. B. Some Forebrain Mechanisms Involved in Expression of Rage with Special Reference to Suppression of Angry Behavior. *Proc. Assn. Res. Nerv. Ment. Dis.,* 1947, 27, 362-404.
73. Bard, P. & Rioch, D. M. A Study of Four Cats Deprived of Neocortex and Additional Portions of the Forebrain. *Johns Hopkins Hosp. Bull.,* 1937, 60, 73-147.
74. Barker, W. The Petit Mal Attack as a Response Within the Central Nervous System to Distress in Organism-Environment Integration. *Psychosom. Med.,* 1948, 10, 73-94.
75. Barker, W. Personality Pattern Situational Stress, and the Symptoms of Narcolepsy. *Psychosom. Med.,* 1948, 10, 193-202.
76. Barker, W. Brain Waves and Behavior. Unpublished.
77. Barker, W. & Barker, S. Experimental Production of Human Convulsive Brain Potentials by Stress-Induced Effects upon Neural Integrative Function, Dynamics of the Convulsive Reaction to Stress. *Proc. Assn. Res. Nerv. Ment. Dis.,* 1949, 29, 90-113.
78. Barker, W., Burgmin, S. & Simons, D. J. The Significance of "Spontaneous" Abnormalities in the Brain Wave Pattern as Observed During Interviews with Epileptic Patients. *J. Nerv. Ment. Dis.,* 1950, 112, 187-205.
79. Barker, W. & Wolf, S. Experimental Induction of Grand Mal Seizure During the Hypnoidal State Induced by Sodium Amytal. *Am. J. Med. Sci.,* 1947, 214, 600-604.
80. Barris, R. W. Cataleptic Symptoms Following Bilateral Cortical Lesions in Cats. *Am. J. Physiol.,* 1937, 119, 213-220.
81. Bartley, S. H. & Bishop, G. H. The Cortical Responses to Stimulation of the Optic Nerve in the Rabbit. *Am. J. Physiol.,* 1933, 103, 159-172.
82. Bateman, J. F. & Papez, J. W. Significance of the Thalamus in Psychoses. *J. Clin. Exp. Psychopath.,* 1951, 12, 89-103.
83. Bateson, G. Cultural Determinants of Personality. In: Hunt (610) Vol. 2, 714-735.
84. Bayley, N. A Study of Fear by Means of the Psychogalvanic Technique. *Psychol. Mon.,* 1928, 38, 1-38.
85. Bayley, N. A Study of Crying in Infants During Mental and Physical Tests. *J. Genet. Psychol.,* 1932, 40, 306-329.
86. Beach, F. A. A Review of Physiological and Psychological Studies of Sexual Behavior in Mammals. *Physiol. Rev.,* 1947, 27, 240-307.
87. Beach, F. A. Evolutionary Changes in the Physiological Control of Mating Behavior in Mammals. *Psychol. Rev.,* 1947, 54, 297-315.
88. Beach, F. A. *Hormones and Behavior.* New York: Paul B. Hoeber, 1948.

89. Beach, F. A. Body Chemistry and Perception. In: Blake & Ramsey (125), pp. 56-94.
90. Bearn, A. G., Billing, B., Edholdm, O. G. & Sherlock, S. Hepatic Blood Flow and Carbohydrate Changes in Man During Fainting. *P. Physiol.*, 1951, 115, 442-455.
91. Beattie, J., Brace, G. R. & Lang, C. N. H. The Hypothalamus and the Sympathetic Nervous System. *Proc. Assn. Res. Nerv. Ment. Dis.*, 1930, 9, 249-316.
92. Beaumont, W. *Experiments and Observations on the Gastric Juices and the Physiology of Digestion.* Plattsburg: F. P. Allen, 1833.
93. Beck, S. J. *Rorschach's Test.* 2 vols. New York: Grune & Stratton, 1945.
94. Beck, S. J. Emotional Experience as a Necessary Constituent in Knowing. In: Reymert (1033), pp. 95-107.
95. Beebe-Center, J. G. *The Psychology of Pleasantness and Unpleasantness.* New York: D. Van Nostrand, 1932.
95a. Beecher, H. K. Perception of Pain and Some Factors that Modify It. In: H. A. Abramson, ed., *Problems of Consciousness.* New York: Josiah Macy, Jr. Foundation, 1951, pp. 89-122.
96. Bell, J. E. *Projective Techniques.* New York: Longmans, Green, 1948.
97. Bellows, R. T. Time Factors in Water Drinking in Dogs. *Am. J. Physiol.*, 1939, 125, 87-97.
98. Bender, M. B. Fright and Drug Contractions in Denervated Facial and Ocular Muscles of Monkeys. *Am. J. Physiol.*, 1938, 121, 609-619.
99. Benedek, T. *Studies in Psychosomatic Medicine: Psychosexual Functions in Women.* New York: Ronald Press, 1952.
100. Benedek, T. & Rubenstein, B.B. The Correlations between Ovarian Activity and Psychodynamic Processes: I. The Ovulative Phase. *Psychosom. Med.*, 1939, 2, 245-270.
101. Benedict, R. *Patterns of Culture.* Boston: Houghton Mifflin, 1934.
102. Benedict, R. Continuities and Discontinuities in Cultural Conditioning. *Psychiatry*, 1938, 1, 161-167.
103. Beneke, F. W. *Die anatomischen Grundlagen der Konstitutionsanomalien des Menschen.* Marburg: N. G. Elwert, 1878.
104. Benussi, V. Die Atmungssymptome der Lüge. *Arch. Ges. Psychol.*, 1914, 31, 244-283.
105. Berger, H. Über das Elektroenzephalogramm des Menschen, I. *Arch. Psychiat. Nervenkr.*, 1929, 87, 527-570.
106. Berger, H. Über das Elektroenzephalogramm des Menschen, III. *Arch. Psychiat. Nervenkr.*, 1931, 94, 16-60.
107. Berger, H. Über das Elektroenzephalogramm des Menschen, IV. *Arch. Psychiat. Nervenkr.*, 1932, 97, 6-26.
108. Berger, H. Über das Elektroenzephalogramm des Menschen, VI. *Arch. Psychiat. Nervenkr.*, 1933, 99, 555-574.
109. Berger, H. Über das Elektroenzephalogramm des Menschen, XII. *Arch. Psychiat. Nervenkr.*, 1937, 106, 165-187.
110. Berger, H. Über das Elektroenzephalogramm des Menschen, XIV. *Arch. Psychiat. Nervenkr.*, 1938, 108, 407-431.
111. Bergler, E. Some Atypical Forms of Impotence and Frigidity. *Psychoanal. Rev.*, 1954, 41, 29-47.
112. Bergmann, G. Theoretical Psychology. *Ann. Rev. Psychol.*, 1953, 4, 435-458.
113. Bernard, C. *Leçons sur les Propriétés physiologiques et les Altérations pathologiques des Liquides de l'Organisme.* 2 vols. Paris: Ballière, 1859.

114. Bernard, C. *An Introduction to the Study of Experimental Medicine.* New York: Macmillan, 1927.
114a. Bernstein, I. C. Psychosomatic Problems in Obstetrics and Gynecology. *Lancet,* 1955, 75, 278-283.
115. Berrien, F. K. Finger Oscillations as Indices of Emotion. *J. Exp. Psychol.,* 1939, 24, 485-498.
116. Bertalanffy, L., van. *Modern Theories of Development.* New York: Oxford University Press, 1933.
117. Bickford, R. G. The Mechanism of Local Sweating in Response to Faradism. *Clin. Sci.,* 1938, 3, 337-341.
118. Binet, A. & Courtier, J. Travaux du Laboratoire de Psychologie de Paris. *L'Année Psychol.,* 1895, 2, 87-254.
119. Binet, A. & Courtier, J. Influence de la Vie émotionnelle sur le Cœur, la Respiration et la Circulation capillaire. *L'Année Psychol.,* 1897, 3, 65-126.
120. Bingham, J. R., Ingelfinger, F. J. & Smithwick R. H. Effect of Combined Sympathectomy and Vagectomy on the Gastrointestinal Tract. *J. Am. Med. Assn.,* 1951, 146, 1406-1408.
121. Bingham, W. E., Jr. Electromagnetic and Electrostatic Fields, a Neglected Area in Physiological Psychology. *J. Psychol.,* 1954, 37, 225-231.
122. Bishop, G. H. Neurophysiology and Behavior. In: Milbank Memorial Fund (903), pp. 159-161.
123. Bishop, L. F. & Kimbro, R. W. Neurocirculatory Asthenia. *J. Am. Med. Assn.,* 1943, 7, 88.
124. Bishop, P. M. F. Sex Hormones and Human Behavior. *Brit. J. Anim. Behav.,* 1953, 1, 20-22.
125. Blake, R. R. & Ramsey, G. V., eds. *Perception: An Approach to Personality.* New York: Ronald Press, 1951.
126. Blake, R. R., Ramsey, G. V. & Moran, L. J. Perceptual Processes as Basic to an Understanding of Complex Behavior. In: Blake & Ramsey (125), pp. 3-24.
127. Blanton, M. G. The Behavior of the Human Infant During the First Thirty Days of Life. *Psychol. Rev.,* 1917, 24, 456-483.
128. Blaschko, H. The Activity of *l* (—) — dopa decarboxylase. *J. Physiol.,* 1942, 101, 337-349.
129. Blatz, W. E. The Cardiac, Respiratory, and Electrical Phenomena Involved in the Emotion of Fear. *J. Exp. Psychol.,* 1925, 8, 109-132.
129a. Blatz, W. E. & Millichamp, D. A. The Development of Emotion in the Infant. *Univ. Toronto Stud.: Child Develop. Series,* 1935, No. 4.
129b. Blau, A. A Unitary Hypothesis of Emotion: 1. Anxiety, Emotions of Displeasure, and Affective Disorders. *Psychoanal. Quart.,* 1955, 24, 75-103.
130. Blaurock, M. F., Low, A. A & Sachs, M. The Influence of Fear, Pharmacologic Action and Convulsion in Metrazol Therapy. *Arch. Neurol. Psychiat.,* 1939, 42, 233-236.
131. Blazer, A. The Psychosomatic Character. *N.Y. State J. Med.,* 1950, 50, 1587-1590.
132. Bleuler, E. *Dementia Praecox or the Group of Schizophrenias.* New York: International Universities Press, 1950.
133. Bleuler, E. *Textbook of Psychiatry.* New York: Macmillan, 1934.
133a. Bliss, E. L., Migeon, C. I., Branch, C. H. H. & Samuels, L. T. Reaction of the Adrenal Cortex to Emotional Stress. *Psychosom. Med.,* 1956, 18, 56-76.
133b. Bloomfield, A. L. & Polland, W. S. Experimental Referred Pain from the Gastro-intestinal tract. *J. Clin. Invest.,* 1931, 10, 435-473.

134. Boas, E. P. & Goldschmidt, E. L. *The Heart Rate.* Springfield, Ill.: C. C Thomas, 1932.
135. Bockus, H. L., Bank, J. & Wilkinson, S. A. Neurogenic Mucous Colitis. *Am. J. Med. Sci.,* 1928, 176, 813-829.
136. Bodo, R. C. & Benagalio, A. E. Hyperglycemia Produced by Sympathin in Emotional Excitement. *Am. J. Physiol.,* 1938, 121, 738-746.
137. Bondy, P. K. Spontaneous Fluctuations in Glucose Content of the Hepatic Venous Blood in Resting Normal Human Beings. *J. Clin. Invest.,* 1952, 31, 231-237.
138. Boring, E. G. Processes Referred to the Alimentary and Urinary Tracts: A Qualitative Analysis. *Psychol. Rev.,* 1915, 22, 306-331.
139. Boring, E. G. *Sensation and Perception in the History of Experimental Psychology.* New York: D. Appleton-Century, 1942.
140. Boring, E. G. *A History of Experimental Psychology.* New York: D. Appleton-Century, 1950.
141. Boring, E. G. A History of Introspection. *Psychol. Bull.,* 1953, 50, 169-189.
142. Boring, E. G. & Titchener, E. B. A Model for the Demonstration of Facial Expression. *Am. J. Psychol.,* 1923, 34, 471-485.
143. Bourne, G. & Wittkower, E. Psychological Treatment of Cases with Cardiac Pain. *Brit. Heart J.,* 1940, 2, 25-32.
144. Bowman, K. M. & Kasanin, J. The Sugar Content of the Blood in Emotional States. *Arch. Neurol. Psychiat.,* 1929, 21, 342-362.
145. Brazier, M. A. B. Tremors of Combat Neurosis. *Arch. Neurol. Psychiat.,* 1945, 54, 175-180.
146. Brazier, M. A. B. *The Electrical Activity of the Nervous System.* London: Isaac Pitman, 1951.
147. Brazier, M. A. B., Finesinger, J. E. & Cobb, S. A Contrast Between the Electroencephalograms of 100 Psychoneurotic Patients and Those of 500 Normal Adults. *Am. J. Psychiat.,* 1945, 101, 443-448.
147a. Bremer, F. The Neurophysiological Problem of Sleep. In: Delefresnaye (287b), pp. 137-162.
147b. Brenner, C. Addendum to Freud's Theory of Anxiety. *Int. J. Psycho-Anal.,* 1953, 34, 18-24.
148. Breuer, J. & Freud, S. *Studies in Hysteria.* New York: Nerv. Ment. Dis. Pub. Co., 1936.
149. Bridges, K. M. B. A Genetic Theory of the Emotions. *J. Genet. Psychol.,* 1930, 38, 514-527.
150. Bridges, K. M. B. Emotional Development in Early Infancy. *Child Develop.,* 1932, 3, 324-341.
151. Brinton, W. *On the Pathology, Symptoms and Treatment of Ulcer of the Stomach.* London: John Churchill, 1857.
152. Brobeck, J. R. Physiology of Appetite. In: Goodenough (470), pp. 36-48.
153. Brobeck, J. R., Tepperman, J. & Long, C. N. H. Experimental Hypothalamic Hyperphagia in the Albino Rat. *Yale J. Biol. Med.,* 1943, 15, 831-853.
153a. Brody, S. *Patterns of Mothering.* New York: International Universities Press, 1956.
154. Brosin, H. W. The Psychology of Overeating. In· Goodhart (470a), pp. 52-69.
155. Brower, D. Respiration and Blood Pressure in Sensory Motor Conflict. *J. Gen. Psychol.,* 1946, 34, 47-58.
156. Brown, C. H. & van Gelder, D. Emotional Reactions Before Examinations, I. Physiological Changes. *J. Psychol.,* 1938, 5, 1-9

157. Brown, E. A. & Goitein, P. L. Some Aspects of Mind in Asthma and Allergy, Comparative Personality Study of 2 Groups of Clinical Cases. *J. Nerv. Ment. Dis.*, 1943, 98, 638-647.

158. Brown, J. S. & Farber, I. E. Emotions Conceptualized as Intervening Variables: With Suggestions Toward a Theory of Frustration. *Psychol. Bull.*, 1951, 48, 465-495.

159. Brown, M., Bresnahan, J., Chalke, F., Peters, B., Poser, E. & Tougas, R. Personality Factors in Duodenal Ulcer. *Psychosom. Med.*, 1950, 12, 1-5.

160. Browning, J. S. & Houseworth, J. H. Development of New Symptoms Following Medical and Surgical Treatment for Duodenal Ulcer. *Psychosom. Med.*, 1953, 15, 328-336.

161. Brožek, J. Semi-Starvation and Nutritional Rehabilitation: A Qualitative Case Study with Emphasis on Behavior. *J. Clin. Nutrition*, 1953, 1, 107-118.

162. Brožek, J., Guetykow, H. & Keys, A. A Study of Personality of Normal Young Men Maintained on Restricted Intake of Vitamins of the B Complex. *Psychosom. Med.*, 1946, 8, 98-109.

163. Brueen, H. G. The Mechanism of Impaired Auriculoventricular Conduction in Acute Rheumatic Fever. *Am. Heart J.*, 1937, 13, 413-425.

164. Brugelmann, R. *Das Asthma, sein Wesen und seine Behandlung, auf Grund 32 jähriger Erfahrungen und Forschungen.* Wiesbaden: Bergmann, 1910.

165. Brugghen, Ver, A. *Neurosurgery in General Practice.* Springfield, Ill.: C. C Thomas, 1952.

166. Brun, R. The Biological Aspect of Freudian Psychoanalysis. *Int. J. Psycho-Anal.*, 1953, 34, 83-95.

167. Bruner, J. S. Emotional Selectivity in Perception and Reaction. *J. Personality,* 1947, 16, 69-77.

168. Bruner, J. S. Perception, Cognition and Behavior. *J. Personality,* 1949, 18, 14-31.

169. Bruner, J. S. Personality Dynamics and the Process of Perceiving. In: Blake & Ramsay (125), pp. 121-147.

170. Brunswick, D. The Effects of Emotional Stimuli on the Gastro-intestinal Tone. *J. Comp. Psychol.*, 1924, 4, 19-79, 225-287.

171. Bucciardi, G. Ricerche sull' Sperglicemia Emotiva. Azione della Pilocarpina. *Arch. di Fisiol.*, 1928, 26, 1-23.

172. Buchanan, A. R. *Functional Neuro-Anatomy, Including an Atlas of the Brain Stem.* Philadelphia: Lea & Febiger, 1951.

173. Burchell, H. B. Cardiac Manifestations of Anxiety. *Proc. Mayo Clin.*, 1947, 22, 433-440.

174. Burrow, T. *The Biology of Human Conflict: An Anatomy of Behavior, Individual and Social.* New York: Macmillan, 1937.

175. Burrow, T. The Law of the Organism, a Neurosocial Approach to the Problems of Human Behavior. *Am. J. Sociol.*, 1937, 42, 814-824.

176. Burrow, T. The Organismic Factor in Disorders of Behavior. *J. Psychol.*, 1937, 4, 233-241.

177. Burrow, T. Kymograph Studies of Physiological (respiratory) Concomitants in Two Types of Attentional Adaptation. *Nature,* 1938, 142, 156-157.

178. Burrow, T. Emotion and the Social Crisis: A Problem in Phylobiology. In: Reymert (1033), pp. 465-486.

179. Burt, C. Experimental Tests of Higher Mental Processes and their Relation to General Intelligence. *J. Exp. Pedag.*, 1911, 1, 93-107.

180. Burt, C. Personality, a Symposium. I, The Assessment of Personality. *Brit. J. Educ. Psychol.*, 1945, 15, 107-121.

181. Burt, C. The Factorial Study of Emotions. In: Reymert (1033), pp. 531-551.
182. Burt, C. The Assessment of Personality. *J. Ment. Sci.,* 1954, 100, 1-28.
183. Burtt, H. E. The Inspiration-Expiration Ratio During Truth and Falsehood. *J. exp. Psychol.,* 1921, 4, 1-23.
183a. Bush, R. R. & Mosteller, F. *Stochastic Models for Learning.* New York: John Wiley, 1955.
184. Button, A. D. An Inquiry into the Psychological Effects of Adrenocorticotropic Hormone Administration. *Dissert. Abstr.,* 1953, 13, 873.
185. Buytendijk, F. J. J. The Phenomenological Approach to the Problem of Feeling and Emotions. In: Reymert (1033), pp. 127-141.
186. Bychowski, G. On Neurotic Obesity. *Psychoanal. Rev.,* 1950, 37, 301-319.
186a. Cain, J., Sarles, H., Bonnefoy, M. Psychiatrie et Gastro-entérologie, Le Point de Vue psychosomatique dans les Affections des Voies biliaires. *Ann. Méd. Psychol.* (Paris), 1955, 2, 15-25.
187. Cannon, W. B. Further Observations on the Movement of the Stomach and Intestines. *Am. J. Physiol.,* 1903, 8, 21-22.
188. Cannon, W. B. The Influence of Emotional States on the Functions of the Alimentary Canal. *Am. J. Med. Sci.,* 1909, 137, 480-487.
189. Cannon, W. B. *The Mechanical Factors of Digestion.* New York: Longmans, Green, 1911.
190. Cannon, W. B. Recent Studies of Bodily Effects of Fear, Rage, and Pain. *J. Phil. Psychol. Sci. Meth.,* 1914, 11, 162-165.
191. Cannon, W. B. The James-Lange Theory of Emotions: A Critical Examination of an Alternative Theory. *Am. J. Psychol.,* 1927, 39, 106.
192. Cannon, W. B. Again the James-Lange and the Thalamic Theories of Emotion. *Psychol. Rev.,* 1931, 38, 281-295.
193. Cannon, W. B. *The Wisdom of the Body.* New York: Norton, 1932.
194. Cannon, W. B. Hunger and Thirst. In: Murchison (940aa), pp. 247-263.
195. Cannon, W. B. *Bodily Changes in Pain, Hunger, Fear and Rage.* New York: D. Appleton-Century, 1939.
196. Cannon, W. B. & Britton, S. W. Studies on the Conditions of Activity in Endocrine Glands: XV, Pseudoaffective Medulliadrenal Secretion. *Am. J. Physiol.,* 1925, 72, 283-294.
197. Cannon, W. B., Lewis J. T. & Britton, S. W. The Dispensability of the Sympathetic Division of the Autonomic Nervous System. *Boston Med. Surg. J.,* 1927, 197, 514-515.
198. Cannon, W. B. & Mendenhall, W. L. Factors Affecting the Coagulation Time of the Blood. *Am. J. Physiol.,* 1914, 34, 225-261.
199. Cannon, W. B., Shohl, A. T. & Wright, W. S. Emotional Glycosuria. *Am. J. Physiol.,* 1911-12, 29, 280-287.
200. Cannon, W. B. & Washburn, A. L. An Explanation of Hunger. *Am. J. Physiol.,* 1912, 29, 568-579.
201. Canter, F. M. Personality Factors in Seizure States with Reference to the Rosenzweig Triadic Hypothesis. *J. Consult. Psychol.,* 1953, 17, 429-435.
201a. Cantril, H. & Hunt, W. A. Emotional Effects Produced by the Injection of Adrenalin. *Am. J. Psychol.,* 1932, 44, 300-307.
202. Capps, J. A. & Coleman, D. H. *An Experimental and Clinical Study of Pain in the Pleura, Pericardium, and Peritoneum.* New York: Macmillan, 1932.
203. Capps, R. B. A Method for Measuring Tone and Reflex Construction of the Capillaries, Venules and Veins of the Human Hand with the Results in Normal and Diseased States. *J. Clin. Invest.,* 1936, 15, 229-239.

204. Carlson, A. J. Contributions to the Physiology of the Stomach, I. *Am. J. Physiol.,* 1912, 31, 151-168.
205. Carlson, A. J. Contributions to the Physiology of the Stomach, II. *Am. J. Physiol.,* 1913, 32, 245-263.
206. Carlson, A. J. The Science Core in Liberal Education. *Scient. Month.,* 1945, 61, 379.
207. Carmichael, L., ed., *Manual of Child Psychology.* New York: John Wiley, 1946, pp. 190-254.
208. Carmichael, L. The Development of Behavior in Vertebrates Experimentally Removed from the Influence of External Stimulation. In: Dennis (293a), pp. 541-546.
209. Carr, H. A. *Psychology, a Study of Mental Activity.* New York: Longmans, Green, 1925.
210. Carr, H. A. Functionalism. In: C. Murchison, *Psychologies of 1930.* Worcester, Mass.: Clark University Press, 1930, pp. 59-78.
211. Carus, C. G. *Symbolik der menschlichen Gestalt.* Leipzig: Brockhaus, 1858.
212. Cason, H. & Cason, E. B. Association Tendencies and Learning Ability. *J. Exp. Psychol.,* 1925, 8, 168-189.
213. Cason, H. & Cason, E. B. Affectivity in Relation to Breathing and Gross Bodily Movement. *J. Gen. Psychol.,* 1933, 9, 130-156.
214. Caster, J. E. Emotional Reactions to Strong Stimuli. *J. Gen. Psychol.,* 1930, 4, 131-153.
215. Cattell, J. P. The Alterations of Ego Functioning After Topectomy. *Phychoanal. Rev.,* 1954, 41, 114-121.
216. Cattell, R. *Description and Measurement of Personality.* New York: World Book Co., 1946.
217. Cattell, R. The Integration of Factor Analysis with Psychology, etc. *J. Educ. Psychol.,* 1948, 39, 227-236.
218. Cattell, R. *Personality: A Systematic Theoretical and Factural Study.* New York: McGraw-Hill, 1950.
219. Cattell, R. *Factor Analysis: An Introduction and Manual for the Psychologist and Social Scientist.* New York: Harper, 1952.
219a. Cattell, R. B. Second-Order Personality Factors in the Questionnaire Realm. *J. Consult. Psychol.,* 1956, 20, 411-418.
220. Chalmers, J. H., Branston, R. W., Taylor, H. L. & Keys, A. Effect of a Psychiatric Interview on Renal Plasma Flow and Finger Skin Temperature. *Fed. Proc.,* 1949, 8, 23.
221. Chalmers, T. M. & Lewis, A. A. G. Stimulation of the Supraoptico-Hypophysial System in Man. *Clin. Sci.,* 1951, 10, 127-135.
222. Chambers, W. N. & Rosenbaum, M. Ulcerative Colitis: Psychosomatic Conference of the Cincinnati General Hospital, March, 1950. *Psychosom. Med.,* 1953, 15, 523-532.
222a. Chapman, A. H., Loeb, D. G. & Young, J. B. A Psychosomatic Study of Five Children with Duodenal Ulcer. *J. Pediat.,* 1956, 48, 248-261.
223. Chapman, W. P. Measurements of Pain Sensitivity in Normal Control Subjects and in Psychoneurotic Patients. *Psychosom. Med.,* 1944, 6, 252-257.
224. Chapman, W. P., Cohen, M. E. & Cobb, S. Measurements Related to Pain in Neurocirculatory Asthenia Anxiety Neurosis, or Effort Syndrome: Levels of Heat Stimulus Perceived as Painful and Producing Wince and Withdrawal Reactions. *J. Clin. Invest.,* 1946, 25, 890-896.
225. Chapman, W. P., Finesinger, J. E. & Chesley, G. The Effect of Direct Sug-

gestion on Pain Sensitivity in Normal Control Subjects and Psychoneurotic Patients. *J. Nerv. Ment. Dis.*, 1953, 118, 19-26.

226. Chapman, W. P., Finesinger, J. C., Jones, C. M. & Cobb, S. Measurements of Pain Sensitivity in Patients with Psychoneurosis. *Arch. Neurol. Psychiat.*, 1947, 57, 321-331.

227. Chapman, W. P. & Jones, C. M. Variations in Cutaneous and Visceral Pain Sensitivity in Normal Subjects. *J. Clin. Invest.*, 1944, 23, 81-91.

228. Chappell, M. N. Blood Pressure Changes in Deception. *Arch. Psychol.*, 1929, 27, 1-39.

229. Chappell, M. N. A Comparison of Blood-Pressure Methods. *J. Genet. Psychol.*, 1931, 39, 398-403.

229a. Charpy, J., Gastaut, H., Calas, E. & Roger, A. L'EEG en Dermatologie réactionnelle, les Tracés de l'Eczéma humain. *Bull. Soc. Franç. Derm. Syph.*, 1952, 5, 433.

230. Chasis, H., Ranger, H. A., Goldring, W. & Smith, H. W. The Control of Renal Blood Flow and Glomerular Filtration in Normal Man. *J. Clin. Invest.*, 1938, 17, 683-697.

231. Clark, L. C., Jr. & Treichler, P. Psychic Stimulation of Prostatic Secretion. *Psychosom. Med.*, 1950, 12, 261-263.

232. Clark, L. D., Bauer, W. & Cobb, S. Preliminary Observation on Mental Disturbances Occurring in Patients under Therapy with Cortisone and ACTH. *New Eng. J. Med.*, 1952, 246, 205-216.

233. Clark, L. P. What Is the Psychology of Organic Epilepsy? *Psychoanal. Rev.*, 1933, 20, 79-85.

234. Clausen, J. Changes in Galvanic Skin Resistances as Indication of Pain Threshold. *J. Gen. Psychol.*, 1953, 49, 261-271.

235. Cleghorn, R. A. Psychosomatic Medicine and Altered Automatic and Humoral Function. *McGill Med. J.*, 1949-1950, 18-19, 25-42.

236. Cleghorn, R. A., Graham, B. F., Campbell, N. K., Rublee, N. K., Elliott, F. H. & Saffron, M. Anxiety States: Their Response to ACTH and to Isotonic Saline. In J. R. Mote, ed., *Proc. First Clin. ACTH Conf.* Philadelphia: Blakiston, 1950, pp. 561-565.

237. Cleghorn, R. A. Endocrine Influence on Personality and Behavior. In: Milbank, Memorial Fund (903), pp. 265-276.

237a. Cleghorn, R. A. The Hypothalamic-Endocrine System. *Psychosom. Med.*, 1955, 17, 367-376.

238. Cleghorn, R. A., Graham, B. F., Saffron, M., & Cameron, D. E. Study of Effect of Pituitary ACTH in Depressed Patients. *Canad. Med. Assn. J.*, 1950, 63, 329-331.

239. Cobb, S. *Emotions and Clinical Medicine.* New York: Norton, 1950.

240. Coghill, G. E. *Anatomy and the Problem of Behavior.* New York: Macmillan, 1929.

241. Coghill, G. E. The Neuro-Embryologic Study of Behavior: Principles, Perspective and Aim. *Science*, 1933, 78, 131-138.

242. Cohen, M. E. & White, P. D. Life Situations, Emotions and Neurocirculatory Asthenia (anxiety neurosis, neurasthenia, effort syndrome). *Proc. Assn. Res. Nerv. Ment. Dis.*, 1949, 29, 832-869.

243. Cohen, M. E. & White, P. D. Life Situations, Emotions, and Neurocirculatory Asthenia (anxiety neurosis, neuroasthenia, effort syndrome). *Psychosom. Med.*, 1951, 13, 335-357.

244. Cohn, R. The Influence of Emotion on the Human Electroencephalogram. *J. Nerv. Ment. Dis.*, 1946, 104, 351-357.

244a. Colby, K. M. *Energy and Structure in Psychoanalysis.* New York: Ronald Press, 1955.
245. Collett, M. E. & Lilgestrand, G. Variations in the Resting Minute Volume of the Heart in Man. *Skandinav. Arch. Physiol.,* 1924, 45, 17-42.
246. Collias, N. E. Aggressive Behavior among Vertebrate Animals. *Physiol. Zool.,* 1944, 17, 83-123.
247. Conn, J. W., Louis, L. H. & Wheeler, C. E. Production of Temporary Diabetes Mellitus in Man with Pituitary ACTH. Relation to Uric Acid Metabolism. *J. Lab. Clin. Med.,* 1948, 33, 651-661.
248. Conn, J. W., Lewis, L. H. & Johnston, M. W. Alleviation of Experimental Diabetes in Man by Administration of Reduced Glutathione (G.S.H.): Metabolic Implications. *Science,* 1949, 109, 279-280.
249. Conrad, A. Psychiatric Study of Hyperthyroid Patients. *J. Nerv. Ment. Dis.,* 1934, 79, 505.
250. Converse, E. The Relationship of Bright and Dull Pressure to Affectivity. *Am. J. Psychol.,* 1932, 44. 740-748.
251. Coon, J. M. & Rothman, S. The Sweat Response to Drugs with Nicotine-Like Action. *J. Pharm. & Exp. Ther.,* 1941, 73, 1-11.
252. Cotton, T. F. & Lewis, T. Observations upon Fainting Attacks Due to Inhibitory Cardiac Impulses. *Heart,* 1918, 7, 23-34.
253. Courts, F. A. Relations between Muscle Tension and Performance. *Psychol. Bull.,* 1942, 34, 347-367.
254. Coutu, W. *Emergent Human Nature.* New York: Knopf, 1949.
255. Craddock, C. G., Jr. Chronic Ulcerative Colitis: Effect of a Specific Psychotherapeutic Measure. *Psychosom. Med.,* 1953, 15, 513-522.
256. Cramer, H. & Wittkower, E. Affektive Kreislaufveränderungen unter besonderer Berüchsicktigung der Herzgrösse. *Klin. Wochnschr.* 1930, 9, 1296-1298.
257. Cranston, R. W., Chalmers, J. H., Taylor, H. L., Henschel, A. & Keys, A. Effect of a Psychiatric Interview on the Blood Pressure Response to Cold Stimuli. *Fed. Proc.,* 1949, 8, 30.
258. Crider, R. J. & Walker, S. M. Physiologic Studies on the Stomach of a Woman with a Gastric Fistula. *Arch. Surg.,* 1948, 57, 1-9.
259. Crosland, H. R. A Qualitative Analysis of the Process of Forgetting. *Psychol. Mon.,* 1921, 29, 1-159.
260. Crossland, J. The Significance of Brain Acetylcholine. *J. Ment. Sci.,* 1953, 99, 247-251.
261. Curry, J. J. Comparative Action of Acetylbeta-Methyl Choline and Histamine on Respiratory Tract in Normals, Patients with Hay Fever and Subjects with Bronchial Asthma. *J. Clin. Invest.,* 1947, 26, 430-438.
262. Cushing, H. Peptic Ulcer and the Interbrain. *Surg. Gynec. Obst.,* 1932, 55, 1-34.
263. Cushing, M. M. The Psychoanalytic Treatment of a Man Suffering with Ulcerative Colitis. *J. A. Psychoanal. Assn.,* 1953, 1, 510-518.
264. DaCosta, J. M. On Irritable Heart, A Clinical study of a Functional Cardiac Disorder and its Consequences. *Am. J. Med. Sci.,* 1871, 61, 17.
265. Daniels, G. E. An Approach to Psychological Control Studies of Urinary Sex Hormones. *Am. J. Psychiat.,* 1943, 100, 231-239.
266. Daniels, G. E. & Tauber, E. L. A Dynamic Approach to the Study of Replacement Therapy in Cases of Castration. *Am. J. Psychiat.,* 1941, 97, 905-918.
267. Darling, R. R. Autonomic Action in Relation to Personality Traits of Children. *J. Abnorm. Soc. Psychol.,* 1940, 35, 246-260.

268. Darrow, C. W. Sensory, Secretory and Electrical Changes in the Skin Following Bodily Excitation. *J. Exp. Psychol.*, 1927, 10, 197-226.
269. Darrow, C. W. Differences in the Physiological Reactions to Sensory and Identical Stimuli. *Psychol. Bull.*, 1929, 26, 185-201.
270. Darrow, C. W. The Galvanic Skin Reflex (Sweating) and Blood-Pressure as Preparatory and Facilitative Functions. *Psychol. Bull.*, 1936, 33, 73-94.
271. Darrow, C. W. Psychological and Psychophysiological Significance of the Electroencephalogram. *Psychol. Rev.*, 1947, 54, 157-168.
272. Darrow, C. W. Mechanisms for the Spread of Epileptic Activity. *EEG Clin. Neurophysiol.*, 1949, 1, 25-27.
273. Darrow, C. W. A New Frontier: Neurophysiological Effects of Emotion on the Brain. In: Reymert (1033), pp. 247-260.
274. Darrow, C. W. The Relation of Cerebral to Autonomic Activity in the Conditioned Emotional Reactions of Children. *Ann. N.Y. Acad. Sci.*, 1953, 56, 289-301.
275. Darrow, C. W. & Freeman, G. L. Palmar Skin Resistance Changes Contrasted with Non-Palmar Changes and Rate of Insensible Weight Loss. *J. Exp. Psychol.*, 1934, 17, 739-748.
276. Darrow, C. W., Jost, H., Solomon, A. P. & Mergener, J. C. Autonomic Indications of Excitatory and Homeostatic Effects on the Electroencephalogram. *J. Psychol.*, 1942, 14, 115-130.
277. Darwin, C. *The Expression of the Emotions in Man and Animals.* New York: D. Appleton, 1896.
278. Davey, L. M., Kaada, B. R. & Fulton, J. F. Effects on Gastric Secretion of Frontal Lobe Stimulation. *Proc. Assn. Res. Nerv. Ment. Dis.*, 1949, 29, 617-627.
279. Davis, F. H. & Malmo, R. B. Electromyographic Recording during Interview. *Am. J. Psychiat.*, 1950-1951, 107, 908-916.
280. Davis, H. & Davis, P. A. The Electrical Activity of the Brain: Its Relation to Physiological States of Impaired Consciousness. *Proc. Assn. Res. Nerv. Ment. Dis.*, 1939, 19, 50-80.
281. Davis, H., Davis, P. A., Loomis, A. L., Harvey, E. W. & Hobart, G. Electrical Reactions of Human Brain to Auditory Stimulation during Sleep. *J. Neurophysiol.*, 1938, 2, 500-514.
282. Davis, K. B. *Factors in the Sex Life of Twenty-two Hundred Women.* New York: Harper, 1929.
283. Davis, P. A. Electroencephalograms of Manic-Depressive Patients. *Am. J. Psychol.*, 1941, 98, 430-433.
284. Davis, P. A. Comparative Study of the EEGs of Schizophrenic and Manic-Depressive Patients. *Am. J. Psychiat.*, 1942, 99, 210-217.
285. Davis, P. A. Effect on the EEG of Changing the Blood Sugar Level. *Arch. Neurol. Psychiat.*, 1943, 49, 186-194.
286. Day, R. & Klingman, W. O. The Effect of Sleep on Skin Temperature Reactions in a Case of Acrocyanosis. *J. Clin. Invest.*, 1939, 18, 271-276.
287. De Groot, J. & Harris, G. W. Hypothalamic Control of the Anterior Pituitary Gland and Blood Lymphocytes. *J. Physiol.*, 1950, 111, 335-346.
287a. Dekker, E. & Green, J. Reproducible Psychogenic Attacks of Asthma, A Laboratory Study. *J. Psychosom. Res.*, 1956, 1, 58-67.
287b. Delefresnaye, J. F., ed., *Brain Mechanisms and Consciousness.* Oxford: Blackwell, 1954.
288. Delgado, J. M. R. & Anand, B. K. Increase of Food Intake Induced by

Electrical Stimulation of the Lateral Hypothalamus. *Am. J. Physiol.*, 1953, 172, 162-168.

289. Delgado, J. M. R. Responses Evoked in the Waking Cat by Electrical Stimulation of the Motor Cortex. *Am. J. Physiol.*, 1952, 171, 436-446.

289a. Delgado, J. M. R. Cerebral Structures Involved in Transmission and Elaboration of Noxious Stimulation. *J. Neurophysiol.*, 1955, 18, 261-275.

289b. Delgado, J. M. R. & Hamlin, H. Surface and Depth Electrography of the Frontal Lobes in Conscious Patients. *EEG Clin. Neurophysiol.*, 1956, 8, 371-384.

290. Dell, P. Corrélations entre le Système végétatif et le Système de la Vie de Relation: Mésencéphale, Diencéphale et Cortex Cérébral. *J. Physiol.*, 1952, 44, 471-557.

291. Dempsey, E. W. Homeostasis. In: Stevens (1197a), pp. 209-235.

292. Dennis, C., Eddy, F. D., Frykman, H. M., McCarthy, A. M. & Westover, D. The Response to Vagotomy in Idiopathic Ulcerative Colitis and Regional Enteritis. *Ann. Surg.*, 1948, 128, 479-496.

293. Dennis, W. Infant Reactions to Restraint: An Evaluation of Watson's Theory. *N. Y. Acad. Sci.*, 1940, 2, 202-218.

293a. Dennis, W. *Readings in the History of Psychology.* New York: Appleton-Century-Crofts, 1948.

294. Dennis, W., Leeper, R., Harlow, H., et al. *Current Trends in Psychological Theory.* Pittsburgh: University of Pittsburgh Press, 1951.

295. Derbes, V. J. & Weiss, T. E. *Untoward Reaction of Cortisone and ACTH.* Springfield, Ill.: C. C Thomas, 1951.

296. Derner, G. F. *Aspects of the Psychology of the Tuberculous.* New York: Paul B. Hoeber, 1953.

297. Deutsch, F. The Choice of Organ in Organ Neurosis. *Int. J. Psycho-Anal.*, 1939, 10, 252-262.

297a. Deutsch, F. *The Production of Somatic Diseases by Emotional Disturbance.* Baltimore: Williams & Wilkins, 1939.

298. Deutsch, F. Psychoanalysis and Psychosomatic Medicine. *Annual Survey of Psychoanalysis*, 1952, 1, 179-199.

299. Deutsch, F., ed. *The Psychosomatic Concept in Psychoanalysis.* New York: International Universities Press, 1953.

299a. Deutsch, F. Basic Psychoanalytic Principles in Psychosomatic Disorders. *Acta Psychother.*, 1953, 1, 102.

299b. Deutsch, F. Analytic Synesthesiology, Analytic Interpretation of Intersensory Perception. *Int. J. Psycho-Anal.*, 1954, 35, 293-301.

300. Dewey, J. *Psychology.* New York: Harper, 1887.

301. Dewey, J. The reflex Arc Concept in Psychology. *Psychol. Rev.*, 1896, 3, 357-370.

302. Dickinson, R. L. *A Thousand Marriages: A Medical Study of Sex Adjustment.* Baltimore: Williams & Wilkins, 1931.

303. Diethelm, O., Fleetwood, M. F. & Milhorat, A. T. The Predictable Association of Certain Emotions and Biochemical Change in the Blood. *Proc. Assn. Res. Nerv. Ment. Dis.*, 1949, 29, 262-278.

303a. Di Mascio, A., Boyd, R. W. & Greenblatt, M. Physiological Correlation of Tension and Antagonism during Psychotherapy. *Psychosom. Med.*, 1957, 29, 99-104.

304. Dobreff, M. & Tomoff, W. Durch Angst hervorgerufene somatische Veränderungen. *Ztschr. Ges. Exp. Med.*, 1932, 84, 695-701.

304a. Dollard, J. & Miller, N. E. *Personality and Psychotherapy.* New York: McGraw-Hill, 1950.

304b. Dongier, M., Wittkower, E. D., Stephens-Newsham, L. & Hoffman, M. M. Psychophysiological Studies in Thyroid Function. *Psychosom. Med.,* 1956, 18, 310-323.

305. Dorfman, A., Apter, N. S., Smull, K., Bergenstal, D. M. & Richter, R. B. Status Epilepticus Coincident with Use of Pituitary Adrenocorticotropic Hormone: Report of Three Cases. *J. Am. Med. Assn.,* 1951, 146, 25-57.

306. Dott, N. M. Surgical Aspects of the Hypothalamus. In: Clark et al., *The Hypothalamus.* Edinburgh: Oliver and Boyd, 1938.

307. Draper, G., Bruenn, H. G. & Dupertuis, C. W. Changes in the Electrocardiogram as Criteria of Individual Constitutions Derived from Its Physiological Panel. *Am. J. Med. Sci.,* 1937, 194, 514-523.

308. Draper, G., Dupertuis, C. W. & Caughey, J. L. *Human Constitution in Clinical Medicine.* New York: Paul B. Hoeber, 1944.

309. Draper, G., Ramsey, H. J. & Dupertuis, C. W. Variations in Behavior of Buffy Coat Culture among Individuals of Different Constitutional Types. *J. Clin. Invest.,* 1944, 23, 864-874.

310. Draper, G. & Touraine, G. A. Man-Environment Unit and Peptic Ulcer. *Arch. Int. Med.,* 1932, 49, 616-662.

311. Draper, P. A. Personality Reactions to ACTH and Related Substances. *Geriatrics,* 1953, 8, 557-563.

312. Dreyfuss, F. & Feldman, S. Eosinopenia Induced by Emotional Stress. *Acta Med. Scandinav.,* 1952, 144, 107-113.

313. Driesch, H. Entwicklungsmechanische Studien. *Z. Wiss. Zool.,* 1891, 53, 160-184.

314. Duffy, E. Emotion: An Example of Need for Reorientation in Psychology. *Psychol. Rev.,* 1934, 41, 184-198.

315. Duffy, E. An Explanation of "Emotional Phenomena" without the Use of the Concept "Emotion." *J. Gen. Psychol.,* 1941, 25, 283-293.

316. Duffy, E. Leeper's "Motivational Theory of Emotions." *Psychol. Rev.,* 1948, 55, 324-328.

316a. Duffy, E. Physiological Approaches to the Study of Individual Differences. Presented at American Psychological Association Convention, New York, 1957.

317. Dumas, G. Le Choc émotional. *J. Psychol. Norm. & Path.,* 1928, 25, 130-164.

318. Dunbar, H. F. *Psychosomatic Diagnosis.* New York: Paul B. Hoeber, 1943.

319. Dunbar, H. F. *Mind and Body: Psychosomatic Medicine.* New York: Random House, 1947.

320. Dunbar, H. F. *Synopsis of Psychosomatic Diagnosis and Treatment.* St. Louis: C. V. Mosby, 1948.

321. Dunbar, H. F. *Emotions and Bodily Changes.* New York: Columbia University Press, 1954.

322. Duncan, C. H., Stevenson, I. P. & Ripley, H. S. Life Situations, Emotions, and Paroxysmal Auricular Arrhythmias. *Psychosom. Med.,* 1950, 12, 23-37.

323. Duncan, C. H., Stevenson, I. P. & Wolff, H. G. Life Situation, Emotion, and Exercise Tolerance. *Psychosom. Med.,* 1951, 13, 36-50.

324. Duncan, C. H. & Taylor, H C., Jr. Psychosomatic Study of Pelvic Congestion. *Am. J. Obst. Gynec.,* 1952, 65, 1-12.

325. Dusser de Barenne, J. G. Recherches expérimentales sur les Fonctions du Système nerveux central, Faites en particulier sur deux Chats dont le Néopallium avait eté enlevé. *Arch. néerl. physiol.,* 1919-1920, 4, 31-123.

326. Dusser de Barenne, J. G. Central Levels of Sensory Integration. *Proc. Assn. Res. Nerv. Ment. Dis.*, 1935, 15, 274-288.
327. Dusser de Barenne, J. G. & McCulloch, W. S. The Direct Functional Interrelation of Sensory Cortex and Optic Thalamus. *J. Neurophysiol.*, 1938, 1, 176-186.
328. Dysinger, W. S. & Ruckmick, C. A., *The Emotional Responses of Children to the Motion Picture Situation*. New York: Macmillan, 1933.
329. Ebbecke, U. Zur physiologischen Deutung des Phantomgliedes. *Deut. Ztschr. Nervenheilk.*, 1950, 163, 337-353.
330. Ectors, L., Brookens, N. L. & Gerard, R. W. Autonomic and Motor Localization in the Hypothalamus. *Arch. Neurol. Psychiat.*, 1938, 39, 789-798.
330a. Eichhorn, E. & Tracktir, J. The Relationship between Anxiety, Hypnotically Induced Emotions and Gastric Secretion. *Gastroenterol.*, 1955, 29, 422-431.
331. Einthoven, W. Filament Galvanometer and Measurement of Heart's Action Current. *Svenska Läk.-Sällsk. Handl.* 1925, 51, 213-226.
331a. Ellingson, R. J. Brain Waves and Problems of Psychology. *Psychol. Bull.*, 1956, 53, 1-34.
331b. Ellingson, R. J. Comments on Schmidt's "The Reticular Formation and Behavioral Wakefulness." *Psychol. Bull.*, 1957, 54, 76-78.
332. Ellis, W. D. *A Source Book of Gestalt Psychology*. New York: Harcourt, Brace, 1938.
333. Emerson, A. E. Dynamic Homeostasis: A Unifying Principle in Organic, Social and Ethical Evolution. *Scient. Month.*, 1954, 78, 67-85.
334. Engel, F. L. General Concepts of Adrenocortical Function in Relation to the Response to Stress. *Psychosom. Med.*, 1953, 15, 565-573.
334a. Engel, G. L. Studies of Ulcerative Colitis: IV, The Significance of Headaches. *Psychosom. Med.*, 1956, 18, 334-346.
335. Engel, G. L. & Margolin, S. Neurosychiatric Disturbances in Internal Disease, Metabolic Factors and EEG Correlations. *Arch. Int. Med.*, 1942, 70, 236-259.
336. Engel, G. L. & Romano, J. Studies of Delirium: II, Reversibility of the Electroencephalogram with Experimental Procedures. *Arch. Neurol. Psychiat.*, 1944, 51, 378-392.
337. English, S. O. & Pearson, G. H. J. *Emotional Problems of Living*. New York: Norton, 1945.
338. Erickson, M. H. Experimental Demonstration of the Psychopathology of Everyday Life. In: Tompkins (1256), pp. 517-528.
339. Erikson, E. H. Childhood and Tradition in Two American Indian Tribes. In: Kluckhohn & Murray (712), pp. 176-203.
340. Escalona, S. & Leitch, M. Progress Report: Early Phases of Personality Development, a Non-normative Study of Infant Behavior. *Report to the U. S. Public Health Service, Project MH-27*, 1951.
340a. Estes, W. K. et al. *Modern Learning Theory: A Critical Analysis of Five Examples*. New York: Appleton-Century-Crofts, 1954.
341. Euler, von, U. S. Visceral Functions of the Nervous System. *Ann. Rev. Physiol.*, 1954, 16, 340-370.
342. Euler, von, U. S. & Hokfelt, B. Influence of Hypophysectomy upon the Distribution of Noradrenaline and Adrenaline in the Spleen of the Rat. *Endocrinology*, 1951, 48, 98-100.
343. Euler, von, U. S. & Luft, R. Effects of ACTH and ACTH Peptides on the Circulating Eosinophils and Urinary Excretion of Adrenaline and Noradrenaline in a Human Subject. *Acta Endocrinol.*, 1949, 3, 323-330.
344. Ewalt, J. R., Randoll, G. C. & Morris, H. D. The Phantom Limb. *Psychosom. Med.*, 1947, 9, 118-123.

345. Eysenck, H. J. Types of Personality: A Factorial Study of 700 Neurotics. *J. Ment. Sci.,* 1944, 90, 851-861.
346. Fahrenkamp, K. *Die psycho-physischen Wechselwirkungen bei den Hypertonic-Erkrankungen. Eine klinische Studie über die praktische Bedeutung der Blutdruckkurve.* Stuttgart: Hippokrates, 1926.
346a. Falstein, E. I. & Judas, I. Juvenile Diabetes and Its Psychiatric Implications. *Am. J. Orthopsychiat.,* 1955, 25, 330-342.
347. Faulkner, W. B., Jr. Influence of Suggestion on Size of Bronchial Lumen. *Northwest Med.,* 1941, 40, 367-368.
348. Faulkner, W. B., Jr., Rodenbaugh, F. A. & O'Neill, J. R. Influence of Emotions upon Esophageal Function. *Radiology,* 1941, 37, 443-453.
349. Fechner, G. T. *Elemente der Psychophysik.* Leipzig: Breitkopf & Härtel, 1860.
350. Fechner, G. T. Elements of Psychophysics. In: Dennis (293a), pp. 206-273.
351. Feichtinger, F. Psychosomatics and Psychoneurosis. *Am. J. Indiv. Psychol.,* 1952-1953, 10, 123-135.
352. Feleky, A. The Influence of the Emotions on Respiration. *J. Exp. Psychol.,* 1916, 1, 218-241.
352a. Fenichel, O. The Nature and Classification of the So-Called Psychosomatic Phenomena. *Psychoanal. Quart.,* 1945, 14, 287-312.
353. Fenichel, O. *The Psychoanalytic Theory of Neurosis.* New York: Norton, 1945.
353a. Fields, W. S., ed. *Brain Mechanisms and Drug Action.* Springfield, Ill.: C. C Thomas, 1957.
354. Finesinger, J. E. Neurotic Symptoms and Emotional Factors in Atopic Dermatitis. *Arch. Derm. Syph.,* 1942, 46, 187.
355. Finesinger, J. E. The Effect of Pleasant and Unpleasant Ideas on the Respiratory Pattern (Spirogram) in Psychoneurotic Patients. *Am. J. Psychiat.,* 1944, 100, 659-667.
356. Finesinger, J. E., Cohen, M. E. & Thompson, K. J. Velocity of Blood Flow in Schizophrenia. *Arch. Neurol. Psychiat.,* 1938, 39, 24-36.
357. Finley, K. H. On Occurrence of Rapid Frequency Potential Changes in the Human Electroencephalogram. *Am. J. Psychiat.,* 1944, 101, 194-200.
358. Finley, K. H. Emotional Physiology and Its influence on Thought Content. *J. Nerv. Ment. Dis.,* 1953, 118, 442-446.
359. Finley, K. H. & Campbell, M. C. Electroencephalography in Schizophrenia. *Am. J. Psychiat.,* 1941, 98, 374-381.
359a. Fischer, L. K. Hospitalism in Six-Month-Old Infants. *Am. J. Orthopsychiat.,* 1952, 22, 522-533.
360. Fishberg, A. M. *Hypertension and Nephritis.* Philadelphia:: Lea & Febiger, 1939.
360a. Fisher, A. Behavioral Effects of Brain Chemical Stimulation in the Rat. Presented at American Psychological Association Convention, New York, 1957.
361. Floyd, W. F. & Welford, A. T., eds. *Symposium on Fatigue.* London: H. K. Lewis, 1953.
361a. Flugel, J. C. *Studies in Feeling and Desire.* London: Gerald Duckworth, 1955.
362. Flynn, J. T., Kennedy, M. A. K. & Wolf, S. Essential Hypertension in one of Identical Twins, An Experimental Study of Cardiovascular Reactions in Y Twins. *Proc. Assn. Res. Nerv. Ment. Dis.,* 1949, 29, 944.
363. Folin, O., Denis, W. & Smillie, W. G. Some Observations on "Emotional Glycosuria" in Man. *J. Biol. Chem.,* 1914, 17, 519-520.
363a. Folkow, B. & von Euler, U. S. Selective Activation of Noradrenaline and Adrenaline Producing Cells in the Cat's Adrenal Gland by Hypothalamic Stimulation. *Circulation Res.,* 1954, 2, 191-195.

363b. Folson, J. P. *Physician's Desk Reference to Pharmaceutical Specialties and Biologicals.* Cradell, N. J.: Medical Economics, 1957.
364. Ford, A. Bioelectrical Potentials and Mental Effort: I, Cardiac Effects. *J. Comp. Physiol. Psychol.,* 1953, 46, 347-351.
365. Fox, H. M. & Gifford, S. Psychological Responses to ACTH and Cortisone: A Preliminary Theoretical Formulation. *Psychosom. Med.,* 1953, 15, 614-631.
366. Frank, L. K. *Feelings and Emotions.* Garden City, N. Y.: Doubleday, 1954.
367. Franklin, J. C., Schiele, B. C., Brozek, J. & Keys, A. Observations of Human Behavior in Experimental Semi-Starvation and Rehabilitation. *J. Clin. Psychol.,* 1948, 4, 28-45.
368. Freeman, F. N. Heredity and Environment in the Light of the Study of Twins. *Scient. Month.,* 1937, 44, 13-19.
369. Freeman, G. L. The Effect of Inhibited Micturition upon Interrupted and Completed Acts of Unrelated Origin. *J. Gen. Psychol.,* 1938, 19, 277-283.
370. Freeman, G. L. Toward a Psychiatric Plimsoll Mark: Physiological Recovery Quotients in Experimentally Induced Frustration. *J. Psychol.,* 1939, 8, 247-252.
371. Freeman, G. L. Postural Tensions and Conflict Situation. *Psychol. Rev.,* 1939, 46, 226-240.
372. Freeman, G. L. *The Energetics of Human Behavior.* Ithaca, N. Y.: Cornell University Press, 1948.
373. Freeman, G. L. *Physiological Psychology.* New York: D. Van Nostrand, 1948.
374. Freeman, W. & Watts, J. W. Interpretation of Functions of Frontal Lobe Based upon Observations in 48 Cases of Prefrontal Lobotomy. *Yale J. Biol. Med.,* 1939, 11, 527-539.
375. Freeman, W. & Watts, J. W. *Psychosurgery.* Springfield, Ill.: C. C Thomas, 1950.
376. Fremont-Smith, F. The Influence of Emotional Factors on Physiological and Pathological Processes. *Bull. N. Y. Acad. Med.,* 1939, 15, 560-596.
376a. French, J. D. Hernández-Peón, R. & Livingston, R. B. Projection from Cortex to Cephalic Brain Stem (Reticular Formation) in Monkey. *J. Neurophysiol.,* 1955, 18, 74-93.
376b. French, J. D., Longmire, R. L., Porter, R. W. & Movius, H. J. Extravagal Influences on Gastric Hydrochloric Acid Secretion Induced by Stress Stimuli. *Surgery,* 1953, 34, 621-632.
376c. French, J. D., Porter, R. W., Cavanaugh, E. B., & Longmire, R. L. Experimental Observations on "Psychosomatic" Mechanisms: Gastrointestinal Disturbances. *Arch. Neurol. Psychiat.,* 1954, 72, 267-281.
376d. French, J. D., Porter, R. W., Cavanaugh, E. B. & Longmire, R. L. Experimental Gastroduodenal Lesions Induced by Stimulation of the Brain. *Psychosom. Med.,* 1957, 19, 209-220.
377. French, T. M., Alexander, F., et al. *Psychogenic Factors in Bronchial Asthma.* Washington, D. C.: Psychosom. Med. Mon. National Research Council, 1941.
378. Frenkel-Brunswick, E. Psychoanalysis and the Unity of Science. *Proc. Am. Acad. Arts Sci.,* 1954, 80, 271-350.
379. Freud, A. *The Ego and the Mechanisms of Defense.* New York: International Universities Press, 1946.
379a. Freud, A. *The Psychoanalytic Treatment of Children.* London: Imago, 1946.
379b. Freud, A. Observations on Child Development. *Psychoanalytic Study of the Child,* 1951, 6, 18-30.
380. Freud, S. *Beyond the Pleasure Principle.* London: Hogarth Press, 1922.
381. Freud, S. The Origin and Development of Psychoanalysis. In: J. van Teslaar, ed., *An Outline of Psychoanalysis.* New York: Modern Library, 1924.

382. Freud, S. *The Problem of Anxiety.* New York: Norton, 1936.
383. Freud, S. *The Basic Writings of Sigmund Freud.* New York: Random House, 1938.
384. Freud, S. *Collected Papers,* 4 vols. London: Hogarth Press, 1938.
385. Freud, S. Infantile Genital Organization. In: Freud (384), Vol. 2, 244-249.
386. Freud, S. On Narcissism: An Introduction. In: Freud (384), Vol. 4, 30-59.
387. Freud, S. *A General Introduction to Psychoanalysis.* New York: Permabook, 1953.
388. Freyberg, R. H., Traeger, C. H., Patterson, M., Squires, W., Adams, C. H. & Stevenson, C. Problems of Prolonged Cortisone Treatment for Rheumatoid Arthritis: Further Investigations. *J. Am. Med. Assn.,* 1951, 147, 1538-1543.
389. Fried, R. I. Socio-Emotional Factors Accounting for Growth Failure in Children as Measured by the Wetzel Grid. *Proc. Assn. Res. Nerv. Ment. Dis.,* 1950, 29, 317-325.
389a. Friedl, F. P. Anxiety and Cortical Alpha in Normal Subjects. *Stud. Psychol. Psychiat. Catholic Univ. Am.,* 1954, 9, vi, 29.
390. Friedman, A. P. & Brenner, C. Psychological Mechanisms in Chronic Headache. *Proc. Assn. Res. Nerv. Ment. Dis.,* 1949, 29, 605-608.
391. Friedman, A. P., deSola Pool, N. & Storch, von, T. J. C. Tension Headache. *J. Am. Med. Assn.,* 1953, 151, 174-177.
392. Friedman, M. Studies Concerning the Etiology and Pathogenesis of Neurocirculatory Asthenia. III, The Cardiovascular Manifestations of Neurocirculatory Asthenia. *Am. Heart J.,* 1945, 30, 478-491.
393. Friedman, M. *Functional Cardiovascular Disease.* Baltimore: Williams & Wilkins, 1947.
394. Friedman, M. Studies Concerning the Etiology and Pathogenesis of Neurocirculatory Asthenia. VI, Episodic Neurogenic Discharge as a Manifestation of Its Syndrome. *Psychosom. Med.,* 1947, 9, 242-245.
395. Friedman, M. H. F. & Snape, W. J. Color Changes in the Mucosa of the Colon in Children as Affected by Food and Psychic Stimulation. *Fed. Proc.,* 1946, 5, 30-31.
396. Fromm, E. *Escape from Freedom.* New York: Rinehart, 1941.
397. Fromm, E. Individual and Social Origins of Neurosis. *Am. Sociol. Rev.,* 1944, 9, 380-384.
398. Fromm, E. *Man for Himself.* New York: Rinehart, 1947.
399. Fromm, E. Sex and Character: The Kinsey Report Viewed from the Standpoint of Psychoanalysis. In: *About the Kinsey Report.* New York: Signet Books, 1948, pp. 47-59.
400. Fromm, E. *The Sane Society.* New York: Rinehart, 1955.
401. Fry, P. C. A Comparative Study of "Obese" Children Selected on the Basis of Fat Pads. *J. Clin. Nutr.,* 1953, 1, 453-468.
402. Fry, W. F., Jr. Pituitary-Adrenal Cortex Reactivity in Schizophrenic Patients. *Arch. Neurol. Psychiat.,* 1953, 70, 598-610.
403. Fryer, D. An Objective and Subjective Measurement of Interest. *J. Appl. Psychol.,* 1930, 14, 549-556.
404. Fuller, J. L. *Nature and Nurture: A Modern Synthesis.* Garden City, N. Y.: Doubleday, 1954.
405. Fulton, J. F. *Physiology of the Nervous System.* New York: Oxford University Press, 1949.
406. Fulton, J. F., *A Textbook of Physiology,* 16th Ed., Philadelphia: Saunders, 1950.

407. Fulton, J. F. Somatic Functions of the Central Nervous System. *Ann. Rev. Physiol.,* 1953, 15, 305-328.
408. Fulton, J. F., Kennard, M. A. & Watts, J. W. Autonomic Representation in the Cerebral Cortex. *Am. J. Physiol.,* 1934, 109, 37.
409. Funkenstein, D. H. Variations in Response to Standard Amounts of Chemical Agents during Alterations in Feeling States in Relation to Occurrence of Asthma. *Proc. Assn. Res. Nerv. Ment. Dis.,* 1949, 29, 566-582.
410. Funkenstein, D. H. Psychophysiologic Relationship of Asthma and Urticaria to Mental Illness. *Psychosom. Med.,* 1950, 12, 377-385.
410a. Funkenstein, D. H. Nor-Epinephrine-Like and Epinephrine-Like Substance in Relation to Human Behavior. *J. Nerv. Ment. Dis.,* 1956, 124, 58-68.
411. Funkenstein, D. H., Greenblatt, M. & Solomon, H. C. Autonomic Nervous System Changes Following Electric Shock Treatment. *J. Nerv. Ment. Dis.,* 1948, 108, 409-422.
411a. Funkenstein, D. H., King, S. H. & Drolette, M. A Study of the Direction of Anger during Laboratory Stress Inducing Situation. *Psychosom. Med.,* 1954, 16, 404-413.
411b. Funkenstein, D. H., King, S. H. & Drolette, H. E. Mastery of Stress. Cambridge: Harvard University Press, 1957.
412. Fuster, B., Gibbs, E. L. & Gibbs, F. A. Pentothal Sleep as an Aid to the Diagnosis and Localization of Seizure Discharges of Psychomotor Type. *Dis. Nerv. Syst.,* 1948, 9, 199-202.
413. Gagel, O. Symptomatologie der Erkrankungen des Hypothalamus. In: Bumke & Foerster, eds., *Handbuch der Neurologie.* Berlin: Springer, 1936, pp. 482-522.
413a. Gangloff, H. & Monnier, M. Electrographic Aspects of an "Arousal" or Attention Reaction Induced in the Unanesthetized Rabbit by the Presence of a Human Being. *EEG Clin. Neurophysiol.,* 1956, 8, 623-629.
414. Gantt, W. H. & Dykman, R. A. Experimental Psychogenic Tachycardia. *Am. J. Physiol,* 1952, 171, 725-736.
415. Gardiner, H. M., Medcalf, R. C. & Beebe-Center, J. G. *Feeling and Emotion.* New York: American Book Co., 1937.
416. Garvin, J. S. Psychomotor Epilepsy: A Clinico-encephalographic Syndrome. *J. Nerv. Ment. Dis.,* 1953, 117, 1-8.
417. Gaskill, H. V. The Objective Measurement of Emotional Reactions. *Genet. Phychol. Mon.,* 1933, 14, 177-280.
418. Gasser, H. S. Pain-Producing Impulses in Peripheral Nerves. *Proc. Assn. Res. Nerv. Ment. Dis.,* 1943, 23, 44-62.
419. Gastaut, H. Combined Photic and Metrazol Activation of the Brain. *EEG Clin. Neurophysiol.,* 1950, 2, 249-261.
419a. Gastaut, H. The Brain Stem and Cerebral Electro-genesis in Relation to Consciousness. In: Delfresnaye (287b), pp. 249-283.
420. Geddes, D. P. *An Analysis of the Kinsey Reports on Sexual Behavior in the Human Male and Female.* New York: Dutton, 1954.
421. Gelb, A. & Goldstein, K. Zur Psychologie des optischen Wahrnehmungs-Erkennungsvorganges. *Z. Ges. Neurol. Psychiat.,* 1918, 41, 1-143.
422. Geldreich, E. W. Some Physiological Concomitants of Mental Work. *Psychol. Mon.,* 1953, 67, 1-28.
423. Gellhorn, E. *Autonomic Regulations: Their Significance for Physiology, Psychology, and Neuropsychiatry.* New York: Interscience, 1943.
424. Gellhorn, E. Recent Investigations on the Physiological Basis of Emotions. In: Hoch & Zubin (583), pp. 205-217.

425. Gellhorn, E. On the Physiological Activity of Carbon Dioxide on the Cortex and Hypothalamus. *EEG Clin. Neurophysiol.*, 1953, 5, 401-413.
426. Gellhorn, E. *Physiological Foundations of Neurology and Psychiatry*. Minneapolis: University of Minnesota Press, 1953.
427. Gellhorn, E. & Ballin, H. M. The Effect of Afferent Impulses on Hypothalamic Potentials. *Am. J. Physiol.*, 1946, 146, 630-635.
428. Gellhorn, E., Ballin, H. M. & Riggle, C. M. Hypothalamus and Thalamus as Pacemakers of Cortical Activity in Asphyxia and Anoxia. *Acta Neuroveg.*, 1951, 2, 237-262.
429. Gellhorn, E., Cortell, R. & Feldman, J. The Autonomic Basis of Emotion. *Science,* 92, 1940, 288-289.
430. Gellhorn, E., Cortell, R. & Feldman, J. The Effect of Emotion, Sham Rage and Hypothalamic Stimulation on the Vago-Insulin System. *Am. J. Physiol.,* 1941, 133, 532-541.
431. Gellhorn, E., Feldman, J. & Allen, A. Effect of Emotional Excitement on the Insulin Content of the Blood. In: Tompkins (1256), pp. 259-269.
432. Gellhorn, E. & Thompson, L. The Influence of Muscle Pain on Cortically Induced Movements. *Am. J. Physiol.,* 1944, 142, 231-239.
433. Gemelli, A. Orienting Concepts in the Study of Affective States. *J. Nerv. Ment. Dis.,* 1949, 110, 198-214; 249-314.
434. George, F. H. Logical Constructs and Psychological Theory. *Psychol. Rev.,* 1953, 60, 1-6.
434a. Gerard, M. W. Genesis of Psychosomatic Symptoms in Infancy. In: Deutsch (299), pp. 82-95.
435. Gerard, R. W., Marshall, W. H. & Saul, L. Electrical Activity of the Cat's Brain. *Arch. Neurol. Psychiat.,* 1936, 36, 675-738.
436. Gesell, A. *The Mental Growth of the Pre-school Child*. New York: Macmillan, 1925.
437. Gesell, A. *Infancy and Human Growth*. New York: Macmillan, 1929.
438. Gesell, A. *The First Five Years of Life*. New York: Harper, 1940.
439. Gesell, A. *The Embryology of Behavior*. New York: Harper, 1945.
440. Gesell, A. Emotions from the Standpoint of a Developmental Morphology. In: Reymert (1033), pp. 393-397.
441. Gesell, A. & Amatruda, C. S. *Developmental Diagnosis: Normal and Abnormal Child Development. Clinical Methods and Pediatric Applications*. New York: Paul B. Hoeber, 1947.
442. Gesell, A. & Ilg, F. L. *Infant and Child in the Culture of Today*. New York: Harper, 1943.
443. Gesell, A. & Ilg, F. L. *The Child from Five to Ten*. New York: Harper, 1946.
444. Gesell, A. & Thompson, H. *Infant Behavior: Its Genesis and Growth*. New York: McGraw-Hill, 1942.
445. Gesell, A. et al. *An Atlas of Child Behavior*. New Haven: Yale University Press, 1934.
446. Gibbs, E. L. & Gibbs, F. A. Diagnostic and Localizing Value of EEG Studies in Sleep. *Proc. Assn. Res. Nerv. Ment. Dis.,* 1947, 26, 366-376.
447. Gibbs, E. L., Gibbs, F. A. & Fustrer, B. Psychomotor Epilepsy. *Arch. Neurol. Psychiat.,* 1948, 60, 331-339.
448. Gibbs, E. L. & Gibbs, F. A. Electroencephalographic Evidence of Thalamic and Hypothalamic Epilepsy. *Neurology,* 1951, 1, 136-144.
449. Gibbs, F. A. & Gibbs, E. L. *Atlas of Electroencephalography*. Cambridge, Mass.: The Authors, 1941.

450. Gibbs, F. A. Psychiatric Implications of Discharging Temporal Lesions. *Tr. Am. Neurol. Assn.*, 1948, 73, 133-137.
451. Gibbs, F. A. & Gibbs, E. L. *Atlas of Electroencephalography,* Vol. 2. Cambridge, Mass.: Addison Wesley Press, 1952.
452. Gibson, T. E. & Shelley, W. B. Sexual and Racial Differences in the Response of Sweat Glands to Acetylcholine and Pilocarpine. *J. Invest. Derm.*, 1948, 11, 137-142.
453. Gildea, E. F. Special Features of Personality Which Are Common to Certain Psychosomatic Disorders. *Psychosom. Med.*, 1949, 11, 273-281.
454. Gillespie, R. D. The Relative Influence of Mental and Muscular Work on the Pulse Rate and Blood Pressure. *J. Physiol.*, 1924, 58, 425-432.
455. Gillespie, R. D. Psychological Factors in Asthma. *Brit. Med. J.*, 1936, 1, 1285-1289.
456. Gilman, A. The Relation Between Blood Osmotic Pressure, Fluid Distribution and Voluntary Water Intake. *Am. J. Physiol.*, 1937, 120, 323-328.
457. Gilmer, von, H. The Glomus Body as a Receptor of Cutaneous Pressure and "Vibrations." *Psychol. Bull.*, 1942, 39, 73-93.
458. Ginsberg, A. Hypothetical Constructs and Intervening Variables. *Psychol. Rev.*, 1954, 61, 119-131.
459. Gjessing, R. Disturbances of Somatic Functions in Catatonia with a Periodic Course and Their Compensation. *J. Ment. Sci.*, 1948, 84, 608-621.
460. Glaser, G. H. Psychotic Reactions Induced by Corticotropin (ACTH) and Cortisone. *Psychosom. Med.*, 1953, 15, 280-291.
460a. Glaser, G. H. Panel Discussion: Recent Concepts of Central Neurophysiology, Their Bearing on Psychosomatic Phenomena. *Psychosom. Med.*, 1955, 17, 337-346.
460b. Glover, E. *Psychoanalysis.* New York: Staples Press, 1939.
460c. Glover, E. *On the Early Development of Mind.* New York: International Universities Press, 1956.
460d. Glover, E. Functional Aspects of the Mental Apparatus. *Int. J. Psycho-Anal.*, 1950, 31, 125-131.
461. Gloyne, H. F. Psychosomatic Aspects of Pain. *Psychoanal. Rev.*, 1954, 41, 135-159.
462. Godtfredsen, E. Psychosomatic Ophthalmology. *Acta Psychother. Pyschosom. Orthopaedagog.*, 1953-1954, 1, 211-219.
463. Gold, H., Kwit, N. T. & Modell, W. The Effect of Extracardiac Pain on the Heart. *Ann. Int. Med.*, 1943, 23, 345-357.
464. Goldberg, H., Elisberg, E. I. & Katz, L. N. The Effect of the Valsalvalike Maneuver upon the Circulation in Normal Individuals and Patients with Mitral Stenosis. *Circulation,* 1951, 5, 38-48.
465. Goldenberg, M., Pines, K. L., Baldwin, E. de F., Gruen, D. G. & Roh, C. E. Hemodynamic Response of Man to Nor-Epinephrine and Epinephrine and Its Relation to the Problem of Hypertension. *Am. J. Med.*, 1948, 5, 792-806.
466. Goldstein, K. *The Organism: A Holistic Approach to Biology Derived from Pathological Data in Man.* New York: American Book Co., 1939.
467. Golightly, C. L. The James-Lange Theory: A Logical Post-Mortem. *Phil. Sci.*, 1953, 20, 286-299.
468. Goltz, F. Über die Verrichtungen des Grosshirns V. Abhandl. *Pflüg. Arch. ges. Physiol.*, 1884, 34, 450-505.
469. Goodell, H., Graham, D. T. & Wolff, H. G. Changes in Body Heat Regulation Associated with Varying Life Situations and Emotional States. *Proc. Assn. Res. Nerv. Ment. Dis.*, 1950, 29, 418-432.

470. Goodenough, F. L. *Developmental Psychology.* New York: D. Appleton-Century, 1945.

470a. Goodhart, R. S. *Overeating, Overweight and Obesity.* New York: National Vitamin Foundation, 1953.

471. Goolker, P. & Schein, J. Psychic Effects of ACTH and Cortisone. *Psychosom. Med.,* 1953, 15, 589-613.

472. Gottlieb, J. S., Ashby, M. C. & Knott, J. R. Studies in Primary Behavior Disorders and Psychopathic Personality: II, The Inheritance of Electrocortical Activity. *Am. J. Psychiat.,* 1947, 103, 823-827.

473. Gottlober, A. B. The Relationship between Brain Potentials and Personality. *J. Exp. Psychol.,* 1938, 22, 67-74.

474. Grace, W. J. Life Situations, Emotions and Chronic Ulcerative Colitis. *Proc. Assn. Res. Nerv. Ment. Dis.,* 1949, 29, 679.

475. Grace, W. J., Holman, C. W., Wolf, S. & Wolff, H. G. The Effect of Vagotomy on the Human Colon. *Gastroenterol.,* 1949, 13, 536-546.

476. Grace, W. J., Wolf, S. & Wolff, H. G. Life Situations, Emotions, and Colonic Function. *Gastroenterol.,* 1950, 14, 93-108.

477. Grace, W. J., Wolf, S. & Wolff, H. G. *The Human Colon.* New York: Paul B. Hoeber, 1951.

478. Graham, B. F. Neuroendocrine Components in the Physiological Response to Stress. *Ann. N.Y. Acad. Sci.,* 1953, 56, 184-199.

479. Graham, D. T. The Pathogenesis of Hives: Experimental Study of Life Situations, Emotions, and Cutaneous Vascular Reactions. *Proc. Assn. Res. Nerv. Ment. Dis.,* 1949, 29, 987-1009.

479a. Graham, D. T. Cutaneous Vascular Reactions in Raynaud's Disease and in States of Hostility, Anxiety, and Depression. *Psychosom. Med.,* 1955, 17, 200-207.

480. Graham, D. T. & Wolf, S. Pathogenesis of Urticaria. *J. Am. Med. Assn.,* 1950, 143, 1396-1402.

481. Grant, R. Physiological Effects of Heat and Cold. *Am. Rev. Physiol.,* 1951, 13, 75-98.

482. Grant, R. T. Observations on the After-Histories of Men Suffering from the Effort Syndrome. *Heart,* 1925, 12, 121-142.

483. Grant, R. T., Pearson, R. S. B. & Comeau, W. J. Observations on Urticaria Provoked by Emotion, by Exercise, and by Warming the Body. *Clin. Sci.,* 1936, 2, 253-272.

484. Gray, S. J., Benson, J. A., Jr., Reifenstein, R. W. & Spiro, H. M. Chronic Stress and Peptic Ulcer: I, Effect of Corticotropin (ACTH) and Cortisone on Gastric Secretion. *J. Am. Med. Assn.,* 1951, 141, 1529-1537.

485. Grayson, H. M. & Tolman, R. S. A Semantic Study of Concepts of Clinical Psychologists and Psychiatrists. *J. Abnorm. Soc. Psychol.,* 1950, 45, 216-231.

486. Grayson, J. Vascular Reactions in the Human Intestine. *J. Physiol.,* 1949, 109, 439-447.

487. Grayson, J. & Swan, H. J. C. Action of Adrenalin, Noradrenalin, and Dihydroergocornine on Colonic Circulation. *Lancet,* 1950, 1, 488-490.

488. Grayson, J. & Swan, H. J. C. Intestinal Blood-Flow Changes in Man during Fainting. *J. Physiol.,* 1951, 112, 44P.

489. Graziani, A. Ricerche sulle Modificazione Citologiche del Sangue nelle Principali Psicosi. *Riv. Speriment. di Freniat.,* 1910, 36, 878-914.

490. Green, E. & Emery, F. E. Emotional Glycosuria in Medical and Dental Students. *Endocrinol.,* 1942, 30, 353-354.

491. Green, J. D. & Morin, F. Hypothalamic-Electrical Activity and Hypothalamo-Cortical Relationships. *Am. J. Physiol.,* 1953, 172, 175-186.
492. Greenacre, P. Infant Reactions to Restraint. *Am. J. Orthopsychiat.,* 1944, 14, 204-218.
492a. Greenacre, P. *Trauma, Growth, and Personality.* New York: Norton, 1952.
493. Greenblatt, M., Healey, M. M. & Jones, G. A. Age and Electroencephalographic Abnormality in Neuropsychiatric Patients: A Study of 1593 cases. *Am. J. Psychiat.,* 1944, 101, 82-90.
494. Greenfield, A. D. M. An Emotional Faint. *Lancet,* 1951, 1, 1302-1303.
495. Greenhill, M. H. & Finesinger, J. E. Neurotic Symptoms and Emotional Factors in Atopic Dermatitis. *Arch. Derm. Syph.,* 1942, 46, 187-200.
496. Grenell, R. G. & McCawley, E. L. Central Nervous System Resistance: III, The Effect of Adrenal Cortical Substances on the Central Nervous System. *J. Neurosurg.,* 1947, 4, 508-518.
497. Grenit, R. Reflex Self-regulation of Muscle Contraction and Autogenetic Inhibition. *J. Neurophysiol.* 1950, 13, 351-372.
498. Grings, W. W. Methodological Considerations Underlying Electrodermal Measurement. *J. Psychol.,* 1953, 35, 271-282.
499. Grinker, R. R. Hypothalamic Functions in Psychosomatic Interrelations. *Psychosom. Med.,* 1939, 1, 19-47.
500. Grinker, R. R. *Psychosomatic Research.* New York: Norton, 1953.
501. Groen, J. *Psychopathogenese van Ulcus Ventriculi et Duodeni.* Amsterdam: Scheltema & Holkema, 1947.
502. Groen, J. A Personal Communication to H. G. Wolff (1937).
503. Grollman, A. Physiological Variations in the Cardiac Output of Man. *Am. J. Physiol.,* 1929, 89, 366-370.
504. Grollman, A. The Effect of Psychic Disturbances on the Cardiac Output, Blood Pressure and Oxygen Consumption of Man. *Am. J. Physiol.,* 1929, 89, 584-588.
505. Groen, J. A Personal Communication to H. G. Wolff (1937). Baillière, Tindall & Cox, 1932.
506. Gross, I. H. & Bartley, S. H. Fatigue in House Care. *J. Appl. Psychol.,* 1951, 35, 206-207.
507. Grossman, M., Weinstein, W. W. & Katz, I.N. The Use of the Exercise Test in the Diagnosis of Coronary Insufficiency. *Ann. Int. Med.,* 1949, 30, 387-397.
508. Guilford, J. P. When not to Factor Analyze. *Psychol. Bull.,* 1952, 49, 26-37.
509. Guthrie, E. R. *The Psychology of Learning.* New York: Harper, 1935.
510. Guthrie, E. R. *The Psychology of Human Conflict.* New York: Harper, 1938.
511. Guthrie, E. R. Personality in Terms of Associative Learning. In: Hunt (610), pp. 1, 49-68.
512. Haggard, E. A. & Jones, H. E. The Comparative Discriminating Value of Various Measures of GSR for Words of Differing Affect Value. *Am. Psychol.,* 1947, 2, 349.
513. Hall, C. S. The Genetics of Behavior. In: Stevens (1197a), pp. 304-329.
514. Hall, K. R. L. Studies of Cutaneous Pain: A Survey of Research Since 1940. *Brit. J. Psychol.,* 1953, 44, 279-294.
515. Hall, K. R. L. & Stride, E. The Varying Response to Pain in Psychiatric Disorder. *Brit. J. Med. Psychol.,* 1954, 27, 48-60.
516. Halliday, J. L. Approach to Asthma. *Brit. J. Med. Psychol.,* 1937, 17, 1-53.
517. Halstead, W. C. Brain and Intelligence. In: L. A. Jeffress, ed., *Cerebral Mechanisms in Behavior, the Hiron Symposium.* New York: John Wiley, 1951, pp. 244-278.
517a. Hamilton, M. *Psychosomatics.* New York: John Wiley, 1955.

518. Hammar, L. & Wainwright, C. W. The Diagnosis of Obscure Fever. I, The Diagnosis of Unexplained, Long Continued Low Grade Fever. *Bull. Johns Hopkins Hosp.*, 1936, 58, 109.
519. Hanson, H. H. & Rutledge, D. J. Auricular Fibrillation in Normal Hearts. *New Eng. J. Med.*, 1949, 240, 947-953.
520. Hardwick, S. W. & Stokes, A. B. Metabolic Investigations in Periodic Catatonia. *Proc. Royal Soc. Med.*, 1941, 34, 733-766.
521. Hardy, J. D., Wolff, H. G. & Goodell, H. Studies on Pain in a New Method for Measuring Pain Threshold: Observations on Spatial Summation of Pain. *J. Clin. Invest.*, 1940, 19, 649-657.
522. Hardy, J. D., Wolff, H. G. & Goodell, H. *Pain Sensations and Reactions.* Baltimore: Williams & Wilkins, 1952.
523. Harlow, H. F. Higher Functions of the Nervous System. *Ann. Rev. Physiol.*, 1953, 15, 493-514.
524. Harlow, H. F. & Stagner, R. Psychology of Feeling and Emotion. I, Theory of Feeling. *Psychol. Rev.*, 1932, 39, 570-589.
525. Harlow, H. F. & Stagner, R. Psychology of Feeling and Emotion. II, Theory of Emotion. *Psychol. Rev.*, 1933, 40, 184-195 and 368-380.
526. Harms, E. A Differential Concept of Feelings and Emotions. In: Reymert (1033), pp. 147-157.
527. Harris, I. D. Mood, Anger, and Somatic Dysfunction. *J. Nerv. Ment. Dis.*, 1951, 113, 152-158.
528. Harris, J. B., Hoff, H. E. & Wise, R. A. Diaphragmatic Flutter as a Manifestation of Hysteria. *Psychosom. Med.*, 1954, 16, 56-66.
529. Harris, M. M., Brand, E. & Hensie, L. E. Studies of the Urinary Excretion of Gonadal Stimulating Substance in Mental Patients. *Am. J. Psychiat.*, 1935, 91, 1239-1261.
530. Harris, R. E., Sokolow, M., Carpenter, L., Jr., Freedman, M. & Hunt, S. Response to Psychologic Stress in Persons Who Are Potentially Hypertensive. *Circulation*, 1953, 7, 874-879.
531. Harrower-Erickson, M. R. & Steiner, M. E. *Large Scale Rorschach Techniques*, Springfield, Ill.: C. C Thomas, 1945.
532. Hart, B. & Spearman, C. General Ability, Its Existence and Nature. *Brit. J. Psychol.*, 1912, 5, 51-84.
532a. Hartfall, S. J. Stress and the Rheumatic Disorders. *Practitioner*, 1954, 172, 29-36.
533. Hartman, G. W. *Gestalt Psychology: A Survey of Facts and Principles.* New York: Ronald Press, 1935.
533a. Hartmann, H. Psychoanalysis and Developmental Psychology. *Psychoanalytic Study of the Child*, 1950, 5, 7-17.
533b. Hartmann, H. Comments on the Psychoanalytic Theory of the Ego. *Psychoanalytic Study of the Child*, 1950, 5, 74-96.
533c. Hartmann, H. The Mutual Influences in the Development of Ego and Id. *Psychoanalytic Study of the Child*, 1952, 7, 9-30.
533d. Hartmann, H. & Kris, E. The Genetic Approach in Psychoanalysis. *Psychoanalytic Study of the Child*, 1945, 1, 11-30.
533e. Hartmann, H., Kris, E & Loewenstein, R. M. Comments on the Formation of Psychic Structure. *Psychoanalytic Study of the Child*, 1946, 2, 11-38.
533f. Hartmann, H., Kris, E., & Loewenstein, R. M. Notes on the Theory of Aggression. *Psychoanalytic Study of the Child*, 1949, 3/4, 9-36.
534. Hartwell, A. S., Burrett, J. B., Graybiel, A. S. & White, P. D. The Effect of Exercise and Four Commonly Used Drugs on the Normal Human Electro-

cardiogram, with Particular Reference to T Wave Changes. *J. Clin. Invest.,* 1942, 21, 409-417.

535. Harvey, W. A. & Sherfey, M. J. Vomiting in Pregnancy. *Psychosom. Med.,* 1954, 16, 1-9.

536. Hassler, R. Über die afferenten Bahnen und Thalamuskerne des motorischen Systems des Grosshirns. *Arch. f. Psychiat.,* 1949, 182, 759-818.

536a. Hayakawa, S. I., ed. *Language, Meaning and Maturity.* New York: Harper, 1954.

537. Hayes, S. P. A Study of the Affective Qualities. *Am. J. Psychol.,* 1906, 17, 358-392.

538. Head, H. On Disturbances of Sensation with Especial Reference to the Pain of Visceral Disease. *Brain,* 1894, 17, 339.

539. Head, H. *Studies in Neurology,* Vol. 2. London: Oxford University Press, 1920.

540. Head, H., Rivers, W. H. R. & Sherren, J. The Afferent Nervous System from a New Aspect. *Brain,* 1905, 28, 99-116.

541. Head, H., and Rivers, W. H. R. A Human Experiment in Nerve Division. *Brain,* 1908, 31, 323-450.

541a. Heath, R. G., ed. *Studies in Schizophrenia.* Cambridge: Harvard University Press, 1954.

542. Hebb, D. O. On the Nature of Fear. *Psychol. Bull.,* 1946, 53, 259-276.

543. Hebb, D. O. Emotion in Man and Animals: An Analysis of the Intuitive Process of Recognition. *Psychol. Rev.,* 1946, 53, 88-106.

544. Hebb, D. O. *The Organization of Behavior.* New York: John Wiley, 1949.

544a. Hecht, I. The Difference in Goal Striving Behavior between Peptic Ulcer and Ulcerative Colitis Patients as Evaluated by Psychological Techniques. In: D. O. McClelland, ed., *Studies in Motivation.* New York: Appleton-Century-Crofts, 1955, pp. 460-465.

545. Heckel, N. J. *The Effect of Hormone upon the Testes and Accessory Sex Organs.* Springfield, Ill.: C. C Thomas, 1951.

546. Heide, C. van der. A Study of the Mechanisms in Two Cases of Peptic Ulcer. *Psychosom. Med.,* 1940, 2, 398.

547. Heilig, R. & Hoff, H. Über hypnotische Beeinflussung der Nierenfunktion. *Deut. Med. Wochnschr.,* 1925, 51, 1615.

548. Heller, M. H., Levine, J. & Sohler, T. P. Gastric Acidity and Normally Produced Anxiety. *Psychosom. Med.,* 1953, 15, 509-512.

549. Helson, H., ed. *Theoretical Foundations of Psychology.* New York: D. Van Nostrand, 1951.

550. Hemingway, A. Cold Sweating in Motion Sickness. *Am. J. Physiol.,* 1944, 141, 172-175.

551. Hemphill, R. E., Hall, K. R. L. & Crookes, T. G. Preliminary Report on Fatigue and Pain Tolerance in Depressive and Psychoneurotic Patients. *J. Ment. Sci.,* 1952, 98, 433-440.

552. Hemphill, R. E. & Reiss, M. The Isotopes in Psychiatry. *Int. Congress Psychiat.,* 1950, 3, 290-291.

553. Hench, P. S., Kendall, E. C., Slocumb, C. H. & Polley, H. F. Effects of Cortisone Acetate and Pituitary ACTH on Rheumatoid Arthritis, Rheumatic Fever and Certain Other Conditions, A Study in Clinical Physiology. *Arch. Int. Med.,* 1950, 85, 545-666.

554. Henry, C. E. & Knott, J. R. A Note on the Relationship between "Personality" and the Alpha Rhythm of the Electroencephalogram. *J. Exp. Psychol.,* 1941, 28, 362-366.

555. Heppenstall, M. E. The Relation Between the Effects of the Blood Sugar Levels and Hyperventilation on the Electroencephalogram. *J. Neurol. Neurosurg. Psychiat.*, 1944, 7, 112-118.

556. Hertz, A. F. The Sensibility of the Alimentary Canal in Health and Disease. *Lancet*, 1911, 1, 1051-1056; 1119-1124; 1187-1193.

557. Hertz, M. A. The Ileo-caecal Sphincter. *J. Physiol.*, 1913-14, 47, 54.

558. Hertzmann, A. R. The Relative Responses of the Dorsal Metacarpal, Digital and Terminal Skin Arteries of the Hand in Vasoconstrictor Reflexes. *Am. J. Physiol.*, 1951, 134, 59-64.

559. Hess, W. R. Die Funktion des vegetativen Nervensystems. *Klin. Wochnschr.*, 1930, 9, 1009.

559a. Hess, W. R. The Diencephalic Sleep Center. In: Delefresnaye (287b), pp. 117-136.

559b. Hess, W. R. & Akert, K. Experimental Data on Role of Hypothalamus in Mechanism of Emotional Behavior. *Arch. Neurol. Psychiat.*, 1955, 73, 127-129.

560. Hickam, J. B., Corgill, W. H. & Golden, A. Cardiovascular Reactions to Emotional Stimuli. *J. Clin. Invest.*, 1948, 27, 290-298.

561. Hilgard, E. R. *Theories of Learning*. New York: Appleton-Century-Crofts, 1948.

562. Hill, D. Cerebral Dysrhythmia: Its Significance in Aggressive Behaviour. *Proc. Royal Soc. Med.*, 1944, 37, 317-330.

563. Hill, D. EEG in Episodic Psychotic and Psychopathic Behavior. A Classification of Data. *EEG Clin. Neurophysiol.*, 1952, 4, 419-422.

564. Hill, D. Clinical Association of Electroencephalographic Foci in the Temporal Lobe. *Arch. Neurol. Psychiat.*, 1953, 69, 379.

565. Hill, D. & Watterson, D. Electroencephalographic Studies of Psychopathic Personalities. *J. Neurol. Psychiat.*, 1942, 5, 47-65.

566. Hill, S. R., Jr., Reiss, R. S., Forsham, P. H. & Thorn, G. W. The Effect of Adrenocorticotropin and Cortisone on Thyroid Function: Thyroid-Adrenocortical Interrelationships. *J. Clin. Endocrinol.*, 1950, 10, 1375-1400.

567. Himwich, H. E. A Review of Hypoglycemia, Its Physiology and Pathology, Symptomatology and Treatment. *Am. J. Digestive Dis.*, 1944, 2, No. 1.

568. Hinkle, L. E., Jr., Conger, G. B. & Wolf, S. Studies on Diabetes Mellitus: The Relation of Stressful Life Situations to the Concentration of Ketone Bodies in the Blood of Diabetic and Non-diabetic Humans. *J. Clin. Invest.*, 1950, 29, 754-769.

569. Hinkle, L. E., Jr., Edwards, C. J. & Wolf, S. The Occurrence of Diuresis in Humans in Stressful Situations and Its Possible Relation to the Diuresis of Early Starvation. *J. Clin. Invest.*, 1951, 30, 809-817.

570. Hinkle, L. E., Jr., Edwards, C. J., Wolf, S., et al. Studies in Diabetes Mellitus. II, The Occurrence of Diuresis in Diabetic Persons Exposed to Stressful Life Situations with Experimental Observations on Its Relation to the Concentration of Glucose in Blood and Urine. *J. Clin. Invest.*, 1951, 30, 818-839.

571. Hinkle, L. E., Jr., Evans, F. M. & Wolf, S. Studies in Diabetes Mellitus. III, Life History of Three Persons with Labile Diabetes, and Relation of Significant Experience in Their Lives to the Onset and Course of the Disease. *Psychosom. Med.*, 1951, 13, 160-183.

572. Hinkle, L. E., Jr., Evans, F. M. & Wolf, S. Studies in Diabetes Mellitus. IV, Life History of Three Persons with Relatively Mild Stable Diabetes, and Relation of Significant Experience in Their Lives to the Onset and Course of the Disease. *Psychosom. Med.*, 1951, 13, 184-202.

573. Hinkle, L. E., Jr. & Wolf, S. Experimental Study of Life Situations, Emotion,

and the Occurence of Acidosis in a Juvenile Diabetic. *Am. J. Med. Sci.*, 1949, 219, 130-135.

574. Hinkle, L. E., Jr. & Wolf, S. Studies in Diabetes Mellitus: Changes in Glucose, Ketone, and Water Metabolism during Stress. *Proc. Assn. Nerv. Ment. Dis.*, 1950, 29, 338-389.

575. Hinkle, L. E., Jr. & Wolf, S. Variations in Blood Sugar in Diabetes Mellitus. *J. Clin. Invest.*, 1951, 30, 649.

576. Hinkle, L. E., Jr. & Wolf, S. Importance of Stress in Course and Management of Diabetes Mellitus. *J. Am. Med. Assn.*, 1952, 148, 513-520.

577. Hinsey, J. C. The Hypothalamus and Somatic Responses. *Proc. Assn. Res. Nerv. Ment. Dis.*, 1947, 2, 363-404.

578. Hinsey, J. C., Ranson, S. W. & McNattin, R. F. The Role of the Hypothalamus and Mesencephalon in Locomotion. *Arch. Neurol. Psychiat.*, 1930, 23, 1-42.

579. Hoagland, H. Some Biochemical Considerations of Psychotic Behavior. *J. Clin. Exp. Psychopath.*, 1951, 12, 111-122.

580. Hoagland, H. Metabolic and Physiologic Disturbances in the Psychoses. In: Milbank Memorial Fund (903), pp. 434-456.

580a. Hoagland, H., Bergen, J. R., Slocombe, A. G. & Hunt, C. A. Studies of Adrenocortical Physiology in Relation to the Nervous System. *Proc. Assn. Res. Nerv. Ment. Dis.*, 1953, 32, 40-60.

581. Hoagland, H., Cameron, D. E. & Rubin, M. A. Emotion in Man as Tested by the Delta Index of the Electroencephalogram. I, *J. Gen. Psychol.*, 1938, 19, 227-245.

582. Hoagland, H., Cameron, D. E. & Tegelberg, J. J. Emotion in Man as Tested by the Delta Index of the Electroencephalogram. II, Simultaneous Records from Cortex and from a Region Near the Hypothalamus. *J. Gen. Psychol.*, 1938, 19, 247-261.

583. Hoch, P. H. & Zubin, J., eds. *Anxiety.* New York: Grune & Stratton, 1950.

583a. Hochberg, J. E. Effects of the Gestalt Revolution. *Psychol. Rev.*, 1957, 62, 73-84.

584. Hochberg, J. E. & Gleitman, H. Towards a Reformulation of the Perception-Motivation Dichotomy. *J. Personality,* 1949, 18, 180-191.

585. Hoefer, P. F. A. & Glaser, G. H. Effects of Pituitary Adrenocorticotropic Hormone (ACTH) Therapy: Electroencephalographic and Neuropsychiatric Changes in 15 Patients. *J. Am. Med. Assn.*, 1950, 143, 620-624.

586. Hoelzel, F. Central Factors in Hunger. *Am. J. Physiol.*, 1927, 82, 665-671.

587. Hoelzel, F. Fear and Gastric Acidity. *Am. J. Digestive Dis.*, 1942, 9, 188.

588. Hoff, H. & Werner, P. Untersuchungen über den Mechanismus der Diuresehemmung durch Pituitin am Menschen. *Arch. Exp. Path. Pharmakol.*, 1926, 119, 153-164.

589. Hoisington, L. B. Pleasantness and Unpleasantness as Modes of Bodily Experience. In: Reymert (1032), pp. 236-246.

590. Hollander, E. Clinical Gauge for Sensitivity to Pain. *J. Lab. Clin. Med.*, 1939, 24, 537.

591. Hollands, E. H. Wundt's Doctrine of Psychical Analysis and the Psychical Elements and Some Recent Criticisms. *Am. J. Psychol.*, 1926, 17, 205-226.

592. Holmes, T. H., Goodell, H., Wolf, S. & Wolff, H. G. Evidence on the Genesis of Certain Common Nasal Disorders. *Am. J. Med. Sci.*, 1949, 218, 16-27.

593. Holmes, T. H., Goodell, H., Wolf, S. & Wolff, H. G. *The Nose: An Experimental Study of Reactions Within the Nose in Human Subjects during Varying Life Experiences.* Springfield, Ill.: C. C Thomas, 1950.

593a. Holmes, T. H., Hawkins, N. G., Bowerman, C. E., Clarke, E. K., Jr. & Jaffe,

J. R. Psychosocial and Psychophysiologic Studies of Tuberculosis. *Psychosom. Med.*, 1957, 29, 134-143.

594. Holmes, T. H., Treuting, T. & Wolff, H. G. Life Situations, Emotions, and Nasal Disease. *Psychosom. Med.*, 1951, 13, 71-82.

595. Holmes, T. H. & Wolff, H. G. Life Situations and Backaches. *Psychosom. Med.*, 1952, 14, 18-33.

596. Holmgren, B. & Kraepelien, S. Electroencephalographic Studies of Asthmatic Children. *Acta Paediat.*, 1953, 42, 432-441.

597. Hopkins, J. G., Kesten, B. M. & Hazel, O. G. Urticaria Provoked by Heat or by Psychic Stimuli. *Arch. Derm. Syph.*, 1938, 38, 679-691.

597a. Hornbostel, E. M. von. The Unity of the Senses. *Psyche,* 1927, 28, 83-89.

598. Horney, K. *The Neurotic Personality of Our Times.* New York: Norton, 1937.

599. Horney, K. *New Ways in Psychoanalysis.* New York: Norton, 1939.

600. Horney, K. *Neurosis and Human Growth.* New York: Norton, 1950.

601. Horowitz, O., Peirce, G. & Montgomery, H. Oxygen Tension of Tissues by the Polarographic Method. III, The Effect of Local Heat on the Oxygen Tension of the Skin of Extremities. *Circulation,* 1951, 4, 111-115.

601a. Hose, W., Cremerius, J., Elhardt, S. & Kilian, H. Ergebnisse der psychosomatischen Diabetes-Forschung. *Psyche,* 1955, 9, 815-840.

602. Hoskins, R. G. Schizophrenia from the Physiological Point of View. *Ann. Int. Med.*, 1933, 7, 445-456.

603. Hoskins, R. G. & Jellinek, E. M. The Schizophrenic Personality with Special Regard to Psychologic and Organic Concomitants. *Proc. Assn. Res. Nerv. Ment. Dis.*, 1933, 14, 211-233.

604. Hotelling, H. Analysis of a Complex of Statistical Variables into Principal Components. *J. Educ. Psychol.*, 1933, 24, 417-441, 498-520.

605. Howard, R. P., Venning, E. H. & Fisk, G. H. Rheumatoid Arthritis. II, Studies of Adrenocortical and Hypophyseal Function and the Effects Thereon of Testosterone and Pregnenolone Therapy. *Canad. Med. Assn. J.*, 1950, 63, 340-342.

606. Howells, W. W. A Factorial Study of Constitutional Type. *Am. J. Phys. Anthrop.*, 1952, 10, 91-118.

607. Howorth, M. D. *A Textbook of Orthopedics.* Philadelphia: Saunders, 1952.

608. Hull, C. L. *Principles of Behavior.* New York: Appleton-Century, 1943.

609. Hume, D. M. & Wittenstein, G. J. The Relationship of the Hypothalamus to Pituitary-Adrenocortical Function. In: J. R. Mote, ed., *Proc. First Clin. ACTH Conf.*, Philadelphia: Blakiston, 1950, pp. 134-147.

610. Hunt, J. McV., ed. *Personality and the Behavior Disorders,* 2 vols. New York: Ronald Press, 1944.

611. Hunt, W. A. The Relation of Bright and Dull Pressure to Affectivity. *Am. J. Psychol.*, 1931, 43, 87-92.

611a. Hunt, W. A. Localization of Bright and Dull Pressure. *Am. J. Psychol.*, 1932, 44, 308-313.

612. Hunt, W. A. The Conscious Correlates of the Galvanic Skin Response. *Psychol. Bull.*, 1934, 31, 699.

612a. Hunt, W. A. Ambiguity of Descriptive Terms for Feeling and Emotion. *Am. J. Psychol.*, 1935, 47, 165-166.

613. Hunt, W. A. A Critical Review of Current Approaches to Affectivity. *Psychol. Bull.*, 1939, 36, 807-828.

614. Hunt, W. A. Recent Development in the Field of Emotion. *Psychol. Bull.*, 1941, 38, 249-276.

615. Hunt, W. A. & Landis, C. The Overt Behavior Pattern in Startle. *J. Exp. Psychol.,* 1936, 19, 309-315.
616. Hunt, W. A., Landis, C. & Jacobsen, C. F. Studies of the Startle Pattern. V, Apes and Monkeys. *J. Psychol.,* 1937, 3, 339-343.
617. Hurst, L. A., Mundy-Castle, A. C. & Beerstecher, D. M. The Electroencephalogram in Manic-Depressive Psychosis. *J. Ment. Sci.,* 1954, 100, 220-240.
618. Hyndman, O. R. & Wolkin, J. Anterior Chordotomy. Further Observations on Physiologic Results and Optimum Manner of Performance. *Arch. Neurol. Psychiat.,* 1943, 50, 129-148.
619. Igersheimer, W. W. Cold Pressor Test in Functional Psychiatric Syndromes. *Arch. Neurol. Psychiat.,* 1953, 70, 794-801.
620. Ingbar, S. H., Relman, A. S., Burrows, B. A., Kass, E. H., Sisson, J. H. & Burnett, C. H. Changes in Normal Renal Function Resulting from ACTH and Cortisone. *J. Clin. Invest.,* 1950, 29, 824.
621. Ingram, W. R., Knott, J. R., Wheatley, M. D. & Summers, T. D. Physiological Relationships between Hypothalamus and Cerebral Cortex. *EEG Clin. Neurophysiol.,* 1951, 3, 37-58.
622. Inman, V. T. & Saunders, J. B. D. M. Referred Pain from Skeletal Structures. *J. Nerv. Ment. Dis.,* 1944, 99, 660-667.
623. Ireland, L. T. *The Principles of Psychophysiology.* New York: D. Van Nostrand, 1921.
624. Isham, A. C. Emotion, Instinct, and Pain-Pleasure. *Psychoanal. Rev.,* 1954, 41, 99-113.
624a. Jacobson, E. Neuromuscular Controls in Man: Methods of Self-direction in Health and in Disease. *Am. J. Psychol.,* 1955, 68, 549-561.
624b. Jacobson, E. The Child's Laughter. *Psychoanalytic Study of the Child,* 1946, 2, 39-66.
624c. Jacobson, E. The Self and the Object World. *Psychoanalytic Study of the Child,* 1954, 9, 75-127.
625. James, W. What Is Emotion? *Mind,* 1884, 9, 188-204.
626. James, W. *Principles of Psychology,* 2 vols. New York: Henry Holt, 1890.
627. James, W. The Emotions. In: James (626), Chapter 25. Republished in Dunlap, K., ed., *The Emotions.* Psychology Classic, Vol. I, Baltimore: Williams & Wilkins, 1922.
628. James, W. & Lange, G. C. *The Emotions.* Baltimore: Williams & Wilkins, 1922.
629. Janet, P. *L'Etat mental des Hystériques.* Paris: Rueff, 1894.
630. Janet, P. *Les Obsessions et la Psychasténie.* Paris: Alcan, 1903.
631. Janet, P. *The Major Symptoms of Hysteria.* New York: Macmillan, 1920.
632. Jasper, H. H. Diffuse Projection Systems: The Integrative Action of the Thalamic Reticular System. *EEG Clin. Neurophysiol.,* 1949, 1, 405-420.
633. Jasper, H. H. Electrical Activity and Mechanisms of Cerebral Integration. In: Milbank Memorial Fund (903), pp. 226-243.
634. Jasper, H. H. & Andrews, H. L. Electroencephalography. III, Normal Differentiation of Occipital and Pre-central Regions in Man. *Arch. Neurol. Psychiat.,* 1938, 39, 96-115.
635. Jasper, H. H. & Droogleeve-Fortuyn, J. Experimental Studies on the Functional Anatomy of Petit Mal Epilepsy. *Proc. Assn. Res. Nerv. Ment. Dis.,* 1947, 26, 272-298.
636. Jasper, H. H., Fitzpatrick, C. P. & Solomon, P. Analogies and Opposites in Schizophrenia and Epilepsy. *Am. J. Psychiat.,* 1939, 95, 831-851.
637. Jasper, H. H., Pertuisset, B. & Flanigin, H. EEG and Cortical Electrograms in

Patients with Temporal Lobe Seizure. *Arch. Neurol. Psychiat.* 1951, 65, 272-290.

638. Jasper, H. H. & Shagass, C. Conditioning the Occipital Alpha Rhythm in Man. *J. Exp. Psychol.,* 1941, 28, 373-388.

639. Jasper, H. H., Solomon, P. & Bradley, C. Electroencephalographic Analysis of Behavior Problem Children. *Am. J. Psychiat.,* 1938, 95, 641-658.

640. Jefferson, G. The Prodromes to Cortical Localization. *J. Neurol. Neurosurg. Psychiat.,* 1953, 16, 59-72.

641. Jeliffe, S. Dynamic Concepts and the Epileptic Attack. *Am. J. Psychiat.,* 1935, 92, 565-574.

642. Jellinek, E. M. & McFarland, R. A. Analysis of Psychological Experiments on the Effects of Alcohol. *Quart. J. Stud. Alcohol,* 1940, 1, 212-371.

642a. Jenkin, N. Affective Process in Perception. *Psychol. Bull.,* 1957, 54, 100-127.

643. Jenkins, W. L. Somesthesis. In: Stevens (1197a), pp. 1172-1190.

644. Jenkins, W. L. & Stone, L. J. Recent Research in Cutaneous Sensitivity. I, Pain and Temperature. *Psychol. Bull.,* 1940, 37, 285-311.

645. Jenkins, W. L. & Stone, L. J. Recent Research in Cutaneous Sensitivity. II, Touch and the Neural Basis of Skin Sense. *Psychol. Bull.,* 1941, 38, 69-91.

646. Johnson, W. The Semantics of Maladjustment. In: Pennington & Berg (985), pp. 498-516.

647. Jones, C. M. *Digestive Tract Pain.* New York: Macmillan, 1938.

648. Jones, C. M. Pain from the Digestive Tract. *Proc. Assn. Res. Nerv. Ment. Dis.,* 1943, 23, 274-288.

649. Jones, E. Fear, Guilt and Hate. *Int. J. Psychoanal.,* 1929, 10, 383-397.

650. Jones, H. E. The Galvanic Skin Reflex in Infancy. *Child Develop.,* 1930, 1, 106-110.

651. Jones, H. E. The Retention of Conditioned Emotional Reactions in Infancy. *J. Genet. Psychol.,* 1930, 37, 485-498.

652. Jones, H. E. The Galvanic Skin Reflex as Related to Overt Emotional Expression. *Am. J. Psychol.,* 1935, 47, 241-251.

653. Jones, H. E. The Study of Patterns of Emotional Expression. In: Reymert (1033), pp. 161-168.

654. Jones, M. & Lewis, A. Effort Syndrome. *Lancet,* 1941, 2, 813.

655. Jost, H. The Genetic Factor in Autonomic Nervous System Function. *Psychosom. Med.,* 1944, 6, 308-310.

656. Jost, H. Some Physiological Changes during Frustration. *Child Develop.,* 1941, 12, 9-15.

657. Jost, H., Ruilmann, C. J., Hill, T. S. & Gulo, M. J. Studies in Hypertension. *J. Nerv. Ment. Dis.,* 1952, 115, 35-48; 152-162.

658. Judovich, B. & Bates, W. *Pain Syndromes.* Philadelphia: F. A. Davis, 1953.

659. Jung, C. G. The Association Method. *Am. J. Psychol.,* 1910, 21, 246-247.

660. Jung, C. G. *Psychological Types or the Psychology of Individualism.* New York: Harcourt, Brace, 1926.

661. Jung, C. G. *The Psychology of the Unconscious.* New York: Dodd, Mead, 1927.

662. Jung, C.G. *The Integration of the Personality.* New York: Farrar & Rinehart, 1939.

663. Jung, C. G. *The Development of Personality.* New York: Pantheon Books, 1954.

664. Jurgens, B. Über vegetative Reaktionen beim Menschen in ihrer Abhängigkeit von verschiedenen Reizen. *Arch. Psychiat. Nervenkr.,* 1940, 111, 88-114.

665. Jurji, E. J. *The Great Religions of the Modern World.* Princeton, N. J.: Princeton University Press, 1947.
666. Kaada, B. R. Somato-Motor, Autonomic and Electrocorticographic Responses to Electrical Stimulation of "Rhinencephalic" and Other Structures in Primates, Cat and Dog. *Acta Physiol. Scandinav.,* 1951, 24, Suppl. 83, 1-285.
667. Kaada, B. R. Electrical Activity of the Brain. *Ann. Rev. Physiol.,* 1953, 15, 39-62.
668. Kahn, D. & Rothman, S. Sweat Response to Acetylcholine. *J. Invest. Dermat.,* 1942, 5, 431-444.
668a. Kalis, B. L., Harris, R. E., Bennett, L. F. & Sokolow, M. Personality and the Predisposition to Essential Hypertension. *Psychosom. Med.,* in preparation.
668b. Kalis, B. L., Harris, R. E., Sokolow, M. & Carpenter, L. G. Response to Psychological Stress in Patients with Essential Hypertension. *Am. Heart J.,* 1957, 53, 572-578.
669. Kallmann, F. J. *The Genetics of Schizophrenia.* New York: J. J. Augustin, 1938.
670. Kallmann, F. J. Genetic Theory of Schizophrenia. *Am. J. Psychiat.,* 1946, 103, 309-322.
671. Kallmann, F. J. Genetic Aspects of Psychoses. In: Milbank Memorial Fund (903), pp. 283-302.
672. Kapp, F. T., Rosenbaum, M. & Romano, J. Psychological Factors in Men with Peptic Ulcers. *Am. J. Psychiat.,* 1947, 103, 700-704.
673. Kardiner, A. & Linton, R. *The Psychological Frontiers of Society.* New York: Columbia University Press, 1945.
674. Karplus, J. P. & Kreidl, A. Gehirn und Sympathicus, IV. *Pflüg. Arch. Ges. Physiol.,* 1918, 171, 192.
675. Karplus, J. P. & Kreidl, A. Gehirn und Sympathicus. V, Latenzbestimmungen unter Anwehdung einer neuen Methode. *Pflüg. Arch. Ges. Physiol.,* 1924, 203, 533.
676. Karplus, J. P. & Kreidl, A. Gehirn und Sympathicus. VII, Über Beziehungen der Hypothalamuszentren zu Blutdruck und innerer Sekretion. *Pflüg. Arch. Ges. Physiol.,* 1927, 215, 667.
677. Karplus, J. P. & Kreidl, A. Gehirn und Sympathicus. VIII, Über Beziehungen der Hypothalamuszentren zu Blutdruck und innerer Sekretion. *Pflüg. Arch. Ges. Physiol.,* 1928, 219, 613.
678. Karush, A. & Daniels, G. Ulcerative Colitis: The Psychoanalysis of Two Cases. *Psychosom. Med.,* 1953, 15, 140-167.
678a. Karush, A., Hiatt, R. B. & Daniels, G. E. Psychophysiological Correlations in Ulcerative Colitis. *Psychosom. Med.,* 1955, 17, 36-56.
679. Katz, D. *Der Aufbau der Tastwelt.* Berlin: Barth, 1925.
680. Katz, L. N., Winton, S. S. & Megibrow, R. S. Psychosomatic Aspects of Cardiac Arrhythmias: A Physiological Dynamic Approach. *Ann. Int. Med.,* 1947, 1, 261-274.
681. Kaufman, W. Some Psychosomatic Aspects of Food Allergy. *Psychosom. Med.,* 1954, 16, 10-40.
682. Kaufmann, J. Treatment of Peptic Ulcer. *Med. Res.,* 1918, 94, 324.
682a. Keegan, J. G. Recent Findings in Neurology. In: Roback (1046a), pp. 9-31.
683. Keller, A. D., Hare, W. K. & d'Amour, M. C. Ulceration in Digestive Tract Following Experimental Lesions in Brain Stem. *Proc. Soc. Exp. Biol. Med.,* 1933, 30, 772-775.
683a. Kelley, K., Daniels, G. E., Poe, J., Esser, R. & Monroe, R. Psychological Correlations with Secondary Amenorrhea. *Psychosom. Med.,* 1954, 16, 127-147.

684. Kelley, T. L. *Crossroads in the Mind of Man*. Stanford: Stanford University Press, 1928.
685. Kellgren, J. H. On the Distribution of Pain Arising from Deep Somatic Structures with Charts of Segmental Pain Areas. *Clin. Sci.*, 1939, 4, 35-46.
686. Kelly, D. M. Psychophysiological Methods in Police Psychiatry. *J. Nerv. Ment. Dis.*, 1953, 118, 385-390.
686a. Kelly, G. A. *The Psychology of Personal Constructs*, 2 vols. New York: Norton, 1955.
687. Kennard, M. A. Effects on EEG of Chronic Lesions of Basal Ganglia, Thalamus, and Hypothalamus of Monkeys. *J. Neurophysiol.*, 1943, 6, 405-415.
688. Kennard, M. A. Inheritance of Electroencephalogram Patterns in Children with Behavior Disorders. *Psychosom. Med.*, 1949, 11, 151-157.
689. Kennard, M. A. The Electroencephalogram in Psychological Disorders, A Review. *Psychosom. Med.*, 1953, 15, 95-115.
690. Kennard, M. A. & Henry, C. E. The Conditioning of the Blocking of the Alpha Rhythm of the Human Electroencephalogram. *J. Exp. Psychol.*, 1941, 28, 134-144.
691. Kennard, M. A. & Levy, S. The Meaning of the Abnormal Electroencephalogram in Schizophrenia. *J. Nerv. Ment. Dis.*, 1952, 116, 413-423.
691a. Kennard, M. A. & Schwartzman, A. E. A longitudinal Study of Changes in EEG Frequency Pattern as Related to Physiological Changes. *J. Nerv. Ment. Dis.*, 1956, 124, 8-20.
692. Kennard, M. A. & Willner, M. D. Significance of Paroxysmal Pattern in Electroencephalograms of Children without Clinical Epilepsy. *Proc. Assn. Res. Nerv. Ment. Dis.*, 1947, 26, 308-327.
693. Kennedy, F. Medical Syndromes of the Hypothalamus. *Proc. Assn. Res. Nerv. Ment. Dis.*, 1940, 20, 864-874.
694. Kepecs, J. G. Some Patterns of Somatic Displacement. *Psychosom. Med.*, 1953, 15, 425-432.
695. Kern, F., Jr., Almy, T. P., Abbot, F. K. & Bogdonoff, M. D. The Motility of Distal Colon in Nonspecific Ulcerative Colitis. *Gastroenterol.*, 1951, 19, 492-503.
696. Kern, F. Jr., Almy, T. P. & Stolk, N. J. An Experimental and Preliminary Clinical Study of the Effect of a New Quaternary Amine, Banthine, upon the Human Colon. *Gastroenterol.*, 1951, 17, 198-208.
697. Kern, F., Jr., Almy, T. P. & Stolk, N. J. Effects of Certain Antispasmodic Drugs on the Intact Human Colon with Special Reference to Banthine (β-Diethylaminoethyl Xanthene-Carboxylate Methobromide). *Am. J. Med.*, 1951, 11, 67-74.
698. Kerr, W. J., Dalton, J. W. & Gliebe, P. A. Some Physical Phenomena Associated with Anxiety States and Their Relation to Hyperventilation. *Ann. Int. Med.*, 1937, 11, 961-992.
699. Kesilman, M. The Incidence of Essential Hypertension in White and Negro Males. *Med. Rec.*, 1941, 154, 16-19.
700. Keys, A. Experimental Induction of Psychoneurosis by Starvation. In: Milbank Memorial Fund (903), pp. 515-530.
701. Kezur, E., Kapp, F. T. & Rosenbaum, M. Psychological Factors in Women with Peptic Ulcers. *Am. J. Psychiat.*, 1951, 108, 373-386.
702. Kibbe, M. H. Electroencephalograms in Neuropsychiatric Disorders among Soldiers: Results in 950 Cases. *New Eng. J. Med.*, 1947, 237, 112-125.
703. King, H. E., Clausen, J. & Scorff, J. E. Cutaneous Thresholds for Pain Before

and After Unilateral Prefrontal Lobotomy. *J. Nerv. Ment. Dis.*, 1950, 112, 93-96.

704. Kinsey, A. C., Pomeroy, W. B. & Martin, C. E. *Sexual Behavior in the Human Male.* Philadelphia: Saunders, 1948.

705. Kinsey, A. C., Pomeroy, W. B., Martin, C. E. & Gebhard, P. H. *Sexual Behavior in the Human Female.* Philadelphia: Saunders, 1953.

706. Kirschbaum, W. B. & Stehle, H. C. Electroencephalographic Studies of Patients with Peptic Ulcer and Functional Gastric Disorders. *EEG Clin. Neurophysiol.*, 1953, 5, 513-520.

707. Klebanoff, S. G., Singer, J. L. & Wilensky, H. Psychological Consequences of Brain Lesions and Ablations. *Psychol. Bull.*, 1954, 51, 1-41.

708. Kleist, K. Brain and Psyche. *J. Nerv. Ment. Dis.*, 1952, 116, 776-782.

709. Kleitman, N. *Sleep and Wakefulness as Alternating Phases in the Cycle of Existence.* Chicago: University of Chicago Press, 1939.

710. Kling, C. The Role of the Parasympathetics in Emotions. *Psychol. Rev.*, 1933, 40, 368-380.

711. Klopfer, B., Ainsworth, M. D., Klopfer, W. G. & Holt, R. R. *Developments in the Rorschach Technique.* New York: World Book Co., 1954.

712. Kluckhohn, C. & Murray, H. E. *Personality in Nature, Society, and Culture.* New York: Knopf, 1950.

713. Klüver, H. & Bucy, P. C. Preliminary Analysis of Functions of the Temporal Lobes in Monkeys. *Arch. Neurol. Psychiat.*, 1939, 42, 979-1000.

714. Koch, S. The Logical Character of the Motivation Concept. *Psychol. Rev.*, 1941, 48, 15-38, 127-154.

715. Koch, S. The Current Status of Motivational Psychology. *Psychol. Rev.*, 1951, 58, 147-154.

716. Koella, W. P. Influence of Hypothalamic and Thalamic Lesions upon the Action of Nociceptive Impulses and CO_2 on the Electroencephalogram. *Federation Proc.*, 1952, 11, 85.

717. Koffka, K. *Principles of Gestalt Psychology.* New York: Harcourt, Brace, 1935.

718. Köhler, W. *Gestalt Psychology.* New York: Liveright, 1947.

719. Kolb, L. C. *The Painful Phantom: Psychology, Physiology and Treatment.* Springfield, Ill.: C. C Thomas, 1954.

720. Korzybski, A. *Science and Sanity: An Introduction to Non-Aristotelian Systems and General Semantics.* Lakeville, Conn.: International Non-Aristotelian Library Publishing Co., 1948.

721. Korzybski, A. The Role of Language in the Perceptual Process. In: Blake & Ramsey (125), pp. 170-205.

722. Kraepelin, E. *Psychiatrie.* Leipzig: Barth, 1899.

723. Kramer, P. & Ingelfinger, F. J. Motility of the Human Esophagus in Control Subjects and in Patients with Esophageal Disorders. *Am. J. Med.*, 1949, 7, 168-173.

724. Kramer, P. & Ingelfinger, F. J. Cardiospasm, a Generalized Disorder of Esophageal Motility. *Am. J. Med.*, 1949, 7, 174-179.

725. Krasner, L. Personality Differences between Patients Classified as Psychosomatic and as Non-psychosomatic. *J. Abnorm. Soc. Psychol.*, 1953, 48, 190-198.

726. Kraus, B. S. Male Somatotypes Among the Japanese of Northern Honshu. *Am. J. Phys. Anthrop.*, 1951, 9, 347-366.

727. Krech, D. Notes toward a Psychological Theory. *J. Person.*, 1949, 18, 66-87.

728. Krech, D. Dynamic Systems, Psychological Fields, and Hypothetical Constructs. *Psychol. Rev.*, 1950, 57, 283-290.

729. Krech, D. Dynamic Systems as Open Neurological Systems. *Psychol. Rev.,* 1950, 57, 345-361.
730. Krech, D. Cognition and Motivation in Psychological Theory. In: Dennis et al. (294), p. 111.
731. Krech, D. & Crutchfield, R. L. *Theory and Problems of Social Psychology.* New York: McGraw-Hill, 1948.
732. Kretschmer, E. *Körperbau und Charakter.* Berlin: Springer, 1921. (*Physique and Character.* London: Kegan Paul, Trench, Trubner, 1925.)
733. Krieg, W. J. S. *Functional Neuroanatomy.* Philadelphia: Blakiston, 1953.
733a. Kris, E. On Preconscious Mental Processes. *Psychoanal. Quart.,* 1950, 19, 540-560.
733b. Kris, E. The Significance of Freud's Earliest Discoveries. *Int. J. Psycho-Anal.,* 1950, 31, 108-116.
733c. Kris, E. Some Comments and Observations on Early Autoerotic Activities. *Psychoanalytic Study of the Child,* 1951, 6, 95-116.
734. Kroeber, A. L., ed. *Anthropology Today, an Encyclopedic Inventory.* Chicago: University of Chicago Press, 1953.
735. Kroetz, C. Physiologische und pathologische Schwankungen der Sauerstoff-Durchlässigkeit der Lungen. *Verhand. d. Deutschen Ges. für Innere Med.,* 1931, 43, 105.
735a. Kroger, W. S. & Freed, C. S. *Psychosomatic Gynecology.* Philadelphia: Saunders, 1951.
736. Kubie, L. S. Some Implications for Psychoanalysis of Modern Concepts of the Organization of the Brain. *Psychoanal. Quart.,* 1953, 22, 21-68.
737. Kunkle, E. C., Goodell, H. & Wolff, H. G. "Unpublished Observations" cited by H. G. Wolff, *Harvey Lect.,* 1943-44, 39, 39.
738. Kuno, Y. The Significance of Sweating in Man. *Lancet,* 1930, 218, 912-915.
739. Kuntz, A. *A Textbook of Neuroanatomy.* Philadelphia: Lea & Febiger, 1950.
740. Kuntz, A. *The Autonomic Nervous System.* Philadelphia: Lea & Febiger, 1945.
741. Kupper, H. J. Psychic Concomitants in Wartime Injuries. *Psychosom. Med.,* 1945, 7, 15-21.
742. Küppers, E. von. Psychologische Analyse im Dienste der Neurologie, zugleich ein von Beitrag zur Lehre von den Reflexen. *Nervenarzt,* 1953, 24, 420-430.
742a. Lacey, J. I. Individual Differences in Somatic Response Patterns. *J. Comp. Physiol. Psychol.,* 1950, 43, 338-350.
743. Lamb, W. M., Ulett, G. A., Masters, W. H. & Robinson, D. W. Premenstrual Tension: EEG, Hormonal and Psychiatric Evaluation. *Am. J. Psychiat.,* 1953, 109, 840-848.
744. Landau, W. M. Autonomic Responses Mediated via the Corticospinal Tract. *J. Neurol. Physiol.,* 1953, 16, 299-311.
745. Landis, C. Studies of Emotional Reactions. V, Severe Emotional Upset. *J. Comp. Psychol.,* 1926, 6, 221-242.
746. Landis, C. The Expression of Emotion. In: Murchison (940aa), pp. 312-351.
747. Landis, C. Psychological Observation on Psychosurgery Patients. *Psychiat. Quart.,* 1951, 25, 409-417.
748. Landis, C. & Gullette, R. Studies of Emotional Reactions. III, Systolic Blood Pressure and Inspiration Expiration Ratios. *J. Comp. Psychol.,* 1925, 5, 221-253.
748a. Landis, C. & Hunt, W. A. Conscious Correlates of Galvanic Skin Response. *J. Exp. Psychol.,* 1935, 18, 505-529.
749. Landis, C. & Hunt, W. A. *The Startle Pattern.* New York: Farrar & Rinehart, 1939.

750. Landis, C. & Slight, D. Studies of Emotional Reactions. VI, Cardiac Responses. *J. Gen. Psychol.,* 1929, 2, 413-420.
751. Lange, G. C. Om Sindsbevagelser. In: K. Dunlap, ed. *The Emotions.* Baltimore: Williams & Wilkins, 1922.
752. Langer, M. & Parks Ochandorena, R. El Espasmo de las Trompas Como Origen de Esterilidad: Sus Causas, Mecanismo y Tratamiento. *Rev. Psicoanal.,* 1953, 10, 103-115.
753. Langfeldt, G. The Importance of Constitution in Psychiatry. *Am. J. Psychiat.,* 1953, 110, 261-268.
754. Larson, J. A. The Cardio-Pneumo-Psychogram in Deception. *J. Exp. Psychol.,* 1923, 6, 420-454.
755. Larson, J. A., Haney, G. W. & Keeler, L. *Lying and Its Detection: A Study of Deception and Deception Tests.* Chicago: University of Chicago Press, 1932.
756. Lashley, K. S. The Thalamus and Emotion. *Psychol. Rev.,* 1938, 45, 42-61.
757. Lashley, K. S. Coalescence of Neurology and Psychiatry. *Am. Philos. Soc.,* 1944, 84, 461-470.
758. Lashley, K. S. Functional Interpretation of Anatomic Patterns. *Proc. Assn. Res. Nerv. Ment. Dis.,* 1952, 30, 529-548.
758a. Lazarus, R. S. Motivation and Personality in Psychological Stress. Progress Report No. 4. G. N. M-734, Feb. 1, 1957, Clark University, Worcester, Mass.
758b. Lazarus, R. S. & Baker, R. W. Personality and Psychological Stress—A Theoretical and Methodological Framework. *Psychol. Newsletter,* 1956, 8, 21-32.
759. Lazarus, R. S. & McLeary, R. A. Autonomic Discrimination Without Awareness: A Study of Subperception. *Psychol. Rev.,* 1951, 58, 113-122.
760. Leavitt, H. C. Bronchial Asthma in Functional Psychoses. *Psychosom. Med.,* 1943, 5, 39-41.
761. Lee, H. N. Theoretical Knowledge and Hypothesis. *Psychol. Rev.,* 1950, 57, 31-37.
762. Lee, I. J. *The Language of Wisdom and Folly.* New York: Harper, 1949.
763. Leeper, R. W. A Motivational Theory of Emotion to Replace: "Emotions as a Disorganized Response." *Psychol. Rev.,* 1948, 55, 5-21.
764. Leigh, D. & Lovett Doust, J. W. Asthma and Psychoses. *J. Ment. Sci.,* 1953, 99, 489-496.
765. Lemere, F. The Significance of Individual Differences in the Berger Rhythm. *Brain,* 1936, 59, 366-375.
766. Lemere, F. Electroencephalography. *Psychiat. Quart.,* 1939, 13, 5-15.
767. Lemere, F. Cortical Energy Production in the Psychoses. *Psychosom. Med.,* 1941, 3, 152-156.
768. Lennox, W. G. *Science and Seizures.* New York: Harper, 1941.
769. Lennox, W. G. Seizure States. In: Hunt (610), 2, 938-967.
770. Leschke, E. Die körperlichen Begleiterscheinungen körperlicher Vorgänge. *Arch. Ges. Psychol.,* 1911, 21, 435-463.
771. Leschke, E. Die Ergebnisse und die Fehlerquellen der bisherigen Untersuchungen über die körperlichen Begleiterscheinungen seelischer Vorgänge. *Arch. Ges. Psychol.,* 1914, 31, 27-37.
771a. Lesse, H., Heath, R. G., Mickle, W. A., Monroe, R. R. & Miller, W. H. Rhinencephalic Activity during Thought. *J. Nerv. Ment. Dis.,* 1955, 122, 433-440.
772. Levitt, M. F. & Bader, M. E. Effect of Cortisone and ACTH on Fluid and Electrolyte Distribution in Man. *Am. J. Med.,* 1951, 11, 715-723.
773. Levy, D. M. Pyschosomatic Studies of Some Aspects of Maternal Behavior. *Psychosom. Med.,* 1942, 4, 223-227.

774. Levy, R. L., White, P. D., Stroud, W. D. & Hillman, C. C. Transient Tachycardia. *J. Am. Med. Assn.,* 1945, 129, 585-588.
775. Levy, S. & Kennard, M. A. The EEG Pattern of Patients with Psychological Disorders of Various Ages. *J. Nerv. Ment. Dis.,* 1953, 118, 416-428.
776. Lewin, K. *Principles of Topological Psychology.* New York: McGraw-Hill, 1936.
777. Lewin, K. *Field Theory in Social Sciences.* New York: Harper, 1951.
778. Lewin, K., Dembo, T., Festinger, L. & Sears, P. S. Level of Aspiration. In: Hunt (610), 1, 333-378.
779. Lewis, G. M. *Practical Dermatology.* Philadelphia: Saunders, 1952.
780. Lewis, N. D. C. *A Short History of Psychiatric Achievement.* New York: Norton, 1941.
781. Lewis, T. *The Blood Vessels of the Human Skin and Their Responses.* London: Shaw, 1927.
782. Lewis, T. *Pain.* New York: Macmillan, 1942.
783. Lhamon, W. T. & Saul, L. J. A Note on Psychosomatic Correlations. *Psychosom. Med.,* 1950, 12, 113.
784. Liberson, W. T. Study of Word Association Processes. Part I, Depression of Alpha Activity during Administration of the Test. *Dig. Neurol. Psychiat.,* 1945, 13, 594-601.
785. Libman, E. Observations on Sensitiveness of Pain. *Tr. Assn. Am. Phys.,* 1926, 41, 305.
786. Liddell, H. S. Conditioned Reflex Method and Experimental Neurosis. In: Hunt (610), 1, 389-412.
787. Liddell, H. S. Animal Origins of Anxiety. In: Reymert (1033), pp. 181-188.
787a. Lidz, T. Emotional Factors in the Etiology of Hyperthyroidism Occurring in Relation to Pregnancy. *Psychosom. Med.,* 1955, 17, 420-427.
788. Lidz, T. & Whitehorn, J. C. Life Situations, Emotions and Graves' Disease. *Proc. Assn. Res. Nerv. Ment. Dis.,* 1950, 29, 445-450.
789. Lief, A., ed., *The Commonsense of Psychiatry of Dr. Adolf Meyer.* New York: McGraw-Hill, 1948.
790. Lindemann, E. Modification in the Course of Ulcerative Colitis in Relationship to Changes in Life Situations and Reactions Patterns. *Proc. Assn. Res. Nerv. Ment. Dis.,* 1949, 29, 706.
791. Lindhard, J. Über das Minutenvolum des Herzens bei Ruhe und bie Muskelarbeit. *Pflüg. Arch. Ges. Physiol.,* 1915, 161, 233-383.
792. Lindsley, D. B. Electrical Activity of Human Motor Units during Voluntary Contraction. *Am. J. Physiol.,* 1935, 114, 92-99.
793. Lindsley, D. B. Electrical Potentials of the Brain in Children and Adults. *J. Gen. Psychol.,* 1938, 19, 285-306.
794. Lindsley, D. B. Electroencephalography. In: Hunt (610), 2, 1033-1103.
795. Lindsley, D. B. Emotions and the Electroencephalogram. In: Reymert (1033), pp. 238-246.
796. Lindsley, D. B. Emotion. In: Stevens (1197a), pp. 473-516.
797. Lindsley, D. B., Bowen, B. J., Magoun, H. W. Effect upon the EEG of Acute Injury to the Brain Stem Activating System. *EEG Clin. Neurophysiol.,* 1949, 1, 475-186.
798. Lindsley, D. B. & Hunter, W. S. A Note on Polarity Potentials from the Human Eye. *Proc. Nat. Acad. Sci. Wash.,* 1939, 25, 180-183.
799. Lindsley, D. B., Schreiner, L. H. & Magoun, H. W. An Electromyographic Study of Spasticity. *J. Neurophysiol.,* 1947, 12, 197-205.

800. Lindzey, G. Hypothetical Constructs, Conventional Constructs, and the Use of Physiological Data in Psychological Theory. *Psychiatry,* 1953, 16, 21-33.
801. Linton, R. *The Cultural Background of Personality.* New York: Appleton-Century-Crofts, 1945.
802. Lippman, H. S. Certain Behavioral Responses in Early Infancy. *J. Genet. Psychol.,* 1927, 34, 424-440.
803. List, C. F. & Peet, M. M. Sweat Secretion in Man. I, Sweating Responses in Normal Persons. *Arch. Neurol. Psychiat.,* 1938, 39, 1228-1237.
804. List, C. F. & Peet, M. M. Sweat Secretion in Man. III, Clinical Observations on Sweating Produced by Pilocarpine and Mecholyl. *Arch. Neurol. Psychiat.,* 1938, 40, 269-290.
805. Lium, R. Etiology of Ulcerative Colitis. II, Effects of Induced Muscular Spasm on Colonic Explants in Dogs with Comment on Relation of Muscular Spasm to Ulcerative Colitis. *Arch. Int. Med.,* 1939, 63, 210.
805a. Livingston, R. B. Some Brain Stem Mechanisms Relating to Psychosomatic Functions. *Psychosom. Med.,* 1955, 17, 347-354.
806. Livingston, W. K. *Pain Mechanisms. A Physiologic Interpretation of Causalgia and the Related States.* New York: Macmillan, 1943.
807. Loewenberg, J. Are Relations Effable? *J. Philos.,* 1930, 27, 309.
808. Loewenstein, R. M., ed., *Drive, Affects, Behavior.* New York: International Universities Press, 1953.
809. London, I. D. Research on Sensory Interaction in the Soviet Union. *Psychol. Bull.,* 1954, 51, 531-568.
810. Loomis, A. V., Harvey, E. N. & Hobart, G. Electric Potentials of the Human Brain. *J. Exp. Psychol.,* 1936, 19, 249-279.
811. Lorenz, T. H., Graham, D. T. & Wolf, S. The Relation of Life Stress and Emotions to Human Sebum Secretion and to the Mechanism of Acne Vulgaris. *J. Lab. Clin. Med.,* 1953, 41, 11-28.
812. Lorenz, T. H., Graham, D. T. & Wolff, H. G. A Method for the Collection and Quantitative Determination of Sebum: Its Application to an Investigation of Human Sebum Secretion. *J. Lab. Clin. Med.,* 1952, 39, 91-104.
813. Lorenz, T. H. & Musser, M. J. Life Stresses, Emotions and Painful Stiff Shoulder. *Ann. Int. Med.,* 1952, 37, 1232-1244.
814. Lorr, M. & Fields, V. A Factorial Study of Body Types. *J. Clin. Psychol.,* 1954, 10, 182-185.
815. Loucks, R. B. & Gantt, W. H. The Conditioning of Striped Muscle Responses Based upon Faradic Stimulation of Dorsal Roots and Dorsal Columns of the Spinal Cord. *J. Comp. Psychol.,* 1938, 45, 415-426.
816. Lovett Doust, J. W. An Oximetric Analysis of Emotion and the Differential Planes of Awareness Seen in Hypnosis. *Am. J. Psychiat.,* 1953, 110, 205.
817. Lovett Doust, J. W. & Leigh, D. Studies on the Physiology of Awareness: The Interrelationships of Emotions, Life Situations, and Anoxemia in Patients with Bronchial Asthma. *Psychosom. Med.,* 1953, 15, 292-311.
818. Lovett Doust, J. W. Studies on the Physiology of Awareness. *J. Clin. Exp. Psychopathol.,* 1953, 14, 113-126.
818a. Lovett Doust, J. W. & Schneider, R. A. Studies on the Physiology of Awareness: An Oximetrically Monitored Controlled Stress Test. *Canad. J. Psychol.,* 1955, 9, 67-78.
819. Lowenstein, J. Asthma und Psychotherapie. *Med. Klin.,* 1926, 22, 994-997.
820. Lown, B., Ganong, W. F. & Levine, S. A. The Syndrome of Short P-R Interval, Normal QRS Complex and Paroxysmal Rapid Heart Action. *Circulation,* 1952, 5, 693-706.

820a. Luborsky, L. Intraindividual Repetitive Measurements (P Technique) in Understanding Psychotherapeutic Change. In: Mowrer (936b), pp. 389-413.
821. Lund, F. H. *Emotions: Their Psychological, Physiological and Educative Implications.* New York: Ronald Press, 1939.
822. Lundervold, A. An Electromyographic Investigation of Tense and Relaxed Subjects. *J. Nerv. Ment. Dis.,* 1952, 115, 512-525.
823. Luria, A. R. *The Nature of Human Conflict.* New York: Liveright, 1932.
824. McCleary, R. A. Palmar Sweat as an Index of Anxiety: A Field Method Suitable for Large Groups. *USAF Sch. Aviat. Med. Proj. Rep.,* 1953, Proj. No. 21-1207-0004, 1-10.
825. McClelland, D. C. & Atkinson, J. W. The Projective Expression of Needs. I, The Effect of Different Intensities of Hunger Drive on Perception. *J. Psychol.,* 1948, 25, 205-222.
826. MacCorquodale, K. & Meehl, P. E. On a Distinction between Hypothetical Constructs and Intervening Variables. *Psychol. Rev.,* 1948, 55, 95-107.
827. McDermott, N. T. & Cobb, S. A Psychiatric Survey of Fifty Cases of Bronchial Asthma. *Psychosom. Med.,* 1939, 1, 203-244.
828. McDougall, W. *Introduction to Social Psychology.* London: Methuen, 1908.
829. McDougall, W. *Outline of Psychology.* New York: Scribner, 1923.
830. McDougall, W. *The Energies of Men, a Study of Fundamentals of Dynamic Psychology.* London: Methuen, 1932.
831. McFarland, R. A. Psycho-Physiological Studies at High Altitude in the Andes. *J. Comp. Psychol.,* 1937, 23, 191-258.
832. McFarland, R. A. Psycho-Physiological Studies of High Altitude in the Andes. *J. Comp. Psychol.,* 1937, 24, 147-220.
833. McFarland, R. A. & Barach, A. L. The Relationship between Alcoholic Intoxication and Anoxemia. *Am. J. Ment. Sci.,* 1936, 192, 186.
834. MacFarlane, J. W. Cattell's Personality: a Systematic Theoretical and Factorial Study. *Psychol. Bull.,* 1952, 49, 89-90.
835. McGinnies, E. Emotionality and Perceptual Defense. *Psychol. Rev.,* 1949, 56, 244-251.
836. McGregor, H. G. *The Emotional Factor in Visceral Disease.* London: Oxford University Press, 1938.
837. McGregor, H. G. The Physical Examination of Two Thousand Cases of Neurosis. *J. Neurol. Psychiat.,* 1947, 7, 21-27.
838. MacGregor, I. A. The Sweating Reaction of the Forehead. *J. Physiol.,* 1952, 116, 26-34.
839. MacInnis, K. B. Allergic Symptoms in the Psychotic Patient. *J. Allergy,* 1936, 8, 73.
840. MacLean, P. D. Psychosomatic Disease and the "Visceral Brain." *Psychosom. Med.,* 1949, 11, 338-353.
841. MacLean, P. D. Some Psychiatric Implications of Physiological Studies on Frontotemporal Portion of Limbic System (Visceral Brain). *EEG Clin. Neurophysiol.,* 1952, 4, 407-418.
841a. MacLean, P. D. The Limbic System ("Visceral Brain") in Relation to Central Gray and Reticulum of the Brain Stem. *Psychosom. Med.,* 1955, 17, 355-366.
841b. MacLean, P. D. The Limbic System ("Visceral Brain") and Emotional Behavior *Arch. Neurol. Psychiat.,* 1955, 73, 130-134.
842. MacLean, P. D. & Delgado, J. M. R. Electrical and Chemical Stimulation of Frontotemporal Portion of Limbic System in the Waking Animal. *EEG Clin. Neurophysiol.,* 1953, 5, 91-100.
843. MacLean, P. D. & Pribram, K. H. Neurographic Analysis of Medical and

Basal Cerebral Cortex Comparing Cat and Monkey. *J. Neurophysiol.*, 1953, 16, 312-340.

844. MacLean, W. C. Disease of the British Army. *Brit. Med. J.*, 1867, 1, 161.

845. McLellan, A. M. & Goodell, H. Pain from the Bladder, Ureter, and Kidney Pelvis. *Proc. Assn. Res. Nerv. Ment. Dis.*, 1943, 23, 252-262.

846. McMahon, J. F. & Walter, W. G. Electro-encephalogram in Schizophrenia. *J. Ment. Sci.*, 1938, 84, 781-787.

847. McMichael, J. & Sharpey-Schafer, E. P. Cardiac Output in Man by a Direct Frick Method. Effects of Posture, Venous Pressure Changes, Atropine, and Adrenaline. *Brit. Heart J.*, 1944, 6, 33-40.

848. McTeer, W. Observational Definitions of Emotions. *Psychol. Rev.*, 1953, 60, 172-180.

849. MacWilliam, J. A. Some Applications of Physiology to Medicine. III, Blood Pressure and Heart Action in Sleep and Dreams, Their Relation to Haemorrhages, Angina, and Sudden Death. *Brit. Med. J.*, 1923, 2, 1196-1200.

850. Macalpine, I. Pruritus Ani, a Psychiatric Study, *Psychosom. Med.*, 1953, 15, 499-508.

850a. Magoun, H. W. The Ascending Reticular System and Wakefulness. In: Delefresnaye (287b), pp. 1-20.

851. Magoun, H. W. & Ranson, S. W. Behavior of Cats Following Bilateral Removal of the Rostral Portion of the Cerebral Hemisphere. *J. Neurophysiol.*, 1938, 1, 39-44.

852. Magoun, H. W., Atlas, D., Ingersoll, E. H. & Ranson, S. W. Associated Facial, Vocal and Respiratory Components of Emotional Expression: An Experimental Study. *J. Neurol. Psychopath.*, 1937, 17, 241-255.

853. Mahl, G. F. The Effect of Chronic Fear on the Gastric Secretion of HCl in Dogs. *Psychosom. Med.*, 1949, 11, 30-44.

854. Mahl, G. F. Anxiety, HCl Secretion, and Peptic Ulcer Etiology. *Psychosom. Med.*, 1950, 12, 158-169.

855. Mahl, G. F. The Relationship between Acute and Chronic Fear and the Gastric Acidity and Blood Sugar Levels in Macaca Rhesus Monkey. *Psychosom. Med.*, 1952, 14, 182-210.

856. Mahl, G. F. & Brody, E. B. Chronic Anxiety, Symptomatology, Experimental Stress and HCl Secretion. *Arch. Neurol. Psychiat.*, 1954, 71, 314-325.

857. Mahl, G. F. & Karpe, R. Emotions and Hydrochloric Acid Secretion during Psychoanalytic Hours. *Psychosom. Med.*, 1953, 15, 312-327.

858. Mainzer, F. & Krause, M. The Influence of Fear on the Electrocardiogram. *Brit. Heart J.*, 1940, 2, 221-230.

859. Malamud. W. A. A Personal Communication. In: Funkenstein (409).

860. Malmo, R. B. Experimental Studies of Mental Patients under Stress. In: Reymert (1033), pp. 169-180.

861. Malmo, R. B. & Shagass, C. Physiological Studies of Reaction in Anxiety and Early Schizophrenia. *Psychosom. Med.*, 1949, 11, 9-24.

862. Malmo, R. B. & Shagass, C. Reaction to Stress in Anxiety and Early Schizophrenia. *Psychosom. Med.*, 1949, 11, 25-29.

863. Malmo, R. B. & Shagass, C. Behavioral and Psychological Changes under Stress After Operating on the Frontal Lobes. *Arch. Neurol. Psychiat.*, 1950, 63, 113-124.

864. Malmo, R. B., Belanger, D. J. & Smith, A. A. Control of Psychiatric Patients under Experimental Stress. *J. Abnorm. Soc. Psychol,*, 1951, 46, 539-547.

865. Malmo, R. B., Shagass, C. & Davis, J. F. Physiologic Study of Symptom

Specificity and Bodily Reaction during Psychiatric Interviews. *Psychosom. Med.,* 1950, 12, 360-376.

866. Malmo, R. B., Shagass, C. & Davis, J. F. Electromyographic Studies of Muscular Tension in Psychiatric Patients under Stress. *J. Clin. Exp. Psychopathol.,* 1951, 12, 45-66.

867. Malmo, R. B., Shagass, C., Davis, J. F., Cleghorn, R. A., Graham, B. F. & Goodman, A. J. Standardized Pain Stimulation as Controlled Stress in Physiological Studies of Psychoneurosis. *Science,* 1948, 108, 509-511.

868. Malmo, R. B., Shagass, C. & Smith, A. A. Responsiveness in Chronic Schizophrenia. *J. Personal.,* 1951, 19, 359-375.

868a. Manhold, J. H., Jr. *Introductory Psychosomatic Dentistry.* New York: Appleton-Century-Crofts, 1956.

868b. Manhold, J. H. & Melton, R. S. A Study of Psychosomatic Factors in Oral Pathology. *U. S. Naval Sch. Aviat. Med. Res. Rep.,* 1954, Proj. No. NM001057.11.03, 7p.

869. Mann. S. A. Blood Sugar Studies in Mental Disorders. *J. Ment. Sci.,* 1925, 71, 443-473.

870. Marañón, G., Rosique, A. & Soler, L. Nota Acera de la Influencia del Vuelo Sobre la Glucemia. *Siglo Med.,* 1919, 66, 573-574.

870a. Margolin, S. G. Genetic and Dynamic Psychophysiological Determinants of Pathophysiological Processes. In: Deutsch (299), pp. 3-36.

871. Margolin, S. G., Orringer, D. & Kaufman, M. R. Variations of Gastric Functions during Conscious and Unconscious Conflict States. *Proc. Assn. Res. Nerv. Ment. Dis.,* 1949, 29, 656-664.

871a. Marrazzi, A. S. The Effect of Drugs on Neurons and Synapses. In: Fields (353a), pp. 45-67.

872. Marston, W. M. Systolic Blood Pressure Symptoms of Deception. *J. Exp. Psychol.,* 1917, 2, 117-163.

873. Marston, W. M. Sex Characteristics of Systolic Blood Pressure Behavior. *J. Exp. Psychol.,* 1923, 6, 387-419.

874. Marston, W. M. A Theory of Emotion and Affection Based upon Systolic Blood Pressure Studies. *Am. J. Psychol.,* 1924, 35, 469-506.

875. Marx, H. Untersuchungen über den Wasserhaushalt. II, Die Psychische Beeinflussung des Wasserhaushalt. *Klin. Wochnschr.,* 1926, 5, 92.

876. Mason, R. E. *The Conscious Approach.* Unpublished paper written at Columbia University, New York, 1941.

877. Mason, R. E. *A Sensory Approach in the Study of "Feeling and Emotion."* Unpublished study submitted for a Master of Arts degree. Dallas, Texas: Southern Methodist University, 1949. In: Mason (879a).

878. Mason, R. E. *An Experimental Investigation Concerning Sensations Accompanying Different Feeling Reactions.* Unpublished Study. Lafayette, Ind.: Purdue University, 1950. In: Mason (879a).

879. Mason, R. E. *Introceptive Sensations Reported by Patient and Non-patient Groups in Situations with Different Feeling Loadings.* Unpublished study in partial fulfillment of degree of Doctor of Philosophy. Lafayette, Ind.: Purdue University, 1952. In: Mason (879a).

879a. Mason, R. E. Three Studies Relating Internal Sensory Experience and Feeling Reactions. *J. Gen. Psychol.,* 1959, 60, 211-228.

880. Masserman, J. H. *Principles of Dynamic Psychiatry.* Philadelphia: Saunders, 1946.

881. Masserman, J. H. A Biodynamic Psychoanalytic Approach to the Problems of Feeling and Emotion. In: Reymert (1033), pp. 40-75.

882. Masserman, J. H. Psychoanalysis and Biodynamics. *Int. J. Psycho-Anal.*, 1953, 34 (Suppl.), 13-42.
883. Masserman, J. H. & Haertig, E. W. The Influence of Hypothalamic Stimulation on Intestinal Activity. *J. Neurophysiol.*, 1938, 1, 350-356.
884. Master, A. M. Effort Syndrome of Neurocirculatory Asthenia in the Navy. *U. S. Navy Med. Bull.*, 1943, 41, 666-669.
885. Master, A. M. The Electrocardiogram and the "Two Step" Exercise. *Am. J. Med. Sci.*, 1944, 207, 435-450.
886. Master, A. M. & Eichert, H. Functional Paroxysmal Auricular Fibrillation. *Am. J. Med. Sci.*, 1946, 211, 336-345.
887. Master, A. M., Friedman, R. & Dock, S. The Electrocardiogram after Standard Exercise as a Functional Test of the Heart. *Am. Heart J.*, 1942, 23, 777-793.
888. Matarazzo, J. D. An Experimental Study of Aggression in the Hypersensitive Patient. *J. Person.*, 1954, 22, 423-447.
888a. Matte-Blanco, I. The Constitutional Approach to the Study of Human Personality. *Psychiat. Res. Rep.*, 1955, 2, 132-154.
889. Mead, M. *Sex and Temperament in Three Primitive Societies, Part II.* New York: William Morrow, 1935.
890. Mead, M. Social Change and Cultural Surrogates. *J. Educ. Sociol.*, 1940, 14, 92-110.
891. Mead, M. & Macgregor, F. C. *Growth and Culture: a Photographic Analysis of Balinese Childhood.* New York: Putnam, 1951.
892. Meadow, A., Greenblatt, M., Funkenstein, D. H. & Solomon, H. C. Relationship Between Capacity for Abstraction in Schizophrenia and Physiologic Response to Autonomic Drugs. *J. Nerv. Ment. Dis.*, 1953, 118, 332-338.
893. Meduna, L. J. A Neurophysiological Theory of Psychoneurosis. *J. Nerv. Ment. Dis.*, 1949, 110, 438-439.
893a. Meerloo, J. A. M. Human Camouflage and Identification with the Environment: The Contagious Effect of Archaic Skin Signs. *Psychosom. Med.*, 1957, 29, 89-98.
893b. Mendelson, M., Hirsch, S. & Webber, C. S. A Critical Examination of Some Recent Theoretical Models in Psychosomatic Medicine. *Psychosom. Med.*, 1956, 18, 362-373.
893c. Menninger, K. A. *Man Against Himself.* New York: Harcourt, Brace, 1938.
893d. Menninger, K. A. Psychological Aspects of the Organism under Stress. *J. Am. Psychoanal. Assn.*, 1954, 2, 67-106; 280-310.
894. Merrill, B. R. Some Psychosomatic Aspects of Pulmonary Tuberculosis: A Review of the English Language Literature. *J. Nerv. Dis.*, 1953, 117, 9-28.
895. Merritt, W. Inversion of the T-waves of the Electrocardiogram in Two Patients with Neurocirculatory Asthenia. *Ann. Int. Med.*, 1944, 20, 773-778.
896. Messerle, N. Puls, Elektrokardiogramm, Atmung, und Galvanogramm bei Schiessversuchen. *Ztschr. f. d. Ges. Neurol. Psychiat.*, 1927, 108, 142-151.
897. Mettler, F. A., ed. *Selective Partial Ablation of the Frontal Cortex.* New York: Paul B. Hoeber, 1949.
898. Mettler, F. A., Mettler, C. C. & Culler, E. Effects of Total Removal of the Cerebral Cortex. *Arch. Neurol. Psychiat.*, 1935, 34 1238-1249.
899. Meyer, A., Bollmeier, L. N. & Alexander, F. Correlation between Emotions and Carbohydrate Metabolism in Two Cases of Diabetes Mellitus. *Psychosom. Med.*, 1945, 7, 335-341.
900. Meyer, H. H. Statistisches zur Frage der "Auslösung" endogener Psychosen durch akute körperliche Erkrankungen oder Generationsvorgänge *Nervenarzt,* 1953, 24, 498-500.

901. Michotte, A. E. The Emotions Regarded as Functional Connections. In: Reymert (1033), pp. 114-126.
902. Mieth, N. Seelische Einflüsse auf den Kohlehydratstoffwechsel. *Inaug. Dissert.*, Berlin, 1933, 29 pp.
903. Milbank Memorial Fund, The Twenty-Seventh Annual Conference of. *The Biology of Mental Health and Disease.* New York: Paul B. Hoeber, 1952.
904. Miles, H. H. W. & Cobb, S. Neurocirculatory Asthenia, Anxiety and Neurosis. *New Eng. J. Med.*, 1951, 245, 711-719.
905. Miles, W. R. The Sex Expression of Men Living on a Lowered Nutritional Level. *J. Nerv. Ment. Dis.*, 1919, 49, 208-224.
906. Miller, H. & Baruch, D. W. Psychological Dynamics in Allergic Patients as Shown in Group and Individual Psycho-therapy. *J. Consult. Psychol.*, 1948, 12, 111-115.
906a. Miller, H. & Baruch, D. W. *The Practice of Psychosomatic Medicine as Illustrated in Allergy.* New York: McGraw-Hill, 1956.
907. Miller, J. G. Discrimination Without Awareness. *Am. J. Psychol.*, 1939, 52, 562-578.
908. Miller, J. G. The Experimental Study of Unconscious Processes. In: Reymert (1033), pp. 261-267.
909. Miller, J. G. Unconscious Processes and Perception. In: Blake & Ramsey (125), pp. 258-282.
910. Miller, M. L. Emotional Conflicts in Asthma. *Dis. Nerv. Syst.*, 1952, 13, 298-302.
911. Miller, N. E. Experimental Studies of Conflict. In: Hunt (610), 1, 431-465.
912. Miller, N. E. Learnable Drives and Rewards. In: Reymert (1033), pp. 435-472.
913. Miller, N. E. & Dollard, J. *Social Learning and Imitation.* New Haven: Yale University Press, 1941.
914. Miller, N. E. & Dollard, J. *Personality and Psychotherapy. An Analysis in Terms of Learning, Thinking, and Culture.* New York: McGraw-Hill, 1950.
915. Miller, R. J., Bergheim, O. & Hawk, P. B. Gastric Response to Foods. IX, the Influence of Worry on Gastric Digestion. *Science,* 1920, 52, 253.
916. Mirsky, I. A. Emotional Hyperglycemia. *Proc. Central Soc. Clin. Res.*, 1946, 19, 74.
917. Mirsky, I. A. Psychoanalysis and the Biological Sciences. In: F. Alexander and H. Ross, eds., *20 Years of Psychoanalysis.* New York: Norton, 1953, pp. 155-185.
918. Mirsky, I. A., Kaplan, S. & Broh-kahn, R. H. Pepsinogen Excretion (Uropepsin) as an Index of the Influence of Various Life Situations on Gastric Functions. *Proc. Assn. Res. Nerv. Ment. Dis.*, 1949, 29, 628-646.
919. Mittelmann, B. Psychogenic Factors and Psychotherapy in Hyperthyreosis and Rapid Heart Imbalance. *J. Nerv. Ment. Dis.*, 1933, 77, 465-488.
920. Mittelmann, B. Emotions and Skin Temperature: Observations on Patients During Psychotherapeutic (Psychoanalytic) Interviews. *Psychosom. Med.*, 1943, 5, 211-231.
921. Mittelmann, B. Psychopathology of Epilepsy. In: P. Hoch and R. Knight, eds. *Epilepsy.* New York: Grune & Stratton, 1947, pp. 136-148.
922. Mittelmann, B. & Wolff, H. G. Affective States and Skin Temperature: Experimental Study of Subjects with "Cold Hands" and Raynaud's Syndrome. *Psychosom. Med.*, 1939, 1, 271-292.
923. Mittelmann, B. & Wolff, H. G. Emotion and Gastroduodenal Function: Ex-

perimental Study of Patient with Gastritis, Duodenitis and Peptic Ulcer. *Psychosom. Med.*, 1942, 4, 5-61.

924. Modlin, H. C. The Hypothalamus and Psychosomatic Medicine. *Bull. Menninger Clin.*, 1951-52, 15-16, 16-20.

925. Moldawsky, P. C. A Study of Personality Variables in Patients with Skin Disorders. *Dissert. Abstr.*, 1953, 13, 1260-1261.

926. Montagu, M. F. A. The Sensory Influences of the Skin. *Tex. Rep. Biol. Med.*, 1953, 11, 291-301.

927. Montgomery, M. F. The Role of Salivary Glands in the Thirst Mechanism. *Am. J. Physiol.*, 1931, 96, 221-227.

928. Morgan, C. T. *Physiological Psychology.* New York: McGraw-Hill, 1943.

929. Morgan, C. T. Some Structural Factors in Perception. In: Blake & Ramsey (125), pp. 25-55.

930. Morgan, J. J. B. *Child Psychology.* New York: Ray Long & R. P. Smith, 1932.

931. Morison, R. S. & Dempsey, E. W. A Study of Thalamocortical relationships. *Am. J. Physiol.*, 1942, 135, 281-292.

932. Morley, J. *Abdominal Pain.* New York: W. Wood, 1931.

933. Morris, D. P. Blood Pressure and Pulse Changes in Normal Individuals under Emotional Stress: Their Relationship to Emotional Instability. *Psychosom. Med.*, 1941, 3, 389-398.

933a. Moruzzi, G. The Physiological Properties of the Brain Stem Reticular System. In: Delefresnaye (287b), pp. 21-53.

934. Moruzzi, G. & Magoun, H. W. Brain Stem Reticular Formation and Activation of the Electroencephalogram. *EEG Clin. Neurophysiol.*, 1949, 1, 453-473.

935. Moses, L. Psychodynamic and Electroencephalographic Factors in Duodenal Ulcer. *Psychosom. Med.*, 1946, 8, 405-409.

935a. Moses, L., Daniels, G. E. & Nickerson, J. L. Psychogenic Factors in Essential Hypertension: Methodology and Preliminary Report. *Psychosom. Med.*, 1956, 18, 471-485.

935b. Moulton, R. Oral and Dental Manifestations of Anxiety. *Psychiatry*, 1955, 18, 261-273.

936. Mowrer, O. H. On the Dual Nature of Learning—A Reinterpretation of "Conditioning" and "Problem-Solving." *Harvard Educ. Rev.*, 1947, 17, 102-148.

936a. Mowrer, O. H. *Learning Theory and Personality Dynamics.* New York: Ronald Press, 1950.

936b. Mowrer, O. H., ed. *Psychotherapy:Theory and Research.* New York: Ronald Press, 1953.

937. Mullahy, P. *Oedipus Myth and Complex.* New York: Hermitage Press, 1948.

938. Mullahy, P., ed. *The Contributions of Harry Stack Sullivan.* New York: Hermitage House, 1952.

938a. Munn, N. L. *The Evolution and Growth of Human Behavior.* Boston: Houghton Mifflin, 1955.

939. Muralt, A. von. Excitation and Conduction in Peripheral Nerves. *Ann. Rev. Physiol.*, 1954, 16, 305-324.

940. Murchison, C., ed. *Psychologies of 1925.* Worcester, Mass.: Clark University Press, 1926, pp. 145-195.

940a. Murphy, G. *Personality.* New York: Harper, 1947.

940aa. Murchison, C., ed. *A Handbook of General Experimental Psychology.* Worcester, Mass.: Clark University Press, 1934.

941. Murphy, J. P. & Gellhorn, E. Further Investigations on Diencephalic-Cortical Relations and Their Significance for the Problem of Emotion. *J. Neurophysiol.*, 1945, 8, 431-448.

942. Murphy, J. P. & Gellhorn, E. Influence of Hypothalamic Stimulation on Cortically Induced Movements and Action Potentials of the Cortex. *J. Neurophysiol.*, 1948, 8, 341-364.
943. Myerson, A. A Personal Communication. In: Funkenstein (409).
944. Naber, J. Dysmenorrhoe und Psychotherapie. *Therap. d. Gegenwart.*, 1931, 72, 108-112.
945. Nafe, J. P. An Experimental Study of the Affective Qualities. *Am. J. Psychol.*, 1924, 35, 507-544.
946. Nafe, J. P. The Psychology of Felt Experiences. *Am. J. Psychol.*, 1927, 39, 367-389.
947. Nakoshima, T. Contribution to the Study of the Affective Processes. *Am. J. Psychol.*, 1909, 20, 157-193.
948. Nathan, P. W. & Smith, M. C. The Centripedal Pathway from the Bladder and Urethra within the Spinal Cord. *J. Neurol. Neurosurg. Psychiat.*, 1951, 14, 262-280.
949. Nauta, W. J. H. Hypothalamic Regulation of Sleep in Rats. An Experimental Study. *J. Neurophysiol.*, 1946, 9, 285-316.
950. Newman, E. B., Perkins, F. T. & Wheeler, R. H. Cannon's Theory of Emotion: A Critique. *Psychol. Rev.*, 1930, 37, 305-326.
951. Newman, H. H., Freeman, F. W. & Holzinger, K. J. *Twins: A Study of Heredity and Environment.* Chicago: University of Chicago Press, 1937.
952. Newman, P. P. Electromyographic Studies of Emotional States in Normal Subjects. *J. Neurol. Neurosurg. Psychiat.*, 1953, 16, 200-208.
953. Nielsen, J. M. & Roth, P. Clinical Spirography. *Arch. Int. Med.*, 1939, 43, 132-138.
954. Novak, J. & Harnik, M. Die psychogene Entstehung der Menstrualkolik und deren Behandlung. *Ztschr. f. Geburtsh. u. Gynäk.* 1929, 96, 239-296.
955. Noyes, A. P. *Modern Clinical Psychiatry.* Philadelphia: Saunders, 1949.
956. Obermann, C. E. The Effect on the Berger Rhythm of Mild Affective States. *J. Abnorm. Soc. Psychol.*, 1939, 34, 84-95.
957. Obendorf, C. P. Psychogenic Factors in Asthma. *N.Y. St. J. Med.*, 1935, 35, 41.
957a. Obermayer, M. E. *Psychocutaneous Medicine.* Springfield, Ill.: C. C Thomas, 1955.
958. Obrador, S. Effect of Hypothalamic Lesions on Electrical Activity of Cerebral Cortex. *J. Neurophysiol.*, 1943, 6, 81-84.
959. Ødegaard, Ø. *The Neurosis of Man: An Introduction to the Science of Behavior.* London: Routledge and Kegan Paul, 1949.
960. Ødegaard, Ø. On the Psychology of Social Groups as Illustrated by Their Incidence of Mental Disorder. In: Reymert (1033), pp. 454-464.
961. Ogden, C. K. *The Meaning of Psychology.* New York: Harper, 1926.
962. Ogden, R. M. Oswald Külpe and the Würzburg School. *Am. J. Psychol.*, 1951, 64, 4-19.
962a. Olds, J. Physiological Mechanisms of Reward. In: M. R. Jones, ed. *Nebraska Symposium on Motivation.* Lincoln: University of Nebraska Press, 1955, pp. 73-139.
962b. Ostfeld, A. M., Chapman, L. F., Goodell, H. & Wolff, H. G. Studies in Headache: Summary of Evidence Concerning a Noxious Agent Active Locally During Migraine Headache. *Psychosom. Med.*, 1957, 19, 199-208.
963. Otani, T. Fatigue as a Failure of Nervous Regulation. *Scientia*, 1953, 88, 272-276.
964. Pacella, B. L., Polatin, P. & Nagler, S. H. Clinical and EEG Studies in Obsessive-Compulsive States. *Am. J. Psychiat.*, 1944, 100, 830-838.

965. Palmer, W. L. The Mechanisms of Pain in Gastric and Duodenal Ulcer. I, Achlorhydria. *Arch. Int. Med.*, 1926, 38, 603.
966. Palmer, W. L. & Heinz, T. E. Further Observations on the Mechanism of Pain in Gastric and Duodenal Ulcers. *Arch. Int. Med.*, 1934, 53, 269.
967. Palmer, W. L. The Pain of Peptic Ulcer. *Proc. Assn. Res. Nerv. Ment. Dis.*, 1943, 23, 302-326.
967a. Panzani, R. & Tuner, M. Etude EEGraphique de la Maladie asthmatique. *Presse Méd.*, 1952, 83, 1826.
968. Papez, J. W. A Proposed Mechanism of Emotion. *Arch. Neurol. Psychiat.*, 1937, 38, 725-743.
969. Papez, J. W. Cerebral Mechanisms. *J. Nerv. Ment. Dis.*, 1939, 89, 145-159.
969a. Papez, J. W. Central Reticular Path to Intralaminar and Reticular Nuclei of Thalamus for Activating EEG Related to Consciousness. *EEG Clin. Neurophysiol.*, 1956, 8, 117-128.
970. Parkinson, J. & Campbell, M. Paroxysmal Auricular Fibrillation. A Record of Two Hundred Patients. *Quart. J. Med.*, 1930, 24, 67.
971. Partridge, M. *Pre-frontal Leucotomy.* Springfield, Ill.: C. C Thomas, 1950.
972. Pattie, F. A. The Production of Blisters by Hypnotic Suggestion. *J. Abnorm. Soc. Psychol.*, 1947, 36, 62-72.
973. Pavlov, I. P. Scientific Study of the So-Called Psychical Processes in the Higher Animals. In: Dennis (293a), pp. 425-438.
974. Pavlov, I. P. *Conditioned Reflexes.* London: Oxford University Press, 1927.
975. Pavlov, I. P. *Conditioned Reflexes and Psychiatry.* New York: International Publishers, 1941.
976. Payne, W. W. & Poulton, E. P. Visceral Pain in the Upper Alimentary Tract. *Quart. J. Med.*, 1923-1924, 17, 53-83.
977. Payne, W. W. & Poulton, E. P. Experiments on Visceral Sensation, Part I. The Relation of Pain to Activity in the Human Esophagus. *J. Physiol.*, 1927, 46, 217-241.
978. Payne, W. W. & Poulton, E. P. Experiments on Visceral Sensation, Part II. The Sensation of "Nausea" and "Sinking"; Esophageal Reflexes and Counter-Irritation. *J. Physiol.*, 1928, 45, 157-172.
979. Peabody, F., Clough, H. D., Sturgis, C. C., Wearn, J. T. & Tompkins, E. H. Effects of the Injection of Epinephrine in Soldiers with Irritable Heart. *J. Am. Med. Assn.*, 1918, 71, 1912.
980. Pearson, K. On Lines and Planes of Closest Fit to Systems of Points in Space. *Philosoph. Mag.*, 1921, 2, 559-572.
981. Pelt, S. J. van. Asthma? Is there any such Disease? *Brit. J. Med. Hypnot.*, 1953, 4, 17-25.
982. Penfield, W. The Cerebral Cortex in Man. I, The Cerebral Cortex and Consciousness. *Arch. Neurol. Psychiat.*, 1938, 40, 417-442.
983. Penfield, W. Memory Mechanisms. *Arch. Neurol. Psychiat.*, 1952, 67, 178-198.
984. Penfield, W. & Rasmusen, T. *The Cerebral Cortex of Man, A Clinical Study of Localization of Function.* New York: Macmillan, 1950.
985. Pennington, L. A. & Berg, I. *An Introduction to Clinical Psychology.* New York: Ronald Press, 1948.
985a. Peretz. Gormim Psihosomatizim b'Alveset. *Harefuah,* 1954, 46, 189-192.
986. Perrin, F. A. L. & Klein, D. B. *Psychology, Its Method and Principles.* New York: Henry Holt, 1926.
987. Persky, H., Gamm, S. R. & Grinker, R. R. Correlation between Fluctuations of Free Anxiety and Quantity of Hippuric Acid Excretion. *Psychosom. Med.*, 1952, 14, 34-40.

988. Peters, H. N. The Judgmental Theory of Pleasantness and Unpleasantness. *Psychol. Rev.*, 1935, 42, 354-386.

989. Peters, H. N. A Note on Verification of the Judgmental Theory of Pleasantness and Unpleasantness. *Psychol. Rev.*, 1937, 44, 533-535.

990. Petrie, A. *Personality and the Frontal Lobes: An Investigation of the Psychological Effects of Different Types of Leucotomy.* Philadelphia: Blakiston, 1952.

991. Pfeiffer, J. B. & Wolff, H. G. Studies in Renal Circulation during Periods of Life Stress and Accompanying Emotional Reactions in Subjects with and without Essential Hypertension; Observations on the Role of Neural Activity in Regulation of Renal Blood Flow. *Proc. Assn. Res. Nerv. Ment. Dis.*, 1949, 29, 929-953.

992. Phantom Limb, The. *Psychiat. Bull. Texas*, 1952-53, 3 (1), 6-8.

993. Piéron, H. Emotions in Animals and Men. In: Reymert (1032), pp. 284-294.

994. Piéron, H. Sensory Affectivity. In: Reymert (1033), pp. 76-83.

994a. Pilot, M. L., Lenkoski, D., Spiro, H. M. & Schafer, R. Duodenal Ulcer in One of Identical Twins. *Psychosom. Med.*, 1957, 19, 221-227.

995. Pincus, G. & Hoagland, H. Adrenal Cortical Responses in Normal Men and in Those with Personality Disorders. *Am. J. Psychiat.*, 1950, 106, 641-659.

996. Pincus, G., Hoagland, H., Freeman, H. & Elmadjian, F. Adrenal Function in Mental Disease, Recent Progress in Hormone Research. *Geriatrics*, 1949, 4, 291-322.

996a. Pinneau, S. R. The Infantile Disorders of Hospitalism and Anaclitic Depression. *Psychol. Bull.*, 1955, 52, 429-452.

996b. Pinneau, S. R. Reply to Dr. Spitz. *Psychol. Bull.*, 1955, 52, 459-462.

997. Plooij, M. Sur quelques Variations fonctionelles de l'Onde T dans l'Electrocardiogramme. *Arch. d. Mal. du Coeur*, 1946, 39, 126-141.

998. Plutchik, R. The Role of Muscular Tension in Maladjustment. *J. Gen. Psychol.*, 1954, 50, 45-62.

998a. Plutchik, R. Some Problems for a Theory of Emotion. *Psychosom. Med.*, 1957, 19, 306-310.

999. Pochin, E. E. Delay of Pain Perception in Tabes dorsalis. *Clin. Sci.*, 1938, 3, 191-196.

1000. Pollock, G. H. The Psychological Response to Estrogenic Therapy in Turner's Syndrome (Ovarian Agenesis). *J. Nerv. Ment. Dis.*, 1955, 121, 420-422.

1001. Pond, D. A., Rey, J. H. & Hill, D. Biological Correlates of Constitutional EEG Abnormalities of the Temporal Lobes. *EEG Clin. Neurophysiol.*, 1950, 2, 111-112.

1002. Poser, E. G. The Use of Psychological Tests in Psychosomatic Research. *Canad. J. Psychol.*, 1953, 7, 177-182.

1003. Pratt, J. P. A Personal Note on Testosterone in Hypogonadism. *J. Clin. Endocrinol.*, 1942, 2, 460-464.

1004. Pratt, K. C., Nelson, A. K. & Sun, K. H. The Behavior of the Newborn Infant. *Ohio St. Univ. Studies*, No. 10, 1930.

1005. Precker, J. A. Toward a Theoretical Brain Model. *J. Person.*, 1954, 22, 310-325.

1005a. Price, D. B., Thaler, M. & Mason, J. W. Preoperative Emotional States and Adrenal Cortical Activity. *Arch. Neurol. Psychiat.*, 1957, 17, 646-656.

1006. Price, H. Dermatitis in Industry. *Am. J. Nurs.*, 1953, 53, 65-66.

1007. Prugh, D. G. Variations in Attitudes, Behavior and Feeling States as Exhibited in the Play of Children during Modifications in the Course of Ulcerative Colitis. *Proc. Assn. Res. Nerv. Ment. Dis.*, 1949, 29, 692.

1007a. Rabinovitch, M. S., Kennard, M. A. & Fister, W. P. Personality Correlates of

Electroencephalographic Patterns: Rorschach Findings. *Canad. J. Psychol.*, 1955, 9, 29-41.

1008. Ramström, M. Über die Funktion der Vater-Pacinischen Körperchen. *Mitt. a. d. Grenzgeb. d. Med. u. Chir.*, 1908, 13, 314.

1009. Randall, L. & Cohen, L. The Serum Lipids in Schizophrenia. *Psychiat. Quart.*, 1939, 13, 441-459.

1010. Randall, W. C. & McClure, W. Quantitation of the Output of Individual Sweat Glands and Their Response to Stimulation. *J. Appl. Physiol.*, 1949, 2, 72-80.

1011. Ranges, H. A. & Bradley, S. E. Systemic and Renal Circulatory Changes Following Administration of Adrenin, Ephedrine and Paredrinol to Normal Man. *J. Clin. Invest.*, 1943, 22, 687-693.

1012. Rank, O. *The Trauma of Birth.* New York: Harcourt, Brace, 1929.

1013. Rank, O. *Modern Education.* New York: Knopf, 1932.

1014. Rank, O. *Will Therapy and Truth and Reality.* New York: Knopf, 1945.

1015. Rank, O. & Ferenczi, S. *The Development of Psychoanalysis.* New York: Nerv. Ment. Dis. Publ. Co., 1925.

1016. Ranson, S. W. The Hypothalamus: Its Significance for Visceral Innervation and Emotional Expression. *Tr. Coll. Phys. Phila.*, 1934, 32, 222.

1017. Ranson, S. W. Somnolence Caused by Hypothalamic Lesions in the Monkey. *Arch. Neurol. Psychiat.*, 1939, 41, 1-23.

1018. Ranson, S. W. Regulation of Body Temperature. *Proc. Assn. Res. Nerv. Ment. Dis.*, 1940, 20, 342-399.

1019. Rapaport, D. *Diagnostic Psychological Testing,* 2 vols. Chicago: Year Book Publishers, 1946.

1020. Rapaport, D. *Emotions and Memory.* New York: International Universities Press, 1950.

1021. Rapaport, D. *Organization and Pathology of Thought.* New York: Columbia University Press, 1951.

1022. Rapaport, D. On the Psychoanalytic Theory of Affects. *Int. J. Psycho-Anal.*, 1953, 34, 177-198.

1023. Raskin, N. J. Analysis of Six Parallel Studies of the Therapeutic Process. *J. Consult. Psychol.*, 1949, 13, 206-220.

1024. Ravitz, L. J. Electrocyclic Phenomena and Emotional States. *J. Clin. Exp. Psychopathol.*, 1952, 13, 69-106.

1025. Ray, G. B., Ray, L. H. & Johnson, J. R. The Change in Reduction Time of Blood After Breathing as a Criterion of Physiological Fitness. *Am. J. Psychiat.*, 1946, 147, 630-646.

1026. Rees, L. Psychosomatic Aspects of the Pre-Menstrual Tension Syndrome. *J. Ment. Sci.*, 1953, 99, 62-73.

1027. Rees, L. Psychological Concomitants of Cortisone and ACTH Therapy. *J. Ment. Sci.*, 1953, 99, 497-504.

1028. Rees, W. L. & Eysenck, H. J. A Factorial Study of Some Morphological and Psychological Aspects of Human Constitution. *J. Ment. Sci.*, 1945, 91, 8-21.

1029. Rehwoldt, F. Über respiratorische Affektsymptome. *Psychol. Studien*, 1911, 7, 141-195.

1030. Rennie, T. A. C. & Howard, J. E. Hypoglycemia and Tension-Depression. *Psychosom. Med.*, 1942, 4, 273-282.

1031. Rey, J. H., Pond, D. A. & Evans, C. C. Clinical and Electroencephalographic Studies of Temporal Lobe Function. *Proc. Royal Soc. Med.*, 1949, 42, 891-904.

1032. Reymert, M. L., ed. *Feelings and Emotions* (The Wittenberg Symposium). Worcester, Mass.: Clark University Press, 1928.

1033. Reymert, M. L., ed. *Feelings and Emotions* (The Mooseheart Symposium). New York: McGraw-Hill, 1950.
1034. Reynolds, S. R. M. & Friedman, M. H. Studies on the Uterus: III. The Activity of the Uterine Fistula in Unanesthetized Rabbits Following Coitus and During Pseudo-Pregnancy. *Am. J. Physiol.*, 1930, 94, 696-704.
1034a. Ribble, M. A. Clinical Studies of Instinctive Reactions in Newborn Babies. *Am. J. Psychiat.*, 1938, 95, 149-160.
1035. Ribble, M. A. Infantile Experience in Relation to Personality Development. In: Hunt (610), 2, 621-651.
1036. Richards, A. N. & Plant, O. H. The Action of Minute Doses of Adrenalin and Pituitrin on the Kidney. *Am. J. Physiol.*, 1922, 59, 191-202.
1037. Richards, C. H., Wolf, S. & Wolff, H. G. The Measurement and Recording of Gastroduodenal Blood Flow in Man by Means of a Thermal Gradientometer. *J. Clin. Invest.*, 1942, 21, 551-558.
1038. Richards, T. W. *Modern Clinical Psychology*. New York: McGraw-Hill, 1946.
1039. Richter, C. P. A Behavioristic Study of the Activity of the Rat. *Comp. Psychol. Mon.*, 1922, 1, 1-55.
1040. Richter, C. P. Factors Determining Voluntary Ingestion of Water in Normals and Individuals with Maximum Diabetes Insipidus. *Am. J. Physiol.*, 1938, 122, 668-675.
1041. Richter, C. P. Behavior and Endocrine Regulations of the Internal Environment. *Endocrinol.*, 1941, 28, 193-195.
1042. Riddock, G. The Reflex Functions of the Completely Divided Spinal Cord in Man as Compared with Those Associated with Less Severe Lesions. *Brain*, 1917, 40, 264-402.
1043. Riddock, G. Phantom Limbs and Body Shape. *Brain*, 1941, 64, 197-222.
1044. Riesen, A. H. The Development of Visual Perception in Man and Chimpanzee. *Science*, 1947, 106, 107-108.
1045. Riggs, H. E., Boles, R. S., Rheinhold, I. G. & Shore, P. S. Observations on the Chemical Composition of the Blood on Some Cardiovascular Reactions in Chronic Peptic Ulcer through One Year. *Gastroenterol.*, 1944, 3, 480-488.
1046. Rioch, D. M. Certain Aspects of Behavior of Decorticate Cats. *Psychiatry*, 1938, 1, 339-345.
1046a. Roback, A. A., ed. *Present-Day Psychology*. New York: Philosophical Library, 1955.
1047. Robertson, T. B. *Principles of Biochemistry for Students of Medicine, Agriculture, and Related Sciences*. Philadelphia: Lea & Febiger, 1920.
1048. Robinson, S. C. On the Etiology of Peptic Ulcer; Analysis of 70 Ulcer Patients. *Am. J. Digest. Dis. Nutr.*, 1935, 2, 333-343.
1049. Rockwell, F. V. & Simons, D. J. The Electroencephalogram and Personality Organization in the Obsessive Compulsive Reactions. *Arch. Neurol. Psychiat.*, 1947, 57, 71-77.
1050. Rogers, C. R. *Counselling and Psychotherapy*. Boston: Houghton Mifflin, 1942.
1051. Rogers, C. R. Some Observations of the Organization of Personality. *Am. Psychol.*, 1947, 2, 358-368.
1052. Rogers, C. R. Significance of the Self-Regarding Attitudes and Perceptions. In: Reymert (1033), pp. 374-382.
1053. Rogers, C. R. *Client-Centered Therapy*. Boston: Houghton Mifflin, 1951.
1053a. Rogers, C. R. Directions of Psychotherapy. In: Moulton (936b), pp. 44-68.
1053b. Rogers, C. R. & Dymond, R. F., eds. *Psychotherapy and Personality Change*. Chicago: University of Chicago Press, 1954.
1054. Rogers, F. T. & Hardt, L. L. J. The Relation of the Digestion Contraction of

the Filled to the Hunger Contraction of the Empty Stomach. *Am. J. Physiol.*, 1915, 38, 274-284.

1055. Rogers, F. T. & Martin, C. L. X-Ray Observations of Hunger Contractions in Man. *Am. J. Physiol.*, 1926, 76, 349-353.

1056. Romano, J. & Engel, G. Studies of Delirium: I. EEG data. *Arch. Neurol. Psychiat.*, 1944, 51, 356-377.

1057. Rome, H. P. & Braceland, F. J. The Role of ACTH, Cortisone and Hydrocortisone in Provocation of Certain Psychologic Responses. *Proc. Assn. Res. Nerv. Ment. Dis.*, 1951, 31, 273-279.

1058. Rooke, A. B. Diuresis by Suggestion. *Brit. Med. J.*, 1946, 1, 776.

1058a. Rosen, S. Emotional Factors in Nausea and Vomiting of Pregnancy. *Psychiat. Quart.*, 1955, 29, 621-633.

1059. Rosenthal, M. J. Neuropsychiatric Aspects of Infantile Eczema. *Arch. Neurol. Psychiat.*, 1953, 70, 428-451.

1060. Ross, N. Psychoanalytic Studies in Development. Instinctual Drives-Ego. *Annual Survey of Psychoanalysis*, 1952, 1, 61-108.

1061. Roth, G. M., Allen, E. V., Barker, N. W. & Hines, E. A. *Peripheral Vascular Diseases*. Philadelphia: Saunders, 1946.

1062. Rothmann, H. Zusammenfassender Bericht über den Rothmannschen grosshirnlosen Hund nach klinischer und anatomischer Untersuchung. *Z. Ges. Neurol. Psychiat.*, 1923, 87, 247-313.

1063. Rowntree, D. W. & Kay, W. W. Clinical, Biochemical, and Physiological Studies in Cases of Recurrent Schizophrenia. *J. Ment. Sci.*, 1952, 98, 100-121.

1063a. Minor, R. W., ed. *The Regulation of Hunger and Appetite*. New York: New York Academy of Sciences, 1955.

1064. Rubin, M. A. Electroencephalography in the Psychoses. *Am. J. Psychiat.*, 1940, 96, 862-873.

1065. Rubin, S. & Bowman, K. M. Electroencephalographic and Personality Correlates in Peptic Ulcer. *Psychosom. Med.*, 1942, 4, 309-318.

1066. Rubin, S. & Moses, L. Electroencephalographic Studies in Asthma with Some Personality Correlates. *Psychosom. Med.*, 1944, 6, 31-39.

1067. Ruch, T. C. Neural Basis of Somatic Sensation. In: Fulton (406), pp. 316-344.

1068. Ruch, T. C. Visceral Sensation and Referred Pain. In: Fulton (406), pp. 360-374.

1069. Ruch, T. C. Somatic Sensation. In: Fulton (406), pp. 292-314.

1070. Ruckmick, C. A. Emotions in Terms of the Galvanometric Technique. *Brit. J. Psychol.*, 1930, 21, 149-159.

1071. Ruckmick, C. A. *Psychology of Feeling and Emotion*. New York: McGraw-Hill, 1936.

1072. Ruckmick, C. A. The Reality of Bright and Dull Pressure. *Am. J. Psychol.*, 1935, 47, 330-333.

1072a. Rudolf, G. de M. Clinical Blood-Pressure in Anxiety. *J. Ment. Sci.*, 1955, 101, 893-894.

1073. Rupp, C., Riggs, H. E., Boles, R. S. & Shore, P. Homeostatic Studies in Patients with So-Called Psychosomatic Disease (Peptic Ulcer). *I. Nerv. Ment. Dis.*, 1951, 114, 384-390.

1074. Russell, R. W. Experimental Studies of Hereditary Influences on Behaviour. *Eugen. Rev.*, 1953, 45, 19-30.

1075. Rydin, H. & Verney, E. B. The Inhibition of Water Diuresis by Emotional Stress and by Muscular Exercise. *Quart. J. Exp. Physiol.*, 1938, 27, 343-374.

1076. Sachs, W. The Vegetative Nervous System in Dementia Praecox. *S. African J. Med. Sci.*, 1936, 1, 142-155.
1077. Saenger, M. *Über Asthma und seine Behandlung*. Berlin: Karger, 1910.
1078. Saltzman, S. S. An Investigation of Certain Psychological Aspects of Personality in Three Allergic Groups. *Dissert. Abstr.*, 1953, 13, 1251.
1079. Sanford, R. N. The Effect of Abstinence from Food upon Imaginal Processes: A Preliminary Experiment. *J. Psychol.*, 1936, 2, 129-136.
1080. Sanford, R. N. et al. Physique, Personality, and Scholarship. *Mon. Soc. Res. Child Dev.*, 1943, 8, Ser. No. 34, No. 1.
1081. Sargent, W. The Hyperventilation Syndrome. *Lancet*, 1940, 238, 314-316.
1082. Saslow, G., Gressel, G. C., Shobe, F. O., DuBois, P. H. & Schroeder, H. A. The Possible Etiological Relevance of Personality Factors in Arterial Hypertension. *Psychosom. Med.*, 1950, 12, 292-302.
1083. Saul, L. J. Physiological Effects of Emotional Tension. In: Hunt (610), pp. 269-305.
1084. Saul, L. J. Brief Therapy of a Case of Torticollis. *Samiksa*, 1953, 7, 139-141.
1085. Saul, L. J. Psychosomatic Aspects of Peptic Ulcer. *Samiksa*, 1953, 7, 225-235.
1086. Saul, L. J., Davis, H. & Davis, P. A. Correlations Between Electroencephalograms and the Psychological Organization of the Individual. *Tr. Am. Neurol. Assn.*, 1937, 63, 167-169.
1087. Saul, L. J., Davis, H. & Davis, P. A. Psychologic Correlations with the Electroencephalogram. *Psychosom. Med.*, 1949, 11, 361-376.
1088. Saxl, S. Ein Fall von Asthma Bronchinole bei einem Manisch-Depressiven. *Wien. Klin. Wochnschr.*, 1933, 46, 1515.
1089. Schaeffer, J. P. *Morris' Human Anatomy*. Philadelphia: Blakiston, 1951.
1090. Schafer, R. *The Clinical Application of Psychological Tests*. New York: International Universities Press, 1948.
1091. Scheflen, A. E. On Bronchial Asthma: A Case Report. *Psychiat. Quart.*, 1953, 27, 650-653.
1091a. Scheibel, M., Scheibel, A., Mollica, A. & Moruzzi, G. Convergence and Interaction of Afferent Impulses on Single Units of Reticular Formation. *J. Neurophysiol.*, 1955, 18, 309-331.
1092. Scheidegger, S. Liver Tissue Changes in Schizophrenia. *J. Neuropath. Exp. Neurol.*, 1953, 12, 397-399.
1093. Schick, A. On Premenstrual Depression. *Am. J. Psychother.*, 1953, 7, 664-671.
1093a. Schilder, P. *The Image and Appearance of the Human Body*. New York: International Universities Press, 1950.
1094. Schilling, R. F. & Musser, M. J. Pain Reaction Thresholds in Psychoneurotic Patients. *Am. J. Med. Sci.*, 1948, 215, 195-197.
1095. Schilling, R. F. & Musser, M. J. Pain Reaction Thresholds in the Menopausal Syndrome. *Am. J. Med. Sci.*, 1949, 218, 204-206.
1096. Schilling, R. F. & Musser, M. J. Pain Reaction Thresholds in Patients with Peptic Ulcer. *Am. J. Med. Sci.*, 1949, 218, 207-208.
1097. Schimmenti, J. M. The Hyperventilating Type of Female. *J. Nerv. Ment. Dis.*, 1953, 118, 223-236.
1098. Schlionsky, H., Sarracino, L. R. & Bishof, L. J. Functional Enuresis in the Army. Report of Clinical Study of 100 Cases. *War Med.*, 1954, 7, 297-303.
1099. Schlosberg, H. Three Dimensions of Emotion. *Psychol. Rev.*, 1954, 61, 81-88.
1100. Schmideberg, M. Some Clinical Implications of the Sense of Bodily Reality. *J. Hillside Hosp.*, 1953, 2, 207-212.
1100a. Schmidt, H., Jr. The Reticular Formation and Behavioral Wakefulness. *Psychol. Bull.*, 1957, 54, 75.

1101. Schneck, J. M. Hypnoanalytic Study of a Patient with Extrasystoles. *J. Clin. Exp. Hypnosis,* 1953, 1, 11-17.
1102. Schneck, J. M. The Hypnotic Trance, Magico-Religious Medicine and Primitive Initiation Rites. *Psychoanal. Rev.,* 1954, 41, 182-190.
1103. Schneider, R. A. Relation of Stress to Clotting Time, Relative Viscosity and Certain other Biophysical Alterations of the Blood in the Normotensive and Hypertensive Subject. *Proc. Assn. Res. Nerv. Ment. Dis.,* 1950, 29, 818-831.
1104. Schneider, R. A. Recurrent Thrombophlebitis: An Experimental Study of Life Situations and Emotions and the Clotting Time and Relative Viscosity of the Blood. *Am. J. Med. Sci.,* 1951, 221, 562-578.
1105. Schneider, R. A. & Zangari, V. M. Variations in Clotting Time, Relative Viscosity, and other Physiochemical Properties of the Blood Accompanying Physical and Emotional Stress in the Normotensive and Hypertensive Subject. *Psychosom. Med.,* 1951, 13, 289-303.
1106. Schoenberg, M. J. Role of States of Anxiety in Pathogenesis of Primary Glaucoma. *Arch. Ophth.,* 1940, 23, 76-90.
1107. Schoenberg, M. J. Psychosomatic Interrelations, Their Therapeutic Implications in Glaucoma. *Arch. Ophth.,* 1940, 23, 91-103.
1108. Schroeder, H. A. Pathogenesis of Hypertension. *Am. J. Med.,* 1951, 10, 189-209.
1109. Schultz, J. H. *Das autogene Training (Konzentrative Selbstentspannung).* Leipzig: Thieme, 1932.
1110. Schulze, V. E. & Schwab, E. H. Arteriolar Hypertension in the American Negro. *Am. Heart J.,* 1936, 11, 66-74.
1110a. Schur, M. Chronic, Exudative, Discoid and Lichenoid Dermatitis (Sulzberger-Garbe's Syndrome): Case Analysis. *Int. J. Psycho-Anal.,* 1950, 31, 73-77.
1110b. Schur, M. Comments on the Metapsychology of Somatization. *Psychoanalytic Study of the Child,* 1955, 10, 119-164.
1111. Schwab, R. S. Psychiatry Attacks Fatigue. *Res. Rev. (ONR),* 1949, June, 17-22.
1112. Schwab, R. S. *Electroencephalography in Clinical Practice.* Philadelphia: Saunders, 1951.
1113. Schwab, R. S. & de Lorme, T. Psychiatric Findings in Fatigue. *Am. J. Psychiat.,* 1953, 109, 621-625.
1114. Schwade, E. D. & Geiger, S. Impulsive-Compulsive Behavior Disorder with Abnormal Electroencephalographic Findings. *Abstr. Third Internat. EEG Congress,* 1953, p. 60.
1114a. Schwartz, T. B. & Shields, D. R. Urinary Excretion of Formaldehydrogenic Steroids and Creatinine, a Reflection of Emotional Tension. *Psychosom. Med.,* 1956, 18, 159-172.
1115. Scodel, A. Passivity in a Class of Peptic Ulcer Patients. *Psychol. Mon.,* 1953, 67, 1-15.
1116. Scott, J. C. Systolic Blood Pressure Fluctuations with Sex, Anger, and Fear. *J. Comp. Psychol.,* 1930, 10, 97-114.
1117. Scott, J. P. The Relative Importance of Social and Hereditary Factors in Producing Disturbances in Life Adjustment during Periods of Stress in Laboratory Animals. *Proc. Assn. Res. Nerv. Ment. Dis.,* 1949, 29, 61-71.
1118. Sears, R. R. *Survey of Objective Studies of Psychoanalytic Concepts.* Washington: Social Science Research Council, 1942, pp. 110-120.
1119. Secord, P. F. & Jourard, S. M. The Appraisal of Body-Cathexis: Body-Cathexis and the Self. *J. Consult. Psychol.,* 1953, 17, 343-347.
1120. Selye, H. *Stress.* Montreal: Acta, Inc., 1950.

1121. Selye, H. *The Physiology and Pathology of Exposure to Stress*. Montreal: Acta, Inc., 1950.

1121a. Selye, H. *Annual Report on Stress*. Montreal: Acta, Inc., 1951, pp. 51, 244, 316, 441, 450.

1122a. Selye, H. *The Stress of Life*. New York: McGraw-Hill, 1956.

1123. Selye, H. & Fortier, C. Adaptive Reaction to Stress. *Psychosom. Med.*, 1950, 12, 149-157.

1124. Sen, I. The Psychological System of Sri Aurobindo. *Indian J. Psychol.*, 1952, 27, 79-89.

1125. Shagass, C. Conditioning the Human Occipital Alpha Rhythm to a Voluntary Stimulus. A Quantitative Study. *J. Exp. Psychol.*, 1942, 31, 367-379.

1126. Shagass, C. & Johnson, E. P. The Course of Acquisition of a Conditioned Response of the Occipital Alpha Rhythm. *J. Exp. Psychol.*, 1943, 33, 201-209.

1127. Shands, H. C. & Finesinger, J. E. Lymphocytes in the Psychoneuroses. *Am. J. Psychiat.*, 1948, 105, 277-285.

1128. Sheldon, S. H. & Ball, R. Physical Characteristics of the Y Twins and Their Relation to Hypertension. *Proc. Assn. Res. Nerv. Ment. Dis.*, 1949, 29, 952.

1129. Sheldon, W. H. Constitutional Factors in Personality. In: Hunt (610), pp. 526-549.

1130. Sheldon, W. H. *Varieties of Delinquent Youth: An Introduction to Constitutional Psychology*. New York: Harper, 1949.

1131. Sheldon, W. H. & Stevens, S. S. *The Varieties of Temperament: A Psychology of Constitutional Differences*. New York: Harper, 1942.

1132. Sheldon, W. H., Stevens, S. S. & Tucker, W. B. *The Varieties of Human Physique: An Introduction to Constitutional Psychology*. New York: Harper, 1940.

1133. Shelley, W. B., Horvath, P. N. & Pillsbury, D. M. Anhidrosis. *Medicine*, 1950, 29, 195-224.

1134. Shepard, J. F. Organic Changes and Feeling. *Am. J. Psychol.*, 1906, 17, 522-584.

1135. Sherif, M. & Cantril, H. *The Psychology of Ego Involvements*. New York: John Wiley, 1947.

1135a. Sherif, M. & Sherif, C. W. *An Outline of Social Psychology*. New York: Harper, 1956.

1136. Sherman, M. The Differentiation of Emotional Response in Infants. *J. Comp. Psychol.*, 1927, 7, 265-284.

1137. Sherman, M. & Jost, H. Frustration Reactions of Normal and Neurotic Persons. *Psychol.*, 1942, 13, 3-19.

1138. Sherman, M. & Sherman, I. C. Sensory-Motor Responses in Infants. *J. Comp. Psychol.*, 1925, 5, 53-67.

1139. Sherman, M. & Sherman, I. C. *The Process of Human Behavior*. New York: Norton, 1929.

1140. Sherrington, C. S. Experiments on the Value of Vascular and Visceral Factors for the Genesis of Emotion. *Proc. Royal Soc.*, 1900, 66, 390-403.

1141. Sherrington, C. S. *The Integrative Action of the Nervous System*. New Haven: Yale University Press, 1947.

1142. Shields, J. Personality Differences and Neurotic Traits in Normal Twin School Children. *Eugen. Rev.*, 1954, 45, 213-246.

1143. Shock, N. W. Physiological Factors in Behavior. In: Hunt (610), 1, 582-618.

1144. Shock, N. W. Physiological Manifestations of Chronic Emotional States. In: Reymert (1033), pp. 277-283.

1145. Sigl, A. Psyche und psychisch ausgelöste Spannungen im Krankheitsgeschehen. *Ztschr. Psychother. Med. Psychol.,* 1954, 4, 33-39.
1146. Silberman, I. A Contribution to the Psychology of Menstruation. *Int. J. Psycho-Anal.,* 1950, 31, 258-267.
1147. Silverman, J. J. & Powell, V. E. Studies on Palmar Sweating. *Am. J. Med. Sci.,* 1944, 208, 297-305.
1148. Simmons, L. W. The Relation Between the Decline of Anxiety-Inducing and Anxiety-Resolving Factors in a Deteriorating Culture and Its Relevance to Bodily Disease. *Proc. Assn. Res. Nerv. Ment. Dis.,* 1949, 29, 127-136.
1149. Simons, D. J., Day, E., Goodell, H. & Wolff, H. G. Experimental Studies on Headache: Muscles of the Scalp and Neck as Sources of Pain. *Proc. Assn. Res. Nerv. Ment. Dis.,* 1943, 23, 228-244.
1150. Sinelnikoff, W. I. Über Hungerbewegungen eines Dünndarmabschnitts beim Menschen. *Pflüg. Arch. Ges. Physiol.,* 1927, 215, 427-430.
1151. Sinha, R. C. A Case of Aspermia. *Samiksa,* 1954, 8, 14-19.
1152. Sirmay, E. A. The Role of Psychotherapy in Allergy, Credits and Debits. *Calif. Med.,* 1953, 78, 456-458.
1153. Skaggs, E. B. Studies in Attention and Emotion. *J. Comp. Psychol.,* 1930, 10, 375-419.
1154. Skaggs, E. B. Changes in Pulse, Breathing, and Steadiness under Conditions of Startledness and Excited Expectancy. *J. Comp. Psychol.,* 1926, 6, 303-317.
1155. Skinner, B. F. *The Behavior of Organisms.* New York: D. Appleton-Century, 1938.
1156. Skinner, C. E. *Readings in Educational Psychology.* Boston: Houghton, Mifflin, 1934.
1157. Skinner, C. E. *Elementary Educational Psychology.* New York: Prentice-Hall, 1950.
1157a. Slater, E. & Shield, J. *Psychotic and Neurotic Illness in Twins* (Medical Research Council, Special Report Series, No. 278). London: Her Majesty's Stationery Office, 1953.
1158. Smith, A. A. An Electromyographic Study of Tension in Interrupted and Completed Tasks. *J. Exp. Psychol.,* 1953, 46, 32-36.
1159. Smith, H. W. Physiology of the Renal Circulation. *Harvey Lect.,* 1939, 35, 166-222.
1160. Smith, H. W. *Lectures on the Kidney.* Lawrence, Kan.: Extension Division, University of Kansas, 1943.
1161. Smith, H. W. The Excretion of Water. *Bull. N.Y. Acad. Med.,* 1947, 23, 177-195.
1162. Smith, H. W. *The Kidney: Structure and Function in Health and Disease.* New York: Oxford University Press, 1951.
1163. Smith, J. J. The Endocrine Bases and Hormonal Therapy of Alcoholism. *N.Y. St. J. Med.,* 1950, 50, 1704-1706.
1164. Smythies, J. R. The Experience and Description of the Human Body. *Brain,* 1953, 76, 132-145.
1165. Snygg, D. & Combs, A. W. *Individual Behavior.* New York: Harper, 1949.
1166. Sodeman, W. A. & Birch, G. E. Regional Variations in Water Loss from the Skin of Diseased Subjects Living in a Subtropical Climate. *J. Clin. Invest.,* 1944, 23, 37-43.
1167. Söderbergh, G. Sur les Moyens actuels d'Exploration du Système Sympathique en Clinique et leur Valeur. *Rev. Neurol.,* 1926, 33, 721-756.
1168. Soley, M. H. & Shock, V. W. The Etiology of Effort Syndrome. *Am. J. Med. Sci.,* 1938, 196, 840.

1160. Sonnemann, E. *Existence and Therapy. An Introduction to Phenomenological Psychology and Existential Analysis.* New York: Grune & Stratton, 1954.

1170. Sontag, L. W. Some Psychosomatic Aspects of Childhood. *Nerv. Child,* 1946, 5, 296-304.

1170a. Sparer, P. J., ed. *Personality, Stress and Tuberculosis.* New York: International Universities Press, 1956.

1171. Spearman, C. The Proof and Measurement of Association Between Two Things. *Am. J. Psychol.,* 1904, 15, 72-101, 202-292.

1172. Spearman, C. *Abilities of Man, Their Nature and Measurement.* London: Macmillan, 1927.

1173. Spemann, H. *Embryonic Development and Induction.* New Haven: Yale University Press, 1938.

1174. Spence, K. W. Postulates and Methods of "Behaviorism." *Psychol. Rev.,* 1948, 55, 67-79.

1174a. Spence, K. W. *Behavior Theory and Conditioning.* New Haven: Yale University Press, 1956.

1175. Spence, K. W. & Farber, I. E. The Relation of Anxiety to Differential Eyelid Conditioning. *J. Exp. Psychol.,* 1954, 47, 127-134.

1176. Spencer, H. *Principles of Psychology.* New York: D. Appleton, 1897.

1177. Spiegel, E. A., ed. *Progress in Neurology and Psychiatry: An Annual Review,* Vol. 8. New York: Grune & Stratton, 1953.

1178. Spiegel, E. A., Miller, E. A. & Oppenheimer, M. J. Forebrain and Rage Reactions. *J. Neurophysiol.,* 1940, 3, 538-548.

1179. Spiegel, E. A. & Wycis, H. T. Thalamic Recordings in Man with Special Reference to Seizure Discharges. *EEG Clin. Neurophysiol.,* 1950, 2, 23-27.

1179a. Spiegel, E. A., Wycis, H. T., Freed, H. & Orchinik, C. The Central Mechanism of Emotions. *Am. J. Psychiat.,* 1951, 108, 426-432.

1180. Spitz, R. A. Anaclitic Depression: An Inquiry into the Genesis of Psychiatric Conditions in Early Childhood. *Psychoanalytic Study of the Child,* 1946, 2, 313-342.

1180a. Spitz, R. A. Autoerotism. *Psychoanalytic Study of the Child,* 1949, 3/4, 85-120.

1181. Spitz, R. A. Anxiety in Infancy: Its Manifestations in the First Year of Life. *Int. J. Psycho-Anal.,* 1950, 31, 138-143.

1182. Spitz, R. A. Relevancy of Direct Infant Observation. *Psychoanalytic Study of the Child,* 1950, 5, 66-73.

1182a. Spitz, R. A. The Psychogenic Diseases in Infancy: An Attempt at Their Etiologic Classification. *Psychoanalytic Study of the Child,* 1951, 6, 255-275.

1182b. Spitz, R. A. Reply to Dr. Pinneau. *Psychol. Bull.,* 1955, 52, 453-459.

1183. Sprague, R. G., Power, M. H., Mason, H. L., Albert, A., Mathieson, D. R., Hench, P. S., Kendall, E. C., Slocumb, D. H. & Polley, H. Observations on the Physiologic Effects of Cortisone and ACTH in Man. *Arch. Int. Med.,* 1950, 85, 199-258.

1184. Stafford-Clark, D. & Taylor, F. H. Clinical and Electroencephalographic Studies of Prisoners Charged with Murder. *J. Neurol. Neurosurg. Psychiat.,* 1949, 12, 325-330.

1185. Starr, H. E. The Hydrogen Ion Concentration of the Mixed Saliva Considered as an Index of Fatigue and of Emotional Excitation, and Applied to a Study of the Metabolic Etiology of Stammering. *Am. J. Psychol.,* 1922, 33, 394-418.

1186. Starr, H. E. Studies of Human Mixed Saliva. II, Variations in the Hydrogen Ion Concentration of Human Mixed Saliva. *J. Biol. Chem.,* 1922, 54, 55-64.

1187. Starr, I., Jr. & Collins, L. H., Jr. Observations on Changes in Respiration and

Circulation Occurring Coincidentally with Sensations of Faintness and Impending Syncope in Normal Individuals. *J. Clin. Invest.*, 1929, 7, 513-514.

1188. Starr, I., Jr. & Collins, L. H., Jr. Studies of Cardiac Output in Normal Men. *Am. J. Physiol.*, 1931, 96, 228-242.

1189. Starr, I., Jr. & Gamble, C. J. A Method for the Determination of Minute Amounts of Ethyl Iodide in Air, Water, and Blood by Means of Its Reaction with Silver Nitrate and Experiments Bearing on the Determination of Blood Flow by Means of Ethyl Iodide. *J. Biol. Chem.*, 1927, 71, 509-535.

1190. Starr, I., Jr. & Gamble, C. J. An Improved Method for the Determination of Cardiac Output in Man by Means of Ethyl Iodide. *Am. J. Physiol.*, 1928, 87, 450-473.

1191. Starzl, T. E., Taylor, C. W. & Magoun, H. W. Collateral Afferent Excitation of Reticular Formation of Brain Stem. *J. Neurophysiol.*, 1951, 14, 479-496.

1191a. Starzl, T. E., Taylor, C. W. & Magoun, H. W. Ascending Conduction in Reticular Activity System, with Special Reference to the Diencephalon. *J. Neurophysiol.*, 1951, 41, 461-477.

1192. Stead, E. A., Jr. & Warren, J. V. Clinical Significance of Hyperventilation. *Am. J. Med. Sci.*, 1943, 206, 183-190.

1193. Stead, E. A., Jr., Warren, J. V., Merrill, A. D. & Brannon, E. S. The Cardiac Output in Male Subjects as Measured by the Technique of Right Arterial Catheterization. *J. Clin. Invest.*, 1945, 24, 326-331.

1194. Stellar, E. The Physiology of Emotion. *Psychol. Rev.*, 1954, 61, 5-22.

1195. Stenberg, S. Psychosis and Blood Lipoids: Quantitative Variation of Total Cholesterin and Total Fatty Acids in the Blood of Dementia Praecox. *Acta Med. Scandinav.*, 1929, 72, 1-49.

1195a. Stennett, R. D. The Relationship of Alpha Amplitude to the Level of Palmar Conductance. *EEG Clin. Neurophysiol.*, 1957, 9, 131-138.

1196. Stephenson, W. The Significance of Q-Technique for the Study of Personality. In: Reymert (1033), pp. 552-570.

1196a. Stevens, J. R., Glaser, G. H. & MacLean, P. D. The Influence of Sodium Amytal on the Recollection of Seizure States. *Tr. Am. Neurol. Assn.*, 1954, 79, 40-45.

1197. Stevens S. S. Mathematics, Measurement, and Psychophysics. In: Stevens (1197a) pp. 1-49.

1197a. Stevens, S. S., ed. *Handbook of Experimental Psychology.* New York: John Wiley, 1951.

1198. Stevenson, I. P. Variations in the Secretion of Bronchial Mucus During Periods of Stress. *Proc. Assn. Res. Nerv. Ment. Dis.*, 1949, 29, 596-601.

1199. Stevenson, I. P. Physical Symptoms during Pleasurable Emotional States. *Psychosom. Med.*, 1950, 12, 98-102.

1200. Stevenson, I. P. & Duncan, C. H. Alterations in Cardiac Function and Circulatory Efficiency during Periods of Life Stress as Shown by Changes in the Rate, Rhythm, Electrocardiographic Pattern and Output of the Heart in Those with Cardiovascular Disease. *Proc. Assn. Res. Nerv. Ment. Dis.*, 1949, 29, 799-817.

1201. Stevenson, I. P., Duncan, C. H., Flynn, J. T. & Wolf, S. Hypertension as a Reaction Pattern to Stress. Correlation of Circulatory Hemodynamics with Changes in the Attitude and Emotional State. *Am. J. Med. Sci.*, 1952, 224, 286-299.

1202. Stevenson, I. P., Duncan, C. H. & Ripley, H. S. Variations in the Electrocardiogram Changes in Emotional State. *Geriatrics*, 1951, 6, 164-178.

1203. Stevenson, I. P., Duncan, C. H. & Wolff, H. G. Circulatory Dynamics Before and After Exercise in Subjects with and without Structural Heart Disease during Anxiety and Relaxation. *J. Clin. Invest.*, 1949, 28, 1534-1543.

1204. Stevenson, I. P. & Mathews, R. A. Fact and Theory in Psychosomatic Medicine. *J. Nerv. Ment. Dis.*, 1953, 118, 289-306.

1205. Stevenson, I. P. & Ripley, H. S. Variations in Respiration and Respiratory Symptoms During Changes in Emotion. *Psychosom. Med.*, 1952, 14, 476-490.

1206. Stevenson, I. P. & Wolff, H. G. Life Situations, Emotions, and Bronchial Mucus. *Psychosom. Med.*, 1949, 11, 223-227.

1207. Stokes, J. H., Kulchar, G. V. & Pillsbury, D. M. Effect on the Skin of Emotional and Nervous States: Etiologic Background of Urticaria with Special Reference to the Psychoneurogenous Factor. *Arch. Derm. Syph.*, 1935, 31, 470-499.

1208. Stone, C. P. & Barker, R. G. The Attitudes and Interest of Premenarcheal and Postmenarcheal Girls. *J. Genet. Psychol.*, 1939, 54, 27-71.

1209. Stone, H. M. Psychological Factors in Infantile Eczema. *Am. J. Nurs.*, 1953, 53, 449-451.

1210. Stopes, M. C. *Married Love*. London: A. C. Fifield, 1921.

1211. Stratton, G. M. Excitement as an Undifferentiated Emotion. In: Reymert (1032), pp. 215-221.

1212. Straub, L., Ripley, H. S. & Wolf, S. J. Disturbance of Bladder Function Associated with Emotional States. *J. Am. Med. Assn.*, 1949, 141, 1139-1143.

1213. Straub, L., Ripley, H. S. & Wolf, S. J. An Experimental Approach to Psychosomatic Bladder Disorder. *N. Y. St. J. Med.*, 1949, 49, 635-638.

1214. Strauss, H. Clinical and Electroencephalographic Studies: The Electroencephalogram in Psychoneurotics. *J. Nerv. Ment. Dis.*, 1945, 101, 19-27.

1215. Strother, G. B. & Cook, D. M. Neurocirculatory Reaction and a Group Stress Situation. *J. Consult. Psychol.*, 1953, 17, 267-268.

1216. Sullivan, A. J. & McKell, T. E. *Personality in Peptic Ulcer*. Springfield, Ill.: C. C Thomas, 1950.

1217. Sullivan, H. S. *Conceptions of Modern Psychiatry*. Washington, D. C.: William Alanson White Foundation, 1947.

1218. Sullivan, H. S. The Meaning of Anxiety in Psychiatry and in Life. *Psychiatry*, 1948, 11, 1-13.

1219. Sullivan, H. S. *The Interpersonal Theory of Psychiatry*. New York: Norton, 1953.

1220. Sulzberger, M. *Dermatologic Allergy*. Springfield, Ill.: C. C Thomas, 1940.

1221. Swartz, H. *The Allergic Child*. New York: Coward-McCann, 1954.

1222. Swartz, J. H. *Dermatology in General Practice*. Baltimore: Williams & Wilkins, 1953.

1223. Symonds, P. M. *Dynamic Psychology*. New York: Appleton-Century, 1949.

1224. Syz, H. Burrow's Differentiation of Tensional Patterns in Relation to Behavior Disorders. *J. Psychol.*, 1940, 9, 153-163.

1225. Szasz, T. S. Psychiatric Aspects of Vagotomy. *Psychosom. Med.*, 1949, 11, 187-199.

1226. Szasz, T. S. Psychosomatic Aspects of Salivary Activity. II, Psychoanalytic Observations Concerning Hypersalivation. *Psychosom. Med.*, 1950, 12, 320-331.

1227. Szasz, T. S. Physiologic and Psychodynamic Mechanisms in Constipation and Diarrhea. *Psychosom. Med.*, 1951, 13, 112-116.

1227a. Szasz, T. S. Contributions to the Psychology of Bodily Feelings. *Psychoanal. Quart.*, 1957, 26, 25-49.

1227b. Szasz, T. S. *Pain and Pleasure: A Study of Bodily Feelings*. New York: Basic Books, 1957.

1228. Szondi, L. & Lax, H. Über die Alimentare Glykämische Reaktion bei Neurasthenie. *Ztschr. Ges. Exp. Med.*, 1929, 64, 274-280.
1229. Talso, P. J., Crosley, A. P., Jr. & Clarke, R. W. Effect of Cold Pressor Test on Glomerular Filtration Rate and Effective Renal Plasma Flow. *J. Lab. Clin. Med.*, 1948, 33, 430-434.
1230. Tarsy, J. M. *Pain Syndromes and Their Treatment.* Springfield, Ill.: C. C Thomas, 1953.
1231. Tasi, S. Y., Bennett, A., May, L. G. & Gregory, R. L. Effect of Insulin Hypoglycemia on Eosinophils and Lymphocytes of Psychotics. *Proc. Soc. Exp. Biol. Med.*, 1950, 74, 782-784.
1232. Tauber, E. S. Effects of Castration upon the Sexuality of the Adult Male. *Psychosom. Med.*, 1940, 2, 74-87.
1233. Taylor, J. H. Innate Emotional Responses in Infants. *Ohio State University Studies in Infant Behavior*, 1934, 12, 81.
1234. Taylor, N. B. G. & Noble, R. L. Anti-Diuretic Substance in the Urine after Fainting. *Fed. Proc.*, 1949, 8, 155.
1235. Teplov, B. M. "Ob ob" Ektiunom Metode v Psikhologii. *Sovetsk. Pedag.*, 1952, 16, 66-86.
1236. Thiesen, J. W. Effects of Certain Forms of Emotion on the Normal Electroencephalogram. *Arch. Psychol.*, 1943, 285, 1-85.
1237. Thompson, C. *Psychoanalysis: Evolution and Development.* New York: Hermitage House, 1950.
1238. Thompson, G. H. *The Factor Analysis of Human Ability.* Boston: Houghton Mifflin, 1939.
1239. Thompson, G. H. Cattell's Study of Personality. *J. Educ. Psychol.*, 1943, 38, 273-282.
1240. Thompson, L. & Gellhorn, E. The Influence of Muscle Pain on Spinal Reflexes. *Proc. Soc. Exp. Biol. Med.*, 1945, 58, 105-108.
1241. Thorn, G. W. Neuropsychiatric Changes. In: *Proceedings of First Clinical ACTH Conference.* Philadelphia: Blakiston, 1950, pp. 541-542.
1242. Thorndike, E. L. Animal Intelligence (1898). In: Dennis (293a), pp. 377-387.
1243. Thorpe, L. P. *Child Psychology and Development.* New York: Ronald Press, 1946.
1244. Thurstone, L. L. *Vectors of the Mind.* Chicago: University of Chicago Press, 1935.
1245. Thurstone, L. L. *Primary Mental Abilities.* Chicago: University of Chicago Press, 1938.
1246. Thurstone, L. L. *Multiple Factor Analysis.* Chicago: University of Chicago Press, 1947.
1247. Tigerstedt, C. Der Blutdruck des Menschen bei psychischer Excitation. *Skandinav. Arch. f. Physiol.*, 1926, 48, 138-146.
1248. Titchener, E. B. Prof. Stumpf's Affective Psychology. *Am. J. Psychol.*, 1917, 28, 263-277.
1249. Titchener, E. B. *A Beginner's Psychology.* New York: Macmillan, 1924.
1250. Titchener, E. B. *A Textbook of Psychology.* New York: Macmillan, 1926.
1251. Titchener, E. B. The Postulates of Structural Psychology. In: Dennis (293a), pp. 366-377.
1252. Todd, T. W. & Kuenzel, W. Studies in the Alimentary Tract of Man. V, Disturbances of Central Origin in Gastric Responses. *J. Lab. Clin. Med.*, 1929, 15, 142-150.
1253. Todd, T. W. & Rowlands, M. E. Studies in the Alimentary Canal of Man. VI,

Emotional Interference in Gastric Behavior Patterns. *J. Comp. Psychol.*, 1930, 10, 167-188.

1254. Tolman, E. L. *Purposive Behavior in Animals and Men.* New York: Appleton-Century, 1932.

1255. Tolstrup, K. On Psychogenic Obesity in Children. *Acta Paediat.*, 1953, 42, 289-304.

1256. Tompkins, S. S., ed. *Contemporary Psychopathology: A Source Book.* Cambridge, Mass.: Harvard University Press, 1943.

1257. Tönnies, J. F. Die Ableitung bioelektrischer Effekte vom uneröffneten Schädel. *J. f. Psychol. u. Neurol.*, 1933, 45, 154-171.

1258. Torda, C. & Wolff, H. G. Effects of Various Concentrations of Adrenocorticotropic Hormone on Electrical Activity of Brain and on Sensitivity to Convulsion-Inducing Agents. *Am. J. Physiol.*, 1952, 168, 406.

1259. Totten, E. Oxygen Consumption During Emotional Stimulation. *Comp. Psychol. Mon.*, 1925, 3, 1-79.

1260. Tow, P. M. & Whitty, C. W. M. Personality Changes after Operations on the Cingulate Gyrus in Man. *J. Neurol. Neurosurg. Psychiat.*, 1953, 16, 186-193.

1261. Travell, J., Berry, C. & Bigelow, N. Effects of Referred Somatic Pain on Structures in the Reference Zone. *Fed. Proc.*, 1944, 3, 49.

1262. Travell, J. & Bigelow, N. H. Referred Somatic Pain Does Not Follow a Simple "Segmental" Pattern. *Fed. Proc.*, 1946, 5, 106.

1263. Travell, J., Rinzler, S. & Herman, M. Pain and Disability of the Shoulder and Arm. *J. Am. Med. Assn.*, 1942, 120, 417-422.

1264. Travis, L. E. & Egan, J. P. Conditioning of the Electrical Response of the Cortex. *J. Exper. Psychol.*, 1938, 22, 524-531.

1265. Travis, L. E. & Lindsley, D. B. The Relation of Frequency and Extent of Action Currents to Intensity of Muscular Contraction. *J. Exp. Psychol.*, 1931, 14, 359-381.

1266. Treuting, T. F. & Ripley, H. S. Life Situations, Emotions, and Bronchial Asthma. *J. Nerv. Ment. Dis.*, 1948, 105, 380-398.

1267. Troland, L. T. *The Principles of Psychophysiology.* New York: D. Van Nostrand, 1929.

1268. Tsang, Y. C. Hunger Motivation in Gastrectomized Rats. *J. Comp. Psychol.*, 1938, 26, 1-17.

1269. Tseng, F. *Differentiation of Anger and Fear in the Emotional Behavior of the Rat.* Unpublished Master's thesis, University of Toronto, 1942.

1269a. Ulett, G. A. & Gleser, G. Psychiatric Screening of Flying Personnel: The Development of Empirical Scales for the Prediction of Anxiety-Proneness from the EEG and Reaction of Intermittent Photic Stimulation. *U.S.A.F. Sch. Aviat., Med. Proj. Rep.*, 1953, Proj. No. 21-0202-0007, No. 4.

1269b. Ulett, G. A., Gleser, G., Lawler, A. & Winekur, G. Psychiatric Screening of Flying Personnel: IV, An Experimental Investigation of an EEG Index of Anxiety Tolerance by Means of Photic Stimulation. *U.S.A.F. Sch. Aviat., Med. Proj. Rep.*, 1952, Proj. No. 21-37-002, No. 4.

1270. Vaughan, W. T. *Practice of Allergy.* St. Louis: C. V. Mosby, 1939.

1271. Verney, E. B. Croonian Lecture: The Anti-Diuretic Hormone and the Factors which Determine Its Release. *Proc. Royal Soc.*, 1947, 135, 25-106.

1272. Viola, G. *La Constituzione Individuale.* Bologna: Cappelli, 1933.

1273. Vollmer, H. Treatment of Warts by Suggestion. *Psychosom. Med.*, 1946, 8, 138-14?

1274. Wada, T. Experimental Study of Hunger in Its Relation to Activity. *Arch. Psychol.*, 1922, 8, 1-65.

1275. Walker, A. E. Central Representation of Pain. *Proc. Assn. Res. Nerv. Ment. Dis.*, 1943, 23, 63-85.
1276. Wall, P. D. & Davis, G. D. Three Cerebral Cortical Systems Affecting Autonomic Function. *J. Neurophysiol.*, 1951, 14, 507-517.
1277. Walter, W. G. Electro-Encephalography in Cases of Mental Disorder. *J. Ment. Sci.*, 1942, 88, 110-121.
1278. Walter, W. G. In: Hill, D. & Parr, G., eds. *Electroencephalography, a Symposium on Its Various Aspects*. London: Macdonald, 1950.
1279. Wang, S. C. Visceral Functions of the Nervous System. *Ann. Rev. Physiol.*, 1953, 15, 329-356.
1280. Warren, H. C. *Elements of Human Psychology*. Boston: Houghton Mifflin, 1922.
1281. Watson, J. B. *Psychology from the Standpoint of a Behaviorist*. Philadelphia: Lippincott, 1924.
1282. Watson, J. B. *Behaviorism*. New York: Norton, 1925.
1283. Watson, J. B. Psychology as the Behaviorist Views It. *Psychol. Rev.*, 1913, 20, 158-177.
1284. Watson, J. B. *Psychological Care of the Infant and the Child*. New York: Norton, 1928.
1285. Watson, J. B. & Morgan, J. J. B. Emotional Reactions and Psychological Experimentation. *Am. J. Psychol.*, 1917, 28, 163-174.
1286. Watson, J. B. & Rayner, R. Studies in Infant Psychology. *Scient. Month.*, 1921, 13, 493-515.
1287. Watts, J. W. & Fulton, J. F. The Effect of Lesions of the Hypothalamus upon the Gastro-Intestinal Tract and Heart in Monkeys. *Ann. Surg.*, 1935, 101, 363-370.
1288. Webb, W. B. A Motivational Theory of Emotions. *Psychol. Rev.*, 1948, 55, 329-335.
1289. Weber, E. *Der Einfluss psychischer Vorgänge auf den Körper, insbesondere auf die Blutverteilung*. Berlin: Springer, 1910.
1290. Weber, E. H. *Tastsinn und Gemeingefühl*. In R. Wagner, *Handwörterbuch der Physiologie*. Braunschweig: F. Ueweg, 1846, pp. 1-122.
1291. Weber, E. H. Concerning Touch. In: Dennis (293a), pp. 155-156.
1292. Weber, E. H. The Sense of Touch and Common Feeling. In: Dennis (293a), pp. 194-196.
1293. Weber, C. O. Homeostasis and Servo-Mechanisms for What? *Psychol. Rev.* 1949, 56, 234-239.
1294. Wechsler, D. & Jones, H. E. A Study of Emotional Specificity. *Am. J. Psychol.*, 1928, 40, 600-606.
1295. Weeks, D. M. Observation of Small and Large Bowel Motility in Men. *Gastroenterol.*, 1946, 6, 185-190.
1296. Weiner, J. S. The Regional Distribution of Sweating. *J. Physiol.*, 1945, 104, 32-40.
1296a. Weisman, A. D. A Study of the Psychodynamics of Duodenal Ulcer Exacerbations: With Special Reference to Treatment and the Problem of "Specificity." *Psychosom. Med.*, 1956, 18, 2-42.
1297. Weiss, E. Psychoanalyse eines Falles von nervösem Asthma. *Int. Ztschr. Psychoanal.*, 1922, 8, 440-455.
1298. Weiss, E. Psychogenic Rheumatism. *Ann. Int. Med.*, 1947, 26, 890-900.
1299. Weiss, E. Psychosomatic Aspects of Dieting. *J. Clin. Nutr.*, 1953, 1, 140-148.
1300. Weiss, E. & English, O. S. *Psychosomatic Medicine*. Philadelphia: Saunders, 1949.
1301. Weiss, P. *Principles of Development*. New York: Henry Holt, 1939.

1302. Weiner, J., Hoff, H. E. & Simon, M. A. Production of Ulcerative Colitis in Dogs by the Prolonged Administration of Mecholyl. *Gastroenterol.*, 1949, 12, 637-647.

1303. Wenger, M. An Attempt to Appraise Individual Differences in Muscular Tension Level. *J. Exp. Psychol.*, 1943, 31, 213-225.

1304. Wenger, M. A. Emotion as Visceral Action: An Extension of Lange's Theory. In: Reymert (1033), pp. 1-10.

1305. Wenger, M. A. & Gilchrist, J. C. A Comparison of Two Indices of Palmar Sweating. *J. Exp. Psychol.*, 1948, 38, 757-761.

1306. Werner, H. & Wapner, S. A Sensory-Tonic Field-Theory of Perception. *J. Person.*, 1949, 18, 88-107.

1307. Werner, S. C. A Quantitative Study of the Urinary Excretion of Hypophyseal Gonadotropin, Estrogen, and Androgen of Normal Women. *J. Clin. Invest.*, 1941, 22, 21-30.

1308. Wertheimer, M. *Productive Thinking.* New York: Harper, 1945.

1309. Westcott, R. N., Fowler, N. O., Scott, R. C., Hauenstein, V. D. & McGuire, J. Anoxia and Human Pulmonary Vascular Resistance. *J. Clin. Invest.*, 1951, 30, 957-970.

1310. Westman, W. A. & Jacobson, D. Experimentelle Untersuchungen über die Bedeutung des Hypophysen-Zwischenhirnsystems für die Produktion gonadotroper Hormone des Hypophysenvorderlappens. *Acta Obst. et Gynec. Scandinav.*, 1937, 17, 235-265.

1311. Wheeler, R. H. *The Laws of Human Nature.* New York: D. Appleton, 1932.

1312. Wheeler, R. H. *The Science of Psychology.* New York: Crowell, 1940.

1313. Wheeler, R. H. & Perkins, F. T. *Principles of Mental Development.* New York: Crowell, 1932.

1313a. Wheeler, W. M., Little, K., Dorcus, R. M., Clemens, T. L., Sternberg, T. H. & Zimmerman, M. C. The Effects of Psychological Stress as Measured by a Decrease in the Number of Circulating Eosinophiles. *J. Clin. Exp. Hypnosis,* 1954, 2, 130-135.

1314. White, B. V., Cobb, S. & Jones, C. M. Mucous Colitis: A Psychological and Medical Study of Sixty Cases. *Psychosom. Med. Mon.*, 1939, No. 1.

1315. White, B. V. & Jones, C. M. The Effect of Irritants and Drugs Affecting the Autonomic Nervous System upon the Mucosa of the Normal Rectum and the Rectosigmoid, with Especial Reference to "Mucous Colitis." *New Eng. J. Med.*, 1938, 218, 791-797.

1316. White, J. C. Autonomic Discharge from Stimulation of the Hypothalamus in Man. *Proc. Assn. Res. Nerv. Ment. Dis.*, 1940, 20, 854-863.

1317. White, J. C. Sensory Innervation of the Viscera: Studies on Visceral Afferent Neurones in Man Based on Neurosurgical Procedures for the Relief of Intractable Pain. *Proc. Assn. Res. Nerv. Ment. Dis.*, 1943, 23, 373-390.

1318. White, P. D., Cohen, M. E. & Chapman, W. P. The Electrocardiogram in Neurocirculatory Asthenia, Anxiety Neurosis, and Effort Syndrome. *Am. Heart J.*, 1941, 34, 390.

1319. White, R. W. *The Abnormal Personality.* New York: Ronald Press, 1948.

1320. Whitehorn, J. C., Kaufman, M. R. & Thomas, J. M. Heart Rate in Relation to Emotional Disturbance. *Arch. Neurol. Psychiat.*, 1935, 33, 712-731.

1321. Whiting, J. W. M. & Child, I. L. *Child Training and Personality: A Cross-Cultural Study.* New Haven: Yale University Press, 1953.

1322. Whiting, J. W. & Mowrer, O. H. Habit Progression and Regression. *J. Comp. Psychol.*, 1943, 36, 229-253.

1323. Widdowson, E. M. Mental Contentment and Physical Growth. *Lancet,* 1951, 260, 1316-1318.
1324. Wiener, N. *Cybernetics: Or Control and Communication in the Animal and the Machine.* New York: John Wiley, 1948.
1325. Wilhelmj, C. M., McGuire, T. F., McDonough, J., Waldmann, E. B. & McCarthy, H. H. Emotional Elevations of Blood Pressure in Trained Dogs: Possible Relation to Origin of Hypertension in Humans. *Psychosom. Med.,* 1953, 15, 390-395.
1326. Willard, H. N., Swan, R. C., Jr. & Wolf, G. A. Life Situations, Emotions, and Dyspnea. *Proc. Assn. Res. Nerv. Ment. Dis.,* 1949, 29, 583-595.
1327. Williams, A. C., Jr. Some Psychological Correlates of the Electroencephalogram. *Arch. Psychol.,* 1939, 240, 5-48.
1328. Wilson, W. C. Some Aspects of Sweat Secretion in Man: With Special Reference to the Action of Pilocarpine. *Brain,* 1934, 57, 422-442.
1329. Wilson, W. C. Observations Relating to the Innervation of the Sweat Glands of the Face. *Clin. Sci.,* 1936, 2, 273-286.
1330. Winsor, A. L. & Korchin, B. The Effect of Different Types of Stimulation upon the pH of Human Parotid Secretion. *J. Exp. Psychol.,* 1938, 23, 62-79.
1331. Winter, J. A. *Are Your Troubles Psychosomatic?* New York: Julian Messner, 1952.
1332. Wishner, J. Neurosis and Tension: An Exploratory Study of the Relationship of Physiological and Rorschach Measures. *J. Abnorm. Soc. Psychol.,* 1953, 48, 253-260.
1333. Wittkower, E. Über den Einfluss der Affekte auf den Gallefluss. *Klin. Wochnschr.,* 1928, 7, 2193-2194.
1334. Wittkower, E. Über affektiv-somatische Veränderungen. II, Die Affektlukozytose. *Klin. Wochnschr.,* 1928, 8, 1082.
1335. Wittkower, E. Studies on the Influence of Emotions on the Function of the Organs. *J. Ment. Sci.,* 1935, 81, 533-682.
1336. Wittkower, E. & Petow, H. Beiträge zur Klinik des Asthma bronchiale und verwandter Zustände. V, Zur Psychogenese des Asthma bronchiale. *Ztschr. f. Klin. Med.,* 1931-1932, 119, 293-306.
1337. Wittkower, E. & Pilz, W. Über affektiv-somatische Veränderungen. VI, Zur Affektiven Beeinflussbarkeit der Speichelsekretion. *Klin. Wochnschr.,* 1932, 11, 718-719.
1338. Wittkower, E., Rogers, T. F. & Wilson, A. T. M. Effort Syndrome. *Lancet,* 1941, 1, 531-535.
1339. Wittkower, E. D. Studies of the Personality of Patients Suffering from Urticaria. *Psychosom. Med.,* 1953, 15, 116-126.
1339a. Wittkower, E. D. Psychological Aspects of Pulmonary Tuberculosis, a General Survey. In: Sparer (1170a), pp. 153-174.
1340. Wolf, A. & Cowen, D. Histopathology of Schizophrenia and Other Psychoses of Unknown Origin. In: Milbank Memorial Fund (903), pp. 469-497.
1341. Wolf, G. A. Effect of Pain on Renal Blood Flow. *Proc. Assn. Res. Nerv. Ment. Dis.,* 1943, 23, 358-364.
1342. Wolf, G. A. & Wolff, H. G. Studies on the Nature of Certain Symptoms Associated with Cardiovascular Disorders. *Psychosom. Med.,* 1946, 8, 293-319.
1343. Wolf, S. J. The Regulation of Gastric Function to Nausea in Man. *J. Clin. Invest.,* 1943, 22, 877-882.
1344. Wolf, S. J. Observation of the Occurrence of Nausea in Army Combat Soldiers. *Gastroenterol.,* 1947, 8, 15-18.
1345. Wolf, S. J. Sustained Contraction of the Diaphragm, the Mechanism of a

Common Type of Dyspnea and Precordial Pain. *J. Clin. Invest.*, 1947, 26, 1201.

1346. Wolf, S. J. Summary of Evidence Relating Life Situation and Emotional Response to Peptic Ulcer. *Ann. Int. Med.*, 1949, 31, 637-649.

1347. Wolf, S. J. & Almy, T. P. Experimental Observations on Cardiospasm in Man. *Gastroenterol.*, 1949, 13, 401-421.

1348. Wolf, S. J. & Andrus, W. de W. The Effect of Vagotomy on the Gastric Function. *Gastroenterol.*, 1947, 8, 429-434.

1349. Wolf, S. J., Pfeiffer, J. B., Ripley, H. S., Winter, O. S. & Wolff, H. G. Hypertension as a Reaction Pattern to Stress: Summary of Experimental Data on Variations in Blood Pressure and Renal Blood Flow. *Ann. Int. Med.*, 1948, 29, 1056-1076.

1350. Wolf, S. J. & Wolff, H. G. Genesis of Peptic Ulcer in Man. *J. Am. Med. Assn.*, 1942, 120, 670-675.

1351. Wolf, S. J. & Wolff, H. G. Life Situation and Gastric Function: A Summary. *Am. Pract.*, 1948, 3, 1-14.

1352. Wolf, S. J. & Wolff, H. G. *Human Gastric Functions*. New York: Oxford University Press, 1947.

1353. Wolf, S. J. & Wolff, H. G. An Experimental Study of Changes in Gastric Functions in Response to Varying Life Experiences. *Rev. Gastroenterol.*, 1947, 14, 419-426.

1354. Wolf, S. J. & Wolff, H. G., *Headaches, Their Nature and Treatment*. Boston: Little, Brown, 1953.

1355. Wolff, H. G. Some Observations on Pain. *Harvey Lect.*, 1943-1944, 39, 39-95.

1356. Wolff, H. G. *Headache and Other Head Pain*. New York: Oxford University Press, 1948.

1357. Wolff, H. G. Life Stress and Bodily Disease—A Formulation. *Proc. Assn. Res. Nerv. Ment. Dis.*, 1949, 29, 1059-1094.

1358. Wolff, H. G. Life Situations, Emotions and Bodily Disease. In: Reymert (1033), pp. 284-324.

1359. Wolff, H. G. Life Stresses and Cardiovascular Disorders. *Circulation*, 1950, 1, 187-203.

1360. Wolff, H. G. *Stress and Disease*. Springfield, Ill.: C. C Thomas, 1953.

1361. Wolff, H. G., Hardy, J. D. & Goodell, H. Studies on Pain: Measurement of the Effect of Ethyl Alcohol on the Pain Threshold and on the "Alarm" Reaction. *J. Pharmacol. Exp. Ther.*, 1942, 75, 38-49.

1362. Wolff, H. G., Grace, W. & Wolf, S. Life Situations, Emotions, and the Large Bowel. *Tr. Assn. Am. Phys.* 1949, 62, 192-195.

1363. Wolff, H. G., Lorenz, T. H. & Graham, O. T. Stress, Emotions, and Human Sebum: Their Relevance to Acne Vulgaris. *Tr. Assn. Am. Phys.*, 1951, 64, 435-444.

1364. Wolff, H. G. & Wolf, S. *Pain*. Springfield, Ill.: C. C Thomas, 1951.

1365. Wood, P. Da Costa's Syndrome. *Brit. Med. J.*, 1941, 1, 767-772.

1366. Woodbury, D. M. Effects of Adrenocortical Steroids and Adrenocorticotropic Hormone on Electroshock Seizure Threshold. *J. Pharmacol. Exp. Ther.*, 1952, 105, 27-36.

1367. Woodworth, R. S. *Dynamic Psychology*. New York: Columbia University Press, 1918.

1368. Woodworth, R. S. *Psychology*. New York: Henry Holt, 1921.

1369. Woodworth, R. S. *Experimental Psychology*. New York: Henry Holt, 1938.

1370. Woodworth, R. S. *Contemporary Schools of Psychology*. New York: Ronald Press, 1948.

1371. Woollard, H. H., Roberts, J. E. H. & Carmichael, E. A. An Inquiry into Referred Pain. *Lancet,* 1932, 222, (1) 337-338.
1372. Wright, M. E. Benedek's Studies in Psychosomatic Medicine: Psychosexual Functions in Women. *Psychol. Bull.,* 1953, 50, 392-393.
1373. Wundt, W. *Outlines of Psychology.* Leipzig: Wilhelm Engelmann, 1903.
1374. Wyss, W. H. von. Über den Einfluss psychischer Vorgänge auf die Innervation von Herz in Gefässen. *Schweiz. Arch. f. Neurol. u. Psychiat.,* 1924, 14, 30-33.
1375. Yaeger, C. L. & Baldes, E. J. The Electro-Encephalogram in Organic and Non-Organic Mental Disorders. *Proc. Mayo Clin.,* 1937, 12, 705-712.
1376. Yeakel, E. H. & Rhoades, R. P. A Comparison of the Body and Endocrine Gland (Adrenal, Thyroid and Pituitary) Weights of Emotional and Non-Emotional Rats. *Endocrinol.,* 1941, 28, 337-340.
1377. Yokoyama, M. The Nature of the Affective Judgments in the Method of Paired Comparisons. *Am. J. Psychol.,* 1921, 32, 357-369.
1378. Young, P. T. An Experimental Study of Mixed Feelings. *Am. J. Psychol.,* 1918, 29, 237-271.
1379. Young, P. T. Pleasantness and Unpleasantness in Relation to Organic Response. *Am. J. Psychol.,* 1921, 32, 38-53.
1380. Young, P. T. Studies in Affective Psychology. *Am. J. Psychol.,* 1927, 38, 157-193.
1381. Young, P. T. *Emotions in Man and Animal.* New York: John Wiley, 1943.
1382. Young, P. T. Emotion as a Disorganized Response: A Reply to Professor Leeper. *Psychol. Rev.,* 1949, 56, 184-191.
1382a. Young, P. T. The Role of Hedonic Processes in Motivation. In: M. R. Jones, ed. *Nebraska Symposium on Motivation.* Lincoln: University of Nebraska Press, 1955, pp. 193-238.
1383. Ziegler, L. H. & Elliott, D. C. The Effect of Emotion on Certain Cases of Asthma. *Am. J. Med. Sci.,* 1926, 172, 860.
1384. Zilboorg, G. & Henry, G. W. *A History of Medical Psychology.* New York: Norton, 1941.
1385. Zotterman, Y. Touch and Tickling: An Electrophysiological Investigation on Cutaneous Sensory Nerves. *J. Physiol.,* 1939, 95, 1-28.

INDEX